W9-CED-301

$7.50

Eleanor Trew Cooley

FUNDAMENTALS OF

Engineering Drawing

Other Books by the Author

Graphics for Engineers, Prentice-Hall, Inc., 1957.
Technical Drafting Essentials, 2nd ed., Prentice-Hall, Inc., 1956.
Problems in Engineering Drawing, 4th ed., Prentice-Hall, Inc., 1959.
Problems for Engineering Graphics, Prentice-Hall, Inc., 1958.
Problems in Drafting Fundamentals, Prentice-Hall, Inc., 1956.
Purdue University Engineering Drawing Films, with J. Rising, *et al.*

FUNDAMENTALS OF

Engineering Drawing

FOR TECHNICAL STUDENTS AND PROFESSIONAL DRAFTSMEN

Fourth Edition

BY **WARREN J. LUZADDER, P.E.**

Professor of Engineering Graphics,
Purdue University. Member,
American Society for Engineering
Education, National Society of
Professional Engineers, Society of
American Military Engineers, etc.

Englewood Cliffs, N.J.
PRENTICE-HALL, INC.
1959

© 1943, 1946, 1952, 1959 BY

PRENTICE-HALL, INC.

ENGLEWOOD CLIFFS, N.J.

ALL RIGHTS RESERVED. NO PART OF THIS
BOOK MAY BE REPRODUCED IN ANY FORM, BY
MIMEOGRAPH OR ANY OTHER MEANS, WITH-
OUT PERMISSION IN WRITING FROM THE
PUBLISHERS.

LIBRARY OF CONGRESS
CATALOG CARD NO.: 59-6531

PRINTED IN THE UNITED STATES OF AMERICA

33840

Preface
to the Fourth Edition

The fourth edition of *Fundamentals of Engineering Drawing* has been in the planning and preparation stage for several years. It became evident, even while the third edition was in the final stages of production, that significant changes in drawing room practices would appear in the various standards, as the committees organized by the American Standards Association (ASA) and the Society of Automotive Engineers (SAE) completed their assignments. Both the author and the publisher agreed that these new practices should be made available for use in the classroom as soon as possible after they had been approved by the ASA and the SAE and accepted by American industry.

Many of the recommended practices that have been approved and incorporated into the ASA and SAE standards during the last few years have been included in this latest edition. In general, the recommended practices that are for use in specialized fields only have been purposely omitted so that the number of pages in the text could be kept within reasonable limits. Those who are interested in a specialized field should purchase the appropriate section of the ASA Y14 standards. Data values given in the tables of the Appendix have been changed where necessary to agree with recent revisions of the standards.

As in the case of the previous editions, the constant aim has been to keep the student in mind by preparing an almost self-teaching book, so clearly written and generously illustrated that the beginner could gain a complete understanding of fundamental principles with a minimum of help. The fact was recognized that those who seek to attain depth in their understanding of a subject must acquire a substantial portion of the necessary knowledge through individual effort.

Much of the credit for the improvements in this edition should be given to the many teachers who have offered constructive suggestions. These ideas have been incorporated into the text for the benefit of all.

Some of the original material has been completely rewritten for greater clarity and new material has been added to modernize particular sections. Many new illustrations and pictorial representations for problems will be found in the chapters that cover the basic fundamentals. More pictorial drawings have been surface-shaded to permit the shape of a part to be visualized quickly by those who find it difficult to visualize a three dimensional object represented by lines drawn on a surface of two dimensions.

Because the decimal system of expressing dimensional values has been adopted in the aircraft and automobile industries, many of the problems and illustrations show decimal dimensions. Both the decimal and fractional systems are widely used at present. How long this coexistence will continue can not be foretold, but it would seem to be desirable that students be able to use either as the occasion may demand.

The chapter dealing with dimensioning practices has been expanded and almost completely revised in order to present changes and incorporate new practices as they have appeared in recent revision of the standards. The fits recommended for use between plain cylindrical parts in the recent ASA B4.1–1955 standard have been included in the chapter. The related tables in the Appendix are in accordance with ABC (American-British-Canadian) conference agreements. The chapter on Welding Drawing has been completely revised to agree with the ASA standard.

Those problems that fulfilled the needs of the users of the third edition have been retained; a considerable number of new problems have been added.

The author wishes to express his thanks to all who have made contributions of ideas and material to this edition and the previous editions. The names of some of these contributors, many of whom are the author's close friends, may be found in the preface to the first edition. Mention must be made of the assistance and advice given over the past years by Professors J. N. Arnold, E. W. Azpell, M. H. Bolds, K. E. Botkin, R. C. Carpenter, J. H. Porsch, W. O. Satterly, C. J. Rogers, L. W. Thomas, H. C. Thompson, and others of the staff at Purdue University.

The author's indebtedness to Mr. William J. Hornung, Director of Training, National Technical Institute, for the material prepared for Architectural Drawing in the third edition, which has been used without change in this latest edition, can not be overlooked.

Once again, the author's close friend, Major Robert H. Hammond of the United States Military Academy, read all of the new manuscript material and checked all of the new problems. I thank him for his kindness.

W. J. LUZADDER

Purdue University,
  W. Lafayette, Indiana.

Preface
to the First Edition

In teaching the present-day large classes, a teacher finds that it is almost impossible to give a student a sufficient amount of individual instruction. Even if he is able to spend as much as five minutes of a period with each student, he finds that the time is taken up explaining some small item that could be just as well presented in some other way. Needless repetition is a waste of the students' time and tends to make the instructor's work monotonous. With this thought in mind, an attempt has been made to create a nearly self-teaching book with simple explanations of all the more common difficulties. An equal effort has been put forth to make each illustration repeat fully in graphical language the ideas presented by the accompanying printed words.

The material for this text has been selected and organized with a full realization of the fact that engineering drawing courses vary somewhat in our many technical schools. The methods of presentation are different because of divergence of opinion among teachers concerning the best scheme for teaching the subject. Course content varies because courses are designed for different purposes. The author does not feel qualified to criticize any method of presentation, because of his deep respect for the intelligence and sincerity of every teacher of the subject, many of whom are more than chance acquaintances.

A majority of teachers seem to agree, however, that engineering drawing, in reality a graphic language, should be taught as any other language. That is, they feel that the elementary principles and rules of composition should be studied and learned step by step before an attempt is made to compose working drawings. The idioms of the language should be taught after the basic principles have been thoroughly mastered. The same teachers frown upon the practice of copying drawings because they realize that engineering drawing requires more than manual skill and that the technical draftsman must possess constructive imagination and a knowledge of industrial practices.

Models of mutilated blocks may be used at the very beginning of the elementary course to help a student to visualize, if they are used judiciously.   Machine parts furnish excellent sketching and working-drawing problems.   In the case of large classes, however, it is almost impossible to handle the great number of models and parts that would be required. The dimensioned pictorials of machine parts given at the end of many of the chapters furnish an answer to this problem and should prove to be excellent substitutes.

Laboratory drawing periods should be supplemented by lectures, recitations, and quizzes.   The instructors at many institutions have found that basic material can be best presented through the use of motion pictures.   More subject matter can be covered in a given amount of time, and each student observes a demonstration equally well.   For a further discussion of the use of motion pictures prepared by Professor Justus Rising and the author, see the Appendix.

The drawing plates used in a beginning course should be small ($8\frac{1}{2}'' \times 11''$ to $11'' \times 17''$) so that no student will become completely discouraged by being forced to work many hours upon a drawing that he feels is not of a quality he desires.   A new start always brings new hope, which in turn leads to better work.   If partial layouts are used, more subject matter can be presented, and many additional experiences may be offered.   By their use, unnecessary work that the student is fully capable of doing can be avoided.

The publication *American Standard Drawings and Drafting Room Practice* (ASA Z14.1-1935) has been used as a guide in the preparation of much of the material presented in this text.   All related standards have also been consulted.   The Appendix contains a considerable amount of handbook material, mostly in the form of tables, many of which were prepared from these standards.   The author highly endorses the valuable work of this association and its allied organizations.   Every effort has been made by the author to keep in step with modern engineering practice.

In the chapters covering the specialized divisions of engineering drawing, sufficient material has been presented to permit the assignment of practical problems.   It has been the intent, however, to avoid the field of design.   The chapters on shop processes should help the student to understand more fully the practices of dimensioning.

Because of the interest and co-operation of many manufacturers, it has been possible to present a number of commercial drawings as illustrations and as problems.   Special acknowledgment of their courtesy has been made throughout the text.

The author wishes to express his appreciation for the ideas of known and unknown persons.   They are so many that their names cannot be given here, but each at some time presented some drawing practice that appears somewhere on these pages.   Grateful acknowledgment is made here for the aid of M. T. Ward and R. S. Green in the preparation of the chapter on structural drawing.   Also to Professors J. N. Arnold and M. R. Graney, who, along with Messrs. C. E. Mayfield and M. H. Bolds, gave constructive criticisms of the manuscript.   Acknowledgment is due to Mr. E. W. Azpell for material on gears and cams and to Professor Justus Rising for his contribution to the chapter on lettering and constant help throughout the entire time that this book was in preparation.   For the aid of G. S. Palmer and others in the preparation of some of the drawings no more need be said than that their work was well done.

Special appreciation must be expressed here for the aid and encouragement given by Dean A. A. Potter, Professor C. W. Beese, and Professor H. F. Owen, all of Purdue University.

Finally, the author wishes to acknowledge with thanks his appreciation for the kindness of Professors E. F. Watts, of Massachusetts Institute of Technology, and Horace P. Fry, of the University of Pennsylvania, who took time during these busy days to review the manuscript and offer many helpful suggestions.

W. J. Luzadder

Purdue University
West Lafayette, Indiana

Contents

FUNDAMENTALS OF

Engineering Drawing

1 | Introduction

1.1. Engineering drawing is a graphic language that is used universally by engineers to describe the shape and size of structures and mechanisms. It has developed through the centuries, much as have various spoken and written languages, until at the present time its fundamental principles are understood by trained persons in all civilized nations. If an engineer is not to be an illiterate member of his profession, he must understand not only the theory of projection and dimensioning as related to working drawings, but he must be familiar with the idioms and conventions as well. It can be truthfully said that any supposedly trained engineer who cannot read a drawing will be of very little value to the firm that employs him. In fact, he can be compared to an unskilled laborer, employed at ordinary work, who cannot read or write.

Engineering drawing is not, as many students are prone to believe, something a draftsman alone need understand. The language belongs to the engineer. It is his means for recording his ideas and conveying his instructions to others. Although many graduates of technical colleges serve an apprenticeship at the drawing board, few remain at it long enough to develop the degree of skill possessed by a good draftsman. The lack of such skill often proves a real handicap, for the ability to execute a neat and accurate drawing can be the one thing that will attract attention and lead to the quick promotion of a young graduate into responsible engineering work.

The usual work of an engineer is to direct the preparation of drawings. To do this he must prepare preliminary design drawings and instructive sketches made in accordance with the basic principles underlying the preparation of working drawings. From time to time he must inspect the draftsmen's work to see that the drawings will convey his ideas as he wishes them to be conveyed.

1.2. The purpose of this text is to present the grammar and composition of drawing so that those who conscientiously study the basic principles will be able to execute satisfactory drawings and, after some practical experience, be capable of directing the work of others. To facilitate study, the subject matter has been separated into its various component parts: lettering, geometry, multiview drawing, dimensioning, pictorial drawing, sketching, and so forth. Later chapters discuss the preparation of working drawings, both detail and assembly, the preparation of topographic drawings, and the construction of charts and graphs. The major

1

portion of the material presented leads up to the preparation of machine drawings, which the prospective members of some branches of the engineering profession think is not of interest to them.   Since the methods used in the preparation of machine drawings, however, are the same methods used in the preparation of drawings in other fields of engineering, a thorough understanding of machine drawing assures a good foundation for later study in some specialized field, such as structural drawing.   For those interested in specific types of drawing, some material has been presented with the assumption that the student already possesses a working knowledge of projection and dimensioning.

1.3. Engineering drawing offers students an insight into the engineer's methods of attacking engineering problems.   Its lessons teach the principles of accuracy, exactness, and positiveness with regard to the information necessary for the production of a nonexisting structure.   Finally, it develops the engineering imagination that is so essential to the creation of successful design.

2 | Technical Lettering

2.1. To impart to the men in the shops all the necessary information for the complete construction of a machine or structure, the shape description, which is conveyed graphically by the views, must be accompanied by size descriptions and instructive specifications in the form of figured dimensions and notes (Fig. 2.1).

All dimensions and notes should be lettered freehand in a plain legible style that can be rapidly executed. Poor lettering detracts from the appearance of a drawing, and often impairs its usefulness, regardless of the quality of the line work.

2.2. Lettering.* "To acquire proficiency in any art one must know what to do, how to do it, and then practice.

"Learning to letter requires:

"(a) A knowledge of the shapes and proportions of the individual characters.

"(b) A knowledge of the order of stroke and direction of stroke used in making them.

"(c) A knowledge of the rules for combining letters into words and words into sentences.

"(d) Practice."

2.3. Single-stroke Gothic letters (Reinhardt). The simplified single-stroke Gothic letters developed by Charles W. Reinhardt are now used universally for working drawings. This style is particularly suitable for most technical purposes because it possesses the qualifications necessary for legibility and speed. On commercial drawings it appears in slightly modified forms, however, as each draftsman finally develops a style that reflects his own individuality.

The expression "single-stroke" means that the width of the straight and curved lines that form the letters are the same width as the stroke of the pen or pencil. The term should not be understood to imply that the entire letter is made with one continuous movement.

2.4. The recommendations of the American Standards Association. After a thorough study of the practices of the leading industrial manufacturing companies and technical schools, the American Standards Association made the following recommendations.

"(a) That single-stroke commercial gothic lettering, either vertical or

---

* By Justus Rising.

3

inclined at a slope of 2 in 5, be used on all working drawings for titles, notes, and so forth [Fig. 2.49].

"(*b*) That only capitals be used in the title box."

2.5. The general proportions of letters. Although there is no fixed standard for the proportions of the letters, certain definite rules in their design must be observed by a draftsman if he wishes to have his lettering appear neat and pleasing to the eye. The recognized characteristics of each letter should be carefully studied, and then thoroughly

WORLD PRODUCTION
OF
CRUDE PETROLEUM
(a) Chart

CLAMP WASHER
C.I   I REQ'D.
(b) Machine Drawing

(c) Structural Drawing

(d) Electrical Diagram
From ASA Y32.2-1954

Fig. 2.1.   Technical Drawings.

learned through practice, before any attempt is made to letter complete notes and sentences.

It is advisable for the beginner, instead of relying on his untrained eye for proportions, to follow the fixed proportions given in this chapter. Otherwise, his lettering most likely will be displeasing to the trained eye of a professional engineer or draftsman. Later, after he has thoroughly mastered the art of lettering, his individuality will be revealed naturally by slight variations in the shapes and proportions of some of the letters.

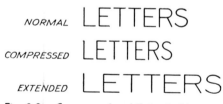

NORMAL   LETTERS

COMPRESSED   LETTERS

EXTENDED   LETTERS

Fig. 2.2.   Compressed and Extended Letters.

It is often desirable to increase or decrease the width of letters in order to make a word or group of words fill a certain space. Letters narrower than normal letters of the same height are called *compressed letters;* those that are wider are called *extended letters.* (See Fig. 2.2.)

2.6. Lettering pencils, pens, and equipment.   Pencil lettering is usually done with a medium-soft pencil.   Since the degree of hardness of the lead required to produce a dark opaque line will vary with the type of paper used, a pencil should be selected only after drawing a few trial lines. In order to obtain satisfactory lines, the pencil should be sharpened to a long conical point and then rounded slightly on a piece of scratch paper. To keep the point symmetrical while lettering, the pencil should be rotated a partial revolution before each new letter is started.

Fig. 2.3.   Pen Points.

The choice of a type of pen point for lettering on ordinary working drawings depends largely upon the personal preference and characteristics of the individual.   The beginner can learn only from experience which of the many types available are best suited to him.   A few of the more popular points and their strokes are illustrated in Fig. 2.3.   Every draftsman should have an assortment of points varied enough in type to suit whatever size of letters and kind of paper he may be called upon to use.

A pen that makes a heavy stroke should be used for bold letters in titles and so forth, while a light-stroke pen is required for the lighter letters in figures and notes.

A very flexible point never should be used for lettering.   Such a point is apt to shade the downward stem strokes as well as the downward portions of curved strokes.   A good point is one that has enough resistance to normal pressure to permit the drawing of curved and stem strokes of uniform width.

Fig. 2.4.   Henry Tank Pen.

There are ordinary steel pen points with special ink-holding devices that make them especially adapted for lettering. The *Henry tank* pen, for example, shown in Fig. 2.4, has an ink reservoir that holds the ink above the point so that it feeds down the slit in an even flow.   The device further assists in maintaining a uniform line by preventing the point from spreading.

Four of the many special pens designed for single-stroke letters are illustrated in Fig. 2.5.   The *Barch-Payzant* pen (*a*) is available in graded sizes from No. 000 (very coarse) to No. 8 (very fine).   The very fine size is suitable for lettering $\frac{1}{8}$ inch to $\frac{3}{16}$ inch high on technical drawings.   The

Edco (*b*) has a patented holder into which any one of a graded set of lettering nibs (ranging in sizes from No. 0 to No. 6) may be screwed. The tubular construction of the point makes it possible to draw uniform lines regardless of the direction of the stroke. Also of tubular construction is the *Leroy* (*c*). The *Speedball* (*d*) may be obtained in many graded sizes.

2.7. Devices for drawing guide lines and slope lines. Devices for drawing guide lines are available in a variety of forms. The two most

BARCH-PAYZANT   EDCO   LEROY   SPEEDBALL

(a)   (b)   (c)   (d)

Fig. 2.5.   Special Lettering Pens.

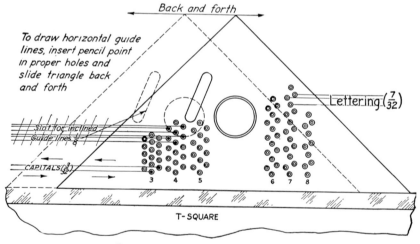

Fig. 2.6.   Braddock Lettering Triangle.

popular are the *Braddock Lettering Triangle* (Fig. 2.6), and the *Ames Lettering Instrument* (Fig. 2.7).

The Braddock Lettering Triangle is provided with sets of grouped countersunk holes that may be used to draw guide lines by inserting a sharp-pointed pencil (4H or 6H) into the holes and sliding the triangle back and forth along the guiding edge of a T-square or a triangle supported by a T-square. The holes are grouped to give guide lines for capitals and lower-case letters. The number below each set indicates the height of the capitals in thirty-seconds of an inch. For example, the No.

3 set is for capitals $\frac{3}{32}''$ high, the No. 4 set is for capitals $\frac{1}{8}''$ high, the No. 5 is for capitals $\frac{5}{32}''$ high, and so on.

The following practice is recommended for drawing guide lines on drawings of ordinary size ($8\frac{1}{2}'' \times 11''$, $9'' \times 12''$, $11'' \times 17''$, and $12'' \times 18''$):

Notes and detail titles.   To draw guide lines for notes and detail titles, use the top and bottom holes of the lower group in size No. 4.

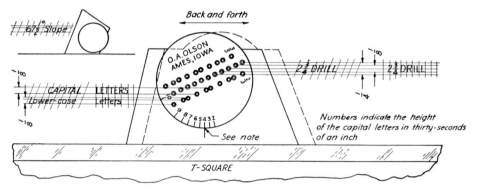

Fig. 2.7.   Ames Lettering Instrument.

Fig. 2.8.   Guide Lines and Slope Lines.

Sheet titles.   To draw guide lines for single-line sheet titles, use the top and bottom holes of the lower group in size No. 6.   For two-line titles use the top and bottom holes of the two lower groups in size No. 4.

Combined whole numbers and fractions.   To draw the seven guide lines required for a whole number and a fraction, use the countersunk holes indicated with black centers in Fig. 2.9.

These lines are made by inserting a sharp pencil in the indicated holes and moving the triangle, guided by a T-square held in a fixed position, back and forth with the pencil point.   The height of a fraction numeral will be three-fourths the height of the whole number, and the total height of the fraction will be twice that of the whole number. If this useful combination is analyzed, it can be observed that the middle hole of the lower group in No. 3 and the top hole of the lower group in No. 6 give the guide lines for the whole number. The upper hole of the lower group in No. 4 gives the fraction bar, while the top and bottom holes in the two lower groups in No. 3 give the guide lines for the numerator and denominator.

Fig. 2.9.   Guide Lines for Fractions.

Fig. 2.10.   Lettering Numerals and Fractions.

UNIFORMITY IN HEIGHT, INCLINATION,
AND STRENGTH OF LINE IS ESSENTIAL
FOR GOOD LETTERING.

Fig. 2.11.   Uniformity in Lettering.

   2.8. Uniformity in lettering.   Uniformity in height, inclination, spacing, and strength of line is essential for good lettering. Professional appearance depends as much upon uniformity as upon the correctness of the proportion and shape of the individual letters. Uniformity in height and inclination is assured by the use of guide lines and slope lines; uniformity in weight and color, by the skillful use of the pencil and proper control of the pressure of its point on the paper. The ability to space letters correctly becomes easy after continued thoughtful practice.

   2.9. Composition.   In combining letters into words, the spaces for the various combinations of letters are arranged so that the areas appear to be equal. For standard lettering, this area should be about equal to one-half the area of the letter M. If the adjacent sides be stems, this area is obtained by making the distance between the letters slightly greater than one-half the height of a letter, and a smaller amount depending on the contours, for other combinations. Examples of good and poor composition are shown in Fig. 2.12.

The space between words should be equal to or greater than the height of a letter, but not more than twice the height. The space between sentences should be somewhat greater. The distance between lines of lettering may vary from one-half the height of the capitals to one and one-half times their height.

2.10. Stability. If the areas of the upper and lower portions of certain letters are made equal, an optical illusion will cause them to appear to be unstable and top heavy. To overcome this effect, the upper portions of the letters B, E, F, H, K, S, X, and Z and the figures 2, 3, and 8 must be reduced slightly in size.

An associated form of illusion is the phenomenon that a horizontal line drawn across a rectangle at the vertical center will appear to be below

Fig. 2.12.   Letter Areas.

the center. Since the letters B, E, F, and H are particularly subject to this illusion, their central horizontal strokes must be drawn slightly above the vertical center in order to give them a more balanced and pleasing appearance.

The letters K, X, S, Z and the figures 2, 3, and 8 are stabilized by making the width of the upper portion less than the width of the lower portion.

2.11. The technique of freehand lettering. Any prospective draftsman or engineer can learn to letter if he practices intelligently and is persistent in his desire to improve. Unguided practice, however, is little better than no practice at all if mistakes are ignorantly repeated. The necessary muscular control, which must accompany the knowledge of lettering, can be developed only through constant repetition.

Pencil letters should be formed with strokes that are dark and sharp; never with strokes that are gray and indistinct. Beginners should avoid the tendency to form letters by sketching, as strokes made in this manner vary in color and width.

When lettering with ink, the results obtained depend largely upon the manner in which the pen is used. Many draftsmen blunder along with incorrect habits, then complain that the execution of good freehand lettering is impossible with an ordinary pen point. The most common result of these habits is an inability to make strokes of uniform width. This may be due to one of four causes: (1) excessive pressure on the pen point; (2) an accumulation of lint, dirt, or dried ink on the point; (3) tilting the point while forming a stroke; or (4) fresh ink on the point. The latter cause requires some explanation, since very few draftsmen know the proper method of "inking" the pen. The pen should be wiped thoroughly clean, and the ink should be deposited on the under side over the slot, as shown in Fig. 2.13. When the pen is filled in this manner, the ink feeds down the slit in an even flow, making possible the drawing of uniform curved and straight lines. If ink is placed on the point or allowed to run to the point, an excessive amount of ink will be deposited on the first letters made, and the width of the strokes will be somewhat wider than the strokes of, say, the sixth or seventh letter. (See Fig. 2.14.)

When lettering, the pen is held

Fig. 2.13. "Inking" the Pen.

INK ON POINT

Fig. 2.14.

as shown in Fig. 2.15. It should rest so loosely between the fingers that it can be slid up and down with the other hand.

The thin film of oil on a new point must be removed by wiping before it is used. However, never "break in" a new point unless absolutely necessary, for an old one that is clean and in good condition will give the most satisfactory results. A lettering pen point is a valuable instrument and must be treated as such. When not in use, it should be removed from the holder and placed in the instrument case. To protect a point from abuse, it should never be loaned.

Fig. 2.15. Holding the Pen.

2.12. Letter groups. The inclined letters shown in the following figures have been arranged in related groups. In laying out the characters, the number of widths has been reduced to the smallest number consistent with good appearance; similarities of shape have been emphasized and minute differences have been eliminated. Each letter is drawn to a large size on a cross-section grid that is two units wider, to facilitate the study of its characteristic shape and proportions. Arrows with numbers indicate the order and direction of the strokes.

INCLINED STRAIGHT-LINE LETTERS

2.13. The I, T, L, E, and F (Fig. 2.16). The letter *I* is the basic or stem stroke. The horizontal stroke of the *T* is drawn first, and the stem

starts at the exact center of the bar.   The L is 5 units wide, but it is often
desirable to reduce this width when an L is used in combination with such
letters as A and T.   It should be observed that the letter L consists of
the first two strokes of the E.   The middle bar of the E is $3\frac{1}{2}$ units long
and is placed slightly above the center for stability.   The top bar is one-
half unit shorter than the bottom bar.   The letter F is the E with the
bottom bar omitted.

2.14. The H and N (Fig. 2.17).   Stroke 3 of the H should be slightly
above the center, for stability.   The outside parallel strokes of the N are
drawn first to permit an accurate estimate of its width.   The inclined
stroke should intersect these accurately at their extremities.

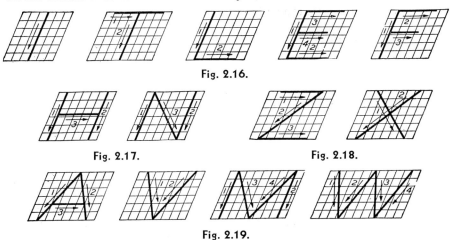

Fig. 2.16.

Fig. 2.17.   Fig. 2.18.

Fig. 2.19.

2.15. The Z and X (Fig. 2.18).   The top of the Z should be one unit
narrower than the bottom, for stability.   In the smaller sizes, this letter
may be formed without lifting the pen.   The X is similar to the Z in that
the top is made one unit narrower than the bottom.   The inclined strokes
cross slightly above center.

2.16. The A, V, M, and W (Fig. 2.19).   The horizontal bar of the A
is located up from the bottom a distance equal to one-third of the height of
the letter.   It should be noted that the bisector of the enclosing parallelogram passes though the vertex, and that the inclined strokes are not
parallel to the slope lines.   The V is the letter A inverted without the
crossbar, and is the same width.   The
letters M and W are the widest letters of
the alphabet.   The outside strokes of the
M are drawn first, so that its width
may be judged accurately.   The outside
strokes of this letter are parallel, and the
inside strokes meet at the center of the

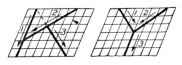

Fig. 2.20.

base.   The W is formed by two modified V's.   Strokes 1 and 3 are practically vertical.   Alternate strokes are parallel.

2.17. The K and Y (Fig. 2.20).   The top of the letter K should be
one unit narrower than the bottom, for stability.   Stroke 2 intersects the

stem one-third up from the bottom.   Stroke 3 is approximately perpendicular to stroke 2, and, if extended, would touch the stem at the top. The strokes of the *Y* meet at the center of the enclosing parallelogram.

INCLINED CURVED-LINE LETTERS

2.18. The O, Q, C, and G (Fig. 2.21).   The letters *O*, *Q*, *C*, and *G* are formed by ellipses.   Stroke 1 of the letter *O* starts just to the right of the top and continues to the left around the side to a point beyond the bottom.   Thus stroke 1 forms more than half of the ellipse.   The *Q* is the letter *O* with the added kern, which is a straight line located slightly to the right of the bottom tangent point.   The *C* is based on the *O*, but since

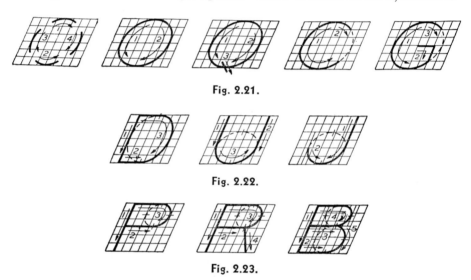

Fig. 2.21.

Fig. 2.22.

Fig. 2.23.

it is not a complete ellipse, it is narrower than either the *O* or *Q*.   The top extends one unit down and the bottom one unit up on the right side.   *G* is similar to *C*.   The horizontal portion of stroke 2 starts at the center, and the inclined portion is parallel to the side of the parallelogram.

2.19. The D, U, and J (Fig. 2.22).   The first two strokes of the *D* form an incomplete letter *L*.   Stroke 3 starts as a horizontal line, and then forms one-half of a perfect ellipse.   The bottom third of the *U* is one-half of an ellipse, and the stroke making it starts one-third up from the base line.   *J* is similar to the letter *U*.   The bottom third is one-half of a perfect ellipse.

2.20. The P, R, and B (Fig. 2.23).   The middle horizontal bar of the *P* is located at the center of stroke 1.   The curved portion of stroke 3 is one-half of a perfect ellipse.   The *R* is constructed similarly to the *P*. The tail joins at the point of tangency of the ellipse and middle bar.   To stabilize the letter *B*, the top is made one-half unit narrower than the bottom and the middle bar is placed slightly above the center.   The curves are halves of ellipses.

Fig. 2.24.

2.21. The S and & (Fig. 2.24). The upper and lower portions of the *S* are perfect ellipses with one-quarter removed. The top ellipse should be made one-half unit narrower than the lower one, for stability. In the smaller sizes this letter may be made with one or two strokes, depending upon its size. The true ampersand is made with three strokes. Professional draftsmen, however, usually represent an ampersand with a character formed by using portions of the upper and lower ellipses of the numeral 8 with the addition of two short bars.

INCLINED NUMERALS

2.22. The 1, 7, and 4 (Fig. 2.25). The stem stroke of the *4* is located one unit in from the right side. The bar is one and one-half units above the base. The stem of the *7* terminates at the center of the base of the parallelogram directly below the left end of the bar.

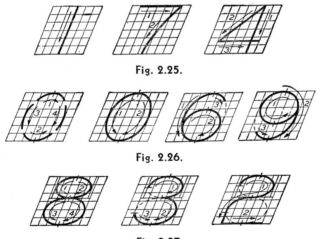

Fig. 2.25.

Fig. 2.26.

Fig. 2.27.

2.23. The 0, 6, and 9 (Fig. 2.26). The cipher, which is one unit narrower than the letter *O*, is the basic form for this group. In the figure *6*, the right side of the large ellipse ends one unit down from the top, and the left side ends at the center of the base. The small loop is slightly more than three-fourths of a perfect ellipse. The *9* is the *6* inverted.

2.24. The 8, 3, and 2 (Fig. 2.27). Each of these figures is related to the letter *S*, and the same rule of stability should be observed in their construction. The top portion of the figure *8* is shorter and one-half unit narrower than the lower portion. Each loop is a perfect ellipse tangent to the sides of its enclosing parallelogram. The figure *3* is the *8* with the lower left quarter of the upper loop and the upper left quarter of the lower loop omitted. The *2* is simply three-quarters of the upper loop of the *8* and the upper left quarter of the lower loop of the *8* with straight lines added.

Fig. 2.28.

2.25. The 5 (Fig. 2.28). This figure is a modification of the related groups previously described. The top is one-half unit narrower than the bottom, for stability. The curve is a segment of a perfect ellipse, ending one unit up from the bottom.

LOWER-CASE LETTERS AND FRACTIONS

2.26. Single-stroke lower-case letters. Single-stroke lower-case letters, either vertical or inclined, are commonly used on map drawings, topographic drawings, structural drawings, and in survey field books. They are particularly suitable for long notes and statements because, first, they can be executed much faster than capitals and, second, words and statements formed with them can be read more easily.

2.27. Inclined lower-case letters. The construction of inclined lower-case letters is based upon the straight line and the ellipse. This basic principle of forming letters is followed more closely for lower-case letters than for capitals. The body portions are two-thirds the height of the related capitals. As shown in Fig.

Fig. 2.29.

2.29, ascenders extend to the cap line, and descenders descend to the drop line. For lower-case letters based on a capital letter six units high, the waistline is two units down from the top and the drop line two units below the base line.

Fig. 2.30.

The order of stroke, direction of stroke, and formation of the letters follow the same principles as for the capitals. The letters are presented in family groups having related characteristics, to enable the beginner to understand their construction.

2.28. The i, l, k, and t (Fig. 2.30). All letters of this group are formed by straight lines of standard slope. The *i* is drawn four units high, and the dot is placed halfway between the waistline and cap line. Stroke 2 of the *k* starts at the waistline and intersects stroke 1 two units above the base. Stroke 3, extended, should intersect stroke 1 at the top. The *t* is five units high, and the crossbar is on the waistline.

2.29. The v, w, x, and z (Fig. 2.31). All of these letters are similar to the capitals. Stroke 1 of the *w* is practically vertical, and the alternate strokes are parallel.   The width of the top of both the x and the z is made one-half unit less than the width across the bottom, for stability.

2.30. The o, a, b, d, p, and q (Fig. 2.32).   The bodies of the letters in this group are formed by the letter o, and they differ only in the position and length of the stem stroke.   The o is made with two strokes, and the first stroke should form more than half of the ellipse.

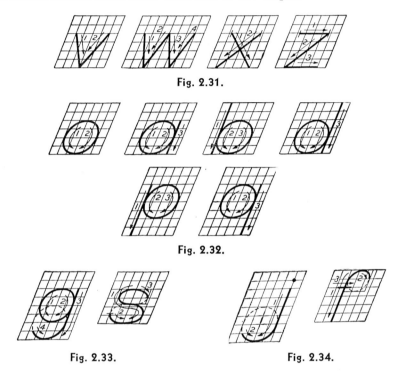

Fig. 2.31.

Fig. 2.32.

Fig. 2.33.   Fig. 2.34.

2.31. The g and s (Fig. 2.33).   The g is related to the letters o and y. Stroke 3 starts at the waistline and ends slightly beyond the point of tangency of the curve with the drop line.   The lower-case s is almost identical to the capital S.

2.32. The j and f (Fig. 2.34).   The portion of the j above the base line is the letter i.   The elliptical curve is the same as that which forms the tail of the g.   The f is two and one-half units wide, stroke 1 starting slightly to the right of the point of tangency with the cap line.

2.33. The c and e (Fig. 2.35).   The c is a modified letter o.   It is not a complete ellipse.   Therefore, its width is less than its height.   Stroke 1 ends one unit up on the right side, stroke 2 one unit down.   The e is

Fig. 2.35.

similarly constructed, except for the fact that stroke 2 continues as a curve and finishes as a horizontal line that terminates at the middle of the back.

2.34. The h, n, r, and m (Fig. 2.36).   The curve of the *h* is the upper portion of the letter *o*.   Stroke 2 starts two units above the bottom of the stem and finishes parallel to stroke 1.   The *n* differs from the *h* in that the stem stroke extends only from the waistline to the base line.   The *r* is a portion of the letter *n*, stroke 2 ending one unit down from the top. The *m* consists of two modified letter *n*'s.   The straight portions of strokes 2 and 3 are parallel to stroke 1.

2.35. The u and y (Fig. 2.37).   The letter *u* is an inverted *n*, and the curve is a portion of the letter *o*.   It should be noted that stroke 2 extends to the base line.   The *y* is a partial combination of the letters *u* and *g*.

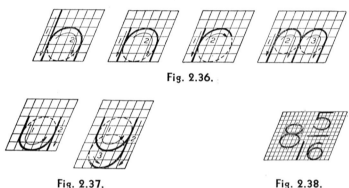

Fig. 2.36.

Fig. 2.37.   **Fig. 2.38.**

2.36. Fractions.   The height of the figures in the numerator and denominator is equal to three-fourths the height of the whole number, and the total height of the fraction is twice the height of the whole number.   The division bar should be horizontal and centered between the fraction numerals as shown in Fig. 2.38.   It should be noted that the sloping center line of the fraction bisects both the numerator and denominator and is parallel to the sloping center line of the whole number.

To assure the best possible appearance, it is advisable to use seven horizontal guide lines for a combined whole number and a fraction (Figs. 2.9 and 2.10).

VERTICAL LETTERS AND NUMERALS

2.37. Vertical capitals.   Although many commercial draftsmen favor the inclined letters, recent surveys indicate that vertical letters are being more generally used.   Since the order and direction of the strokes as well as the general proportions of the vertical letters are the same as previously explained for the inclined form, there is no need for further description.   Their general formation is illustrated in Fig. 2.39.

2.38. Vertical lower-case.   The vertical lower-case letters, illustrated in Fig. 2.40, are constructed in the same manner as inclined letters. The order and direction of strokes, as well as the proportions, are essentially the same.

Fig. 2.39. Vertical Capitals.

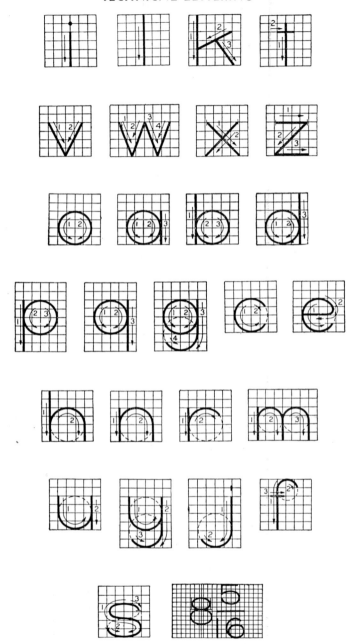

Fig. 2.40.   Vertical Lower-Case Letters and Fractions.

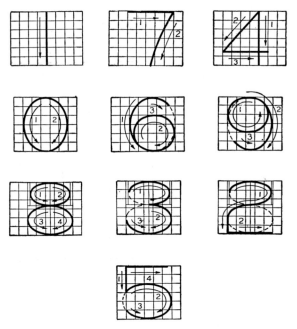

Fig. 2.41. Vertical Numerals.

2.39. Vertical numerals. Vertical numerals are made with the same order and direction of stroke and have the same proportions as the inclined numerals (Fig. 2.41).

2.40. Large caps and small caps in combination. Many commercial draftsmen use a combination of large caps and small caps in forming words, as illustrated in Fig. 2.42. When this style is used, the height of the small caps should be approximately four-fifths the height of the first capital letter of the word.

HANDLE PIN
C.R.S. I REQ'D.

Fig. 2.42. Use of Large and Small Caps.

2.41. Titles. Every drawing, sketch, graph, chart, or diagram has some form of descriptive title to impart certain necessary information and to identify it. On machine drawings, where speed and legibility are prime requirements, titles are usually single-stroke Gothic. On display drawings, maps, architectural designs, and so on, which call for an artistic effect, the titles are usually composed of "built-up" ornate letters.

APPROVED BY CUSTOMER	ROSS-SHOER CO.
ADAMS MFG. CO.	
AURORA. ILL.	

ASSEMBLY
STANDARD DUTY
FLANGE UNIT

SCALE FULL SIZE	DATE JAN.3,1959
DRAWN BY CARL KING	CHECKED BY J.B.JONES
TRACED BY K.BODINE	APPROVED BY W.L.KOE
ORDER NO. M:L:24631	DRG. S-19-9612

Fig. 2.43. A Machine-Drawing Title Block.

Figure 2.43 shows a title block that might be used on a machine drawing. It should be noted that the important items are made more prominent by the use of larger letters formed with heavier lines. Less important data, such as the scale, date, drafting information, and so on, are given less prominence.

To be pleasing in appearance, a title should be symmetrical about a vertical center line and should have some simple geometrical form (Fig. 2.44).

An easy way to insure the symmetry of a title is first to count the letters and word spaces, then, working to the left and right from the middle space or letter on the vertical center line, to sketch the title lightly in pencil, before lettering it in finished form (Fig. 2.45a). An alternate method is to letter a trial line along the edge of a piece of scrap paper and place it in a balanced position just above the location of the line to be lettered, as shown in Fig. 2.45(b).

Fig. 2.44.   Symmetrical Titles.

FAN DETAILS

FAN DETAILS

FAN DETAILS

(a)   (b)

Fig. 2.45.   Spacing Letters in a Balanced Line.

2.42. Mechanical lettering devices and templates. Although mechanical lettering devices produce letters that may appear stiff to an expert, they are used in many drafting rooms for the simple reason that they enable even the unskilled to do satisfactory lettering with ink.

Fig. 2.46.   Leroy Lettering Device.

The average draftsman rightly prefers stiff uniformity to wavy lines and irregular shapes. One of the oldest instruments of this sort on the market is the *Wrico* outfit. With a satisfactory set of Wrico pens and templates, letters ranging in size from $\frac{3}{32}''$ to $\frac{1}{2}''$ in height may be executed. The letters are formed by a stylographic pen that is guided around the sides of openings in a template made of transparent pyralin.

The *Leroy* device, shown in Fig. 2.46, is possibly even more efficient than the Wrico, for it does not require the sliding of a template to complete a letter.

2.43. Commercial Gothic.   All the letters in the commercial Gothic alphabet (see Fig. 2.47) are seven units high.   Although the stems of the letters shown in the illustration are one unit thick, stem thickness may vary from one-tenth to one-fifth of a letter's height depending upon the effect desired.   Since all their curves are circle arcs, Gothic letters are comparatively easy to construct.   They are drawn first in outline, in skeleton form, and then are filled in with a ball-pointed pen.   This style,

Fig. 2.47.   Gothic Letters.

Fig. 2.48. Modern Roman Letters.

TYPE 1

ABCDEFGHIJKLMNOP
QRSTUVWXYZ&
1234567890 $\frac{1}{2} \frac{3}{4} \frac{5}{8} \frac{7}{16}$
TO BE USED FOR MAIN TITLES
& DRAWING NUMBERS

TYPE 2

ABCDEFGHIJKLMNOPQR
STUVWXYZ&
1234567890 $\frac{13}{64} \frac{5}{8} \frac{1}{2}$
TO BE USED FOR SUB-TITLES

TYPE 3

ABCDEFGHIJKLMNOPQRSTUVWXYZ&
1234567890 $\frac{1}{2} \frac{3}{4} \frac{5}{8} \frac{7}{16}$
FOR HEADINGS AND PROMINENT NOTES

TYPE 4

ABCDEFGHIJKLMNOPQRSTUVWXYZ&
1234567890 $\frac{1}{2} \frac{1}{4} \frac{3}{8} \frac{5}{16} \frac{7}{32} \frac{1}{8}$
FOR BILLS OF MATERIAL, DIMENSIONS & GENERAL NOTES

TYPE 5

OPTIONAL TYPE SAME AS TYPE 4 BUT USING TYPE 3 FOR FIRST LETTER OF PRINCIPAL WORDS. MAY BE USED FOR SUB-TITLES & NOTES ON THE BODY OF DRAWINGS.

TYPE 6

abcdefghijklmnopqrstuvwxyz
Type 6 may be used in place of
Type 4 with capitals of Type 3

Fig. 2.49. Lettering—American Standard.*

from which the single-stroke engineering letters are derived, is used to some extent for titles on machine drawings, but more frequently it appears on maps, charts, and graphs that are prepared for display purposes.

———

*ASA Y14.2—1957.

2.44. Modern Roman. The Modern Roman letters shown in Fig. 2.48 are used extensively by engineers for names and titles on maps. Students should be familiar with this alphabet, for it appears in all modern publications. As in the case with the Gothic style, these letters must be drawn first in outline, in skeleton form, and then be filled in with a ball-pointed or wide-line pen. The straight lines are usually drawn with a ruling pen. The curved lines, except for the serifs, may be formed either mechanically or freehand. When attempting to construct this type of letter it is wise to bear in mind the following facts: (1) All vertical strokes are heavy except those forming the letters *M, N,* and *U.* (2) All horizontal strokes are light. (3) The serif extends about one unit on either side of the body of the stem. (4) The width of the heavy strokes may vary from one-eighth to one-sixth of the height of the letter.

Roman letters may be drawn either extended or compressed, depending upon the area to be covered or the space restrictions determined by other lettering, such as on maps. If a draftsman using the Roman-style letter would have his work look professional, he must pay particular attention to detail. Care must be taken to keep the proportions of a letter appearing more than once in a name or title identical. Most persons experienced at drawing should have little difficulty with these letters, if they follow carefully the details and proportions given in Fig. 2.48.

2.45. Problems. It should be noted that while these exercises are offered for the purpose of giving the student practice in letter forms and word composition, they also contain statements of important principles of drawing, shop notes, and titles with which every engineering draftsman should be familiar. Each lettering exercise should be submitted to the instructor for severe criticism before the student proceeds to the next. Sec. 2.2 should be reread before starting the first exercise.

1. Letter the statement given in Fig. 2.50 in $\frac{5}{32}''$ capital letters using an appropriate pencil that is suited to the type of paper being used and one that will produce uniform opaque lines. The necessary guide lines should be drawn with a hard pencil.

POOR LETTERING DETRACTS FROM THE APPEARANCE OF A DRAWING

Fig. 2.50.

2–3. Letter the statements given in Figs. 2.51–2.52 in $\frac{1}{8}''$ capital letters using an appropriate pencil that is suited to the type of paper being used and one that will produce uniform opaque lines. The necessary guide lines should be drawn with a hard pencil.

IN LEARNING TO LETTER CERTAIN DEFINITE RULES OF FORM & DESIGN MUST BE OBSERVED

Fig. 2.51.

WHEN LETTERING WITH INK, THE INK SHOULD BE WELL ABOVE THE TIP OF THE POINT

Fig. 2.52.

4. Letter the statement given in Fig. 2.53 in $\frac{5}{32}''$ capital letters using an appropriate pencil that is suited to the type of paper being used and one that will produce uniform opaque lines. The necessary guide lines should be drawn with a hard pencil.

#26 (.1470) DRILL AND REAM FOR #1×1 TAPER PIN WITH PC #41 IN POSITION

Fig. 2.53.

5–6. Letter the statements given in Figs. 2.54–2.55 in $\frac{1}{8}''$ capital letters using an appropriate pencil that is suited to the type of paper being used and one that will produce uniform opaque lines. The necessary guide lines should be drawn with a hard pencil. (See Fig. 2.9.)

S.A.E. 1020 - COLD DRAWN STEEL BAR
1-14NF-3   1-8NC-2   1-5 SQUARE
BREAK ALL SHARP CORNERS UNLESS OTHERWISE SPECIFIED

Fig. 2.54.

$\frac{5}{16}$ DRILL-$\frac{3}{8}$-16NC-2 $\frac{21}{32}$DRILL - C'BORE $\frac{29}{32}$D ×$\frac{7}{8}$DEEP -2 HOLES

Fig. 2.55.

7–16. Letter the following statements in $\frac{1}{8}''$ capital letters using an appropriate pencil that is suited to the type of paper being used and one that will produce uniform opaque lines. The necessary guide lines should be drawn with a hard pencil.

(7) A GOOD STUDENT REALIZES THE IMPORTANCE OF NEAT AND ATTRACTIVE LETTERING.

A GOOD STUDENT REALIZES THE IMPORTANCE OF NEAT AND ATTRACTIVE LETTERING

DOE, J.X.

Fig. 2.56.

(8) THE CIRCUMFERENCE OF A CIRCLE MAY BE DIVIDED INTO TWENTY-FOUR EQUAL ARCS USING ONLY A T-SQUARE IN COMBINATION WITH THE 30–60° AND 45° TRIANGLES.

(9) A TRUE ELLIPSE MAY BE CONSTRUCTED BY THE TRAMMEL METHOD.

(10) THE POSITION OF THE VIEWS OF AN ORTHOGRAPHIC DRAWING MUST BE IN STRICT ACCORDANCE WITH THE UNIVERSALLY RECOGNIZED ARRANGEMENT ILLUSTRATED IN FIG. 6.4.

(11) THE VIEWS OF AN ORTHOGRAPHIC DRAWING SHOULD SHOW THE THREE DIMENSIONS, LENGTH, HEIGHT, AND DEPTH.

(12) AN INVISIBLE LINE SHOULD START WITH A SPACE WHEN IT FORMS AN EXTENSION OF A SOLID LINE.

(13) THE FRONT VIEW OF AN ORTHOGRAPHIC DRAWING SHOULD BE THE VIEW THAT SHOWS THE CHARACTERISTIC SHAPE OF THE OBJECT.

(14) AN AUXILIARY VIEW SHOWS THE TRUE SIZE AND SHAPE OF AN INCLINED SURFACE.

(15) A SECTIONAL VIEW SHOWS THE INTERIOR CONSTRUCTION OF AN OBJECT.

(16) #404 WOODRUFF KEY.

DRILL AND REAM FOR #2 TAPER PIN WITH PC#10 IN POSITION.

17–21. Using a hard pencil, draw two or more sets of horizontal and inclined guide lines for $\frac{5}{32}$" letters, then execute directly with India ink the following exercises in lower-case letters:

(17) "The front and top views are always in line vertically."

(18) "The front and side views are in line horizontally."

(19) "The depth of the top view is the same as the depth of the side view."

(20) "If a line is perpendicular to a plane of projection, its projection will be a point."

(21) "If a line is parallel to a plane of projection, its projection on the plane is exactly the same length as the true length of the line."

22–26. Draw two or more sets of both horizontal and inclined guide lines, and letter the following series of words, whole numbers, and fractions, once in pencil and once in India ink.   If a Braddock Lettering Triangle is available, draw the seven guide lines shown in Fig. 2.9.

(22) $1\frac{1}{2}$, $3\frac{3}{4}$, $2\frac{7}{8}$, $1\frac{9}{16}$, $9\frac{17}{32}$, $4\frac{5}{8}$, $9\frac{13}{32}$, $7\frac{13}{64}$, $8\frac{1}{2}$, $\frac{11}{16}$, $5\frac{3}{8}$.

(23) $\frac{1}{2}$" $\times$ $2\frac{3}{4}$" HEX. HD. CAP SCREW, $\frac{3}{8}$ $\times$ $1\frac{1}{4}$UNC HEX. HD. BOLT & HEX. NUT.

(24) $\frac{3}{16}$ DRILL—$\frac{3}{8}$ DEEP, $\frac{1}{4}$ DRILL—4 HOLES, $\frac{1}{8}$ $\times$ 45° CHAMFER.

(25) $\frac{1}{8}$ AM. STD. PIPE TAP, $\frac{1}{2}$—13UNC—2B.

(26) $2\angle s$ $2\frac{1}{2}$ $\times$ $2\frac{1}{2}$ $\times$ $\frac{1}{4}$ $\times$ 8'–4", 10" I 30#, 24" W74#.

27. Draw horizontal and inclined guide lines and letter the following detail titles.   Use $\frac{5}{32}$" capitals for the part names and $\frac{1}{8}$" capitals for the remainder of the titles.

BASE		BUSHING		SPINDLE	
C.I.	1 REQ'D	BRO.	1 REQ'D	C.R.S.	1 REQ'D

28. Letter the following map title in Modern Roman.   The letters of the first and third lines are to be $\frac{1}{2}$" high, and those of the second line, which give the name of the county, are to be $\frac{3}{4}$" high.   Draw all necessary guide lines.

MAP OF

TIPPECANOE COUNTY

INDIANA

3

Drawing Equipment
and Use of Instruments

ESSENTIAL EQUIPMENT

3.1. The necessary instruments and materials needed for making ordinary engineering drawings are shown in Fig. 3.1. The instruments in the plush-lined case should be particularly well made and easy to service, for with cheap, inferior ones, it is often difficult to produce accurate drawings of professional quality. Since good equipment will last many years if treated with reasonable care, it is poor economy for the beginner to purchase an inferior set, simply because it is cheap, with the intention of later obtaining a better one. It is not easy to distinguish good instruments from poor ones merely by observing their general appearance or by studying the figures on price tags. The student, before purchasing his equipment, should seek the advice of an expert or consult the catalogs of dealers whom he knows to be reliable. He should then procure the very best he can afford.

Fig. 3.1. Essential Drafting Equipment.

3.2. List of equipment and materials. The following list is a practical selection of equipment and materials necessary for making pencil drawings and ink tracings.

(1) Case of drawing instruments containing the following: 6″ compass with lengthening bar, pencil leg, and pen leg; 6″ dividers (with hairspring adjustment); ruling pens; bow pencil; bow pen; bow dividers

(2) Drawing board.
(3) T-square.
(4) 10″ 30°–60° triangle.
(5) French curve.

*(6) 45° triangle.
(7) Scale (either one triangular or three flat scales).
(8) Drawing pencils (6H, 4H, 2H, and F or H).
(9) Pencil pointer (file or sandpaper pad).
(10) Thumb tacks, brad machine, or Scotch tape.
(11) Pencil eraser.
(12) Cleaning eraser.
(13) Erasing shield.
(14) Dusting brush.
(15) Bottle of black waterproof drawing ink.
(16) Pen wiper.
(17) Penholder.
(18) Lettering pens.
(19) Protractor.
(20) Pad of sketching paper (plain or ruled).
(21) Drawing paper.
(22) Tracing paper.
(23) Tracing cloth.

To these may be added the following useful items:

(24) Hard Arkansas oilstone.
(25) Piece of soapstone.
(26) Ink-bottle holder.
(27) Lettering instrument.
(28) Steel eraser.
(29) Tack lifter.
(30) Slide rule.

3.3. The set of instruments. A standard set of drawing instruments in a velvet-lined case and an alternate set, which is capable of fulfilling the needs of most draftsmen, are shown in Figs. 3.2 and 3.3

Fig. 3.2.   A Standard Set of Drawing Instruments.

respectively.   It should be remembered that while good instruments may seem costly, they are carefully and accurately made from select materials by master craftsmen, and are of simple, sturdy construction.   The cheap ones are usually poorly made imitations, a fact that becomes evident after a short period of use.

A purchaser should not be misled by a large set containing many pieces that is offered at the same price as a small set containing only a

---

* A 6″ 45° Braddock Lettering Triangle, which may be used as either a triangle or a lettering instrument, may be substituted for this item.

Fig. 3.3. The Purdue Riefler Set.

few.   The instruments in the smaller set are better, and will prove more satisfactory and economical over a period of years.   If an additional instrument is required for a special type of drawing, it is advisable to purchase it as a separate piece.

Fig. 3.4. The Compass (Standard Set).

3.4. Compasses and dividers (standard set).   Although good instruments may be obtained in three common patterns, the best ones offered by leading manufacturers are of the square form, the type favored by draftsmen in the United States (Fig. 3.4).

The legs of a modern high-grade compass are fastened by a pivot joint. Usually the joint consists of two discs held in a yoke between adjustable cone-shaped or ball-shaped pivots. The screws in the yoke regulate the pressure between the discs so that the friction will be sufficient to allow the legs of the compass to be adjusted easily and yet maintain settings.

Most instruments have a convenient handle with some form of straightening device for keeping the handle centered in a vertical position when the instrument is in use.

Fig. 3.5. Testing a Compass for Alignment.

One leg of nearly all compasses is manufactured with a socket joint, which allows the insertion of either the pen leg for ink work or the lengthening bar for a longer working radius. It is essential for the shank of an attachment to be well fitted. Both legs of a compass are provided with knee joints. These allow the legs to be adjusted perpendicular to the paper when a large circle is being drawn. Figure 3.5 shows the method for testing a compass for alignment. It should be observed that the alignment of the compass is perfect only if the point of the needle touches the end of the closed nibs exactly at the center of the point. A few compasses are equipped with a hairspring on the pivot leg for making minute adjustments in the distance between the points.

PLAIN DIVIDERS
(a)

HAIRSPRING DIVIDERS
(b)

Fig. 3.6.   Dividers.

Since dividers are used to transfer measurements or to divide lines into any number of equal parts, they differ from the compass in that both legs terminate in sharp steel points. The legs may be alike, as shown in Fig. 3.6(a) or one leg may be provided with a hairspring adjustment, as in Fig. 3.6(b). The hairspring is convenient for making minute variations between the points, and is therefore to be preferred.

3.5. Bow instruments (standard set). The bow instruments include the bow dividers, bow pencil, and bow pen. These instruments are of two general designs: (1) the continuous or single type (Fig. 3.7a, b), and (2) the hook or loop-spring type (Fig. 3.7c).   Either pattern may be purchased with side-screw (see *a*) or center-screw (see *b*, *c*) adjustment.

The spring in either type should be strong enough to keep the legs apart and insure a steady setting throughout the range of the instrument, particularly when it is open to the extreme working limit.

3.6. Ruling pens.   The most satisfactory type of ruling pen consists of two steel blades formed from one solid piece of high-grade steel, a thumb screw for regulating the distance between the ends (nibs) of the blades, and a handle made of wood (sometimes ebony), or metal.   The best drawing pens have blades of high-speed steel or noncorrosive stainless steel with butt-welded, high-speed steel points.   Pens of this type cost more than ordinary pens, but the points retain their shape and edge four

Fig. 3.7.   The Bow Instruments (Standard Set).

or five times as long as ordinary points, even when the ordinary points are made of the finest carbon steel.   Good pens, coming from the factory correctly shaped and sharpened as they do, rarely require touching up, and the excellent quality of line work that can be achieved with them justifies the higher price they command.   Cheap pens usually require frequent sharpening and are an annoyance from the start.

Many devices have been invented for opening the blades for cleaning without changing the setting of the adjusting screw (Fig. 3.8*b*, *c*, *d*), but most of these are troublesome and are not as satisfactory as the plain spring-blade type.   The slide-catch design (Fig. 3.8*b*) is the type usually found in medium-priced drawing sets.

3.7. Large-bow sets.   Large-bow sets are preferred by many draftsmen, especially in the aircraft and automotive fields.   A complete set might include the following: large bow (compass), beam compass with an extension bar for drawing very large circles, dividers, small bow, and a slip-handle ruling pen.   See Fig. 3.3.   The pen attachment, shown assembled with the slip handle to form the ruling pen, may be removed and used with the large bow as the pen leg.   Through the use of the

PLAIN SPRING BLADE TYPE
(a)

SLIDE CATCH TYPE
(b)

SPRING HINGE TYPE
(c)

CLICK TYPE
(d)

Fig. 3.8.   Ruling Pens.

attachments the small bow may be converted into bow dividers, bow pencil, or bow pen as needed.   Large-bow sets may be purchased with various combinations of the instruments listed.   Since the large bow (Fig. 3.9) is particularly suited for drawing circles of very small size up to ten inches in diameter, its range covers that of both the bow instruments and the compass (without the extension bar) of the standard set.

The large bow is preferred by its advocates because its sturdy construction permits the draftsman to exert the pressure necessary to secure black, opaque lines on pencil drawings that are to be used for making prints.

3.8. The drawing board.   Drawing boards should be made of selected straight-grained, soft wood strips that have been thoroughly seasoned.   The most popular type is constructed of $\frac{3}{4}''$ to $1''$ soft white pine or basswood reinforced by end strips (cleats), which are attached to the main body with tongue-and-groove or dovetailed and glued joints.   The cleats provide for expansion, prevent splitting and warping, and furnish a smooth guiding edge for the T-square head.   The working surface (top) must be smooth as well as a true plane, and both edges should be perfectly straight so that either may be used as a working edge.   The board shown in Fig. 3.28 has two working surfaces.

Fig. 3.9.   Large Bow (Vemco).

3.9. The T-square.   The most popular T-square for ordinary work (Fig. 3.10a) is made with a head of hardwood to which is fastened rigidly a blade lined with transparent material to resist warping and to permit lines of the drawing to be seen beneath the edge.   The working edges, which are the upper edge of the blade and the inside edge of the head, should be perfectly straight.   Although it is not necessary, it is desirable that these edges be at right angles to each other.

T-squares usually have ebonized hardwood heads and straight-grained maple blades, although such woods as ash, boxwood, mahogany, and

ORDINARY
(a)

ADJUSTABLE HEAD
(b)

Fig. 3.10.   T-Square.

pearwood are often used.   Occasionally T-squares with steel blades and metal heads are desirable for very accurate work.

Some draftsmen prefer a T-square with an adjustable double head. The type of head shown in Fig. 3.10(b) is designed for drawing parallel inclined lines.

In commercial drafting rooms, either a Universal Drafting Machine (Fig. 3.88) or a parallel-rule attachment is often used in preference to a T-square.   The parallel rule is chosen by many draftsmen because the straightedge, when properly handled, usually remains in perfect alignment.

3.10. The triangles (Fig. 3.11).   Triangles are made of various materials, but the transparent amber-colored celluloid ones are to be preferred, for they not only permit the drawing to be seen beneath them, but also are less likely to warp or nick than are those made of wood. The working edges of a triangle should be perfectly straight and all the angles between them should be true.

The 45° and the 30° × 60° triangles are the ones commonly used for

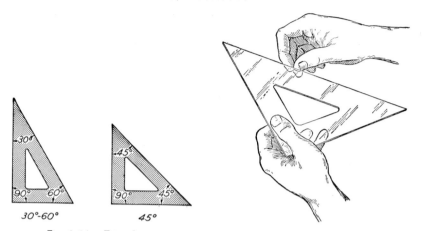

30°-60°   45°

Fig. 3.11.   Triangles.   **Fig. 3.12.   Testing a Triangle for Nicks.**

ordinary work. Special triangles, such as the 15° × 75°, and the 22½° × 67½°, are convenient but not essential.

A popular combination consists of a 10″ or 12″ 30° × 60° triangle and an 8″ or 10″ 45° triangle. These should be at least 0.06″ in thickness and have finger lifts.

3.11. Scales. A number of kinds of scales are available for varied types of engineering design. For convenience, however, all scales may be classified according to their use as mechanical engineer's scales (both fractional and decimal), civil engineer's scales, architect's scales, or metric scales.

Fig. 3.13.   Mechanical Engineer's Scale (Full-Divided).

The mechanical engineer's scales are generally of the full-divided type, graduated proportionally to give reductions based on inches. On one form the principal units are divided into the common fractions of an inch: 4, 8, 16, 32 parts (Fig. 3.13). The scales are indicated on the stick as eighth size (1½″ = 1′), quarter size (3″ = 1′), half size (6″ = 1′), and full size.

Since the decimal system, employed in automotive design for more than twenty years and in aircraft design since World War II, has been rapidly spreading into other fields in recent years, decimals of an inch may soon replace the use of fractions in most of the divisions of American industry. In any case, the use of decimal scales has become so widespread that the American Standards Association found it desirable to establish the standard ASA Z75.1–1955 for markings on scales used with decimal-inch dimensioning. The full-size scale, which has the principal units (inches) divided into fiftieths, is particularly suited for use with the two place decimal system (Fig. 3.14). The half-size, three-eighths size, and quarter-size scales have the principal units divided into tenths (Fig. 3.39).

The civil engineer's (chain) scales are full-divided, and are graduated in decimal parts, usually 10, 20, 30, 40, 50, 60, 80, and 100 divisions to the inch (Fig. 3.15).

Fig. 3.14. Engineer's Decimal Scale.

Fig. 3.15. Civil Engineer's Scale.

Fig. 3.16. Architect's Scale (Open-Divided).

Fig. 3.17. Scale Forms.

Architect's scales differ from mechanical engineer's scales in that the divisions represent a foot, and the end units are divided into inches, half inches, quarter inches, and so forth (6, 12, 24, 48, or 96 parts). The usual scales are $\frac{1}{8}'' = 1'$, $\frac{1}{4}'' = 1'$, $\frac{3}{8}'' = 1'$, $\frac{1}{2}'' = 1'$, $\frac{3}{4}'' = 1'$, $1'' = 1'$, $1\frac{1}{2}'' = 1'$, and $3'' = 1'$ (Fig. 3.16).

Practically all scales are made of thoroughly seasoned boxwood, with the divisions indicated along the edges. The cheaper ones are of natural wood finish, while the better ones are coated with white celluloid. Scales are available in either the triangular form (Fig. 3.17a and b) or one of the flat forms shown in Fig. 3.17(c), (d), (e), and (f).

3.12. Curves. Irregular or french curves are used for drawing curves other than circular arcs. Their ruling edges are composed of combinations of spirals, ellipses, and parabolas.   Although many commercial draftsmen own a variety of curves or have access to specialized sets of curves that are suitable for their particular type of work, students in technical schools usually find that a curve similar to any of those shown in Fig. 3.18 is adequate.

Probably the most satisfactory curves are those made of transparent amber celluloid through which the lines of the drawing may be seen.

Courtesy Keuffel & Esser Co.

Fig. 3.18.   Irregular Curves.

3.13.   Pencils.   Good quality drawing pencils, having uniform leads enclosed in straight-grained wood that will sharpen well, are essential to good technical drawing.   Cheap pencils should be avoided.

Pencil manufacturers grade drawing pencils from 9H (hard) to 6B (very soft).   Ordinarily, the professional draftsman has available a selection of good, well-sharpened pencils graded from hard to medium soft.   Pencil leads are graded as follows: 9H, 8H, 7H, and 6H, very hard; 5H and 4H, medium hard; 3H and 2H, medium; H and F, medium soft; HB and B, soft; 2B, 3B, 4B, 5B, and 6B, very soft.   The grades from 2B to 6B are suited for sketching and rendering. A few manufacturers offer additional grades, indicated as tracing pencils, which produce very opaque lines on tracing paper and pencil cloth.   In selecting the grade of pencil to be used, consideration always must be given to the type of surface and the hardness of the paper to be employed.

SANDPAPER PAD
(a)

ORDINARY FILE
(b)

SPECIAL FILE
(c)

Fig. 3.19.   Pencil Pointers.

Drawing pencils are made with either round or rectangular leads, the latter being for draftsmen who prefer the wedge point.

3.14.   Pencil pointers.   Either a sandpaper pad or an ordinary flat file is satisfactory for sharpening pencil and compass leads (Fig. 3.19).

3.15. Thumb tacks (Fig. 3.20). The thumb tacks best suited for use on drawing boards have thin-edge, nickel-silver heads into which short, tapering, steel pins are screwed and riveted. These offer no obstruction to the T-square. They are easy to insert and remove, and at the same time grip firmly. The stamped steel tacks are a poor investment. Their points frequently break off and their thick flat heads obstruct the movement of the T-square.

Some draftsmen use regular Scotch drafting tape instead of thumb tacks, because its smooth surface allows the T-square and triangles to slide easily, and it eliminates punching holes in the drawing board. Scotch tape, however, frequently rolls up under the T-square or straightedge.

A stapling machine, which fastens a sheet of paper to a drawing board with wire brads, may also be used.

Fig. 3.20.   Thumb Tacks.   Fig. 3.21.   Drafting Brush.

3.16. Drafting brush (Fig. 3.21). The drafting brush is useful for brushing away eraser crumbs and for removing loose graphite from newly-drawn lines before it can be spread over the paper by the T-square and triangles. Read Sec. 6.16.

3.17. Erasers. A *hard pencil eraser*, only moderately gritty, is the only eraser that should ever be used for erasing pencil and ink lines on drawing paper, tracing paper, or tracing cloth. A large-size pencil eraser with beveled ends, or its equivalent, is favored by many commercial draftsmen. Although ink erasers are highly abrasive and remove ink lines more quickly, they damage the paper to such an extent that it is difficult to redraw or draw other ink lines over surfaces where they have been used. A *soft cleaning eraser* is needed for erasing light pencil lines and cleaning soiled spots on drawings. This eraser (about $2'' \times 1'' \times \frac{3}{4}''$ in size) should be self cleaning, should not crumble, and should not weaken ink lines.

Fig. 3.22.   Erasing Shield.

3.18. The erasing shield (Fig. 3.22). An erasing shield is a thin sheet of celluloid or metal used to prevent any wrinkling of the paper and to protect other lines near a line that is being erased. A shield made of tempered spring steel, which will resist wear and will spring back flat after being bent, is to be preferred. Celluloid shields and those made of soft steel soon wear or kink.

3.19. Drawing ink. A good waterproof black drawing ink (India ink) is absolutely essential to successful drafting. It must be free-flowing and quick-drying and should make very black, opaque lines that will not smudge. It should not contain chemicals that will injure instruments, or ingredients that will separate out of solution or evaporate quickly and cause the ink to become thick and gummy.

3.20. Pen points and penholders.   The selection of penholders and pen points depends so much upon personal preference that individual experience is probably the best guide.   It is recommended, however, that the selection of pen points be made from the assortment illustrated in Fig. 2.3.

Fig. 3.23.   Protractor.

3.21. The protractor (Fig. 3.23).   The protractor, which is used for measuring and laying off angles, is usually semicircular in form.   Although the best protractors are made of nickel silver, those made of celluloid or sheet metal are suitable for ordinary work.

Fig. 3.24.   Inexpensive Protractor.

3.22. Drawing paper.   Drawing papers are available in a variety of types, weights, and colors.   For ordinary engineering drawings in pencil (working drawings, design drawings, and so forth), a heavy buff-color detail paper is preferred.   It should have a slightly grained surface in order to take pencil marks readily, and should be able to withstand repeated erasing without serious damage.   Paper of this type may be purchased in sheets or rolls.

White papers are preferred in commercial practice for display drawings of mechanisms, architectural drawings, sketches, and water-color paintings.   For these, Whatman's handmade papers in the three finishes, *HP* (hot-pressed) suitable for fine-line ink work, *CP* (cold-pressed) suitable for pencil drawing and water-color sketches, and *R* (rough) suitable for charcoal work and water sketches, are quite generally used.   Bristol (ply) board is also excellent because it is suitable for fine line work and has the added advantage of being stiff.

White lightweight bond paper, on which pencil drawings can be made and from which blueprints can be produced without making tracings, is used in many commercial drafting rooms in order to keep labor costs at a minimum.

3.23. Tracing papers and cloth.   A large variety of natural and specially prepared tracing papers are available for making ink tracings and pencil drawings from which blueprints, ozalid prints, and so forth, are made for the shop.   It is important that the paper selected be highly translucent and able to hold a workable surface under repeated erasing. The types that are treated with undesirable oils should be avoided, because they become brittle and discolor with age.

The two general types of cloth available are ink cloth and pencil cloth. The cloth used for ink is clear and transparent, dull on one side, and glossy on the other.   Pencil cloth is a white cloth with a surface specially prepared to take pencil marks readily.   It may be dull on one side only or on both sides.

USE OF INSTRUMENTS AND EQUIPMENT

3.24.   It is essential that a beginner acquire a knowledge of the proper manipulation and adjustment of drawing instruments and practice the correct technique before attempting even simple engineering drawings. If he concentrates on the right methods of handling at the very start, he will be rewarded later by neat and accurate work of professional quality.   Speed will develop naturally, and he will acquire a snap and swing that is free of unnecessary motions and awkward handling.

3.25. Pencils.   As stated in a preceding section, the grade of pencil to be used for various purposes depends upon the type of line desired, the kind of paper employed, and the humidity, which affects the surface of the paper.   On a humid day the paper surface is less resistant to the pencil and will therefore require a softer grade than when the air has much less moisture.   There is a considerable difference of opinion among teachers and draftsmen on pencil grades because of the variation among different brands of pencils of the same grade.   Drafting-room standards for line quality usually will govern.   Ordinarily, however, a draftsman should have available at least one hard pencil (6H) for the light construction lines in layout work where accuracy is required, some softer pencils (2H-4H) for repenciling finished lines, and two medium-soft ones (F-H) for freehand work.

Many draftsmen prefer the conical point for general use (Fig. 3.25), while others find the wedge point more suitable for straight-line work, because it requires less sharpening and makes a denser line (Fig. 3.26).

When sharpening a pencil, the wood should be cut away (on the unlettered end) with a knife or a pencil sharpener equipped with draftsman's cutters.   About $\frac{3}{8}$ inch of the lead should be exposed and should form a cut, including the wood, about 1½ inches long.   The lead then should be shaped to a conical point on the pointer (file or sandpaper pad). This is done by holding the file stationary in the left hand and drawing the lead toward the handle while rotating the pencil against the movement (Fig. 3.25).   All strokes should be made in the same manner, a new grip being taken each time so that each stroke starts with the pencil

REMOVE WOOD FROM UNLETTERED END

SHAPE THE POINT   CORRECTLY SHARPENED

Fig. 3.25.   Conical Point.

REMOVE WOOD FROM UNLETTERED END   SHAPE THE POINT   CORRECTLY SHARPENED

Fig. 3.26.   Wedge Point.

in the same rotated position as at the end of the preceding stroke.   The pointer always should be within easy reach because frequent sharpening of the point is necessary to obtain lines of uniform width.

3.26. Drawing pencil lines.   Pencil lines should be sharp and uniform along their entire length, and sufficiently distinct to fulfill their ultimate purposes.   Construction lines (preliminary lines) should be drawn *very* lightly so that they may be easily erased.   Finished lines should be made boldly and distinctly, with definite contrast between object lines and auxiliary lines, such as dimension lines, center lines, and section lines.   To give this contrast, which is necessary for clearness and ease in reading, object lines should be of medium width and very black. Auxiliary lines should be dark and not so wide as object lines.

When drawing a line, the pencil should be inclined slightly (about 60°) in the direction in which the line is being drawn (Fig. 3.27).   The pencil should be "pulled" (never pushed) at the same inclination for the full length of the line. If it is rotated (twirled) slowly between the fingers as the line is drawn, a symmetrical point will be maintained and a straight uniform line will be insured. This procedure helps keep the line straight and parallel to the ruling edge.

3.27. Placing and fastening the paper (Fig. 3.28). For accuracy and ease in manipulating the T-square, the drawing paper should be located well up on the board and near the left-hand edge. The lower edge of the sheet (if plain) or the lower border

Fig. 3.27.   Using the Pencil.

line (if printed) should be aligned along the working edge of the T-square before the sheet is fastened down at all four corners with thumb tacks,

Fig. 3.28.   A Sheet of Drawing Paper Fastened Down.

Scotch tape, or staples. The T-square should be in complete contact with the working edge of the board while squaring the paper.

3.28. The T-square. The T-square is used primarily for drawing horizontal lines and for guiding the triangles when drawing vertical and inclined lines.   It is manipulated by sliding the working edge (inner face) of the head along the left edge of the board until the blade is in the required position. The left hand then should be shifted to a position near the center of the blade to hold it in place and to prevent its deflection while drawing the line. Experienced draftsmen hold the T-square, as

(a)   (b)

Fig. 3.29. Manipulating the T-Square.

Fig. 3.30. Drawing Horizontal Lines.

shown in Fig. 3.29(b), with the fingers pressing on the blade and the thumb on the paper. Small adjustments may be made with the hand in this position by sliding the blade with the fingers.

If a horizontal line is to be drawn through a given point, the T-square is moved into position by placing the pencil on the point at the ruling angle and sliding the T-square into contact with the pencil point.

Horizontal lines are drawn from left to right along the upper edge of the T-square (Fig. 3.30). (*Exception:* left-handed persons should use the T-square head at the right side of the board and draw from right to left.) While drawing the line, the ruling hand should slide along the blade on the little finger. The beginner should cultivate the habit of making certain the T-square head has made perfect contact with the board before he begins drawing a line.

The T-square should never be used with the head against the top or bottom edges of the board because manufacturers do not true-up these edges to make 90° with the end strips.

3.29. Vertical lines. Vertical lines are drawn upward along the vertical leg of a triangle whose other (horizontal) leg is supported and guided by the T-square blade. The blade is held in position with the palm and thumb of the left hand, and the triangle is adjusted and held by the fingers as shown in Fig. 3.31. In the case of a right-handed person, the triangle should be to the right of the line to be drawn.

If the vertical line is to be drawn through a given point, the triangle is moved into position by placing the pencil on the point at the ruling angle, and sliding the triangle along the guiding edge of the T-square until the vertical leg is in contact with the pencil point. To insure that the line will pass accurately through the point, always place the T-square well below the starting point. Never draw to or from an extreme corner of a triangle.

Fig. 3.31.   Drawing Vertical Lines.

Either the 30° × 60° or the 45° triangle may be used since both triangles have a right angle. However, the 30° × 60° is generally preferred because it usually has a longer perpendicular leg.

3.30. Inclined lines. Triangles also are used for drawing inclined lines. Lines that make angles of 30°, 45°, or 60° with the horizontal may be drawn with the 30° × 60° or the 45° triangle in combination with the T-square, as shown in Fig. 3.32. If the two triangles are combined, lines that make 15° or a multiple of 15° may be drawn with the horizontal. Several possible arrangements and the angles that result are shown in Fig. 3.33. It is interesting to note that whenever the hypotenuse of one triangle is placed against the hypotenuse of the other, a 15° and a 75° angle are both available from the single setting; whereas, if the leg of one rests against the hypotenuse of the other, either a 15° or a 75° angle and another, such as a 30°, 45°, or 60° angle, results. The length of a line drawn along the hypotenuse may be extended by shifting the T-square and triangles, as shown in Fig. 3.34.

Fig. 3.32.   Inclined Lines.

Fig. 3.33.   Drawing Inclined Lines with Triangles.

The triangles used singly or in combination offer a useful method for dividing a circle into four, six, eight, twelve, or twenty-four equal parts. For angles other than those divisible by 15, a protractor must be used.

3.31. Parallel lines. The triangles are used in combination to draw a line parallel to a given line. To draw such a line, place a ruling edge of a triangle, supported by a T-square or another triangle, along the given line; then slip the triangle, as shown in Fig. 3.35(a), to the required position and draw the parallel line along

Fig. 3.34. To Extend an Inclined Line.

the same ruling edge that previously coincided with the given line. If the line is to be drawn through a given point, the ruling edge should be moved beyond the point so that the pencil may be placed on the point at the ruling angle, and the ruling edge moved into contact with the pencil point, as in Fig. 3.35(b).

(a)   (b)

Fig. 3.35. To Draw a Line Parallel to a Given Line.

3.32. Perpendicular lines. Either the sliding triangle method (Fig. 3.36a) or the revolved triangle method (Fig. 3.36b) may be used to draw a line perpendicular to a given line. When using the sliding triangle method, adjust to the given line a side of a triangle that is adjacent to the right angle. Guide the side opposite the right angle with a second triangle as shown in Fig. 3.36(a); then slide the first triangle along the guiding triangle until it is in the required position for drawing the perpendicular along the other edge adjacent to the right angle.

Although the revolved triangle method is not so quickly done, it is widely used (Fig. 3.36b). To draw a perpendicular using this method, align along the given line the hypotenuse of a triangle, one leg of which is guided by the T-square or another triangle; then hold the guiding member in position and revolve the triangle about the right angle until the other leg is against the guiding edge. The new position of the hypotenuse will be perpendicular to its previous location along the given line

and, when moved to the required position, may be used as a ruling edge
for the desired perpendicular.

**3.33. Inclined lines making 15°, 30°, 45°, 60°, or 75° with an
oblique line.**   A line making with an oblique line an angle equal to any
angle of a triangle may be drawn with the triangles.   The two methods

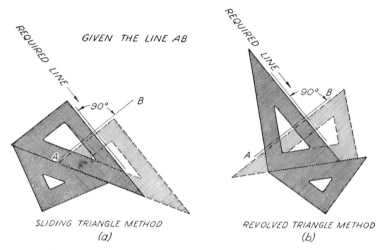

SLIDING TRIANGLE METHOD   REVOLVED TRIANGLE METHOD
(a)   (b)

Fig. 3.36.   To Draw a Line Perpendicular to Another Line.

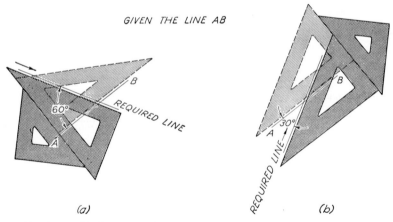

(a)   (b)

Fig. 3.37.   To Draw Lines Making 30°, 45°, or 60° with a Given Line.

previously discussed for drawing perpendicular lines are applicable with
slight modifications.   To draw an oblique line using the revolved triangle
method (Fig. 3.37a), adjust along the given line the edge that is opposite
the required angle, then revolve the triangle about the required angle,
slide it into position, and draw the required line along the side opposite
the required angle.

To use the sliding triangle method, illustrated in Fig. 3.37(b), adjust
to the given line one of the edges adjacent to the required angle, and

guide the side opposite the required angle with a straightedge; then slide the triangle into position and draw the required line along the other adjacent side.

To draw a line making 75° with a given line, place the triangles together so that the sum of a pair of adjacent angles equals 75°, and adjust one side of the angle thus formed to the given line; then slide the triangle, whose leg forms the other side of the angle, across the given line into position, and draw the required line, as shown in Fig. 3.38(a).

GIVEN THE LINE AB

(a)   (b)

Fig. 3.38.   To Draw Lines Making 15° or 75° with a Given Line.

To draw a line making 15° with a given line, select any two angles whose difference is 15°.   Adjust to the given line a side adjacent to one of these angles, and guide the side adjacent with a straightedge.   Remove the first triangle and substitute the other so that one adjacent side of the angle to be subtracted is along the guiding edge, as shown in Fig. 3.38(b); then slide it into position and draw along the other adjacent side.

3.34. The scale.   The sole purpose of the scale is to reproduce the dimensions of an object full size on a drawing or to reduce or enlarge them to some regular proportion such as eighth size, quarter size, half size, or double size.   The scales of reduction most frequently used are as follows:

Fractional

Mechanical
Engineer's
Scales
$\begin{cases} \text{Full Size} & (1'' = 1'') \\ \text{Half Size} & (\frac{1}{2}'' = 1'') \\ \text{Quarter Size} & (\frac{1}{4}'' = 1'') \\ \text{Eighth Size} & (\frac{1}{8}'' = 1'') \end{cases}$

Architect's or
Mechanical
Engineer's
Scales
$\begin{cases} \text{Full Size} & (12'' = 1') \\ \text{Half Size} & (\ 6'' = 1') \\ \text{Quarter Size} & (\ 3'' = 1') \\ \text{Eighth Size} & (1\frac{1}{2}'' = 1') \\ 1'' = 1' & \frac{1}{4}'' = 1' \\ \frac{3}{4}'' = 1' & \frac{3}{16}'' = 1' \\ \frac{1}{2}'' = 1' & \frac{1}{8}'' = 1' \\ \frac{3}{8}'' = 1' & \frac{3}{32}'' = 1' \end{cases}$

Decimal

Mechanical Engineer's Scales	Full Size	$(1.00'' = 1.00'')$
	Half Size	$(0.50'' = 1.00'')$
	Three-eighths Size	$(0.375'' = 1.00'')$
	Quarter Size	$(0.25'' = 1.00'')$

Civil Engineer's Scales	10 Scale: $1'' = 1'$; $1'' = 10'$; $1'' = 100'$; $1'' = 1000'$
	20 Scale: $1'' = 2'$; $1'' = 20'$; $1'' = 200'$; $1'' = 2000'$
	30 Scale: $1'' = 3'$; $1'' = 30'$; $1'' = 300'$; $1'' = 3000'$
	40 Scale: $1'' = 4'$; $1'' = 40'$; $1'' = 400'$; $1'' = 4000'$
	50 Scale: $1'' = 5'$; $1'' = 50'$; $1'' = 500'$; $1'' = 5000'$
	60 Scale: $\qquad 1'' = 60'$; etc.
	80 Scale: $\qquad 1'' = 80'$; etc.

The first four scales, full size, half size, quarter size, and eighth size, are the ones most frequently selected for drawing machine parts although other scales can be used. Since objects drawn by structural draftsmen and architects vary from small to very large, scales from full size to

Fig. 3.39. Decimal Scales.*

$\frac{3}{32}'' = 1'$ ($\frac{1}{128}$ size) are commonly encountered. For maps the civil engineer's decimal scales having 10, 20, 30, 40, 50, 60, and 80 divisions to the inch are used for representing 10', 20', 30', and so forth to the inch.

The decimal scales shown in Fig. 3.39 have been approved by the American Standards Association for making machine drawings when the decimal system is used. Read Sec. 3.11.

It is essential that a draftsman always think and speak of each dimension as full size when scaling measurements, because the dimension

---

* ASA Z75.1–1955.

figures given on the finished drawing indicate full-size measurements of the finished piece, regardless of the scale used.

The reading of an open-divided scale is illustrated in Fig. 3.40 with the eighth-size ($1\frac{1}{2}'' = 1'$) scale shown. The dimension can be read directly as 21 inches, the 9 inches being read in the divided division to the left of the cipher. Each long open division represents twelve inches (one foot).

To lay off a measurement, using a scale starting at the left of the stick, align the scale in the direction of the measurement with the zero of the

Fig. 3.40.   Reading a Scale.

Fig. 3.41.   To Lay Off a Measurement.

scale being used toward the left. After it has been adjusted to the correct location, make short marks opposite the divisions on the scale that establish the desired distance (Fig. 3.41). For ordinary work most draftsmen use the same pencil employed for the layout work. When extreme accuracy is necessary, however, it is better practice to use a pricker and make slight indentations (not holes) at the required points. If a regular pricker is not available, the dividers may be opened to approximately 60° and the point of one leg used as a substitute.

To insure accuracy, place the eye directly over the division to be marked, hold the marking instrument perpendicularly to the paper directly in front of the scale division, and mark the point. Always check the location of the point before removing the scale. If a slight indentation is made, it will be covered by the finished line; if a short mark is made, and it is *very* light, it will be unnoticeable on the finished drawing.

To set off a measurement (say 2'-9") to half scale, the scale indicated either as $\frac{1}{2}$ (Fig. 3.42) or $\frac{1}{2}'' = 1'$ should be used. If the measurement is to be made from left to right, place the 9-inch fractional division mark (counted toward the left from the cipher) on the given line, and make an indentation (or mark) opposite the 2-foot division point. (See Fig. 3.42*a*.) The distance from the line to the point represents 2'-9", although it is actually $1\frac{3}{8}$ inches. To set off the same measurement from right to left, place the 2-foot mark on the given line, and make an indentation opposite the 9-inch fractional division mark. (See Fig. 3.42*b*.)

Fig. 3.42. To Lay Off a Measurement.   **Fig. 3.43. To Lay Off a Measurement (Full Size).**

The procedure for setting off a distance to full size is illustrated in Fig. 3.43. The scale that is full divided into inches and sixteenths is best suited for this purpose.

To set off a measurement (say $1\frac{9}{16}$ inches) from left to right, place the initial mark at the start of the scale on the given line, and make an indentation opposite the $1\frac{9}{16}$-inch mark (Fig. 3.43*a*). To set off the same measurement from right to left, place the $1\frac{9}{16}$-inch mark on the given line, and make an indentation opposite the initial division mark at the start of the scale.

When scaling, there are certain practices that, if observed, will insure great accuracy and will speed up the layout work. Although the practices recommended in the following paragraphs refer principally to the full-size scale, any scale that is full divided may be used similarly.

Whenever it is necessary to divide a dimension by two, divide the whole number and fraction separately and add them on the scale. The fraction is divided by multiplying its denominator by the divisor. For example, it is necessary to draw a circle $3\frac{7}{8}$ inches in diameter.   One half of the whole number, 3 inches, equals $1\frac{1}{2}$ inches, and one half of $\frac{7}{8}$ of an inch equals $\frac{7}{8} \times \frac{1}{2}$ or $\frac{7}{16}$ of an inch.   To lay off the measurement, set the $1\frac{1}{2}$-inch mark at the center, move the scale $\frac{7}{16}$ of an inch to the left, and mark (or indent) opposite the 0-inch and $3\frac{7}{8}$-inch division marks.

Fig. 3.44.   Consecutive Measurements.

In order to avoid cumulative errors and to provide a check on the work, consecutive measurements along a line should be set off by keeping

Fig. 3.45.   Reading the Decimal Scale.

the stick stationary and marking off the distances (from the 0 division mark) one after another, by adding each distance to the preceding ones. The last scale reading should equal the over-all dimension. (See Fig. 3.44.)

The reading of the decimal scale is illustrated in Fig. 3.45.

3.35. The compass. The compass is used principally for drawing circles and circle arcs having radii beyond the working range of the bow pencil and bow pen.   For drawing pencil circles, the style of point illustrated in Fig. 3.47(*c*) should be used because it gives more accurate results and is easier to maintain than most other styles.   This style of point is formed by first sharpening the outside of the lead to a long flat bevel approximately $\frac{1}{4}$ of an inch long (see Fig. 3.47*a*), and then finishing it (see Fig. 3.47*b*) with a slight

Fig. 3.46.   Sharpening the Compass Lead.

rocking motion to reduce the width of the point.   Although a hard lead

(4H to 6H) will maintain a point longer without resharpening, it gives a finished object line that is too light in color. Soft lead (F or H) gives a darker line but quickly loses its edge and, on larger circles, gives a thicker line at the end than at the beginning. Some draftsmen have found that a medium grade (2H-3H) lead is a satisfactory compromise for ordinary working drawings. For design drawings, layout work, and graphical solutions, however, a harder lead will give better results.

(a)   (b)   (c)

Fig. 3.47. Shaping the Compass Lead.

The needle point should have the shouldered end out, and should be adjusted (approximately $\frac{3}{8}$ of an inch beyond the end of the split sleeve) so that it is slightly longer than the pen point. When the pencil leg is

Fig. 3.48. The Adjustment of the Needle Point.

used, the lead should be adjusted slightly shorter and, as it is resharpened, should be readjusted (Fig. 3.48). The length of the needle point must never be changed after it once has been set for the pen.

3.36. Using the compass or large bow. To draw a circle, it is first necessary to draw two intersecting center lines at right angles and mark off the radius as previously explained. The pivot point may be guided accurately into position at the center with the little finger of the left hand. After the pencil point has been adjusted to the radius mark, the circle is drawn in a clockwise direction by holding the compass or large bow as shown in Fig. 3.49, and rotating the handle between the thumb and forefinger. While drawing the circle, the compass should be inclined slightly forward. If the pencil line is not dark enough, it may be brightened by drawing around it again.

For a radius larger than 2 inches, the legs of a compass should be bent at the knee joints to stand approximately perpendicular to the paper (Fig. 3.50). It is particularly important that this adjustment be made when drawing ink circles, otherwise both nibs will not touch the paper. For circles whose radii exceed 5 inches, the lengthening bar should be added to the compass or a beam compass should be used. Either instru-

Fig. 3.49. Using the Large Bow (Vemco).

ment is manipulated similarly by steadying the pivot leg with one hand, and rotating the marking leg with the other (Fig. 3.51). Care must be taken to avoid changing the adjustment while drawing the circle.

3.37. The dividers. The dividers are used principally for dividing curved and straight lines into any number of equal parts, and for transferring measurements. If the instrument is held with one leg between the forefinger and second finger, and the other leg between the thumb and third finger, as illustrated in Fig. 3.52, an adjustment may be quickly and easily made with one hand. The second and third fingers are used to "open out" the legs, and the thumb and forefinger to close them. This

Fig. 3.50. Using the Compass (Legs Bent).

Fig. 3.51. Drawing Large Circles (Vemco Beam Compass).

method of adjusting may seem awkward to the beginner at first, but with practice absolute control can be developed. Close variations to the smallest fraction of an inch are possible with the hairspring. When its use is necessary, the grip on the instrument must be changed so that the forefinger and thumb may be used to turn the adjusting screw.

Fig. 3.52. To Adjust the Large Dividers.

3.38. Use of the dividers. The trial method is used to divide a line into a given number of equal parts. (See Fig. 3.53.) To divide a line into a desired number of equal parts, open the dividers until the distance between the points is estimated to be equal to the length of a division, and step off the line *lightly*. If the last prick mark misses the end point, increase or decrease the setting by an amount estimated to be equal to the error divided by the number of divisions, before lifting the dividers from the paper. Step off the line again. Repeat this procedure until the dividers are correctly set, then space the line again and indent the division points. When stepping off a line, the dividers are rotated alternately in an opposite direction on either side of the line, each half revolution, as shown in Fig. 3.53.

Fig. 3.53.   Use of the Dividers.

Although the dividers are used to transfer a distance on a drawing, they should never be used to transfer a measurement from the scale, as the method is slow and inaccurate and results in serious damage to the graduation marks. Care should be taken to avoid pricking large unsightly holes with the divider points. It is the common practice of many expert draftsmen to draw a small freehand circle around a very light indentation to establish its location.

3.39. Use of the bow instruments. The bow pen and bow pencil are convenient for drawing small circles having a radius of 1 inch or less

(Fig. 3.54).   The needle points should be adjusted slightly longer than the marking points, as in the case of the compass.

Small adjustments are made by the fingers of the hand holding the instrument, with the pivot point in position at the center of the required

Fig. 3.54.   Use of the Bow Pencil.   Fig. 3.55.   Small Adjustments.

Fig. 3.56.   Large Adjustments (Side-Screw Instruments).

circle or arc (Fig. 3.55).   When a side screw type of instrument is being used, and it is necessary to make a large change, damaging wear on the thread can be minimized by closing the legs with the fingers of the left hand to relieve the pressure while setting the adjustment nut in the required position (Fig. 3.56).

The bow dividers are used for the same purposes and in the same manner as the large dividers. Since they hold a setting better, however, they are more suited for very accurate or small work.

3.40. Use of the french curve. A french curve is used for drawing irregular curves that are not circle arcs. After sufficient points have been located, the french curve is applied so that a portion of its ruling edge passes through at least three points, as shown in Fig. 3.57. It should be so placed that the increasing curvature of the section of the ruling edge being used follows the direction of that part of the curve that is changing most rapidly. To insure that the finished curve will be free of humps and sharp breaks, the first line drawn should start and stop short of the first and last points to which the french curve has been fitted. Then the curve is adjusted in a new position with the ruling edge coinciding with a section of the line previously drawn. Each successive segment should

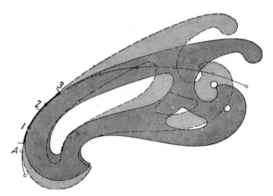

Fig. 3.57.   Using the Irregular Curve.

stop short of the last point matched by the curve. When inking a curve, overlapping should be avoided because sharp changes in the thickness or the color of the line may result. In Fig. 3.57, the curve fits the three points, A, 1, and 2. A line is drawn from between point A and point 1 to between point 1 and point 2. Then, the curve is shifted, as shown, to again fit points 1 and 2 with an additional point 3, and the line is extended to between point 2 and point 3.

Draftsmen sketch a smooth continuous curve through the points in pencil before drawing the mechanical line. This procedure makes the task of drawing the curve less difficult, since it is easier to adjust the ruling edge to segments of the freehand curve than to the points. When tracing a curve in ink the pen must be held perpendicular to the paper and the blades kept parallel to the ruling edge. A beginner's inability to control a pen is usually due to the instrument being held incorrectly.

A curve that cannot be fitted accurately may sometimes be drawn by varying the distance of the marking point from the guiding edge. This should be done only as a last resort, however, and should not be practiced to avoid the sometimes tedious task of finding a portion of the curve that will match at least three points.

3.41. Use of the erasing shield and eraser. An erasure is made on a drawing by placing an opening in the erasing shield over the work to be erased and rubbing with a pen-cil eraser (never an ink eraser) until it is removed (Fig. 3.58). Excessive pressure should not be applied to the eraser, be-cause, although the lines will disappear more quickly, the surface of the paper is likely to be permanently damaged.

Fig. 3.58. Using the Erasing Shield.

The fingers holding the erasing shield should rest partly on the drawing paper to prevent the shield from slipping.

INK TRACING

3.42. Inking a working drawing. An original working drawing is never sent to the shop. Instead, it is safely filed away in the engineering department. The shop gets a blueprint. Prints may be made from pencil drawings that have been executed on light bond tracing paper or pencil cloth, or from inked tracings done on cloth.

Fig. 3.59. Using the Ruling Pen.   Fig. 3.60. Holding the Pen.

3.43. Use of the ruling pen. The ruling pen is used to ink mechan-ical lines. It is always guided by the working edge of a T-square, triangle, or french curve, and is never used freehand (Fig. 3.59).

When ruling a line, the pen should be in a vertical plane and inclined slightly (approximately 60°) in the direction of the movement. It is held by the thumb and forefinger, as illustrated in Fig. 3.60, with the blade against the second finger and the adjusting screw on the outside away from the ruling edge. The third and fourth fingers slide along the T-square blade and help control the pen. Short lines are drawn with a hand movement; long lines with a free arm movement that finishes with a finger movement. While drawing, the angle of inclination and speed must remain constant to obtain a line of uniform width and straightness. Particular attention should be given to the position of the pen, as practically all faulty lines are due to incorrect inclination or to leaning the pen so that the point is too close to the straightedge or too far away from it. The correct position of the pen for drawing a satisfactory line is illustrated in Fig. 3.60.

If the pen is held so that it leans outward, as shown in Fig. 3.61(*a*), the point will be against the straightedge, and ink will run under and cause a blot; or, if it leans inward, as in Fig. 3.61(*b*), the outer nib will not touch the paper and the line will be ragged.

(*a*)   (*b*)

(*c*) T-SQUARE SLIPPED INTO LINE
(*d*) PEN PRESSED AGAINST T-SQUARE BLADE
(*e*) NOT ENOUGH INK IN PEN
(*f*) INK ON OUTSIDE OF PEN BLADE
(*g*) PEN AWAY FROM GUIDING EDGE NEAR END OF LINE

Fig. 3.61. Common Faults in Handling a Ruling Pen.

Unnecessary pressure against the straightedge changes the distance between the nibs, which in turn may either reduce the width of the line along its entire length or cause its width to vary as in Fig. 3.61(*d*).

It will not take any beginner long to discover that care must be taken when removing a T-square or triangle away from a wet ink line.

The ruling pen is filled by inserting the quill or dropper device between the nibs. Care must be taken, while filling, to see that there is enough ink to finish the line and that none of the ink from the filler gets on the outside of the blades. No more than $\frac{1}{4}$ inch should ever be put in; there is a danger of blotting if the pen is used with a greater amount.

The width of a line is determined by the distance between the nibs, which is regulated by the adjusting screw. When setting the pen, a

Fig. 3.62. Testing a Trial Line on a "Try Sheet."

series of test lines should be drawn with a straightedge on a small piece of the same kind of paper or cloth to establish the setting for the desired width of the line (Fig. 3.62). The draftsman's line gauge, shown in Fig. 3.63, is convenient for testing the widths of trial lines as illustrated in Fig. 3.62. If the first trial line is not of the desired width, another and another should be drawn until the final one agrees with the selected width as given on the gauge.

Ruling pens will not perform satisfactorily unless kept clean. For the best results, the ruling pen or any inking instrument *always* must be wiped before each refilling, and before laying it down, so that it will be ready for use again. A dirty pen in which the ink has been allowed to thicken will not draw any better than a dull one. To avoid changing the setting of the pen when cleaning it, fold the pen wiper twice at 90° (see Fig. 3.64) and draw the corner of the fold between the ends of the blades. After

Fig. 3.63. Gauge for Determining Widths of Lines.

a few lines have been drawn, a small speck of ink frequently lodges on the outside of the tip of one or both blades and increases the width of the lines being drawn or makes the drawing of fine lines impossible. These specks may be removed by inclining the pen at a slight angle and rubbing the sides of the tips of the blades on a piece of paper laid on a flat surface.   Either a speck of ink or a small piece of loose dirt or lint will cause the width of a line to change suddenly for no apparent reason, or will cause the second of two consecutively drawn lines to be broader than the first, even though the setting of the pen has not been changed.

If the ink refuses to flow when the pen is touched to the paper, either the ink has thickened or the opening between the nibs has become clogged.   To start it flowing, draftsmen often touch the point to the back of a finger or pinch the blades together.   Whenever this fails to produce an immediate flow, the pen should be cleaned and refilled.

3.44.   Conventional ink lines. The American Standards Association conventional symbols for ink lines for different purposes are

Fig. 3.64.   Cleaning the Ruling Pen.

shown in Fig. 3.71.   They have been reproduced full width so that they appear as required for a well-executed ink tracing.   Recommended line widths have been given in Fig. 3.63 for the conventional lines most commonly used, such as the visible object line, invisible object line, center line, etc.

3.45.   Tracing.   Often, when it is necessary to make duplicate copies (blueprints) of important drawings for a machine or structure, the original pencil drawings are traced in ink on a tracing medium, usually tracing cloth.   Contrary to the practice of old-time draftsmen and the intention of the early manufacturers of this medium, the dull side is now almost universally used for the inking surface instead of the slick side because it produces less light glare, it will take both pencil and ink lines better, and it will withstand more erasing.   The fact that the dull side will take pencil lines is important because, on some occasions, in order to save time, drawings are made directly on the cloth and then traced.   Upon completion of the tracing, all pencil lines including the guide lines and slope lines for the lettering may be removed by wiping the surface of the cloth with a rag moistened with a small amount of gasoline, benzine, or cleaning fluid.

When the tracing cloth has been fastened down over the drawing, a small quantity of tracing cloth powder may be sprinkled over the surface to make it take the ink evenly and smoothly.   After it has been well rubbed in, the excess must be thoroughly removed by wiping with a clean cloth, for even a small amount of loose powder left on the surface can cause clogging of the pen.   Powder is also used by some persons over a spot where an erasure has been made; but a better practice is to use a piece of soapstone, which will put a smooth, slick finish over the damaged area.   In applying the soapstone, rub the spot and then wipe a finger over it a few times. Following this treatment, the erased area will take ink almost as well as the original surface.

Since ink lines are made much wider than pencil lines, in order to get a good contrast on a blueprint, they should be carefully centered over the pencil lines when tracing. The center of an ink line should fall directly on the pencil line as shown correctly in Fig. 3.65. For ink work it might be said that ink lines are tangent when their center lines touch. In this same illustration, note the poor junctures obtained when ink lines are not centered so that their center lines are tangent.

Figure 3.66(a) shows the filled-in corner effect that frequently appears to the disgust of the draftsman, when an ink line is drawn from or to another previously drawn line that is still wet.

When a working drawing is traced in ink on either paper or cloth, the lines should be "inked" in a definite order. Otherwise, the necessity of

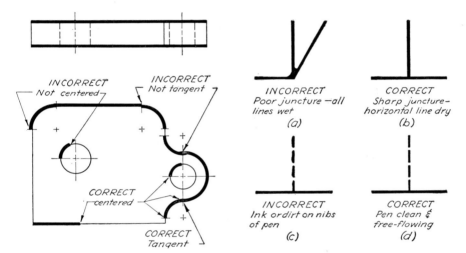

Fig. 3.65.   Inking over Pencil Lines.   Fig. 3.66.   Ink Lines.

waiting for the ink to dry after every few lines not only wastes time, but often results in a line here and there being left out. Furthermore, hit-and-miss inking may produce lines of unequal width. It is therefore recommended that the student make a conscientious attempt to follow the order of inking suggested in this chapter.

After the paper or cloth has been fastened down over the drawing, and before the inking is begun, each tangent point should be marked and all centers should be indented.

ORDER OF INKING

  I. Curved Lines:
     1. Circles and circle arcs (small circles first) in the order of (a), (b), and (c).
       (a) Visible.
       (b) Invisible.
       (c) Circular center lines and dimension lines.

2. Irregular curves.
    (*a*) Visible.
    (*b*) Invisible.
II. Straight Lines:
    1. Visible.
        (*a*) Horizontal, from the top of the sheet down.
        (*b*) Vertical, from the left side of the sheet to the right.
        (*c*) Inclined, from the left to the right.
    2. Invisible.
        (*a*) Horizontal.
        (*b*) Vertical.
        (*c*) Inclined.
    3. Auxiliary (center, extension, dimension lines, etc.).
        (*a*) Horizontal.
        (*b*) Vertical.
        (*c*) Inclined.
        (*d*) Section lines.
III. Arrowheads and Dimension Figures.
IV. Notes and Titles.
V. Border.

Figure 3.67 illustrates the application of this order of inking.

3.46. Use of the drawing ink. All pens are filled by means of a quill or dropper, and *never* by dipping them in the ink.

The ink bottle should always be set off the board and to the right so that it will be handy and yet not be accidentally upset. When the ink is to be used, the cork may be removed with very little effort by twisting it out with the thumb and forefinger while holding the neck of the bottle between the third and fourth fingers of the same hand.

The bottle should be kept tightly corked at all times when not in use, to prevent the ink from thickening and evaporating.

3.47. Sharpening a ruling pen. Ruling pens, whether they have been used continuously or intermittently, eventually show signs of wear. When a pen's nibs have lost their elliptical shape and have become so dull that the ink spreads under their tips, fine lines cannot be drawn until the pen has been sharpened. The way to detect this condition is to examine the tips. If bright spots may be seen on the tips, the pen is too dull for satisfactory work. Examples of worn points are illustrated in Fig. 3.68(*a*) and (*b*).

Since even new pens are seldom sharpened properly and often require retouching, every draftsman should be able to reshape and sharpen his own pen. A beginner should consult his instructor or an experienced draftsman regarding the condition of his pens before attempting to use them.

Incorrectly sharpened points are illustrated in Fig. 3.68(*c*) and (*d*). Points shaped as shown in either (*c*) or (*d*) are aggravating, because if a point is rounded as in (*c*), the ink flows too freely; if it is too pointed as in (*d*), the ink cups up and the flow is difficult to start. Only a pen that is correctly shaped and sharpened, as shown in Fig. 3.68(*e*), will give the results that should be expected.

Although blades should be sharpened to a thin edge, care should be

Fig. 3.67.   Order of Inking.

Fig. 3.68.   Incorrectly Shaped, Worn, and Correctly Shaped Blades.

taken not to make them sharp enough to cut the surface of the paper.   A pen should never be sharpened, even the slightest amount, on the inside of the blades.   Such treatment causes the blades to flare at the point and prevents the ink from feeding down to the paper, making it difficult or impossible to start a line.

A fine-grained Arkansas oilstone is the best all-purpose stone for sharpening a ruling pen.   The first step in sharpening is to equalize the length of the nibs and correct their shape.   This may be done by bringing the blades together so that they barely touch, and then drawing them lightly back and forth across the stone while swinging the pen through an arc of approximately 120 degrees each stroke.   (See Fig. 3.69.)   During this operation, it is essential that the pen be held in a vertical plane and that an even pressure be maintained against the stone.   When an inspection, under a magnifying glass, reveals that the nibs have been restored

Fig. 3.69. Shaping the Nibs.   Fig. 3.70. Sharpening the Blades.

to their correct shape, the blades should be opened and each nib sharpened all around the outside to a thin edge.   A blade is sharpened by holding the pen as shown in Fig. 3.70 and sliding it back and forth across the stone with a slight rolling motion to preserve its original convex shape. The pen should be examined from time to time so that the sharpening can be stopped as soon as the bright point disappears.

Finally, a test should be made by filling the pen and drawing a series of lines of various weights on a piece of tracing paper or tracing cloth.   If the instrument is capable of drawing satisfactory lines of any weight, particularly very fine lines, it has been correctly sharpened.   If the ink feeds too freely, however, the nibs are too rounded, as shown in Fig. 3.68(c); or if the ink cups high in the point, the nibs are too pointed, as in Fig. 3.68(d).   In either case, the entire sharpening process must be repeated.   If the blades cut the paper, even when the usual light working pressure is applied, the nibs should be slightly dulled and brought to an edge that is not quite so sharp.

Occasionally, if the pen has not been correctly sharpened, a featheredge or burr appears on the inside edge of a nib.   It may be removed by laying the inside of the blade flat on the stone and grinding it lightly.

3.48. Conventional line symbols. Symbolic lines of various weights are used in making technical drawings. The recommendations of the American Standards Association as given in ASA Y14.2–1957 are:

Three widths of lines—thick, medium, and thin—are recommended for use on drawings [Fig. 3.71]. Pencil lines in general should be in proportion to the ink lines except that the thicker pencil lines will be necessarily thinner than the corresponding ink lines, but as thick as practicable for pencil work. Exact thicknesses may vary according to the size and type of drawing. For example, where lines are close together, the lines may be slightly thinner.

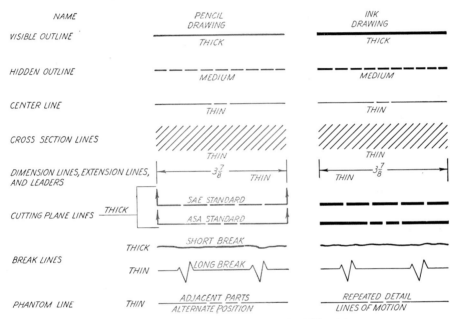

Fig. 3.71. Alphabet of Lines (Finished Weight).

Pencil lines may be further simplified, if desired, to two widths of lines—*medium-thick* for visible, hidden, cutting-plane, and short-break lines; and *thin* for section, center, extension, dimension, long-break, and phantom lines.

The lines illustrated in Fig. 3.71 are shown full size. When symbolic lines are used on a pencil drawing they should not vary in color. For example, center lines, extension lines, dimension lines, and section lines should differ from object lines only in width. The resulting contrast makes a drawing easier to read. All lines, except construction lines, should be very dark and bright to give the drawing the "snap" that is needed for good appearance. If the drawing is on tracing paper the lead must be "packed on" so that a satisfactory print can be obtained. Construction lines should be drawn *very* fine so as to be unnoticeable on the finished drawing. The lengths of the dashes and spaces, shown in Figs. 6.26 and 9.22, are recommended for the hidden lines, center lines, and cutting plane lines on average-size drawings.

USEFUL INSTRUMENTS AND EQUIPMENT

3.49. A few of the many other instruments and pieces of equipment that are convenient for drawing are shown in Figs. 3.72 to 3.87.

Fig. 3.72.   Esco Board.

The parallel rule shown attached to a small board in Fig. 3.72 serves as a substitute for the T-square.   It is preferred by many persons because as it moves it is always parallel to the original position.   In commercial drawing rooms, parallel-rule attachments are used on large boards. Alignment is maintained through a combination of pulleys and cords.

Fig. 3.73.   Line-O-graph Triangle.

The Line-O-graph triangle shown in Fig. 3.73 combines the functions of the triangles, scale, protractor, and lettering instrument.

The Wrico triangle is one of several types of special triangles that may also be used for drawing the end views of standard bolt heads and nuts (Fig. 3.74).

Although it is not widely used, the protractor angle (Fig. 3.75) is a useful device.   It is hinged in such a manner that it may be substituted for a protractor and a set of triangles.

Because of the time consumed in cutting back the wood to repoint an ordinary drawing pencil, some draftsmen favor the use of artist's automatic pencils (Fig. 3.76).   Separate leads for these pencils may be pur-

Fig. 3.74. Wrico Triangle.

Fig. 3.75. Protractor Angle.

Fig. 3.76. Artist's Pencils.

chased in any of the seventeen degrees of hardness obtainable in regular drawing pencils.

A steel eraser (Fig. 3.77), razor blade, or pocketknife is useful to a draftsman for clipping off small projections, but should *never* be used for scratching or removing inked lines or even small segments of inked lines. Its use seriously damages the surface of the paper.

Valuable drafting time can be saved through the use of a scale guard on a triangular stick having multiple scales (Fig. 3.78). The annoyance

Fig. 3.77.   Steel Eraser.

Fig. 3.78.   Scale Guard.

of repeated searching for a selected scale is eliminated, since the scale guard establishes the correct position for the stick.

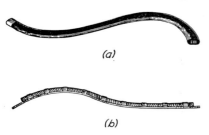

(a)

(b)

Fig. 3.79.   Flexible Curves.

The flexible curves shown in Fig. 3.79, (a and b), because of their limitless variations, are extremely convenient. The type shown in (a) consists of a lead bar enclosed in rubber. Unfortunately, rubber becomes brittle with age and cracks off. The more desirable one shown in (b) has a steel ruling edge attached to a spring enclosing a lead core.

The electric erasing machine saves valuable drafting time of those persons who prepare reproductions in ink and who find it necessary to make frequent erasures (Fig. 3.80).

Fig. 3.80.   Erasing Machine.

Fig. 3.81.   Drop Pen (Pencil).

The drop pen (pencil) is designed for repeated drawing of circles of small diameter, such as the circles representing rivet heads (Fig. 3.81).

Mechanical pencil sharpeners are available with special cutters that expose the proper length of lead for a drawing pencil (Fig. 3.82). A draftsman's pencil sharpener does not point the lead.

A special ink bottle holder and filler is a convenience that saves time when filling a pen, because only one hand is needed to raise the stopper and insert the ink (Fig. 3.83).

The detail or Swede (Fig. 3.84) wide-blade pen holds more ink than an ordinary ruling pen, and thus is better suited to drawing very long or very wide lines.

Fig. 3.82. Draftsman's Pencil Sharpener.　　Fig. 3.83. Special Ink Bottle Holder and Filler.

Fig. 3.84. Detail Pen (Swede).

CONTOUR PEN
(a)

RAILROAD PEN
(b)

FOUNTAIN RULING PEN
(c)

BORDER PEN
(d)

Fig. 3.85. Special Ruling Pens.

Fig. 3.86. Proportional Dividers.

Electro Symbol Template

Chemistry Template

Tooling Template

Tilt-Hex Drafting Template

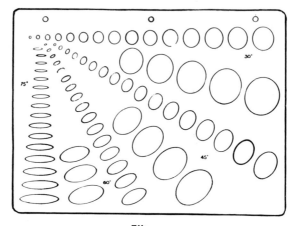

Ellipses

Fig. 3.87.   Special Templates.

Several of a number of special ruling pens that are available are shown in Fig. 3.85. The contour pen (*a*) is used freehand for tracing contours on a map. The inking leg is free to swivel in the handle. The railroad pen (*b*) draws parallel lines that may represent roads or railroad tracks. The fountain ruling pen (*c*) is useful when much inking is to be done. It does not require frequent filling. The border pen (*d*) draws a line of fixed width. It is desirable to have a set of these pens available, since a separate pen is required for each different line width.

Fig. 3.88. Drafting Machine.

Proportional dividers are convenient for enlarging or reducing a drawing. Scales are marked on the instrument for obtaining desired linear proportions and for the division of a circle (Fig. 3.86).

A few of the many forms of special templates that are convenient for drawing are shown in Fig. 3.87. Their use results in the saving of valuable drafting time.

The drafting machine (Fig. 3.88) is a device that is designed to combine the functions of the T-square, triangles, scale, and protractor. Drafting machines are used extensively in commercial drafting rooms because it has been estimated that their use leads to a 25 to 50 per cent saving in time.

3.50. Exercises in instrumental drawing. The following elementary exercises have been designed to offer experience in the use of the drafting instruments. The designs should be drawn *lightly* with a hard pencil. After making certain that all constructions shown on a drawing are correct, the lines forming the designs should be heavied with a medium hard pencil. The light construction lines need not be erased if the drawing has been kept relatively clean. All dimensions and letters should be omitted except in problem 11.

Fig. 3.89.

1. (Fig. 3.89.) On a sheet of drawing paper reproduce the line formations shown. If the principal border lines have not been printed on the sheet, they may be drawn first so that the large $5\frac{1}{2}'' \times 8\frac{1}{4}''$ rectangle can be balanced horizontally and vertically within the border. To draw the inclined lines, first draw the indicated measuring lines through the lettered points at the correct angle, and mark off $\frac{1}{4}''$ distances. These division points establish the locations of the required lines of the formation. The six squares of the formation are equal in size.

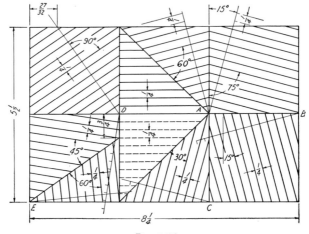

Fig. 3.90.

2. (Fig. 3.90.)   Reproduce the line formations shown, following the instructions given for problem 1.

3. (Fig. 3.91.)   This exercise is designed to give the student practice with the bow pencil and compass by drawing some simple geometrical figures.   The line work within each large circle may be reproduced with the knowledge only that the diameter is $3\frac{1}{4}''$.   All circles and circle arcs are to be made finished weight when they are first drawn, since retracing often produces a double line.   Do not "over-run" the straight lines or stop them too short.

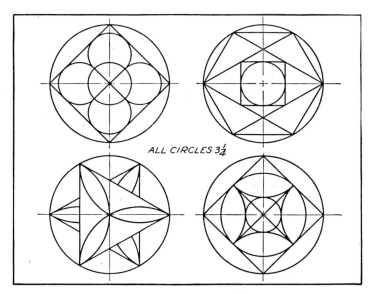

ALL CIRCLES $3\frac{1}{4}$

Fig. 3.91.

4. (Fig. 3.92.)   Reproduce the contour view of the stamping.

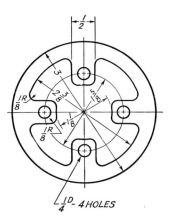

Fig. 3.92. Stamping.

5–7. (Figs. 3.93, 3.94, 3.95.)   Reproduce the designs following the instructions given for problem 3, making the dashes of the arcs approximately $\frac{1}{8}''$ long.

Fig. 3.93.

Fig. 3.94.

Fig. 3.95.

Fig. 3.96.

Fig. 3.97.

Fig. 3.98.

Fig. 3.99.

8–10. (Figs. 3.96, 3.97, 3.98.)   Reproduce the line work within each square using the dimensions given.   The dimensions shown, however, are for the student's use only and should not appear on the finished drawing.   Arcs should be made finished weight when first drawn.   The straight lines of each design may be drawn with a hard pencil and later heavied with a softer pencil.   Do not erase the construction lines.

11. (Fig. 3.99.)   Select a suitable scale and reproduce the design of the highway intersection shown.   Using $\frac{3}{16}''$ capital letters, letter the words HIGHWAY INTERSECTION.   Using $\frac{1}{8}''$ letters and numerals, letter the dimensions. Draw the arrows indicating the direction of traffic flow.

12–15. (Figs. 3.100, 3.101, 3.102, 3.103.)   Reproduce the geometrical shapes.

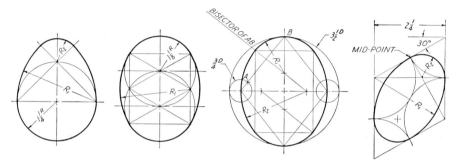

Fig. 3.100. Oval.   Fig. 3.101. Ellipse   Fig. 3.102. Ellipse   Fig. 3.103. Ellipse
                       (Approximate).   (Approximate).   (Pictorial).

4 | Engineering Geometry

4.1. Introduction. The simplified geometrical constructions presented in this chapter are those with which a draftsman should be familiar, for they frequently occur in engineering drawing. The methods are applications of the principles found in textbooks on plane geometry. The constructions have been modified to take advantage of time-saving methods made possible by the use of drawing instruments.

Since a study of the subject of plane geometry should be a prerequisite for a course in engineering drawing, the mathematical proofs have been omitted intentionally. Geometrical terms applying to lines, surfaces, and solids, however, are given in Figs. 4.53 and 4.54 for the purpose of review.

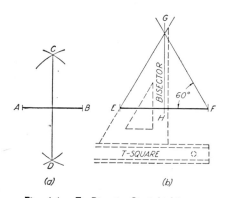

Fig. 4.1. To Bisect a Straight Line.

Fig. 4.2. To Trisect a Straight Line.

4.2. To bisect a straight line (Fig. 4.1).

(a) With A and B as centers, strike the intersecting arcs as shown using any radius greater than one-half of AB. A straight line through points C and D bisects AB.

(b) Draw either 60° or 45° lines through E and F. Through their intersection draw the perpendicular GH that will bisect EF.

The use of the dividers to divide or bisect a line by the trial method is explained in Sec. 3.38.

4.3. To trisect a straight line (Fig. 4.2). Given the line AB. Draw the lines AO and OB making 30° with AB. Similarly, draw CO and OD making 60° with AB. AC equals CD equals DB.

4.4. To bisect an angle (Fig. 4.3).

76

(a) Given the angle BAC. Use any radius with the vertex A as a center, and strike an arc that intersects the sides of the angle at D and E. With D and E as centers and a radius larger than one-half of DE, draw intersecting arcs. Draw AF. Angle BAF equals angle FAC.

(b) Given an angle formed by the lines KL and MN having an inaccessible point of intersection. Draw BA parallel to KL and CA parallel to MN at the same distance from MN as BA is from KL. Bisect angle BAC using the method explained in (a). The bisector FA of angle BAC bisects the angle between the lines KL and MN.

4.5. To draw parallel curved lines about a curved center line (Fig. 4.4). Draw a series of arcs having centers located at random along the given center line AB. Using the french curve, draw the required curved lines tangent to these arcs.

Fig. 4.3.   To Bisect an Angle.

Fig. 4.4.   To Draw Parallel Curved Lines.   Fig. 4.5.   To Trisect an Angle.

4.6. To trisect an angle (Fig. 4.5). Given the angle BAC. Lay off along AB any convenient distance AD. Draw DE perpendicular to AC and DF parallel to AC. Place the scale so that it passes through A with a distance equal to twice AD intercepted between the lines DE and DF. Angle HAC equals one-third of the angle BAC.

4.7. To divide a straight line into a given number of equal parts (Fig. 4.6). Given the line LM, which is to be divided into five equal parts.

(a) Step off, with the dividers, five equal divisions along a line making any convenient angle with LM. Connect the last point P with M, and through the remaining points draw lines parallel to MP intersecting the given line. These lines divide LM into five equal parts.

(b) Some commercial draftsmen prefer a modification of this construction known as the scale method. For the first step, draw a vertical PM

through point M. Place the scale so that the first mark of five equal
divisions is at L and the last mark falls on PM. Locate the four interven-
ing division points, and through these draw verticals intersecting the
given line. The verticals will divide LM into five equal parts.

Fig. 4.6.   To Divide a Straight Line into a Number of Equal Parts.

4.8. To divide a line proportionally (Fig. 4.7). Given the line
AB. Draw BC perpendicular to AB. Place the scale across A and BC so

Fig. 4.7. To Divide a Line
Proportionally.

that the number of divisions intercepted is
equal to the sum of the numbers representing the proportions. Mark off these proportions and draw lines parallel to BC to
divide AB as required. The proportions in
Fig. 4.7 are $1:2:3$.

**4.9. To construct an angle equal to
a given angle** (Fig. 4.8). Given the angle
BAC and the line $A'C'$ that forms one side
of the transferred angle. Use any convenient radius with the vertex A as a center,
and strike the arc that intersects the sides
of the angle at D and E. With A' as a
center, strike the arc intersecting $A'C'$ at E'. With E' as a center and the
chord distance DE as a radius, strike a short intersecting arc to locate
D'. $A'B'$ drawn through D' makes angle $B'A'C'$ equal angle BAC.

**4.10. To draw a line through a given point and the inaccessible
intersection of two given lines** (Fig. 4.9). Given the lines KL and

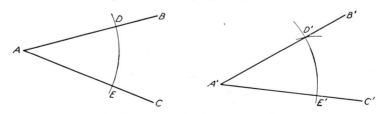

Fig. 4.8.   To Construct an Angle Equal to a Given Angle.

MN, and the point *P*. Construct any triangle such as *PQR* having its vertices falling on the given lines and the given point. At some convenient location construct triangle *STU* similar to *PQR*, by drawing *SU* parallel to *PR*, *TU* parallel to *QR*, and *ST* parallel to *PQ*. *PS* is the required line.

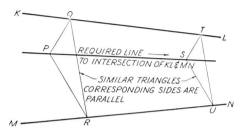

Fig. 4.9. To Draw a Line Through a Given Point and the Inaccessible Intersection of Two Given Lines.

Fig. 4.10. To Construct an Angle, Tangent Method.

4.11. To construct an angle, tangent method (Fig. 4.10). Draftsmen often find it necessary to draw long lines having an angle between them that is not equal to an angle of a triangle. Such an angle may be laid off with a protractor, but it should be remembered that as the lines are extended any error is multiplied. To avoid this situation, the tangent method may be used. The tangent method involves trigonometry but, since it is frequently used, a discussion of it here is pertinent. (See Table XXXV of the Appendix.)

In this method, a distance D_1 is laid off along a line that is to form one side of the angle, and a distance D_2, equal to D_1 times the natural tangent of the angle, is marked off along a perpendicular through point *P*. A line through point *X* is the required line, and angle *A* is the required angle. In laying off the distance D_1, unnecessary multiplication will be eliminated if the distance is arbitrarily made 10″ or ten units on any decimal scale.

This method is also used for angles formed by short lines whenever a protractor is not available.

4.12. To construct a triangle having its three sides given (Fig. 4.11). Given the three sides *AB*, *AC*, and *BC*. Draw the side *AB* in its correct location. Using its end points *A* and *B* as centers and radii equal to *AC* and *BC*, respectively, strike the two intersecting arcs locating point *C*.

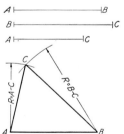

Fig. 4.11. To Construct a Triangle with Three Sides Given.

ABC is the required triangle. This construction is particularly useful for developing the surface of a transition piece by triangulation.

4.13. To construct an equilateral triangle (Fig. 4.12). Given the side *AB*.

(*a*) Using the end points *A* and *B* as centers and a radius equal to the length of *AB*, strike two intersecting arcs to locate *C*. Draw lines from *A* to *C* and *C* to *B* to complete the required equilateral triangle.

(*b*) Using a 30–60° triangle, draw through *A* and *B* lines that make 60° with the given line.   If the line *AB* is inclined, the 60° lines should be drawn as shown in Fig. 3.37.

4.14. To transfer a polygon (Fig. 4.13).   Given the polygon *ABCDE*.

(*a*) Enclose the polygon in a rectangle.   Draw the "enclosing rectangle" in the new position and locate points *A*, *B*, *C*, *D*, and *E* along the sides by measuring from the corners of the rectangle.   A compass may be used for transferring the necessary measurements.

(*b*) To transfer a polygon by the triangle method, divide the polygon into triangles and, using the construction explained in Sec. 4.12, reconstruct each triangle in its transferred position.

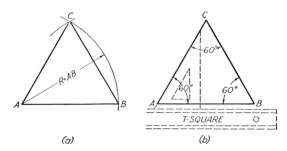

(a)   *(b)*

Fig. 4.12.   To Construct an Equilateral Triangle.

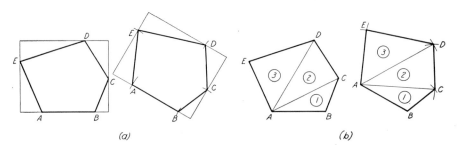

(a)   *(b)*

Fig. 4.13.   To Transfer a Polygon.

4.15. To construct a square (Fig. 4.14).

(*a*) Given the side *AB*.   Using a T-square and a 45° triangle, draw perpendiculars to line *AB* through points *A* and *B*.   Locate point *D* at the intersection of a 45° construction line through *A* and the perpendicular from *B*.   Draw *CD* parallel to *AB* through *D* to complete the square. To eliminate unnecessary movements the lines should be drawn in the order indicated.

(*b*) Given the diagonal length *EF*.   Using a T-square and a 45° triangle, construct the square by drawing lines through *E* and *F* at an angle of 45° with *EF* in the order indicated.

(*c*) The construction of an inscribed circle is the first step in one method for drawing a square when the location of the center and the length of one side are given.

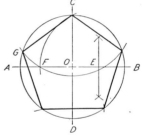

Fig. 4.14. To Construct a Square.

Using a T-square and a 45° triangle, draw the sides of the square tangent to the circle. This construction is used in drawing square bolt-heads and nuts.

4.16. To construct a regular pentagon (Fig. 4.15). Given the circumscribing circle. Draw the perpendicular diameters AB and CD. Bisect OB and, with its mid-point E as a center and EC as a radius, draw the arc CF. Using C as a center and CF as a radius, draw the arc FG. The line CG is one of the equal sides of the required pentagon. Locate the remaining vertices by striking off this distance around the circumference.

If the length of one side of a pentagon is given, the construction shown in Fig. 4.18 should be used.

4.17. To construct a regular hexagon (Fig. 4.16).

Fig. 4.15. To Construct a Regular Pentagon.

(*a*) Given the distance AB across corners. Draw a circle having AB as a diameter. Using the same radius and with points A and B as centers, strike arcs intersecting the circumference. Join these points to complete the construction.

(*b*) Given the distance AB across corners. Using a 30–60° triangle and a T-square, draw the lines in the order indicated by the numbers on the figure.

(*c*) Given the distance across flats. Draw a circle whose diameter equals the distance across flats. Using a 30–60° triangle and a T-square, as shown, draw the tangents that establish the sides and vertices of the required hexagon.

This construction is used in drawing hexagonal boltheads and nuts.

4.18. To construct a regular octagon (Fig. 4.17).

(*a*) Given the distance across flats. Draw the circumscribed square and its diagonals. Using the corners as centers and one-half the diagonal as a radius, strike arcs across the sides of the square. Join these points to complete the required octagon.

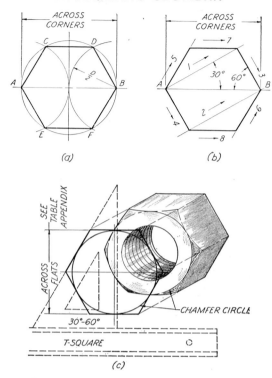

Fig. 4.16. To Construct a Regular Hexagon.

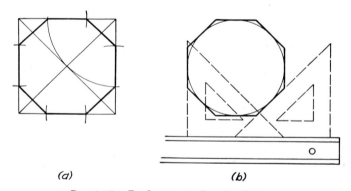

Fig. 4.17. To Construct a Regular Octagon.

(b) Given the distance across flats.   Draw the inscribed circle; then, using a 45° triangle and T-square, draw the tangents that establish the sides and vertices of the required octagon.

4.19. To construct any regular polygon having one side given (Fig. 4.18).   Given the side LM.   With LM as a radius, draw a semi-circle and divide it into the same number of equal parts as the number of sides needed for the polygon.   Suppose the polygon is to be seven-sided. Draw radial lines through points 2, 3, and so forth.   Point 2 (the second division point) is always one of the vertices of the polygon, and line $L2$ is a side. Using point M as a center and LM as a radius, strike an arc across the radial line $L6$ to locate point N. Using the same radius with N as a center, strike another arc across $L5$ to establish O on $L5$. Although this procedure may be continued with point O as the next center, more accurate results will be obtained if point R is used as a center for the arc to locate Q, and Q as a center for P.

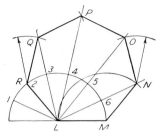

4.20. To divide the area of a triangle or trapezoid into a given number of equal parts (Fig. 4.19).

Fig. 4.18. To Construct Any Regular Polygon, Having One Side Given.

(a) Given the triangle ABC. Divide the side AC into (say five) equal parts, and draw a semicircle having AC as the diameter. Through the division points (1, 2, 3, and 4) draw perpendicular lines to points of intersection with the semicircle (5, 6, 7, and 8). Using C as a center, strike arcs through these points (5, 6, 7, and 8) that will cut AC. To complete the construction, draw lines parallel to AB through the points (9, 10, 11, and 12) at which the arcs intersect the side AC.

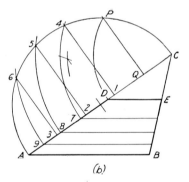

Fig. 4.19. To Divide the Area of a Triangle or Trapezoid into a Given Number of Equal Parts.

(b) Given the trapezoid $DEBA$. Extend the sides of the trapezoid to form the triangle ABC and draw a semicircle on AC with AC as a diameter. Using C as a center and CD as a radius, strike an arc cutting the semicircle at point P. Through P draw a perpendicular to AC to locate point Q. Divide QA into the same number of equal parts as the number of equal areas required (in this case four), and proceed using the construction explained in (a) for dividing the area of a triangle into a given number of equal parts.

4.21. To find the center for a circle through three given points not in a straight line (Fig. 4.20). Given the three points A, B, and C. Join the points with straight lines (which will be chords of the required circle), and draw the perpendicular bisectors. The point of intersection

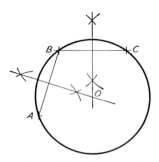

Fig. 4.20. To Find the Center of a Circle Through Three Points.

O of the bisectors is the center of the required circle, and OA, OB, or OC is its radius.

4.22. Tangent circles and arcs. Figure 4.21 illustrates the geometry of tangent circles. In (a) it can be noted that the locus of centers for circles of radius R tangent to AB is a line that is parallel to AB at a distance R from AB. The locus of centers for circles of the same radius tangent to CD is a line that is parallel to CD at R (radius) distance from CD. Since point O at which these lines intersect is R distance from both AB and CD, a circle of radius R with center at O must be tangent to both AB and CD.

In (b) the locus of centers for circles of radius R_3 that will be tangent to the circle with a center at O and having a radius R_1 is a circle that is concentric with the given circle at R_3 distance. The radius of the locus of centers will be $R_1 + R_3$. In the case of the circle with center at point P, the radius of the locus of centers will be $R_2 + R_3$. Points Q and Q_1 where these arcs intersect are points that are R_3 distance from both circles. Therefore, circles of R_3 radius that are centered at Q and Q_1 will be tangent to both circles with centers at O and P.

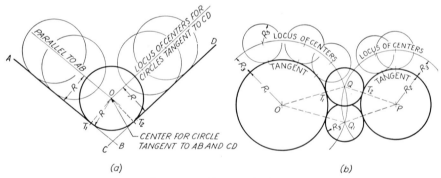

(a) (b)

Fig. 4.21. Tangent Circles.

4.23. To draw a circular arc of radius R tangent to two lines (Fig. 4.22).

(a) Given the two lines AB and CD at right angles to each other, and the radius of the required arc R. Using their point of intersection X as a center and R as a radius, strike an arc cutting the given lines at T_1 and T_2 (tangent points). With T_1 and T_2 as centers and the same radius, strike the intersecting arcs locating the center O of the required arc.

(b) and (c) Given the two lines AB and CD, not at right angles, and the radius R. Draw lines EF and GH parallel to the given lines at a distance R. Since the point of intersection of these lines is distance R from both given lines, it will be the center O of the required arc. Mark the tangent points T_1 and T_2 that lie along perpendiculars to the given lines through O.

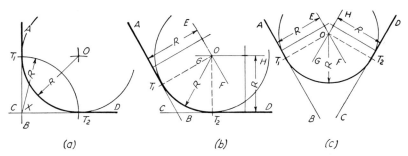

Fig. 4.22.   To Draw a Circular Arc Tangent to Two Lines.

These constructions are useful for drawing fillets and rounds on views of machine parts.

4.24. To draw a circular arc of radius R_1 tangent to a given circular arc and a given straight line (Fig. 4.23).   Given the line AB and the circular arc with center O.

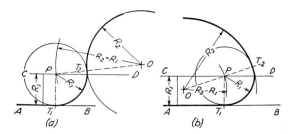

Fig. 4.23.   To Draw a Circular Arc Tangent to a Given Circular Arc and a Line.

(a) and (b) Let R_1 be the radius of the required arc.   Draw line CD parallel to AB at a distance R_1.   Using the center O of the given arc and a radius equal to its radius plus or minus the radius of the required arc (R_2 plus or minus R_1), swing a parallel arc intersecting CD.   Since the line CD and the intersecting arc will be the loci of centers for all circles of radius R_1, tangent respectively to the given line AB and the given arc, their point of intersection P will be the center of the required arc.   Mark the points of tangency T_1 and T_2. T_1 lies along a perpendicular to AB through the center P, and T_2 along a line joining the centers of the two arcs.

This construction is useful for drawing fillets and rounds on views of machine parts.

4.25. To draw a circular arc of a given radius R_1 tangent to two given circular arcs (Fig. 4.24).   Given the circular arcs AB and CD with centers O and P, and radii R_2 and R_3, respectively.   Let R_1 be the radius of the required arc.

(a) and (b) Using O as a center and R_2 plus R_1 as a radius, strike an arc parallel to AB.   Using P as a center and R_3 plus R_1 as a radius, strike an intersecting arc parallel to CD.   Since each of these intersecting arcs is the locus of centers for all circular arcs of radius R_1 tangent to the given arc to which it is parallel, their point of intersection S will be the center for the required arc that is tangent to both. Mark the points of tangency T_1 and T_2 that lie on the lines of centers PS and OS.

(c) Using O as a center and R_2 plus R_1 as a radius, strike an arc parallel to AB. Using P as a center and R_3 minus R_1 as a radius, strike an intersecting arc parallel to CD. The point of intersection of these arcs is the center for the required arc.

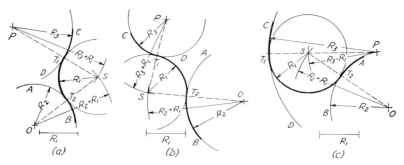

Fig. 4.24. To Draw a Circular Arc Tangent to Two Given Arcs.

4.26. To draw a reverse (ogee) curve (Fig. 4.25). Given the two parallel lines AB and CD. At points B and C, the termini and tangent points of the reverse curve, erect perpendiculars. Join BC with a straight line and assume a point E that will be the point at which the curves will be tangent to each other. Draw the perpendicular bisectors of BE and EC. Since an arc tangent to AB at B must have its center on the perpendicular BP, point of intersection P of the bisector and the perpendicular is the center for the required arc that is to be tangent to the line at B and the other required arc at point E. For the same reason, point Q is the center for the other required arc.

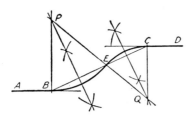

Fig. 4.25. To Draw a Reverse Curve.

This construction is useful to architects in drawing mouldings, and to engineers in laying out center lines for railroad tracks, pipe lines, and so forth.

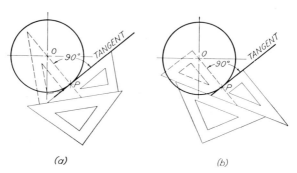

(a)   (b)

Fig. 4.26. To Draw a Line Tangent to a Circle at a Point on the Circumference.

4.27. To draw a line tangent to a circle at a given point on the circumference (Fig. 4.26). Given a circle with center O and point P on its circumference. Place a triangle supported by a T-square or another triangle in such a position that one side passes through the center O and point P. When using the method illustrated in (a), align the hypotenuse of one triangle to the center of the circle and the point of tangency; then, with a guiding triangle held in position, revolve the triangle about the 90° angle and slide it into position for drawing the required tangent line.

Another procedure is shown in (b). To draw the tangent by this method, align one leg of a triangle, which is adjacent to the 90° angle, through the center of the circle and the point of tangency; then, slide it along the edge of a guiding triangle into position.

This construction satisfies the geometrical requirement that a tangent must be perpendicular to a radial line drawn to the point of tangency.

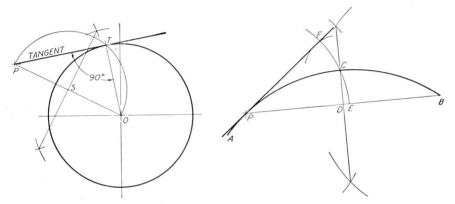

Fig. 4.27. To Draw a Line Tangent to   Fig. 4.28. To Draw a Tangent to a Circular
a Circle Through a Given Point Outside.   Arc Having an Inaccessible Center.

4.28. To draw a line tangent to a circle through a given point outside the circle (Fig. 4.27). Given a circle with center O, and an external point P.

Join the point P and the center O with a straight line, and bisect it to locate point S. Using S as a center and SO (one-half PO) as a radius, strike an arc intersecting the circle at point T (point of tangency). Line PT is the required tangent.

4.29. To draw a tangent through a point P on a circular arc having an inaccessible center (Fig. 4.28). Draw the chord PB; then, erect a perpendicular bisector. With point P as a center swing an arc through point C where the perpendicular bisector cuts the given arc. With C as a center and a radius equal to the chord distance CE, draw an arc to establish the location of point F. A line drawn through points P and F is the required tangent.

4.30. To draw a line tangent to a circle through a given point outside the circle (Fig. 4.29). Place a triangle supported by a T-square or another triangle in such a position that one leg passes through point P tangent to the circle, and draw the tangent. Slide the triangle along the

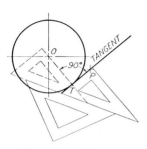

Fig. 4.29. To Draw a Line Tangent to a Circle Through a Given Point Outside.

guiding edge until the other leg coincides with the center O, and mark the point of tangency. Although this method is not as accurate as the geometrical one explained in Sec. 4.28, it is frequently employed by commercial draftsmen.

4.31. To draw a line tangent to two given circles (Fig. 4.30). Given two circles with centers O and P and radii R_1 and R respectively.

(*a*) Open belt—Using P as a center and a radius equal to R minus R_1, draw an arc. Through O draw a tangent to this arc using the method explained in Sec. 4.28. With the location of tangent point T established, draw line PT and extend it to locate T_1. Draw OT_2 parallel to PT_1. The line from T_2 to T_1 is the required tangent to the given circles.

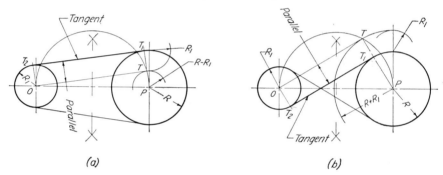

(*a*)   (*b*)

Fig. 4.30.   To Draw a Line Tangent to Two Given Circles.

(*b*) Crossed belt—Using P as a center and a radius equal to R plus R_1, draw an arc. With the location of tangent point T determined through use of the method shown in Fig. 4.27, locate tangent point T_1 on line TP and draw OT_2 parallel to PT. The line T_1T_2, drawn parallel to OT, is the required tangent.

4.32. To approximate a curve with tangent circular arcs (Fig. 4.31). Draftsmen often find it desirable to approximate a noncircular curve with a series of tangent arcs. If the curve consists of a number of points, a pleasing curve should be sketched lightly through the points before starting to draw the arcs. The centers and radii are selected by

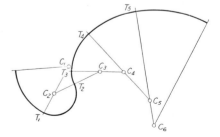

Fig. 4.31.   To Approximate a Curve with Tangent Circular Arcs.

trial, but it must be remembered after the first arc has been drawn as far as it coincides with the sketched curve that when arcs are tangent the centers are on a common normal through their point of tangency. Sometimes draftsmen use this method to draw curves in ink instead of using a french curve.

4.33. To lay off the approximate length of the circumference of a circle (Fig. 4.32).   Draw a line through point A tangent to the circle and lay off along it a distance AB equal to three times the diameter ($3D$). Using point E on the circumference as a center and a radius equal to the radius of the circle, strike an arc to establish the location of point C. Draw CD perpendicular to the vertical center line through point A. DB is the rectified length of the circumference; however, it is slightly longer

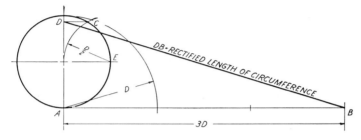

Fig. 4.32.   To Lay Off the Approximate Length of the Circumference of a Circle.

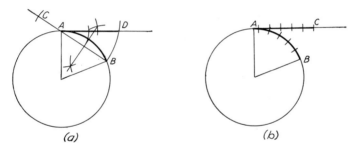

(a)   (b)

Fig. 4.33.   To Lay Off the Approximate Length of a Circular Arc on Its Tangent.

than the true circumference by a negligible amount (approximate error 1/21,800).

4.34. To lay off the approximate length of a circular arc on its tangent (Fig. 4.33).   Given the arc AB.

(a) Draw the tangent through A, and extend the chord BA.   Locate point C by laying off AC equal to one-half the length of the chord AB. With C as a center and a radius equal to CB, strike an arc intersecting the tangent at D.   The length AD along the tangent is slightly shorter than the true length of the arc AB by an amount that may be disregarded, for, when the angle between the chord and the tangent is less than 60°, the length of AD differs from the true length of the arc AB by less than 6′ in one mile; when 30°, the error is $4\frac{1}{2}''$ in one mile.

(b) Draw the tangent through A. Using the small dividers, start at B and step off equal chord distances around the arc until the point nearest A is reached.   From this point (without raising the dividers) step off along the tangent an equal number of distances to locate point C.   If the point nearest A is indented into the tangent instead of the arc, the almost negligible error in the length of AC will be still less.

Since the small distances stepped off are in reality the chords of small arcs, the length AC will be slightly less than the true length of the arc. For most practical purposes the difference may be disregarded.

4.35. Conic sections (Fig. 4.34). When a right circular cone of revolution is cut by planes at different angles, four curves of intersection are obtained that are called conic sections.

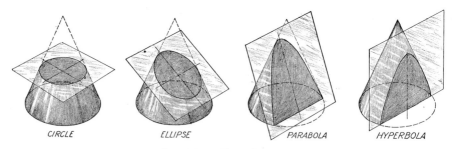

Fig. 4.34. Conic Sections.

When the intersecting plane is perpendicular to the axis, the resulting curve of intersection is a circle.

If the plane makes a greater angle with the axis than do the elements, the intersection is an ellipse.

If the plane makes the same angle with the axis as the elements, the resulting curve is a parabola.

Finally, if the plane makes a smaller angle with the axis than do the elements or is parallel to the axis, the curve of intersection is a hyperbola.

The geometric methods for constructing the ellipse, parabola, and hyperbola are discussed in succeeding sections.

4.36. The ellipse. Mathematically, the ellipse is a curve generated by a point moving so that at any position the sum of its distances from two fixed points (foci) is a constant (equal to the major diameter). It is encountered very frequently in orthographic drawing when holes and circular forms are viewed obliquely. Ordinarily, the major and minor diameters are known.

Fig. 4.35. To Construct an Ellipse, Trammel Method.

4.37. To construct an ellipse, trammel method (Fig. 4.35).
Given the major axis AB and the minor axis CD. Along the straight edge of a strip of paper or cardboard, locate the points O, C, and A, so that the distance OA is equal to one-half the length of the major axis and the distance OC is equal to one-half the length of the minor axis. Place the

marked edge across the axes so that point A is on the minor axis and point C is on the major axis. *Point O will fall on the circumference of the ellipse.* Move the strip, keeping A on the minor axis and C on the major axis, and mark at least five other positions of O on the ellipse in each quadrant. Using a french curve, complete the ellipse by drawing a smooth curve through the points. The ellipsograph, which draws ellipses mechanically, is based on this same principle. The trammel method is an accurate method.

An alternate method for marking off the location of points A, O, and C is given in Fig. 4.35.

4.38. To construct an ellipse, concentric circle method (Fig. 4.36). Given the major axis AB and the minor axis CD. Using the center of the ellipse (point O) as a center, describe circles having the major and minor axes as diameters. Divide the circles into equal central angles and draw diametrical lines such as P_1P_2. From point P_1 on the

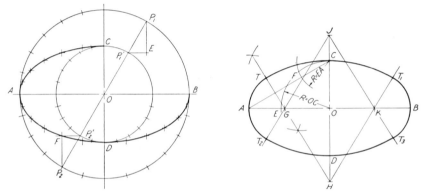

Fig. 4.36. To Construct an Ellipse, Concentric Circle Method.   Fig. 4.37. To Construct an Ellipse, Center Method.

circumference of the larger circle, draw a line parallel to CD, the minor axis, and from point P_1' at which the diameter P_1P_2 intersects the inner circle, draw a line parallel to AB, the major axis. The point of intersection of these lines, point E, is on the required ellipse. At points P_2 and P_2' repeat the same procedure and locate point F. Thus, two points are established by the line P_1P_2. Locate at least five points in each of the four quadrants. The ellipse is completed by drawing a smooth curve through the points.

This is one of the most accurate methods used to form ellipses.

4.39. To construct an ellipse, four-center method (Fig. 4.37). Given the major axis AB and the minor axis CD. Draw the line AC. Using the center of the ellipse O as a center and OC as a radius, strike an arc intersecting OA at point E. Using C as a center and EA as a radius, strike an arc intersecting the line AC at F. Draw the perpendicular bisector of the line AF. The points G and H, at which the perpendicular bisector intersects the axes AB and CD (extended), are the centers of two of the arcs forming the ellipse. Locate the other two centers, J and K,·

by laying off OJ equal to OH and OK equal to OG. To determine the junction points (tangent points), T, T_1, T_2, and T_3, for the arcs, draw lines through the centers of the tangent arcs. The figure thus formed by the four circle arcs approximates a true ellipse.

4.40. To construct an ellipse, parallelogram method (Fig. 4.38). Given the major axis AB and the minor axis CD. Construct the circumscribing parallelogram. Divide AO and AE into the same number of equal parts (say four) and number the division points from A. From C draw a line through point 3 on line AE, and from D draw a line through

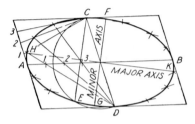

Fig. 4.38. To Construct an Ellipse, Parallelogram Method.

Fig. 4.39. To Draw the Major and Minor Axes of an Ellipse, Given the Conjugate Diameters.

point 3 on line AO. The point of intersection of these lines is on the required ellipse. Similarly, the intersections of lines from C and D through points numbered 1 and 2 are on the ellipse. A similar construction will locate points in the other three quadrants of the ellipse. Use of a french curve will permit a smooth curve to be drawn through the points. Had the circumscribing parallelogram not been a rectangle as in Fig. 4.38, the completed construction would appear as in Fig. 4.39, and AB and CD would be conjugate axes. To establish the major and minor axes, draw a semicircle on CD as a diameter, intersecting the ellipse at E.

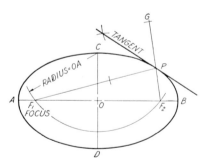

Fig. 4.40. To Draw a Tangent to an Ellipse.

FG, running parallel to CE through the center of the ellipse, will be the required minor axis. HK, running through the center of the ellipse parallel to DE and perpendicular to FG, will be the major axis.

4.41. To draw a tangent to an ellipse at any given point (Fig. 4.40). Given any point, such as P, on the perimeter of the ellipse $ABCD$. Using C as a center and a radius equal to OA (one-half the major diameter), strike arcs across the major axis at F_1 and F_2. From these points, which are foci of the ellipse, draw F_1P and F_2G. The bisector of the angle GPF_1 is the required tangent to the ellipse.

4.42. To draw a tangent to an ellipse from a given point P outside of the ellipse (Fig. 4.41). With the end of the minor axis as a center and a radius R equal to one-half of the length of the major axis, strike an arc to find the foci F_1 and F_2.   With point P as a center and the distance PF_2 as a radius, draw an arc. Using F_1 as a center and the length AB as a radius strike arcs cutting the arc with center of P at points G and H. Draw lines GF_1 and HF_1 to establish the location of the tangent points T_1 and T_2. Draw the required tangent.

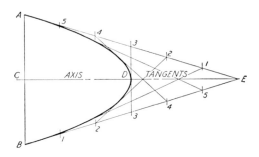

Fig. 4.41. To Draw a Tangent to an Ellipse Through a Point Outside of the Ellipse.

4.43. The parabola. Mathematically, the parabola is a curve generated by a point moving so that at any position its distance from a fixed point (the focus) is always exactly equal to its distance to a fixed line (the directrix). The construction shown in Fig. 4.42 is based on this definition.

In engineering design, the parabola is used for parabolic sound and light reflectors, for vertical curves on highways, and for bridge arches.

4.44. To construct a parabola (Fig. 4.42). Given the focus F and the directrix AB. Draw the axis of the parabola perpendicular to the directrix. Through any point on the axis, for example point C, draw a line parallel to the directrix AB. Using F as a center and the distance OC as a radius, strike arcs intersecting the line at points P_4 and P_4'. Repeat this procedure until a sufficient number of additional points have been located to determine a smooth curve. The vertex V is located at a point midway between O and F.

Fig. 4.42. To Construct a Parabola.

Fig. 4.43. To Construct a Parabola, Tangent Method.

To construct a tangent to a parabola, say at point P_6, draw the line P_6D parallel to the axis; then, bisect the angle DP_6F. The bisector of the angle is the required tangent.

4.45. To construct a parabola, tangent method (Fig. 4.43). Given the points A and B and the distance CD from AB to the vertex. Extend the axis CD, and set off DE equal to CD. EA and EB are tangents to the parabola at A and B respectively.

Divide EA and EB into the same number of equal parts (say six), and number the division points as shown. Connect the corresponding

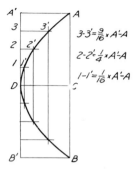

points 1 and 1, 2 and 2, 3 and 3, and so forth. These lines, as tangents of the required parabola, form its envelope. Draw the tangent curve.

$3\text{-}3'=\frac{9}{16}\times A'\text{-}A$

$2\text{-}2'=\frac{1}{4}\times A'\text{-}A$

$1\text{-}1'=\frac{1}{16}\times A'\text{-}A$

4.46. To construct a parabola, offset method (Fig. 4.44). Given the enclosing rectangle $A'ABB'$. Divide DA' into any number of equal parts (say four), and draw from the division points the perpendiculars parallel to DC, along which the offset distances are to be measured off. The offsets vary as the square of their distances from D. For example, since $D1$ is one-fourth of the distance from A' to D, $1\text{-}1'$

Fig 4.44. To Construct a Parabola, Offset Method.

will be $(\frac{1}{4})^2$, or $\frac{1}{16}$ of $A'A$. Similarly, $2\text{-}2'$ will be $(\frac{1}{2})^2$, or $\frac{1}{4}$ of $A'A$; and $3\text{-}3'$ will be $\frac{9}{16}$ of $A'A$. To complete the parabola, lay off the computed offset values along the perpendiculars and form the figure with a french curve.

This method is preferred by civil engineers for laying out parabolic arches and computing vertical curves for highways.

4.47. To construct a curve of parabolic form through two given points (Fig. 4.45). Given the points A and B. Assume a point C. Draw the tangents CA and CB, and construct the parabolic curve using the tangent method shown in Fig. 4.43. This method is frequently used in machine design to draw curves that are more pleasing than circular arcs.

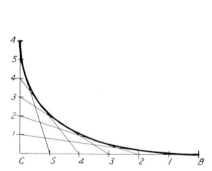

Fig. 4.45. To Construct a Curve of Parabolic Form.

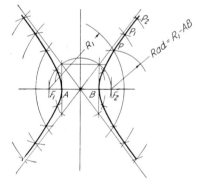

Fig. 4.46. To Construct a Hyperbola.

4.48. The hyperbola. Mathematically, the hyperbola can be described as a curve generated by a point moving so that at any position the difference of its distances from two fixed points (foci) is a constant (equal to the transverse axis of the hyperbola). This definition is the basis for the construction shown in Fig. 4.46.

4.49. To construct a hyperbola (Fig. 4.46). Given the foci F_1 and F_2, and the transverse axis AB. Using F_1 and F_2 as centers and any radius R_1 greater than F_1B, strike arcs. With these same centers and a radius equal to $R_1–AB$, strike arcs intersecting the first arcs at point P.   Point P is on the required hyperbola.   Repeat this procedure and locate as many additional points, such as P_1, P_2, and so forth, as are required to form the hyperbola accurately with a french curve.

The tangent to the hyperbola at any point, such as P, is the bisector of the angle between the focal radii F_1P and F_2P.

4.50. An involute.   The spiral curve traced by a point on a chord as it unwinds from around a circle or a polygon is an involute curve.   Figure 4.47(a) shows an involute of a circle, while (b) shows that of a square. The involute of a polygon is obtained by extending the sides and drawing arcs using the corners, in order, as centers.   The circle in (a) may be considered to be a polygon having an infinite number of sides.

4.51. To draw an involute of a circle (Fig. 4.47a).   Divide the circumference into a number of equal parts.   Draw tangents through the division points.   Then, along each tangent, lay off the rectified length of the corresponding circular arc, from the starting point to the point of

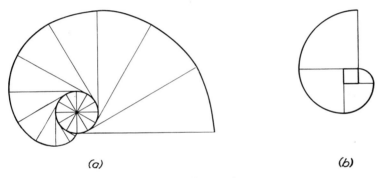

(a)   (b)

Fig. 4.47.   The Involute.

tangency.   The involute curve is a smooth curve through these points. The involute of a circle is used in the development of tooth profiles in gearing.

4.52. To draw the involute of a polygon (Fig. 4.47b).   Extend the sides of the polygon as shown in (b).   With the corners as centers, in order around the polygon, draw arcs terminating on the extended sides.   The first radius is equal to the length of one side of the polygon.   The radius of each successive arc is the distance from the center to the terminating point of the previous arc.

4.53. A cycloid.   A cycloid is the curve generated by a point on the circumference of a moving circle when the circle rolls in a plane along a straight line, as shown in Fig. 4.48.

4.54. To draw a cycloid (Fig. 4.48).   Draw the generating circle and the line AB tangent to it.   The length AB should be made equal to the circumference of the circle.   Divide the circle and the line AB into the same number of equal parts.   With this much of the construction completed, the next step is to draw the line of centers CD through point O and project the division points along AB to CD by drawing perpendiculars. Using these points as centers for the various positions of the moving circle, draw circle arcs. For the purpose of illustration, assume the circle is moving to the left. When the circle has moved along CD to x, point P will have moved to point P_x. Similarly, when the center is at y, P will be at P_y. To locate positions of P along the cycloidal curve, project the division points of the divided circle in their proper order, across to the position circles. A smooth curve through these points will be the required cycloid.

4.55. An epicycloid (Fig. 4.49). An epicycloid is the curve generated by a point on the circumference of a circle that rolls in a plane on

Fig. 4.48. A Cycloid.

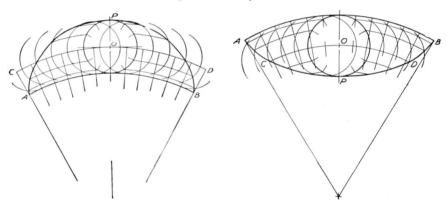

Fig. 4.49. An Epicycloid. Fig. 4.50. A Hypocycloid.

the outside of another circle. The method used in drawing an epicycloid is similar to the one used in drawing the cycloid.

4.56. A hypocycloid (Fig. 4.50). A hypocycloid is the curve generated by a point on the circumference of a circle that rolls in a plane on the inside of another circle. The method used to draw a hypocycloid is similar to the method used to draw the cycloid.

Practical examples of the use of cycloidal curves to form the outlines of cycloidal gear teeth are shown in the chapter on gears in this text.

4.57. Spiral of Archimedes. Archimedes' spiral is a plane curve generated by a point moving uniformly around and away from a fixed point. In order to define this curve more specifically, it can be said that it is generated by a point moving uniformly along a straight line while the line revolves with uniform angular velocity about a fixed point.

The definition of the Spiral of Archimedes is applied in drawing this curve as illustrated in Fig. 4.51.   To find a sufficient number of points to allow the use of an irregular curve for drawing the spiral it is the practice to divide the given circle into a number of equal parts (say twelve) and draw radial lines to the division points.   Next, divide a radial line into the same number of equal parts as the circle and number the division points on the circumference of the circle beginning with the radial line adjacent to the divided one.   With the center of the circle as a center, draw concentric arcs that in each case will start at a numbered division point on the divided radial line and will end at an intersection with the radial line that is numbered correspondingly.   The

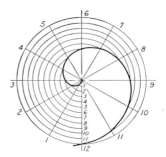

Fig. 4.51.   Spiral of Archimedes.

arc starting at point 1 gives a point on the curve at its intersection with radial line 1; the arc starting at 2 gives an intersection point on radial line 2; etc.   The spiral is a smooth curve drawn through these intersection points.

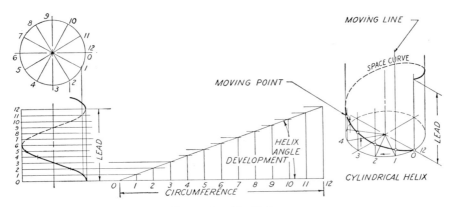

Fig. 4.52.   The Helix.

4.58. The helix (Fig. 4.52).   The cylindrical helix is a space curve that is generated by a point moving uniformly on the surface of a cylinder. The point must travel parallel to the axis with uniform linear velocity while at the same time it is moving with uniform angular velocity around the axis.   The curve can be thought of as being generated by a point moving uniformly along a straight line while the line is revolving with uniform angular velocity around the axis of the given cylinder.   Study the pictorial drawing.

The first step in drawing a cylindrical helix is to lay out the two views of the cylinder.   Next, the lead should be measured along a contour element and divided into a number of equal parts (say twelve).   Divide the circular view of the cylinder into the same number of parts and number the division points.

The division lines of the lead represent the various positions of the moving point as it travels in a direction parallel to the axis of the cylinder along the moving line.   The division points on the circular view are the related positions of the moving line.   For example, when the line has moved from the 0 to the 1 position, the point has traveled along the line a distance equal to one-twelfth of the lead; when the line is in the 2 position the point has traveled one-sixth of the lead.   (See pictorial drawing.) In constructing the curve the necessary points are found by projecting

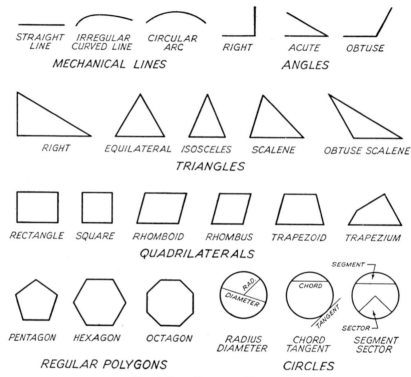

STRAIGHT   IRREGULAR   CIRCULAR
LINE   CURVED LINE   ARC   RIGHT   ACUTE   OBTUSE

MECHANICAL LINES   ANGLES

RIGHT   EQUILATERAL ISOSCELES   SCALENE   OBTUSE SCALENE

TRIANGLES

RECTANGLE   SQUARE   RHOMBOID   RHOMBUS   TRAPEZOID   TRAPEZIUM

QUADRILATERALS

PENTAGON   HEXAGON   OCTAGON   RADIUS   CHORD   SEGMENT
                                    DIAMETER   TANGENT   SECTOR

REGULAR POLYGONS   CIRCLES

Fig. 4.53.   Geometric Shapes.

from a numbered point on the circular view to the division line of the lead that is numbered similarly.

A helix may be either right-hand or left-hand.   The one shown in Fig. 4.52 is a left-hand helix.

When the cylinder is developed, the helix becomes a straight line on the development as shown.   It is inclined to the base line at an angle known as the "helix angle."

A screw thread is an example of a practical application of the cylindrical helix.

4.59. Problems.   The following exercises not only require the student to study and use certain common geometrical constructions, but also furnish additional practice in applying good line technique to the drawing of instrumental figures and practical designs.   All work should

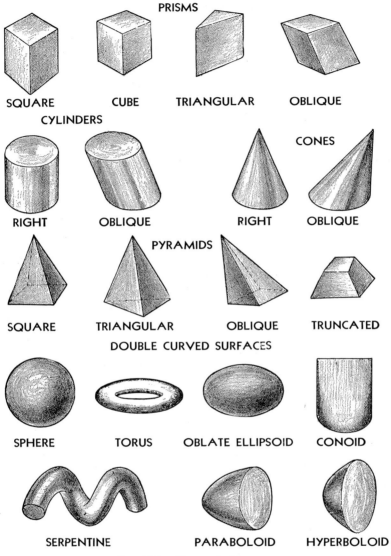

Fig. 4.54. Geometric Shapes.

be very accurately done.   Tangent points should be indicated by a light, short dash across the line.

1. Draw a horizontal line $4\frac{3}{8}''$ long. Bisect it by the method shown in Fig. 4.1(*b*).

2. Draw a line $3\frac{3}{4}''$ long, inclined at 30° to the horizontal. Divide it into five equal parts. Use the method illustrated in Fig. 4.6(*a*).

3. Draw a line $3\frac{1}{4}''$ long. Divide it into three equal parts. Use the method shown in Fig. 4.2.

4. Draw a line $3\frac{1}{8}''$ long. Divide it proportionally in the ratio $1:2:3$. Use the method shown in Fig. 4.7.

5. Using a line $3\frac{1}{4}''$ long as the base line, construct a triangle having sides $2\frac{1}{2}''$, $3\frac{1}{4}''$, and $3\frac{3}{4}''$ long, respectively. Study the method that is illustrated in Fig. 4.11.

6. Construct a regular hexagon having a $2\frac{1}{2}''$ distance across flats. Select the most practical procedure.

7. Construct a regular hexagon having a $3\frac{1}{4}''$ distance across corners. Select the most practical method.

8. Construct a regular pentagon having $1\frac{1}{4}''$ sides. Use the method illustrated in Fig. 4.18.

9. Divide the area of the triangle in problem 5 into four equal parts. Use the method shown in Fig. 4.19(a).

10. Trisect the angle between the $3\frac{1}{4}''$ and $3\frac{3}{4}''$ sides of the triangle in problem 5. Use the method illustrated in Fig. 4.5.

11. Draw two horizontal lines $2''$ apart. Locate two points $3''$ apart horizontally, one on each line. Draw an ogee curve tangent to these lines. Study the procedure illustrated in Fig. 4.25.

12. Draw a $2\frac{1}{2}''$ circle. Select a point $2''$ from the center and draw a line tangent to it, using the method illustrated in Fig. 4.27.

13. Draw a $2\frac{3}{4}''$ circle, and draw tangent to it a line that makes $15°$ with the horizontal. Draw a $1\frac{1}{2}''$ circle tangent to the line and the $2\frac{3}{4}''$ circle. Use the method illustrated in Fig. 4.23.

14. Draw a $3''$ circle. Inside this circle, and tangent to it, draw a $1\frac{3}{4}''$ circle. See that the centers of both circles are on the same vertical center line. Draw two $1''$ circles tangent to the $3''$ and the $1\frac{3}{4}''$ circles. Use the method illustrated in Fig. 4.24.

15. Construct an ellipse having a major diameter of $4\frac{1}{4}''$ and a minor diameter of $2\frac{3}{4}''$. Use the trammel method illustrated in Fig. 4.35.

16. Construct an ellipse having a major diameter of $4''$ and a minor diameter of $2\frac{3}{4}''$. Use the concentric circle method illustrated in Fig. 4.36. Find a sufficient number of points to obtain a smooth curve.

17. Construct the ellipse required in problem 16, using the four-center method. Study Sec. 4.39 and Fig. 4.37.

18. Construct an ellipse having conjugate axes $3\frac{3}{4}''$ and $2\frac{1}{2}''$ long inclined one to the other at $75°$. Determine the major and minor axes (Fig. 4.39).

19. Construct a parabola with axis vertical. Make the focus $\frac{3}{4}''$ from the directrix. Select a point on the curve and draw a line tangent to the parabola. Study Sec. 4.44 and Fig. 4.42.

20. Construct a hyperbola having a transverse axis of $1''$ and foci $1\frac{5}{8}''$ apart. Study Sec. 4.49 and Fig. 4.46.

21. Construct the involute of an equilateral triangle with $1''$ sides. Study Sec. 4.52.

22. Construct the involute of a circle $\frac{7}{8}''$ in diameter. Study Sec. 4.51 and Fig. 4.47(a).

23. Construct the cycloid generated by a $1\frac{1}{2}''$ circle. Study Sec. 4.54 and Fig. 4.48.

24. Construct the epicycloid generated by a $1\frac{1}{2}''$ circle rolling on a $5''$ circle. Study Sec. 4.55 and Fig. 4.49.

25. Construct the hypocycloid generated by a $1\frac{1}{2}''$ circle rolling on a $4\frac{1}{2}''$ circle. Study Sec. 4.56 and Fig. 4.50.

26. Reconstruct the view of the wrench shown in Fig. 4.55. Mark all tangent points with short lines.

Fig. 4.55. Wrench.   Fig. 4.56. Gasket.

27. Reconstruct the view of the gasket shown in Fig. 4.56. Mark all tangent points with short marks across tangent lines.

28. Reconstruct the view of the cam shown in Fig. 4.57. Mark all tangent points.

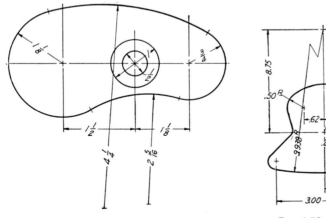

Fig. 4.57. Cam.   Fig. 4.58. Dolly Block.

29. Reconstruct the view of the dolly block shown in Fig. 4.58. Mark all tangent points.

30. Construct the shape of the slotted guide shown in Fig. 4.59. Show all construction for locating centers and mark points of tangency.

Fig. 4.59. Slotted Guide.

Fig. 4.60. Adjustable Y-Clamp.

31. Construct the adjustable Y-clamp shown in Fig. 4.60. Show all construction for locating centers and mark points of tangency.

32. Reconstruct the geometrical design shown in Fig. 4.61. Mark all tangent points with short marks across tangent lines, as shown in the given view.

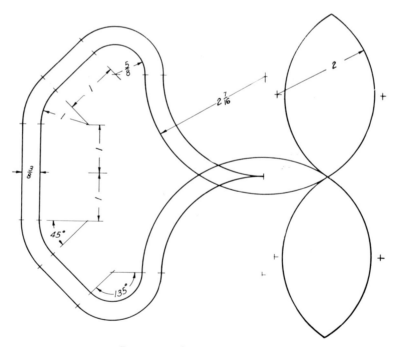

Fig. 4.61. Geometrical Design.

33. Reconstruct the view of the cover gasket shown in Fig. 4.62.

Fig. 4.62. Cover Gasket.   **Fig. 4.63. C-Ring.**

34. Reconstruct the view of the C-ring shown in Fig. 4.63.

35. (Fig. 4.64.) Using an eighth-size scale, make a one-view drawing of the housing gasket. Use approved geometrical constructions and mark all tangent points with $\frac{1}{8}''$ dash across the line. Be prepared to explain to your instructor the procedure for determining the locations for centers and tangent points and demonstrate the manipulation of the triangles for the 15° angles. Study Sec. 4.11. *Supplementary information:* (1) the three small circular holes are to be 6'' in diameter, (2) the large hole in the center of the gasket must have a $10\frac{1}{2}''$ diameter, (3) all small radii are 2'', (4) the gasket is to be cut from $\frac{1}{16}''$ fiber stock.

Fig. 4.64. Housing Gasket.

36. (Fig. 4.65.) Part *A* is free to pivot about a shaft. If this part should be revolved in a counterclockwise direction as indicated by the arrows, it would contact surface C. Reproduce the drawing as given and show part A revolved until it is in contact with surface C. Use the symbolic line for showing an alternate position for part A in this new position. Show all geometrical constructions clearly and do not erase construction lines.

Fig. 4.65. Geometrical Construction.   **Fig. 4.66. Geometrical Construction.**

37. (Fig. 4.66.) Part A revolves about shaft B in a clockwise direction from the position shown until surface C comes into contact with the cylindrical surface of the roller. Reproduce the drawing as given and show part A in its revolved position using the symbolic alternate position line for this new position. Show all geometrical constructions clearly and do not erase construction lines.

Fig. 4.67. A Plat of a Land Survey.

38. Reconstruct the plat of a land survey shown in Fig. 4.67. Use the tangent method, as explained in Sec. 4.11, to determine the direction of the center line of state road 26. The triangles used in combination will produce the other angles.

Use a graphical method
to locate center with
value for R unknown

Fig. 4.68. Electrode.

39. Reconstruct the view of the electrode shown in Fig. 4.68. Find mathematically the lengths of the center lines of the 3.50 inch and 1.12 inch arcs. Determine the lengths of the two remaining arcs using proper graphical methods. Record the total length of the electrode. It is customary to use the length of the center line as the length of an electrode.

5 | The Theory of Projection

5.1. Since engineering draftsmen are confronted with the task of recording the shapes and sizes of three-dimensional objects on the plane of a sheet of drawing paper, it is obvious that they must follow generally recognized procedures if their finished drawings are to be read easily. Size description and shape description are of equal importance, but, in order to simplify the presentation of the fundamentals underlying the making of working drawings, this chapter is concerned entirely with the methods commonly employed in describing shape. A later chapter will discuss size description.

Fig. 5.1. Perspective Projection.

Each of the different methods, axonometric, oblique, and orthographic, is based on some form of projection. The theory governing a method should be understood thoroughly before it is used to produce a drawing.

5.2. Perspective (scenographic) projection. In perspective projection, the projecting lines (visual rays) converge to a point, as shown in Fig. 5.1. The representation upon the transparent picture plane may be considered the view that would be seen by one eye located at a definite point in space. The picture is established on the imaginary plane by the piercing points of the projecting lines from the eye to the object. The size of the view depends upon the distance from the observer to the plane and the distance from the plane to the object.

Perspective projection is not suitable for working drawings because a perspective view does not reveal exact size and shape. It is used mainly by architects in preparing preliminary sketches and display drawings of proposed houses and buildings.

5.3 Orthographic projection (parallel projection). If the observer in Fig. 5.1 moves straight back from the picture plane until he is an infinite distance from it, the projecting lines (projectors) from the eye to the object become parallel to each other and perpendicular to the picture plane. The resulting projection (see Fig. 5.2) will then be the same shape and size as the front surface of the object. From a practical viewpoint, the projection may be thought of as being formed by perpendicular projectors extended from the object to the plane. The view is called an orthographic projection.

Since the view shown in Fig. 5.2 does not reveal the thickness of the object, one or more additional projections (see Figs. 5.3 and 5.4) are necessary to complete the description. Two projections are usually

Fig. 5.2. Orthographic Projection.

sufficient to describe simple objects, but three or more are necessary for complicated ones.

The picture planes are customarily called the principal or co-ordinate planes of projection, and the perpendiculars, projectors. In engineering drawing, the planes are usually arranged as shown in Fig. 5.4. Since all three are mutually perpendicular, they are called the horizontal, frontal, and profile co-ordinate planes. To maintain this mutual relationship when laying out views, it is the usual practice to consider the frontal plane as lying in the plane of the paper and the horizontal and profile planes as being revolved into position. Note in Fig. 5.5 the manner in which the planes are revolved. This theoretical treatment of the co-ordinate planes establishes an absolute relationship between the views. Visualizing an object would be considerably more difficult than it is, if it were not for this fixed relationship, for it would be impossible to determine quickly the direction of sight for a particular view.

Fig. 5.3.   Planes of Projection.

Fig. 5.4.   Planes of Projection.

Fig. 5.5.   The Revolution of the Planes of Projection.

Fig. 5.6.   The Planes Resolved into the Plane of the Paper.

Fig. 5.7.   Axonometric Projection.

PENCILS SHOW THE DIRECTION
OF PROJECTORS

Fig. 5.8. Oblique Projection.

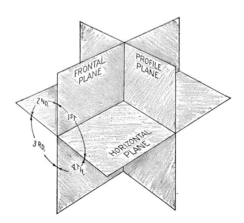

Fig. 5.9. Planes of Projection.

5.4. One-plane projection.   If the object is turned and then tilted so that three faces are inclined to the plane projection, the resulting projection is a special type of orthographic projection known as axonometric projection.   Figure 5.7 illustrates an axonometric projection of a cube.   Note that the projectors from the object to the plane are perpendicular to the plane.   The three recognized subdivisions of axonometric projection, namely, isometric, dimetric, and trimetric, are explained in Chapter 11.

Another form of one-plane projection is known as oblique projection. This form differs from orthographic projection in that, although one face is imagined to be parallel to the plane of projection, the projectors make

Fig. 5.10.   Third-Angle Projection.

an angle other than 90° with it (Fig. 5.8).   Obviously an infinite number of different views are possible, depending upon the angle the parallel projectors make with the plane of projection (picture plane).   The various subdivisions are cavalier projection, cabinet projection, and clinographic projection (Chapter 11).

Axonometric projection, oblique projection, and perspective projection may all be classed together as one-plane pictorial projection.

5.5 First- and third-angle projection.   If the horizontal and frontal planes are assumed to extend indefinitely on one side of the profile plane, four dihedral angles are formed and are designated as the *first*, *second, third*, and *fourth* angles (see Fig. 5.9).   The lines of intersection of these planes are called co-ordinate axes.   Their point of intersection is called the origin.   In this discussion of first- and third-angle projection, it should be remembered that no matter in which angle the object is placed, the observer views it from in front of the frontal plane and from above the horizontal plane.   To avoid misunderstanding, the directions for revolving the horizontal and profile planes into the frontal plane are illustrated in Fig. 5.10.   Note that the first and third quadrants are "opened" and the second and fourth are "closed" in revolving the horizontal plane into the frontal plane.

If an object, such as the one shown in Fig. 5.10, is placed so that its main faces are parallel to the principal planes, the respective projection on each plane will show the true size and shape of all surfaces that are parallel to that principal plane.   Theoretically, the object could have been

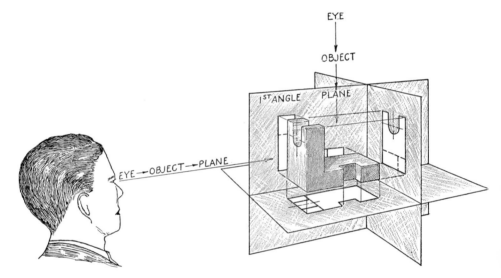

Fig. 5.11.   First-Angle Projection.

shown in any one of the four quadrants.   It has been placed in the third quadrant simply because engineering custom in the United States dictates the use of the third.   This quadrant is used because the views, when revolved into the frontal plane, are in their natural positions.   That is: the top view appears *above* the front view, as is expected, and the profile view, showing the *right side*, falls on the *right* of the front view.

In many foreign countries, "first-angle projection" is used for working drawings.   (Study Fig. 5.11.)   Observe that the top view is projected upon the horizontal plane and the front view upon the frontal plane.   For this reason, the top view falls below the front view when the co-ordinate planes are revolved.

In this country, the use of first-angle projection for working drawings was abandoned by engineering draftsmen some fifty years ago, although it is still used by architects and structural designers.

The different systems of projection may be conveniently classified as follows:

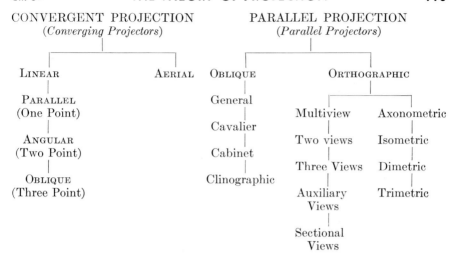

CONVERGENT PROJECTION
(Converging Projectors)

LINEAR

PARALLEL
(One Point)

ANGULAR
(Two Point)

OBLIQUE
(Three Point)

AERIAL

PARALLEL PROJECTION
(Parallel Projectors)

OBLIQUE

General

Cavalier

Cabinet

Clinographic

ORTHOGRAPHIC

Multiview

Two views

Three Views

Auxiliary
Views

Sectional
Views

Axonometric

Isometric

Dimetric

Trimetric

6 | Multiview Drawing

6.1. Industrial draftsmen use the orthographic system of projection for describing the shape of machine parts and structures. Practical application of this method of describing an object results in a drawing consisting of a number of systematically arranged views that reproduce the object's exact shape. It was explained in the preceding chapter, Sec. 5.3, that a set of views show-

TOP VIEW

FRONT VIEW
BOTTOM OF SLOT

EDGE OR SURFACE OF SLOT

RIGHT SIDE VIEW

Fig. 6.1. Three Views of an Object.

ing the object from different positions is always taken. The position of these views, in strict accordance with a universally recognized arrangement, must show the three dimensions, length, height, and depth. Although three views (Fig. 6.1) are usually required to describe an ordinary object, only two may be needed for a particularly simple one. A very complicated object may require four or more views. A view projected upon an auxiliary plane also may be desirable (see Chapter 7). Such a view often makes possible the elimination of one of the principal views. Therefore, it is up to the draftsman to determine the number and type of views needed to produce a satisfactory drawing. He will soon develop a knack for this, if he bears in mind that the number of views required depends entirely upon the complexity of the shape to be described.

6.2. Definition. Multiview (multiplanar) projection is a method by means of which the exact shape of an object can be represented by two or more separate views produced upon projection planes that are usually at right angles to each other.

6.3. Methods of obtaining the views. The views of an object may be obtained by either of two methods:

(1) The natural method.
(2) The glass box method.

Since the resulting views will be the same in either case, the beginner should adopt the method he finds the easiest to understand. Both methods are explained here in detail.

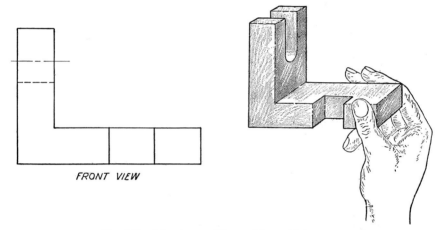

FRONT VIEW

Fig. 6.2. Viewing an Object (Natural Method).

6.4. The natural method. This method is commonly used by experienced commercial draftsmen. Each of the necessary views is obtained looking directly at the particular side of the object the view is to represent. The front view in Fig. 6.2 represents the object as seen by an imaginary observer stationed directly in front of it at an infinite distance away.

Figure 6.3 shows three of the principal views of an object, the front, top, and side views. They were obtained by looking directly at the front, top, and right side, respectively. In the application of this method, some draftsmen consider the position of the object as fixed and the position of the observer as shifted for each view; others find it easier to consider the observer's position as fixed and the position of the object as changed (Fig. 6.3) for each view. Regardless of which procedure is followed, the top and side views must be arranged in their natural positions relative to the front view.

Figure 6.4 illustrates the natural relationship of views.   Note that the top view is *vertically above* the front view, and the side view is *horizontally in line with* the front view.   In both of these views the *front of the block is toward the front view.*

Fig. 6.3.   Obtaining Three Views of an Object.

6.5. The "glass box" method.   An imaginary "glass box" is used widely by drawing instructors to explain the arrangement of orthographic views.   An explanation of this scheme can be best made by reviewing the use of planes of projection (Chapter 5).   It may be considered that planes of projection placed parallel to the six faces of an object form an enclosing "glass box" (see Fig. 6.5).   The observer views the enclosed object from the outside.   The views are obtained by running projectors from points on the object to the planes.   This procedure is in accordance with the theory of orthographic projection explained in Sec. 5.3, as well as the definition in Sec. 6.2.   The front, top, and right side of the box represent the H (horizontal), F (frontal), and P (profile) projection planes.

Fig. 6.4.   Position of Views.

Since the projections on the sides of the three-dimensional transparent box are to appear on a sheet of drawing paper, it must be assumed that the box is hinged (see Fig. 6.6) so that, when it is opened outward into the plane of the paper, the planes assume the positions illustrated in Figs. 6.6

Fig. 6.5.   The Glass Box.

Fig. 6.6.   Opening the Glass Box.

and 6.7.   Note that all of the planes, except the back one, are hinged to the frontal plane.   In accordance with this universally recognized assumption, the top projection must take a position directly above the front projection, and the right side projection must lie horizontally to the right of the front projection.   To identify the separate projections, draftsmen call the one on the frontal plane the *front view* or *front elevation,* the one on the horizontal plane the *top view* or *plan,* and the one on the side or profile plane the *side view, side elevation,* or *end view.*   Figure 6.7 shows the six views of the same object as they would appear on a sheet of drawing paper.   Ordinarily, only three of these views are necessary (front, top, and right side).   A bottom or rear view will be required in comparatively few cases.

Fig. 6.7.   Six Views of an Object on a Sheet of Drawing Paper.

6.6. The "second-position."   Sometimes, especially in the case of a broad flat object, it is desirable to hinge the sides of the box to the horizontal plane so that the side view will fall to the right of the top view, as illustrated in Fig. 6.8.   This arrangement conserves space on the paper and gives the views better balance.

6.7. The principles of multiview drawing.   The following principles should be studied carefully and understood thoroughly before any attempt is made to prepare an orthographic drawing.

1. The front and top views are *always* in line vertically (Fig. 6.4).

2. The front and side views are in line horizontally, except when the second position is used (Fig. 6.4).

3. The front of the object in the top view faces the front view (Fig. 6.10).

4. The front of the object in the side view faces the front view (Fig. 6.10).

5. The depth of the top view is the same as the depth of the side view (Fig. 6.9).

Fig. 6.8.   The "Second Position" for the Side View.

Fig. 6.9.   View Terminology.

Fig. 6.10.   View Analysis.

6. The length of the top view is the same as the length of the front view (Fig. 6.9).

7. The height of the side view is the same as the height of the front view (Fig. 6.9).

8. If a line is parallel to a plane of projection, its projection on the plane is exactly the same length as the true length of the line (Fig. 6.11a, b, c).

9. If a line is inclined to a plane of projection, its projection on the plane will be shorter than the true length of the line (Fig. 6.11d).

10. If a line is perpendicular to a plane of projection, its projection will be a point.

11. If a surface is parallel to a plane of projection, its projection on the plane will show its true size and shape.

12. If a surface is inclined to a plane of projection, its projection on the plane will be foreshortened.

13. If a surface is perpendicular to a plane of projection, its projection on the plane will be a line.

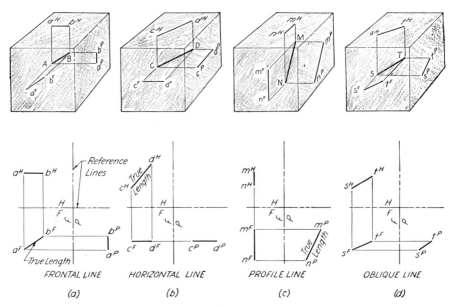

Fig. 6.11. Some Typical Line Positions.

The student should study Fig. 6.11 and attempt to visualize the space position of each of the given lines.   It is very necessary both in preparing and reading graphical representations to recognize the position of a point, line, or plane and to know whether the projection of a line is true length or foreshortened or whether the projection of a plane shows the true size and shape.   The indicated reference lines may be thought of as representing the edges of the glass boxes shown.   The projections of a line are identified as being on either a frontal, horizontal, or profile plane by the use of the letters F, H, or P with the lower-case letters that identify the end points of the line. For example, in Fig. 6.11(a), $a^H b^H$ is the horizontal projection of line AB, $a^F b^F$ is the frontal projection, and $a^P b^P$ is the profile projection.

6.8. Relationship of views. Following a recognized order in the relationship of views prevents confusion in reading drawings, just as following an expected order of words in statements leads to faster reading and interpretation. Locating views in the wrong relationship to the front view, such as drawing a bottom view above the front view, or placing a right-side view to the left of the front view is equivalent to lettering a word of a statement upside-down and to having words out of an expected

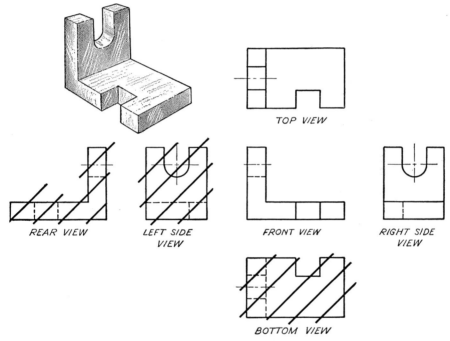

Fig. 6.12. Superfluous Views.

order. The following principles of the relationship of views should be carefully read and understood.

1. A view taken from above is a top view and *must* be drawn above the front view and in line with it vertically.

2. A view taken from the right, in relation to the selected front, is a right-side view and *must* be drawn to the right of the front view and in line with it horizontally.

3. A view taken from the left is a left-side view and *must* be drawn to the left of the front view.

4. A view taken from below is a bottom view and *must* appear below the front view.

6.9. The selection of views. Careful study should be given to the outline of an object before the views are selected (Fig. 6.13). Otherwise, there is no assurance that the object will be described completely from the reader's viewpoint (Fig. 6.14).   Only those views that are necessary for a clear and complete description should be selected.   Since the repetition of information only tends to confuse the reader, superfluous views should be avoided.   In Fig. 6.12, six views of a block are shown.   Note that three views (front, top, and right side) describe the object fully.   The other three views are unnecessary.

GOOD CHOICE
(a)

POOR CHOICE
(b)

VIEW DOES NOT REVEAL THE CONTOUR SHAPE OF EITHER THE HOLE OR THE SLOT NOR DOES IT SHOW THAT THE CORNERS ARE CUT AT 45°

GOOD CHOICE
(c)

POOR CHOICE
(d)

VIEW DOES NOT SHOW THE CHARACTERISTIC SHAPE

Fig. 6.13. Choice of Views.

Although some objects, such as cylinders, bushings, bolts, and so forth, require only two views (front and side), more complicated pieces may require an auxiliary or sectional view in addition to the ordinary three views.

The space available for arranging the views often governs the choice between the use of a top or side view.   The difference between the descriptive values of the two frequently is not great.   For example, a draftsman often finds that the views of a long object will have better balance if a top view is used (see Fig. 6.15*a*); while, in the case of a short object (see *b*), the use of a side view may make possible a more pleasing arrangement.   It should be remembered that the choice of views for many objects is definitely fixed by the contour alone, and no choice is offered as far as spacing is concerned.   In commercial work, it is more important to have a set of views that describes an object clearly than one that is artistically balanced.

Fig. 6.14. Choice of Views.

Fig. 6.15. Selection of Views.

Often there is a choice between two equally important views, such as between a right-side and left-side view (Fig. 6.16) or between a top and bottom view (Fig. 6.17). In such cases, most commercial draftsmen adhere to the following rule: *A right-side view should be used in preference to a left-side view, and a top view in preference to a bottom view.* When this rule is applied to irregular objects, the front (contour) view should be drawn so that the most irregular outline is toward the top and right side.

Another rule, one that must be considered in selecting the front view, is as follows: *If possible, place the object so as to obtain the smallest number of hidden lines.*

6.10. The principal (front) view. The principal view is the one that shows the characteristic contour of the object. See Fig. 6.18(*a*) and (*b*). Good practice dictates that this be used as the front view on a drawing. It should be clearly understood that the view of the natural front of an object is not always the principal view, because frequently it fails to show the object's characteristic shape. Therefore, another rule to be followed is: *Ordinarily, select the view showing the characteristic contour shape as the front view, regardless of the normal or natural front of the object.*

Fig. 6.16.   The Preferred Side View.   Fig. 6.17.   The Preferred Choice of a Top View.

(*a*)   (*b*)

Fig. 6.18.   The Principal View of an Object.

When an object does have a definite normal position, however, the front view should be in agreement with it. In the case of most machine parts, the front view can assume any convenient position that is consistent with good balance.

6.11. Invisible lines. Dotted lines are used on an external view of an object to represent surfaces and intersections invisible at the point from which the view is taken. In Fig. 6.19(*a*), one invisible line represents a line of intersection or edge line while the other invisible line may be considered to represent either the surface or lines of intersection. On the side view in (*b*) there are invisible lines which represent the contour elements of the cylindrical holes.

6.12. Treatment of invisible lines. The short dashes that form an invisible line should be drawn carefully in accordance with the recommendations in Fig. 6.26. An invisible line always starts with a dash in contact with the object line from which it starts, unless it forms a continuation of a visible line. In the latter case, it should start with a space, in order to establish at a glance the exact location of the end point of the visible line. Correct and incorrect methods of starting and finishing

(a)   (b)

Fig. 6.19.   Invisible Lines.

Fig. 6.20.   Correct and Incorrect Junctures of Invisible Outlines.

invisible lines are illustrated in Fig. 6.20. Note that the effect of definite corners is secured at points A, B, E, and F, where, in each case, the end dash touches the intersecting line. Obviously this treatment is to be preferred to the treatment at points A', B', E', and F' in the column labeled "incorrect." When the point of intersection of an invisible line and another object line does not represent an actual intersection on the object, the intersection should be open as at points C and D rather than closed as at C' and D'. An open intersection tends to make the lines appear to be at different distances from the observer.

In all cases similar to the one illustrated at C, the visible line will appear to be extended if the hidden line starts with a dash, as in C'.

Parallel invisible lines should have the breaks staggered, as shown in Fig. 6.20, for the sake of appearance.

The correct and incorrect treatment for starting invisible arcs is illustrated at G and G'. Note that an arc should start with a dash at the point of tangency. This treatment enables the reader to determine the exact end points of the curvature.

6.13. Omission of invisible lines. Although it is common practice for commercial draftsmen to omit hidden lines when their use tends to

Fig. 6.21. Steps in Making a Three-View Drawing of an Object.

confuse further an already overburdened view or when the shape description of a feature is sufficiently clear in another view, it is not advisable for a beginning student to do so. The beginner, until he has developed the discrimination that comes with experience, will be wise to show all hidden lines.

6.14. To make an orthographic drawing. The location of all views should be determined before a drawing is begun. This will insure balance in the appearance of the finished drawing. The contour view is usually started first. After the initial start, the draftsman should construct his views simultaneously by projecting back and forth from one to the other. It is poor practice to complete one view before starting the others, as much more time will be required to complete the drawing. Figure 6.21 shows the procedure for laying out a three-view drawing. The general outline of the views first should be drawn in lightly with a hard pencil and then heavily with a medium grade pencil. Although *(a)*   *(b)*

Fig. 6.22.   Methods of Projecting from the Top View.

Fig. 6.23.   Steps in Making a Two-View Drawing of a Circular Object.

experienced draftsmen sometimes deviate from this procedure by drawing the lines of known length and location in finished weight while constructing the views, it is not recommended that beginners do so.   The graphic language must be learned by the painful process of trial and error, if individual technique is to be attained.

The common geometric methods for projecting from the top view to the side view, and vice versa, are shown in Fig. 6.22.   The more accurate method is the one at the left, at (a), where only the T-square and triangles are required for construction.   The location of the 45° measuring line, shown in (a), may be obtained by extending the construction lines representing the front edge of the top view and the front edge of the side view to an intersection.   The center for the measuring arcs in (b) is found in the same manner.

When constructing a two-view drawing of a circular object, the pencil work must start with the drawing of the center lines, as shown in Fig. 6.23. This is necessarily the first step, because the construction of the circular (contour) view is based upon a horizontal and a vertical center line. The horizontal object lines of the rectangular view are projected from the circles. In order to space the views properly, the horizontal center line should be located so that the distances D_1 and D_2 are approximately equal. In the case of complete working drawings, the spacing of the views must be modified to take into account notes, dimensions, titles, and so forth.

6.15. Penciling a drawing. The correct procedure for making a pencil drawing is shown in Fig. 6.24. Before any drawing can be done, it

PRELIMINARY PROCEDURE
(a)

LOCATE CENTER LINES   STEP I

BLOCK IN VIEWS   STEP II

PUT IN FILLETS   STEP III

DARKEN OBJECT LINES STEP IV

ORDER OF PENCILING
(b)

Fig. 6.24. Procedure in Penciling a Drawing.

is necessary to select the scale to be used, care being taken that the one chosen is large enough to show all details to the best advantage.   Ordinarily, the procedure of balancing the views on the sheet (see Sec. 6.14 and Fig. 6.24a) can be simplified by a preliminary freehand sketch showing their arrangement.   When balancing views, it should be attempted to make the distance D_1 on the left side equal to the distance D_1 on the right side.   In the vertical direction, the views should be so located that the shaded area between the top view and the border is approximately equal to the area between the front view and the lower border.   The location of each view relative to the border and the adjacent views may be calculated and recorded.   It is, as every wide-awake student soon discovers, much better to sketch a fully organized plan than to "draw and erase" on a sheet of good drawing paper.

Following the preliminary planning, the views should be penciled in accordance with the following steps.

1. Draw the center lines, using a hard pencil with a sharp, conical point.   These lines should be light and continuous at this stage in the development of a drawing.

2. Draw arcs and circles, and block in the views.   The arcs and circles should be drawn in their finished weight, if possible.

3. Draw the fillets and rounds in finished weight, using a medium grade lead.   These frequently are drawn freehand by commercial draftsmen, but the use of a bow pencil is permissible.

4. Retrace the object lines with a medium grade pencil.   Transform the center lines into symbolic center lines by retracing with a sharp medium hard pencil.

6.16. The technique of pencil drawing.   Since a majority of commercial drawings are executed in pencil on drawing paper or tracing paper, a training course in drafting should include extensive practice in pencil work.   Practice alone, however, will not develop the necessary skill.   It must be tempered with some knowledge of what is desired in line work and lettering, and judgment on how to achieve the best results (Fig. 6.25).

The term "technique," as applied to drawing, may be defined as the style or quality of individual workmanship.   Although the style of every good draftsman is characterized by his own individuality, the workmanship of all such draftsmen is distinguished by sharp, snappy lines and well-formed letters.

When penciling, the beginner should endeavor to use the line weights recommended in Sec. 3.48.   The object lines should be made very dark and bright, to give snap to the drawing as well as to create the contrast necessary to cause the shape of the object to stand out.   Special care should be taken to gauge the dashes and spaces in invisible object lines. On ordinary drawings, $\frac{1}{8}''$ dashes and $\frac{1}{32}''$ spaces are recommended (Fig. 6.26).

Center lines consist of alternate long and short dashes.   The long dashes are from $\frac{3}{4}''$ to $1\frac{1}{2}''$ long, the short dashes $\frac{1}{8}''$, and the spaces $\frac{1}{32}''$ (Fig. 6.26).   On manila paper, they should be made with a medium hard pencil.   The following technique is recommended in drawing center lines.

Fig. 6.25.   Drawing Technique.

1. Where center lines cross, the short dashes should intersect sym-metrically (see Fig. 6.27a).   In the case of very small circles, the method shown in (b), omitting the breaks, may be used.

2. The breaks should be so located that they will stand out and at the same time allow the center line to be recognized as such.

Fig. 6.26.   Invisible Lines and Center Lines.

3. Center lines should extend $\frac{1}{8}''$ beyond the outline of the part whose symmetry they indicate (Fig. 6.28).

4. Center lines should not end at object lines (Fig. 6.28).

5. Center lines, which are the extensions of object lines, should start with a $\frac{1}{16}''$ space (Fig. 6.29).

For a finished drawing to be pleasing in appearance, all lines of the same type must be uniform, and each type must have proper contrast with other symbolic types.   The contrast between the types of pencil lines is similar to that of ink lines (Fig. 3.71), except that pencil lines are never as wide as ink lines. Read Sec. 3.48. On commercial drawings, the usual practice is to "burn in" the object lines by applying heavy pressure.

If reasonable care is taken not to soil a drawing, it will not be necessary to clean any part of it with an eraser. Since the practice in most commercial drawing rooms is not to erase construction lines if they have been drawn lightly, the student, at the very beginning of his first course, should try to acquire habits that insure cleanliness. First, he should

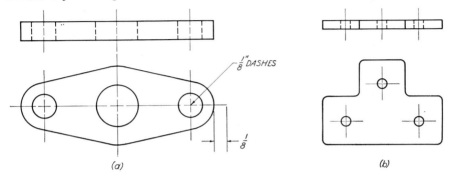

Fig. 6.27. Intersection of Center Lines.

realize that dirty, perspiring hands produce a large amount of soil that frequent washing can do much to eliminate. Second, that dirty equipment causes even more soil than dirty hands. This is due partly to the constant slipping back and forth, across the paper, of the ruling instruments. Many draftsmen wash their T-squares and triangles with soap

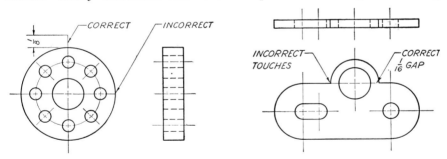

Fig. 6.28. Treatment of Center Lines.   Fig. 6.29. Treatment of Center Lines.

and water, but a better, more convenient way is to clean the instruments with an eraser. Third, loose graphite contributes more toward accumulated soil than either of the other two factors, and yet it is the one most frequently overlooked. A draftsman may take all recognized precautions and still produce drawings that show soil, if he does not bother to brush the invisible loose graphite from the lines as they are drawn. Every line on a drawing should be brushed before a ruling instrument (T-square, triangle, and so forth) is moved over it. After brushing, the amount of such soil may be still further reduced by raising the triangles and the T-square blade when moving them into new positions.

6.17. Visualizing an object from given views. Most students in elementary drawing courses find it difficult to visualize an object from two or more views. This trouble is largely due to the lack of systematic procedure for analyzing complex shapes.

The simplest method of determining shape is illustrated pictorially in Fig. 6.30. This method of "breaking down" may be applied to any object, since all objects may be thought of as consisting of elemental geometrical forms, such as prisms, cylinders, cones, and so on (Fig. 6.31). These imaginary component parts may be additions in the form of projections or subtractions in the form of cavities. Following such a detailed geometric analysis, a clear picture of an entire object can be obtained by mentally assembling a few easily visualized forms.

Fig. 6.30.   "Breaking Down" Method.

It should be realized, when analyzing component parts, that it is impossible ordinarily to determine whether a form is an addition or a subtraction by looking at one view. For example, the small circles in the top view in Fig. 6.31 indicate a cylindrical form, but they do not reveal whether the form is a hole or a projection. By consulting the front view, however, the form is shown to be a hole (subtracted cylinder).

Fig. 6.31.   "Breaking Down" Method.

The graphic language is similar to the written language in that neither can be read at a glance. A drawing must be patiently read by referring systematically back and forth from one view to another. The reader at the same time must imagine a three-dimensional object and not a two-dimensional flat projection.

Figure 6.32 illustrates further the scheme of "breaking down" objects into their component geometrical shapes.

6.18. Analysis of surfaces, lines, and points in three principal views. An analysis of the representation of the surfaces of a mutilated block is given pictorially in Fig. 6.33. It can be noted that each of the

Fig. 6.32.   "Breaking Down" Method.

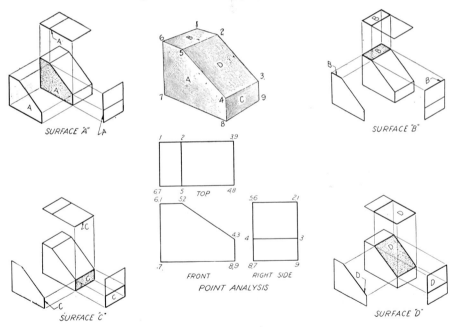

Fig. 6.33.   Analysis of Surfaces, Lines, and Points.

surfaces A, B, and C appears in true size and shape in one view, and as a line in each of the other two related views.   Surface D, which is inclined, appears with foreshortened length in the top and side views, and as an inclined line in the front view.

Three views of each of the visible points are shown on the multiview drawing.   At the very beginning of an elementary course in drawing, a student will often find it helpful to number the corners of an object in all views.

Figure 6.34 shows a pictorial drawing and a three-view orthographic drawing of a mutilated block. The accompanying table gives an orderly analysis of the reading of the three views of the object. A table similar to this one may be prepared by a student to facilitate study of a particular drawing. Such a table, however, is never prepared by a commercial draftsman.

SURFACE NUMBER ON PICTORIAL	PROJECTS AS LINE OR SURFACE		
	NUMBER ON TOP VIEW	NUMBER ON FRONT VIEW	NUMBER ON END VIEW
I	5	24	4
II	1	2	15
III	26	11	27
IV	23	8	17
V	13	14	18
VI	23	9	28
VII	20	12	19
VIII	6	7	25
IX	3	16	15
X	21	22	10

Fig. 6.34.   Lines and Surfaces.

All lines and surfaces are numbered at random on the orthographic drawing so that the student may take each surface designated in the pictorial drawing and identify it by a different number on each of the three views. For example, surface *I* on the pictorial view appears as a surface in the top view and is identified by the number 5. The same surface appears as surface 24 in the front view, and as line 4 in the end view.

6.19. Problems. The problems that follow are intended primarily to furnish study in multiview projection through the preparation of sketches and instrumental drawings. Many of the problems in this chapter may be prepared in more complete form. Their views may be dimensioned as are the views of working drawings, if the student will study carefully the beginning of the chapter on dimensioning before attempting to record size description (Chapter 15). All dimensions should be placed in accordance with the general rules of dimensioning.

The views shown in a sketch or drawing should be spaced on the paper with aim for balance within the border lines. Ample room should be allowed between the views for the necessary dimensions. If the views are not to be dimensioned, the distance between them may be made somewhat less than would be necessary otherwise.

Before starting to draw, the student should reread Sec. 6.15 and study Fig. 6.24, which shows the steps in making a multiview drawing. The preparation of a preliminary sketch, such as the one shown in this illustration, always proves helpful to the beginner.

All construction work should be done in light lines with a sharp hard pencil. A drawing should be checked by an instructor before the lines are "heavied in," unless the preliminary sketch was checked beforehand.

1–2. (Figs. 6.35, 6.36.) Draw a table similar to that shown in Fig. 6.34 and fill in the required information for each of the surfaces designated on the pictorial drawing by a Roman numeral. Draw the necessary guide lines and letter the column headings and information in $\frac{1}{8}''$ capitals.

3. (Fig. 6.37.) A line is missing from each of the three-view drawings. When the correct missing line is found, the three views of each object will be consistent with one another. *Suggestion:* A good method of visualizing these objects is to sketch them pictorially or to cut a model from a piece of modeling clay, a cake of soap, or an ordinary potato.

4. (Fig. 6.38.) Add the missing line or lines in one view of each of the three-view drawings. When the missing line or lines have been determined, the three views of each object will be consistent with one another.

5. (Fig. 6.39.) Draw or sketch the third view for each of the given objects.

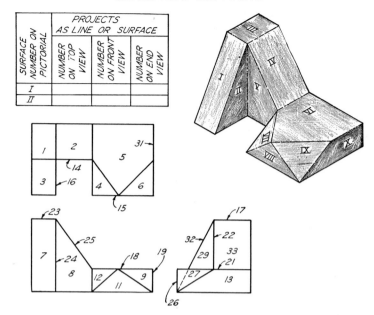

SURFACE NUMBER ON PICTORIAL	PROJECTS AS LINE OR SURFACE		
	NUMBER ON TOP VIEW	NUMBER ON FRONT VIEW	NUMBER ON END VIEW
I			
II			

Fig. 6.35. Reading Exercise.

SURFACE NUMBER ON PICTORIAL	PROJECTS AS LINE OR SURFACE		
	NUMBER ON TOP VIEW	NUMBER ON FRONT VIEW	NUMBER ON END VIEW

Fig. 6.36. Reading Exercise.

Fig. 6.37. Missing-Line Exercises.

Fig. 6.38.

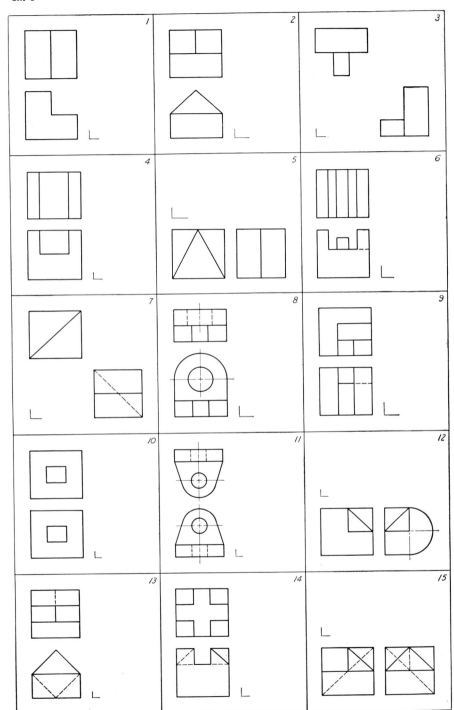

Fig. 6.39.

6–25. (Figs. 6.40–6.59.)   Sketch, freehand, the necessary views of the given objects as assigned.   The selected length for the unit will determine the size of the views.   Assume any needed dimensions that are not given in units.

Fig. 6.40.   Stop Block.

Fig. 6.41.   Angle Block.

Fig. 6.42.   Adjustment Block.

Fig. 6.43.   Slip Block.

Fig. 6.44.   Alignment Block.

Fig. 6.45.   Slide Block.

Fig. 6.46.   Link.

Fig. 6.47.   Collar Bracket.

Fig. 6.48.   Bell Crank.

Fig. 6.49.   Shifter.

Fig. 6.50.   Guide.

Fig. 6.51.   Support Bracket.

Fig. 6.52.   Index Bracket.

Fig. 6.53.   Control Bracket.

Fig. 6.54.   Shaft Bracket.

Fig. 6.55.   Offset Guide.

Fig. 6.56.   Feed Rod Bracket.

Fig. 6.57.   Automatic Feed Bracket.

Fig. 6.58.   Support Bracket.

Fig. 6.59.   Offset Bracket.

26–35. (Figs. 6.60–6.69.) Reproduce the given views and draw the required view. Show all hidden lines.

Fig. 6.60.

Fig. 6.61.

Fig. 6.62.

Fig. 6.63.

Fig. 6.64.

Fig. 6.65.

Fig. 6.66.

Fig. 6.67.

Fig. 6.68.

Fig. 6.69.

36. (Fig. 6.70.)   Make an orthographic drawing or sketch of the bench stop. The views may be dimensioned.   The shaft portion that fits into the hole in the bench top is $\frac{3}{4}''$ in diameter and $2''$ long.

Fig. 6.70.   Bench Stop.

37. (Fig. 6.71.) Reproduce the front and side views of the mutilated block and draw the top view. Balance the drawing on the sheet. Show all hidden lines.

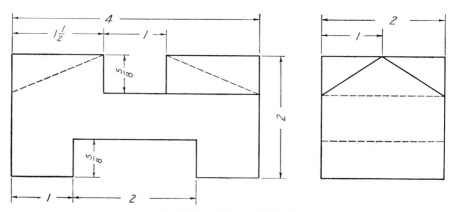

Fig. 6.71. Mutilated Block.

38–78. (Figs. 6.72–6.112.) These problems are designed to give the student further study in multiview drawing and, at the same time, offer him the opportunity to apply good line technique to the preparation of elementary working drawings. The views of the drawings of the given objects may or may not be dimensioned.

Only the necessary views on which all of the hidden lines are to be shown should be drawn. It is suggested that a preliminary sketch be made on a piece of scratch paper before starting to draw. The sketch should show the proposed arrangement of the views and the calculated location of each view in relation to the border and the other views. The student should keep in mind the fact that the drawing is to be well balanced on the sheet and that the views are not to be crowded. If dimensions are to be given, ample space must be allowed between the views for their placement. It is usually wise for a student to consult his class instructor about the scale he has selected before reaching a final decision.

Fig. 6.72. Clamp Block.

Fig. 6.73.   V-Rest.

Fig. 6.74.   Rest Block.

Fig. 6.75.   Adjustment Block.

Fig. 6.76.   Stop Block.

Fig. 6.77.   Corner Block.

Fig. 6.78.   Angle Block.

Fig. 6.79.   Ash Tray.

Fig. 6.80.   Cam.

Fig. 6.81.   Hinge Link.

Fig. 6.82.   Bearing Block.

Fig. 6.83.   Connecting Link.

Fig. 6.84.   Support Base.

Fig. 6.85. Regulator Cover.

Fig. 6.86. Guide.

Fig. 6.87. Support Cap.

Fig. 6.88. Bearing Bracket.

Fig. 6.89. Control Bracket.

Fig. 6.90. Corner Stop.

Fig. 6.91.   Support Bracket.

Fig. 6.92.   Stanchion Support.

Fig. 6.93.   Shifter Link.

Fig. 6.94.   Shifter Bracket.

Fig. 6.95.   Control Guide.

Fig. 6.96.   Control Plate.

Fig. 6.97.   Socket.

Fig. 6.98.   Guide Bracket.

Fig. 6.99.   Tool Rest.

Fig. 6.100.   Support Bracket.

Fig. 6.101.   Shaft Guide.

Fig. 6.102.   Control Rod Guide.

Fig. 6.103.   Anchor Bracket.

Fig. 6.104.   Trip.

Fig. 6.105. Guide Bracket.

Fig. 6.106. Stud Bracket.

Fig. 6.107. Shifter.

Fig. 6.108. Offset Trip Lever.

Fig. 6.109. Stud Guide.

FILLETS & ROUNDS .12^R

Fig. 6.110. Shifter.

$\frac{7}{16}$ UNF HEX. HD. BOLT & NUT

FILLETS & ROUNDS .12^R

Fig. 6.111. Shaft Bracket.

Fig. 6.112.   Motor Bracket.

79. (Fig. 6.113.)   Make a complete orthographic drawing of the anchor bracket.

Fig. 6.113.   Anchor Bracket.

80. (Fig. 6.114.)   Make a complete orthographic sketch or drawing of the trip. *Supplementary information:* (1) The diameter of the shaft is $1\frac{3}{8}''$. There should be a rather tight fit between the shaft and the broached hole.   (2) The diameter of the hub is $2\frac{1}{4}''$.   (3) The thickness of the rib is $\frac{5}{16}''$.   (4) The rectangular surface shown in contact with the semi-spherical end of the trip pin is $\frac{7}{16}'' \times 1\frac{1}{2}''$. (5) The radius of the contact surface of the trip is $8''$.   (6) Fillets and rounds $\frac{1}{8}''$ R.   (7) Fillets and rounds have been purposely omitted from the pictorial drawing. They are to be shown by the student where necessary and desirable. (8) Mark all tangent points with a short dash across the line.

Fig. 6.114. Trip.

81. (Fig. 6.115.)   Make a complete orthographic drawing of the offset shaft bracket.   *Supplementary information:* (1) The center line of the main shaft is $1\frac{3}{8}''$ above the finished surface of the pad.   The hole in the bracket is to be reamed to accommodate a $1\frac{1}{4}''$ O.D. bushing as shown.   (2) The length of the cylindrical part is $1\frac{1}{4}''$.   Both faces, which are raised $\frac{1}{8}''$ on both sides, are contact faces. The O.D. is $1\frac{3}{4}''$.   (3) The over-all dimensions of the pad are to be $2\frac{3}{8}'' \times 2\frac{7}{8}''$. The $2\frac{3}{8}''$ dimension is in the direction parallel to the axis of the main shaft.   (See bottom view.)   (4) The small holes in the base are to be drilled oversize for $\frac{1}{2}''$-UNC cap screws.   (5) The hole for the small shaft should be reamed larger for a $\frac{1}{2}''$ shaft.   (6) The rib is to be $\frac{5}{16}''$ thick.   It should finish tangent to the large cylinder.   (7) Fillets and rounds are $\frac{1}{8}''$ R except as noted.   (8) Pay particular attention to tangent runouts.   (9) The near side of the $\frac{3}{8}''$ thick portion of the base is tangent to the $\frac{1}{2}''$ R of the $\frac{7}{16}''$ thick base.

Fig. 6.115.   Offset Shaft Bracket.

82. (Fig. 6.116.)   Make a complete orthographic drawing of the tube holder.

Fig. 6.116.   Tube Holder.

83. (Fig. 6.117.)   Make a complete three-view drawing of the motor base. The ribs are $\frac{3}{8}''$ thick.   At points A, four holes are to be drilled for $\frac{1}{2}''$ bolts that are to be $2\frac{1}{2}''$ center to center in one direction and $3\frac{1}{8}''$ in the other.   At points B, four holes are to be drilled for $\frac{1}{2}''$ bolts that fasten the motor base to a steel column. Fillets and rounds are $\frac{1}{8}''$ R.

Fig. 6.117.   Motor Base.

84–85. (Fig. 6.118.)   Make a complete three-view drawing of the tool rest and/or the tool rest bracket.   The rectangular top surface of the tool rest is to be $1\frac{1}{8}''$ above the center line of the hole for the $\frac{7}{16}''$ bolt.   The over-all dimensions of the top are $1\frac{1}{4}'' \times 2\frac{1}{2}''$.   It is to be $\frac{1}{4}''$ thick.   The over-all dimensions of the rectangular pad of the bracket are $1\frac{1}{4}'' \times 1\frac{7}{8}''$.   The center line of the adjustment slot is $\frac{9}{16}''$ above the center line of the top holes in the rectangular pad and the distance from center line to center line of the slot is $1\frac{3}{8}''$.   The bracket is to be fastened to a housing with $\frac{1}{4}''$ round head machine screws.

Fig. 6.118.   Tool Rest and Tool Rest Bracket.

7 | Auxiliary Views

PRIMARY AUXILIARY VIEWS

7.1. When it is desirable to show the true size and shape of an irregular surface, which is inclined to two or more of the co-ordinate planes of projection, a view of the surface must be projected on a plane parallel to it. This imaginary projection plane is called an auxiliary plane, and the view obtained is called an auxiliary view (Fig. 7.1).

Fig. 7.1. Theory of Projecting an Auxiliary View.

The theory underlying the method of projecting principal views applies also to auxiliary views. In other words, an auxiliary view shows an inclined surface of an object as it would appear to an observer stationed an infinite distance away (Fig. 7.2).

163

7.2. The use of auxiliary views. In commercial drafting, an auxiliary view ordinarily is a partial view showing only an inclined surface. The reason for this is that a projection showing the entire object adds very little to the shape description. The added lines are likely to defeat the intended purpose of an auxiliary view. For example, a complete drawing

Fig. 7.2. An Auxiliary View.

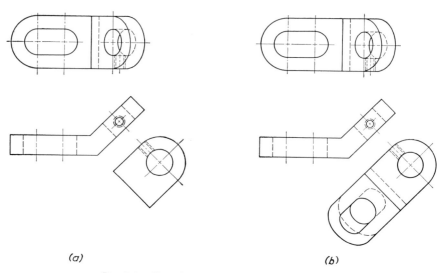

(a)   *(b)*

Fig. 7.3. Partial and Complete Auxiliary Views.

of the casting in Fig. 7.3 must include an auxiliary view of the inclined surface in order to show the true shape of the surface and the location of the holes. Compare the views in *(a)* and *(b)* and note the confused appearance of the view in *(b)*. In technical schools, some instructors require that an auxiliary view show the entire object, including all invisible lines. Such a requirement, though impractical commercially, is justified in the classroom, for the construction of a complete auxiliary view furnishes excellent practice in projection.

A partial auxiliary view often is needed to complete the projection of a foreshortened feature in a principal view. This second important function of auxiliary views is illustrated in Fig. 7.15 and explained in Sec. 7.11.

7.3. Types of auxiliary views. Although auxiliary views may have an infinite number of positions in relation to the three principal planes of projection, primary auxiliary views may be classified into three general types in accordance with position relative to the principal planes. Figure 7.4 shows the first type where the auxiliary plane is perpendicular to the frontal plane and inclined to the horizontal plane of projection. Here the auxiliary view and top view have one dimension that is common to both, the depth. Note that the auxiliary plane is hinged to the frontal plane, and that the auxiliary view is projected from the front view.

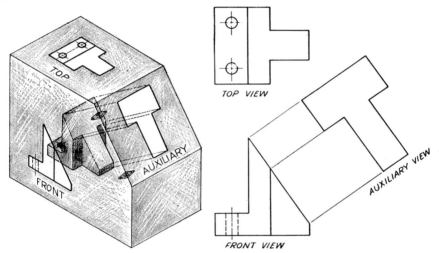

Fig. 7.4. Auxiliary View Projected from Front View.

In Fig. 7.5 the auxiliary plane is perpendicular to the horizontal plane and inclined to the frontal and profile planes of projection. The auxiliary view is projected from the top view, and its height is the same as the height of the front view.

The third type of auxiliary view, as shown in Fig. 7.6, is projected from the side view and has a common dimension with both the front and top views. To construct it, distances may be taken from either the front or top view.

All three types of auxiliary views are constructed similarly. Each is projected from the view that shows the surface as an oblique line, and the distances for the view are taken from the other principal view that has a common dimension with the auxiliary. A careful study of the three illustrations will reveal the fact that the inclined auxiliary plane is always hinged to the principal plane to which it is perpendicular.

7.4. Symmetrical and unsymmetrical auxiliary views. Since auxiliary views are either symmetrical or unsymmetrical about a center line or reference line, they may be termed (1) symmetrical, (2) unilateral, or (3) bilateral, according to the degree of symmetry. A symmetrical view is drawn symmetrically about a center line, the unilateral view entirely on one side of a reference line, and the bilateral view on both sides of a reference line.

Fig. 7.5. Auxiliary View Projected from Top View.

Fig. 7.6. Auxiliary View Projected from Side View.

7.5. To draw a symmetrical auxiliary view. When an inclined surface is symmetrical, the auxiliary view is "worked" from a center line (Fig. 7.7). The first step in drawing such a view is to draw a center line parallel to the oblique line that represents an edge view of the surface. If the object is assumed to be enclosed in a glass box, this center line may be considered the line of intersection of the auxiliary plane and an imaginary vertical center plane. There are professional draftsmen who, not acquainted with the "glass" box, proceed without theoretical explanation.

Their method is simply to draw a working center line for the auxiliary view and a corresponding line in one of the principal views.

Although, theoretically, this working center line may be drawn at any distance from the principal view, actually it should be so located to give the whole drawing a balanced appearance. If not already shown, it also must be drawn in the principal view showing the true width of the inclined surface.

The next step is to draw projection lines from each point of the sloping face, remembering that the projectors make an angle of 90° with the inclined line representing the surface. With the projectors drawn, the location of each point in the auxiliary can be established by setting the dividers to each point's distance from the center line in the principal

Fig. 7.7. A Symmetrical Auxiliary View of an Inclined Surface.

view and transferring the distance to the auxiliary view. For example, point X is projected to the auxiliary by drawing a projector from point X in the front view perpendicular to the center line. Since its distance from the center line in the top view is the same as it is from the center line in the auxiliary view, the point's location along the projector may be established by using the distance taken from the top view. In the case of point X, the distance is set off from the center line toward the front view. Point Y is set off from the center line away from the front view. A careful study of Fig. 7.7 reveals the fact that if a point lies between the front view and the center line of the top view, it will lie between the front view and the center line of the auxiliary view, and, conversely, if it lies away from the front view with reference to the center line of the top view, it will lie away from the front view with reference to the center line of the auxiliary view.

Figure 7.8 shows an auxiliary view of an entire object. In constructing such a view, it should be remembered that the projectors from all points of the object are perpendicular to the auxiliary plane, since the observer views the entire figure by looking directly at the inclined surface.

The distances perpendicular to the auxiliary reference line were taken from the front view.

7.6. Unilateral auxiliary views. When constructing a unilateral auxiliary view, it is necessary to work from a reference line that is drawn in a manner similar to the working center line of a symmetrical view.

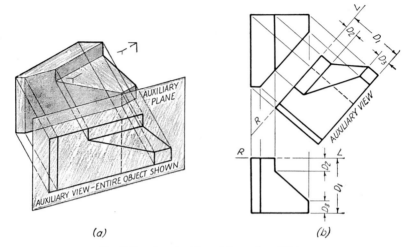

(a)   (b)

Fig. 7.8.   An Auxiliary View of an Object.

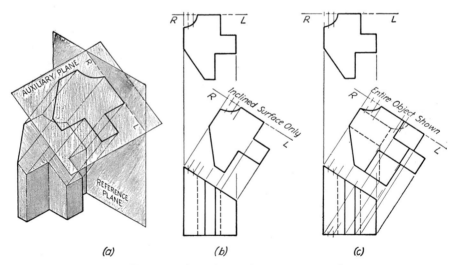

(a)   (b)   (c)

Fig. 7.9.   A Unilateral Auxiliary View.

The reference line for the auxiliary view may be considered to represent the line of intersection of a reference plane coinciding with an outer face and the auxiliary plane (Fig. 7.9). The intersection of this plane with the top plane establishes the reference line in the top view. All the points are projected from the oblique line, as in a symmetrical view, and it should be noted in setting them off that they all fall on the same side of the reference line.

7.7 Bilateral auxiliary views. The method of drawing a bilateral view is similar to that of drawing a unilateral view, the only difference

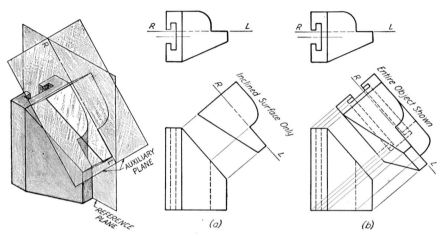

Fig. 7.10.   A Bilateral Auxiliary View.

Fig. 7.11.   Choice of Position of Reference Plane.

being that in a bilateral view the inclined face lies partly on both sides of the reference plane, as shown in Fig. 7.10.

7.8. Curved lines in auxiliary views. To draw a curve in an auxiliary view, the draftsman must plot a sufficient number of points to insure a smooth curve (see Fig. 7.12). The points are projected first to the oblique line representing the surface in the front view and then to the auxiliary view. The distance of any point from the center line in the

Fig. 7.12. Curved Line Auxiliary View.

auxiliary view is the same as its distance from the center line in the end view.

7.9. To construct an auxiliary view, practical method. The usual steps in constructing an auxiliary view are shown in Fig. 7.13. The illustration should be studied carefully, as each step is explained on the drawing.

Fig. 7.13. Steps in Constructing an Auxiliary View.

7.10. Auxiliary and partial views. Often the use of an auxiliary view allows the elimination of one of the principal views (front, top, or side) or makes possible the use of a partial principal view. The shape description furnished by the partial views shown in Fig. 7.14 is sufficient for a complete understanding of the shape of the part. The use of partial views simplifies the drawing, saves valuable drafting time, and tends to make the drawing easier to read.

A break line is used at a convenient location to indicate an imaginary break for a partial view.

7.11. The use of an auxiliary view to complete a principal view. As previously stated, it is frequently necessary to project a foreshortened feature in one of the principal views from an auxiliary view. In the case

Fig. 7.14. Partial Views.

of the object shown in Fig. 7.15, the foreshortened projection of the inclined face in the top view can be projected from the auxiliary view. The elliptical curves are plotted by projecting points from the auxiliary view to the front view and from there to the top view. The location of these points in the top view with respect to the center line is the same as

Fig. 7.15.   Use of Auxiliary to Complete a Principal View.

Fig. 7.16.   Steps in Preparing an Auxiliary View and Completing a Principal View.

their location in the auxiliary view with respect to the auxiliary center line.   For example, the distance D_1 from the center line in the top view is the same as the distance D_1 from the auxiliary center line in the auxiliary view.

The steps in preparing an auxiliary view and using it to complete a principal view are shown in Fig. 7.16.

7.12. To determine the true length of a line. An observer can see the true length of a line when he looks in a direction perpendicular to it. It is suggested that the student hold a pencil before him and move it into the following typical line positions to observe the conditions under which the pencil, representing a line, appears in true length. (See Fig. 7.17.)

1. Vertical line. The vertical line is perpendicular to the horizontal and will therefore appear as a point in the *H* (top) view. It will appear in true length in the *F* (frontal) view, in true length in the *P* (profile) view and in true length in any auxiliary view that is projected upon an auxiliary plane that is perpendicular to the horizontal plane of projection.

2. Horizontal line. The horizontal line will appear in true length when viewed from above because it is parallel to the *H*-plane of projection and its end points are theoretically equidistant from an observer looking downward.

3. Inclined line. The inclined line is any line not vertical or horizontal that is parallel to either the frontal plane or the profile plane of projection.

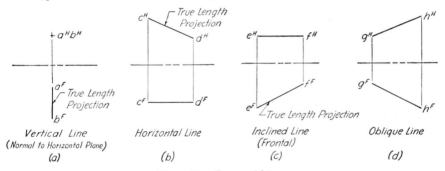

Fig. 7.17.   Types of Lines.

An inclined line will show true length in the *F* (frontal) view or *P* (profile) view and in any auxiliary view that is projected upon an auxiliary plane that is parallel to the line.

4. Oblique line. The oblique line will not appear in true length in any of the principal views because it is inclined to all of the principal planes of projection. It should be apparent that in viewing the pencil alternately from the directions used to obtain the principal views, namely from the front, above, and side, that one end of the pencil is always farther away from the observer than the other. Only when looking directly at the pencil from such a position that the end points are equidistant from the observer can the true length be seen. On a drawing, the true length projection of an oblique line will appear in a supplementary *A* (auxiliary) view projected on a plane that is parallel to the line (Fig. 7.18).

7.13. To determine the true length of an oblique line. To find the true length of an oblique line, it is necessary to use an auxiliary plane of projection which will be parallel to the line (Figs. 7.18 and 7.19).

In this discussion reference lines will be labeled *H-F*, *H-A*, or *F-A*, to enable the reader to associate a particular reference line with the adjacent views on either side of it.

Given: The F (frontal) view $a^F b^F$ and the H (top) view $a^H b^H$ of the oblique line AB (Fig. 7.18).

Solution: (1) Draw the reference line $H\text{-}A$ parallel to the projection $a^H b^H$. The A-plane for this reference line will be parallel to AB and perpendicular to the H-plane. See pictorial drawing. (2) Draw lines of

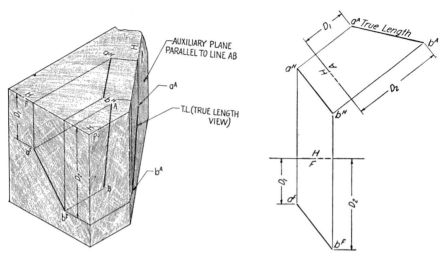

Fig. 7.18.   To Find the True Length of an Oblique Line.

projection from points a^H and b^H perpendicular to the reference line.

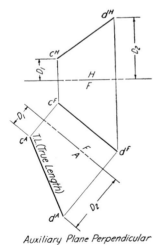

Auxiliary Plane Perpendicular to Frontal Plane

Fig. 7.19.   To Find the True Length of a Line.

(3) Transfer height measurements from the F-view to the A-view to locate a^A and b^A. In making this transfer of measurements, the student should attempt to visualize the space condition for the line and understand that, since the F-view and A-view both show height and because the planes of projection for these views are perpendicular to the H-plane, the perpendicular distance D_1 from the reference line $H\text{-}F$ to point a^F must be the same as the distance D_1 from reference line $H\text{-}A$ to point a^A.

The projection $a^A b^A$ shows the true length of the line AB.

It was not necessary to use an auxiliary plane perpendicular to the H-plane to find the true length of line AB in Fig. 7.18. The auxiliary plane could just as well have been perpendicular to either the F- or P-planes. Figure 7.19 illustrates the use of an auxiliary plane perpendicular to the frontal plane to find the true length of the line CD. In this case the auxiliary view has depth distances in common with the top view as indicated.

SECONDARY (OBLIQUE) AUXILIARY VIEWS

7.14 Secondary (oblique) auxiliary views. Frequently an object will have an inclined face that is not perpendicular to any one of the principal planes of projection. In such cases it is necessary to draw a primary auxiliary view and a secondary auxiliary or oblique view (Fig. 7.20). The primary auxiliary view is constructed by projecting the figure upon a primary auxiliary plane that is perpendicular to the inclined surface and one of the principal planes. This plane may be at any convenient location. In the illustration, the primary auxiliary plane is perpendicular to the frontal plane. Note that the inclined face appears as a straight line in the primary auxiliary view. Using this view as a regular view, the secondary auxiliary view may be projected upon a plane parallel to the inclined face. Figure 7.20(*b*) shows a practical application of the theoretical principles shown pictorially in (*a*).

7.15. To find the true shape (*TSP*) of an oblique plane. To see the true size and shape of any oblique plane an observer must view it with a line of sight perpendicular to it. To do this he must, as the first step in the construction, obtain an edge view of the plane. A secondary auxiliary (oblique) view taken from the primary *A*-view will then show the true shape of the plane.

The edge view of an oblique plane can be obtained by viewing the plane in a direction that will give a point view of a principal line in the plane. A principal line may be either a horizontal line, a frontal line, or a profile line (Fig. 7.21). Principal lines are true length lines and one such line may be drawn in any plane so as to appear true length in any one of the principal views as desired. In the construction shown in Fig. 7.20, it was not necessary to draw a principal line in the inclined plane, because the inclined edge line on the front surface is a principal (frontal) line showing true length in the front view.

The point view of a principal line and the needed edge view of the plane will appear in an auxiliary view projected upon a plane that is perpendicular to the line. See Fig. 7.22.

Perpendicularity between the principal line and the *A*-plane can be observed from the view showing the true length projection of the line. On the drawing, the reference line will be perpendicular to the true length projection of the principal line.

For convenience and ease in identifying the projected views of a point on the supplementary planes, the supplementary planes have been designated as an *A*-plane (primary auxiliary plane) and an *O*-plane (secondary auxiliary or oblique plane). Point a^A is the view of *A* on the *A*-plane. The view of *A* on the *O*-plane is designated a^O.

Given: The *F*- and *H*-views of plane *ABC*.

Solution: (1) Draw a frontal line *CD* in plane *ABC* (Fig. 7.22). (2) Draw reference line *F-A* perpendicular to $c^F d^F$ and construct the *A*-view showing the edge view of plane. The auxiliary view has depth in common with the *H*-view. (3) Draw reference line *A-O* parallel to the edge view in the *A*-view and construct the *O*-view (secondary auxiliary) which will show the true size and shape of plane *ABC*. The needed

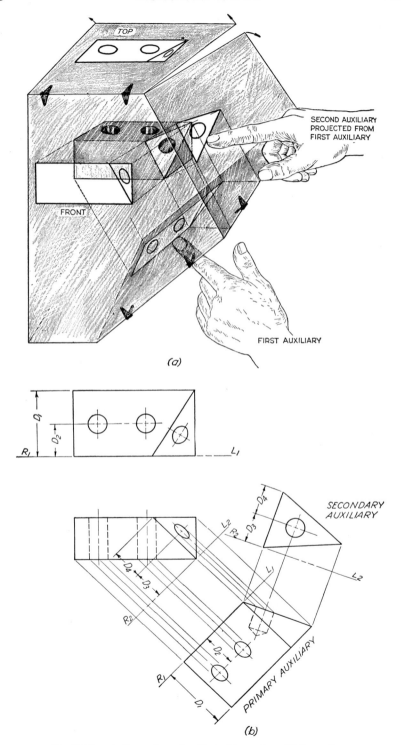

Fig. 7.20. A Secondary Auxiliary View of an Oblique Face.

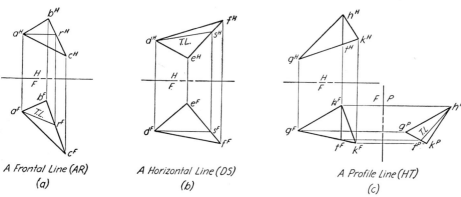

A Frontal Line (AR)   A Horizontal Line (DS)   A Profile Line (HT)
        (a)   (b)   (c)

Fig. 7.21. The Location of a Principal Line in a Plane.

distances from the reference line to points in the O-view are found in the F-view.

7.16. Use of a secondary auxiliary view to complete a principal view. Figure 7.23 shows the progressive steps in preparing and using a secondary auxiliary view of an oblique face to complete a principal view. Reference planes have been used as datum planes from which to take the necessary measurements. Step II shows the partial construction of the primary auxiliary view in which the inclined surface appears as a line. Step III shows the secondary auxiliary view projected from the primary view and completed, using the known measurements of the lug. The primary auxiliary view is finished by projecting from the secondary auxiliary view. Step IV illustrates the procedure for projecting from the secondary auxiliary view to the top view through the primary auxiliary in order to complete the foreshortened view of the lug. It should be noted that distance D_1 taken from reference plane R_2P_2 in the secondary auxiliary is transferred to the top view because both views show the same width distances in true length. A sufficient

Fig. 7.22.   To Find the True Shape (TSP) of an Oblique Plane.

number of points should be obtained to allow the use of an irregular curve. Step V shows the projection of these points on the curve to the front view. In this case the measurements are taken from the primary auxiliary view because the height distances from reference plane R_1P_1 are the same in both views.

Fig. 7.23.   Steps in Drawing a Secondary Auxiliary View and Using It to Complete a Principal View.

Fig. 7.24.   Line of Intersection.

7.17. Line of intersection. It is frequently necessary to represent a line of intersection between two surfaces when making a multiview drawing involving an auxiliary view. Figure 7.24 shows a method for drawing the line of intersection on a principal view. In this case the scheme commonly used for determining the intersection involves the use of elements drawn on the surface of the cylindrical portion of the part as shown on the pictorial drawing. These elements, such as AB, are common to the cylindrical surface. Point B, where the element pierces the flat surface, is a point that is common to both surfaces and, therefore, lies on the line of intersection.

On the orthographic views, element AB appears as a point on the auxiliary view and as a line on the front view. The location of the projection of the piercing point on the front view is visible upon inspection. Point B is found in the other principal view by projecting from the front view and setting off the distance D taken from the auxiliary view. The distance D of point B from the center line is a true distance for both views. The center line in the auxiliary view and side view can be considered as the edge view of a reference plane or datum plane from which measurements can be made.

7.18. Problems. The problems shown in Figs. 7.25 and 7.26 are designed to give the student practice in constructing auxiliary views of the inclined surfaces of simple objects formed mainly by straight lines. They will provide needed drill in projection if, for each of the objects in Fig. 7.26, an auxiliary is drawn showing the entire object. Complete drawings may be made of the objects shown in Figs. 7.27–7.39. If the views are to be dimensioned, the student should adhere to the rules of dimensioning given in Chapter 15 and should not take too seriously the locations for the dimensions on the pictorial representations.

1. (Fig. 7.25.) Using instruments, reproduce the given views and draw an auxiliary view of the inclined surface of each of the given objects.

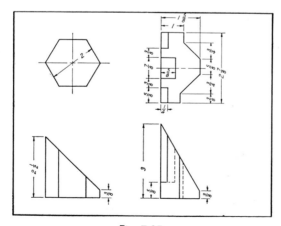

Fig. 7.25.

2. (Fig. 7.26.)   Using instruments, reproduce the given views of an assigned object and draw an auxiliary view of its inclined surface.

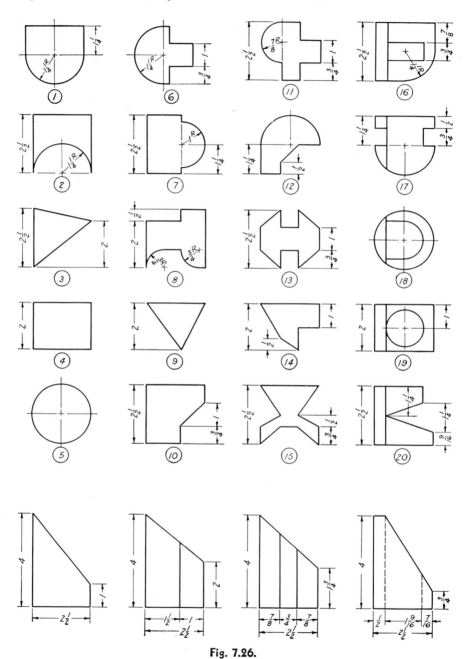

Fig. 7.26.

3. (Fig. 7.27.) Draw the views that are necessary to describe fully the sliding guide. The auxiliary view should show only the inclined surface.

Fig. 7.27. Sliding Guide.

4. (Fig. 7.28.) Draw the necessary views of the anchor clip. It is suggested that the top view be a partial one and that the auxiliary view show only the inclined surface.

Fig. 7.28. Anchor Clip.

5. (Fig. 7.29.)   Draw the views that would be necessary on a working drawing of the angle bearing.

Fig. 7.29.   Angle Bearing.

6. (Fig. 7.30.)   Draw the views that would be necessary on a working drawing of the boiler bracket.

Fig. 7.30.   Boiler Bracket.

7. (Fig. 7.31.)   Draw the views that would be necessary on a working drawing of the dovetail bracket.

Fig. 7.31.   Dovetail Bracket.

8. (Fig. 7.32.)   Draw the necessary views of the offset guide.   It is suggested that partial views be used, except in the view where the inclined surface appears as a line.

Fig. 7.32.   Offset Guide.

9. (Fig. 7.33.)   Draw the necessary views of the anchor bracket.   Make partial views for the top and end views.

Fig. 7.33.   Anchor Bracket   **Fig. 7.34.   Hinge Bracket.**

10. (Fig. 7.34.)   Draw the necessary views of the hinge bracket.

11. (Fig. 7.35.)   Draw the necessary views of the feeder guide.

Fig. 7.35.   Feeder Guide.   **Fig. 7.36.   Angle Bracket.**

12. (Fig. 7.36.)   Draw the views that would be necessary on a working drawing of the angle bracket.   Note that two auxiliary views will be required.

13. (Fig. 7.37.)   Draw the views that would be needed on a working drawing of the gear cover.   The opening on the inclined face is circular.   The pictorial drawing shows an unfinished casting.   Show finished surfaces where necessary.

Fig. 7.37.   Gear Cover.   Fig. 7.38.   45° Elbow.

14. (Fig. 7.38.)   Draw the views that would be necessary on a working drawing of the 45° elbow.

15. Make a multiview drawing of the airplane engine mount shown in Fig. 7.39.   The engine mount is formed of three pieces of steel plate welded to a piece of steel tubing.   The completed drawing is to consist of four views.   It is suggested that the front view be the view obtained by looking along and parallel to the axis of the tube.   The remaining views that are needed are an auxiliary view showing only the inclined lug, a side view that should be complete with all hidden lines shown, and a partial top view with the inclined lug omitted.

Fig. 7.39.   Airplane Engine Mount.

16. (Fig. 7.40.)   Draw the views as given.   Complete the auxiliary view and the front view.

Fig. 7.40.   Sliding Tool Base.

17. (Fig. 7.41.)   Draw the views as given.   Complete the top view.

Fig. 7.41.   Housing Cover.

18. (Fig. 7.42.) Using instruments, reproduce the given views of an assigned object and draw a secondary auxiliary view that will show the true size and shape of the inclined surface.

Fig. 7.42.

19. (Fig. 7.43.) Draw the views as given and add the required primary and secondary auxiliary views.

Fig. 7.43. Cross Anchor.

20. (Fig. 7.44.)   Draw the layout for the support anchor as given and then, using the double auxiliary view method, complete the views as required.

The plate and cylinder are to be welded.   Since the faces of the plate show as oblique surfaces in the front and top views, double auxiliary views are necessary to show the thickness and the true shape.

Start the drawing with the auxiliary views that are arranged horizontally on the paper, then complete the principal views.   The inclined face of the cylinder will show as an ellipse in top and front views; but do not show this in the auxiliary view that shows the true shape (4.00″ square) of the plate.

How would you find the view that shows the true angle between the inclined face and the axis of the cylinder?

Fig. 7.44.   Support Anchor.

21. (Fig. 7.45.)   Reproduce the given views of the line or lines of a problem as assigned and determine the true length or lengths using the auxiliary view method explained in Sec. 7.13.

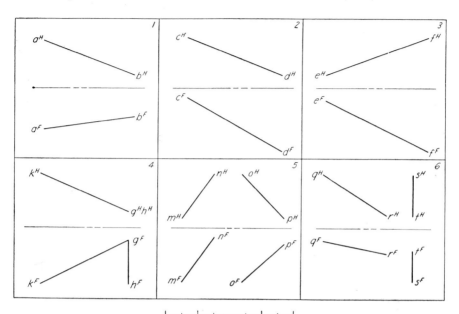

Fig. 7.45.   True Length of a Line.

22. (Fig. 7.46.)   Reproduce the given views of the plane of a problem as assigned and draw the view showing the true size and shape.   Use the method explained in Sec. 7.15.

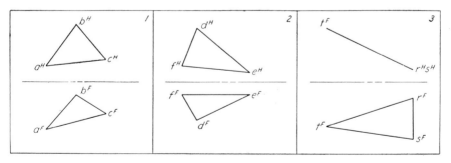

Fig. 7.46.   True Size and Shape of a Plane.

8 | Revolution

8.1. Revolution. Although in general the views on a working drawing represent satisfactorily an object in a fixed natural position, in order to improve the representation or to reveal the true size and shape of a principal surface, it sometimes is desirable to revolve an elemental part until it is parallel to a co-ordinate plane.

The distinguishing difference between this method and the method of auxiliary projection is that, in the procedure of revolution, the observer turns the object with respect to himself instead of shifting his viewing position with respect to an oblique surface of the object.

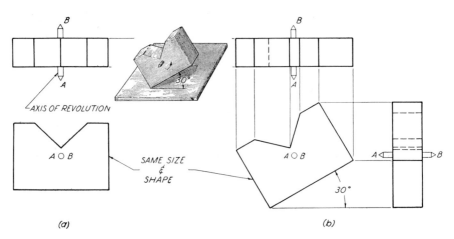

Fig. 8.1.   A Single Revolution About an Axis Perpendicular to the Frontal Plane.

Despite the fact that the revolution of an entire object, as illustrated in Fig. 8.1, rarely has a practical application in commercial drafting, the making of such a drawing provides excellent drill in projection.   Therefore, since the following related articles are intended primarily to aid in the training of embryo engineers and drafting students, the practical applications of revolution purposely have been ignored, while the procedures for making simple and successive revolutions of entire objects are explained in detail.

8.2. Simple (single) revolution. When the regular views are given, an object may be drawn in any oblique position by imagining it to

190

be revolved about an axis perpendicular to one of the principal co-ordinate (frontal, horizontal, or profile) planes.   A single revolution about such an axis is known as a "simple revolution."   Figures 8.1, 8.2, and 8.3 illustrate the three general cases.

8.3. Revolution about a horizontal axis perpendicular to the frontal plane.   A simple revolution about an axis perpendicular to the frontal plane is illustrated in Fig. 8.1.   The object is first revolved about an imaginary assumed axis, AB, until it is in the desired position.   The views of it then are obtained by orthographic projection, as in the case of any ordinary multiview drawing.   Because the front face revolves parallel to the frontal plane, the projection on that plane will change in position but will retain its true size and shape.   For this reason, the most convenient drawing procedure is to copy first the front view, as it is shown in (a), in its new revolved position (say at 30°).   Then, since the depth of

Fig. 8.2.   A Single Revolution About an Axis Perpendicular to the Horizontal Plane.

the top view is unchanged by the revolution of the object, the required top view can be drawn easily by projecting each point horizontally from the top view in (a) to a projection line drawn upward through the corresponding point on the revolved front view in (b).   The side view may be constructed by regular projection.

The front view may be drawn directly in a revolved position, without first drawing the normal orthographic front view.   If this procedure is followed, the depth of the top and side views may be set off to the known dimensions.

8.4. Revolution about a vertical axis perpendicular to the horizontal plane.   If an object is revolved about an imaginary axis perpendicular to the horizontal plane, as shown in Fig. 8.2, the top view changes in position but not in size and shape.   The top view, therefore, should be drawn first in its revolved position, and the front and side views should be projected from it.   The height of the front view and the side view is the same as the height of the normal front view in (a) and, for this reason, vertical dimensions can be conveniently projected from the initial views.

8.5. Revolution about a horizontal axis perpendicular to the profile plane. A single revolution of an object about an axis perpendicular to the profile plane is illustrated in Fig. 8.3. Since in this case it is the side view that is perpendicular to the axis and that revolves parallel to a co-ordinate plane, it is the side view that remains unchanged in size and shape. The length of the top and front views is not affected by the revolution. Therefore, horizontal dimensions for these views may be set off by measurement.

Fig. 8.3. A Single Revolution About an Axis Perpendicular to the Profile Plane.

Fig. 8.4. Direction of Revolution.

From these general cases of simple revolution, two principles have appeared that can be stated as follows:

1. The view that is perpendicular to the axis of revolution changes only in position.

2. The lengths of the lines parallel to the axis do not change during the revolution and, therefore, may be either measured or projected from the normal views of the object.

8.6. Clockwise and counterclockwise revolution. An object may be revolved either clockwise or counterclockwise about an axis of revolution. The direction is indicated by the view to which the axis is perpendicular. For example, front views, when revolved as in Fig. 8.4(*b*), show a clockwise revolution. When revolved as in Fig. 8.4(*a*), their revolution is counterclockwise. Top views show a clockwise revolution when revolved to the right. Right-side views indicate a clockwise direction of revolution when they have been revolved to the right, and a counterclockwise direction when revolved to the left.

8.7. Successive (multiple) revolution.   Since it is possible to draw an object in any oblique position relative to the co-ordinate planes, it is possible to show it revolved through a series of successive simple revolutions.   Usually such a series is limited to three or four stages.   Figure 8.5 shows an object revolved successively about three separate axes.   The normal orthographic views are shown in space I.   In space II, the object has been revolved clockwise through an angle of 30 degrees about an axis perpendicular to the frontal plane.   A system of numbers by which each corner is identified, as shown, is not necessary in the case of a simple object.   If the object is in the least complex, however, possible confusion is avoided by the use of identification symbols of some type.   In space

Fig. 8.5.   Successive Revolution.

III, the object has been revolved counterclockwise from its position in space II through an angle of 15 degrees about an axis perpendicular to the horizontal plane.   From this position, represented in space III, the object is revolved clockwise through 15 degrees into the position shown in space IV.   This last simple revolution completes a series of three simple revolutions involving the three general cases previously discussed.

8.8 To find the true length of a line by revolution.   In engineering drafting, it frequently is necessary to determine the true length of a line when constructing the development of a surface (Chapter 14).   The true lengths must be found of those lines that are not parallel to any co-ordinate plane and, therefore, appear foreshortened in all the principal views.   (See Sec. 6.7, "Principles of multiview drawing.")   The practical as well as the theoretical procedure is to revolve any such oblique line into a position parallel to a co-ordinate plane so that its projection on that particular plane will be the same length as the line.   In Fig. 8.6(a), this is illustrated by the edge AB on the pyramid. AB is oblique to the co-ordinate planes and its projections are foreshortened. If this edge line is imagined to be revolved until it becomes parallel to the frontal plane, then the projection ab_r in the front view will be the same length as the true length of AB.

A practical application of this method is shown in Fig. 8.6(c). The true length of the edge AB, in Fig. 8.6(a), would be found by revolving its top projection into the position ab_r representing AB revolved parallel to the frontal plane, and then projecting the end point b_r down into its new position along a horizontal line through b. The horizontal line represents the horizontal plane of the base in which the point B travels as the line AB is revolved.

Commercial draftsmen who are unfamiliar with the theory of co-ordinate planes find the true length projection of a line by visualizing the

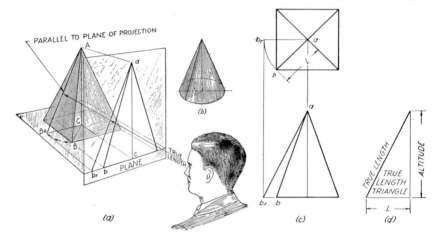

Fig. 8.6.　True Length of a Line, Revolution Method.

line's revolution. They think of an edge as being revolved until it is in a plane perpendicular to the line of sight of an observer stationed an infinite distance away (Figs. 14.11, 14.12, and 14.13). The process corresponds to that used in drawing regular orthographic views (see Sec. 6.4). Usually this method is more easily understood by a student.

Note in Fig. 8.6(a and b) that the true length of a line is equal to the hypotenuse of a right triangle whose altitude is equal to the difference in the elevation of the end points and whose base is equal to the top projection of the line. With this fact in mind, many draftsmen determine the true length of a line by constructing a true-length triangle similar to the one illustrated in Fig. 8.6(d).

8.9. True-length lines. Students who, lacking a thorough understanding of the principles of projection (Sec. 6.7), find it difficult to determine whether or not a projection of a line in one of the principal views shows the true length of the line, should study carefully the following facts:

1. If the projection of a line shows the true length of a line, one of the

other projections must appear as a horizontal line, a vertical line, or a point on one of the other views of the drawing.

2. If the top and front views of a line are horizontal, then both views show the true length.

3. If the top view of a line is a point, the front and side views show the true length.

4. If the front view of a line is a point, the top and side views show the true length.

5. If the top and front views of a line are vertical, the side view shows the true length.

6. If the side projection of a line is a point, the top and front views show the true length.

7. If the front view of a line is horizontal and the top view is inclined, the top inclined view shows the true length.

8. If the top view of a line is horizontal and the front view is inclined, the front inclined view shows the true length.

8.10. Problems. The following problems in revolution furnish excellent drill in projection and offer the student a chance to develop further his imagination and ability to visualize in three dimensions. It will be found worth while to number all the corners of each object used, both on the normal views and on the views of the successive stages.

1–8. Divide, into four equal areas, the space inside the border line of a sheet of drawing paper. In the upper left-hand space, draw the normal orthographic

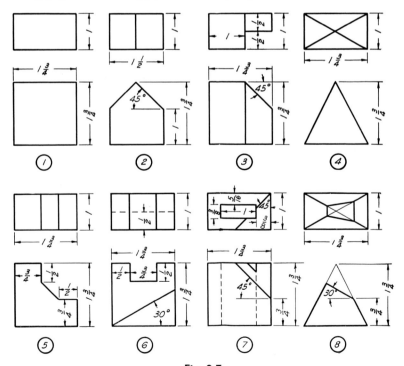

Fig. 8.7.

views of an object assigned from Fig. 8.7.   In the lower left-hand space, show
the object revolved through an angle of 30° about an axis perpendicular to the
front plane (see Fig. 8.1).   In the upper right-hand space, show a simple revolution from the normal orthographic view about an axis perpendicular to the top
plane (see Fig. 8.2).   Revolve the object through an angle of 30°.   Complete
the drawing by making a simple revolution about an axis perpendicular to the
side or profile plane (see Fig. 8.3).   Revolve the object from the original normal
position through an angle of 30°.

9–16. Divide a sheet of drawing paper into four equal areas and make a series
of successive revolutions of an object assigned from Fig. 8.7.   Revolve the object
through the three stages shown in Fig. 8.5.   Make the revolutions in the following order: (1) in the lower left-hand space, revolve the object through an angle
of 30° about an axis perpendicular to the front plane; (2) in the lower right-hand
space, revolve the object from its previous position through an angle of 15° about
an axis perpendicular to the top plane; (3) in the upper right-hand space, make
a revolution through an angle of 15° about an axis perpendicular to the side or
profile plane.

9 | Sectional Views

9.1. Sectional views (Fig. 9.1). Although the invisible features of a simple object usually may be described on an exterior view by the use of hidden lines, it is unwise to depend upon a perplexing mass of such lines to describe adequately the interior of a complicated object or an assembled mechanism. Whenever a representation becomes so confused that it is difficult to read, it is

Courtesy Warner and Swasey Co.

Fig. 9.1. A Working Drawing with Sectional Views.

customary to make one or more of the views "in section" (Fig. 9.2). A view "in section" is one obtained by imagining the object to have been cut by a cutting plane, the front portion being removed so as to reveal clearly the interior features. Figure 9.3(a) illustrates the use of an imaginary cutting plane. The resulting section (front) view, accompanied by a top view, is shown in Fig. 9.3(c). At this point it should be understood that a portion is shown removed only in a sectional view, not in any of the other views. (See Fig. 9.3c.)

197

When the cutting plane cuts an object lengthwise, the section obtained is commonly called a longitudinal section; when crosswise, it is called a cross section. It is designated as being either a full section, a half section, or a broken section. If the plane cuts entirely across the object, the section represented is known as a full section. If it cuts only halfway

EXTERIOR VIEW   SECTIONAL VIEW

Fig. 9.2.   A Sectional View.

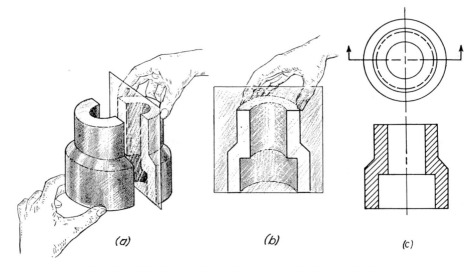

(a)   (b)   (c)

Fig. 9.3.   The Theory of the Construction of a Sectional View.

across a symmetrical object, the section is a half section. A broken section is a partial one which is used when less than a half section is needed.

On a completed sectional view, fine section lines are drawn across the surface cut by the imaginary plane, to emphasize the contour of the interior (see Sec. 9.8).

9.2. A full section. Since a cutting plane that cuts a full section passes entirely through an object, the resulting view will appear as illus-

FULL SECTION

Fig. 9.4.　An Offset Cutting Plane.

ONE-HALF
REMOVED

ONE-QUARTER
REMOVED

SMALL PORTION
REMOVED

Either form of line acceptable

FULL SECTION　　　　HALF SECTION　　　　BROKEN SECTION

Fig. 9.5.　Types of Sectional Views.

trated in Fig. 9.3(c). Although the plane usually passes along the main axis, it may be offset (see Fig. 9.4) to reveal important features.

A full sectional view, showing an object's characteristic shape, usually replaces an exterior front view; however, one of the other principal views, side or top, may be converted into a sectional view if some interior feature thus can be shown to better advantage or if such a view is needed in addition to a sectioned front view.

The procedure in making a full sectional view is simple, in that the sectional view is an orthographic one. The imaginary cut face of the object simply is shown as it would appear to an observer looking directly at it from a point an infinite distance away. In any sectional view, it is considered good practice to omit all invisible lines unless such lines are necessary to clarify the representation. Even then they should be used sparingly.

9.3. A half section. The cutting plane for a half section removes one quarter of an object. The plane cuts halfway through to the axis or center line so that half the finished sectional view appears in section and half appears as an external view. (See Fig. 9.5.) This type of sectional view is used when a view is needed showing both the exterior and interior construction of a symmetrical object. Good practice dictates that hidden lines be omitted from both halves of the view unless they are absolutely necessary for dimensioning purposes or for explaining the construction. Although the use of a solid line object line to separate the two halves of a half section has been approved by the Society of Automotive Engineers and has recently been accepted by the American Standards Association (Fig. 9.6a), many draftsmen prefer to use a center line as shown in 9.6(b). They reason that the removal of a quarter of the object is theoretical and imaginary and that an actual edge, which would be implied by a solid line, does not exist. The center line is taken as denoting a theoretical edge.

Fig. 9.6.   A Half Section.

SOLID LINE
ASA STANDARD
(a)

CENTER LINE
ASA STANDARD
(b)

9.4. A broken section. A broken or partial section is used mainly to expose the interior of objects so constructed that less than a half section is required for a satisfactory description (Fig. 9.7). The object theoretically is cut by a cutting plane and the front portion is removed by breaking it away. The "breaking away" gives an irregular boundary line to the section.

9.5. A revolved section. A revolved section is useful for showing the true shape of the cross section of some elongated object, such as a bar,

Fig. 9.7. A Broken Section.   Fig. 9.8. A Revolved Section.*

(a)

(b)

Fig. 9.9. A Revolved Section and Cutting Plane.

or some feature of an object, such as an arm, spoke, or rib (Figs. 9.1 and 9.8).

To obtain such a cross section, an imaginary cutting plane is passed through the member perpendicular to its axis, and then is revolved through 90° to bring the resulting view into the plane of the paper (Fig. 9.9). When revolved, the section should show in its true shape and in its true revolved position, regardless of the location of the lines of the exterior view. If any lines of the view interfere with the revolved section,

* ASA Y14.2–1957.

they should be omitted (Fig. 9.10).   It sometimes is advisable to provide an open space for the section by making a break in the object (see Fig. 9.8).

9.6. Detail or removed sections.   A detail section is similar to a revolved section, except that it does not appear on an external view but, instead, is drawn "out of place," and appears adjacent to it (Fig. 9.11).

Fig. 9.10.   Revolved Sections.

Fig. 9.11.   Detail Sections.

There are two good reasons why detail sections frequently are desirable. First, their use may prevent a principal view of an object, the cross section of which is not uniform, from being cluttered with numerous revolved sections (Fig. 9.11).   Second, they may be drawn to an enlarged scale in order to emphasize detail and allow for adequate dimensioning (Fig. 9.12).

Whenever a detail section is used, there must be some means of identifying it.   Usually this is accomplished by showing the cutting plane on the principal view and then labeling both the plane and the resulting view, as shown in Fig. 9.11.

9.7. Phantom sections. A phantom or hidden section is a regular exterior view upon which the interior construction is emphasized by cross-hatching an imaginary cut surface with dotted section lines (see Fig. 9.13). This type of section is used only when a regular section or a broken section would remove some important exterior detail, or, in some instances, to show an accompanying part in its relative position with regard to a particular part (Fig. 9.14). Instead of using a broken line with dashes of

Fig. 9.12.   A Detail Section.

Fig. 9.13.   A Phantom Section.

Fig. 9.14.   Phantom Sectioning—Adjacent Parts.

equal length, the phantom line shown in Fig. 3.71 could have been used to represent the outline of the adjacent parts shown in Fig. 9.14.

9.8. Section lining. Section lines are light continuous lines drawn across the imaginary cut surface of an object for the purpose of emphasizing the contour of its interior. Usually they are drawn at an angle of 45° except in cases where a number of adjacent parts are shown assembled. (See Fig. 9.18.)

To be pleasing in appearance, these lines must be correctly executed. While on ordinary work they are spaced about $\frac{3}{32}''$ apart, there is no set rule governing their spacing. They simply should be spaced to suit the drawing and the size of the areas to be crosshatched. For example, on small views having small areas, the section lines may be as close as $\frac{1}{32}''$, while on large views having large areas they may be as far apart as $\frac{1}{8}''$. In the case of very thin plates, the cross section is shown "solid black" (Fig. 9.15).

The usual mistake of the beginning student is to draw the lines too close together. This, plus the unavoidable slight variations, causes the section lining to appear streaked. Although several forms of mechanical

Fig. 9.15.   Thin Sections.

Fig. 9.16.   Faults in Section Lining.

section liners are available, most draftsmen do their spacing by eye. The student is advised to do likewise, being careful to see that the initial pitch, as set by the first few lines, is maintained across the area. To accomplish this, he should check back from time to time to make sure there has been no slight general increase or decrease in the spacing. An example of correct section lining is shown in Fig. 9.16(a), and, for comparison, examples of faulty practice may be seen in Fig. 9.16(b), (c), and (d). Experienced draftsmen realize that nothing will do more to ruin the appearance of a drawing than carelessly executed section lines.

As shown in Fig. 9.17, the section lines on two adjacent pieces should slope at 45 degrees in opposite directions.   If a third piece adjoins the two other pieces, as in Fig. 9.18(a), it ordinarily is section-lined at 30 degrees. An alternate treatment, which might be used, would be to vary the spacing without changing the angle.   On a sectional view showing an assembly of related parts, *all portions of the cut surface of any part must be section-lined in the same direction, for a change would lead the reader to consider the portions as belonging to different parts.   Furthermore, to allow quick identification, each piece (and all identical pieces)* in every view of the assembly drawing should be section-lined in the same direction.

Fig. 9.17.   Two Adjacent Pieces.

Shafts, bolts, pins, rivets, balls, and so on, whose axes lie in the plane of section are not treated the same as ordinary parts.   Having no interior construction to be shown, they are drawn in full and thus tend to make the adjacent sectioned parts stand out to better advantage (Fig. 9.19).

(a)

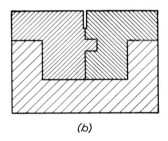

(b)

Fig. 9.18.   Three Adjacent Pieces.

Whenever section lines drawn at 45° with the horizontal are parallel to part of the outline of the section (see Fig. 9.20), it is advisable to draw them at some other angle (say 30° or 60°).   Those drawn as in (a) and (c) produce an unusual appearance that is contrary to what is expected. Note the more natural effect obtained in (b) and (d) by sloping the lines at 30° and 75°.

9.9 Outline sectioning.   Very large surfaces may be section-lined around the bounding outline only, as illustrated in Fig. 9.21.

9.10. The symbolic representation for a cutting plane.   The symbolic lines that are used to represent the edge view of a cutting plane are shown in Fig. 9.22.   The line is as heavy as an object line and is composed of either alternate long and short dashes or a series of dashes of equal length.   The latter form is used in the automobile industry and has been approved by the SAE (Society of Automotive Engineers) and the American Standards Association.   On drawings of ordinary size, when alternate long and short dashes are used for the cutting plane line, the long dashes are $\frac{3}{4}''$ long, the short dashes $\frac{1}{8}''$ long, and the spaces $\frac{1}{16}''$ wide.

Courtesy New Departure, Division General Motor Sales Corp.

Fig. 9.19.   Treatment of Shafts, Fasteners, Ball Bearings, and Other Parts.

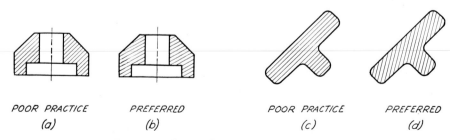

POOR PRACTICE   PREFERRED   POOR PRACTICE   PREFERRED

(a)   *(b)*   *(c)*   *(d)*

Fig. 9.20.   Section Lining at 30°, 60°, or 75°,

When drawn in ink, the dashes are $\frac{1}{40}''$ to $\frac{1}{32}''$ wide, depending on the size of the drawing. When drawn in pencil on manila paper, they are made with a medium pencil.

Arrowheads are used to show the direction in which the imaginary cut surface is viewed, and reference letters are added to identify it (Fig. 9.23).

Whenever the location of the cutting plane is obvious, it is common practice to omit the edge-view representa-tion, particularly in the case of symmetrical objects. If it is shown, however, and coin-cides with a center line, it takes precedence over the center line.

9.11. Summary of the practices of sectioning.

1. A cutting plane may be offset in order to cut the object in such a manner as to reveal an important detail that would not be shown if the cutting plane were con-tinuous (Fig. 9.4).

Fig. 9.21. Outline Sectioning.

2. All visible lines beyond the cutting plane for the section are usually shown.

3. Invisible lines beyond the cutting plane for the section are usually not shown, unless they are absolutely necessary to clarify the construction of the piece. In a half section, they are omitted in the unsectioned half, and either a center line or a solid line is used to separate the two halves of the view (Figs. 9.5 and 9.6).

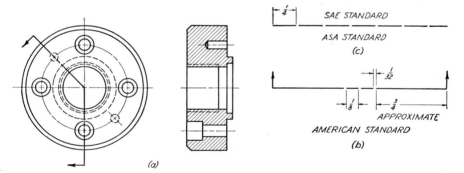

Fig. 9.22. Cutting Plane Lines (American Standard).

4. On a view showing assembled parts, the section lines on adjacent pieces are drawn in opposite directions at an angle of 45° (Fig. 9.17).

5. On an assembly drawing, the portions of the cut surface of a single piece in the same view or different views always should be section-lined in the same direction, with the same spacing (Fig. 9.19).

6. The symbolic line indicating the location of the cutting plane may be omitted if the location of the plane is obvious (Fig. 9.1).

7. On a sectioned view showing assembled pieces, an exterior view is preferred for shafts, rods, bolts, nuts, rivets, and so forth, whose axes are in the plane of section (Fig. 9.19).

SECT B–B

SECT. A–A

Fig. 9.23.   A Sectional View.*

9.12. Auxiliary sections. A sectional view, projected upon an auxiliary plane, is sometimes necessary to show the shape of a surface cut by a plane, or to show the cross-sectional shape of an arm, rib, and so forth, inclined to any two or all three of the principal planes of projection (Fig. 9.24). When a cutting plane cuts an object, as in Fig. 9.24, arrows should show the direction in which the cut surface is viewed. Auxiliary sections are drawn by the usual method for drawing auxiliary views. When the bounding edge of the section is a curve, it is necessary to plot enough points to obtain a smooth one. Sec. 7.9

AUXILIARY VIEW

AUXILIARY SECTION A-A

Fig. 9.24.   An Auxiliary Section.

explains in detail the method for constructing the required view. A section view of this type usually shows only the inclined cut surface.

9.13. Conventional sections. Sometimes a less confusing sectioned representation is obtained if certain of the strict rules of projection are

* ASA Y14.2–1957.

violated as explained in Chapter 10. For example, an unbalanced and confused view results when the sectioned view of the pulley shown in Fig. 9.25 is drawn in true projection, as in (*a*). It is better practice to preserve symmetry by showing the spokes as if they were aligned into one plane, as in (*c*). Such treatment of unsymmetrical features is not misleading, since their actual arrangement is revealed in the circular view. The spokes are not sectioned in the preferred view. If they were, the first impression would be that the wheel had a solid web (*b*). (See Fig. 9.26.)

POOR PRACTICE   POOR PRACTICE   PREFERRED
(*a*)   (*b*)   (*c*)

Fig. 9.25. Conventional Treatment of Spokes in Section.

Preferred   Poor Practice

Fig. 9.26. Spokes in Section.*

The holes in a flange should be shown in a sectioned view at their true distance apart, across the bolt circle, even though their axes do not fall in the plane of section. (See Fig. 9.27.) The unbalanced view in (*b*) conveys no impression of symmetry, nor does it reveal the true location of the holes with reference to rim. The view in (*a*), showing the upper hole as if it had been swung into the plane of section, is less misleading and is therefore to be preferred.

In Fig. 9.28 is shown another example of conventional representation. The sectional view is drawn as if the upper projecting lug had been swung until the portion of the cutting plane through it formed a continuous plane with the other portion. (See Sec. 10.3.) It should be noted that the hidden lines in the sectioned view are necessary for a complete description of the construction of the lugs.

---

* ASA Y14.2–1957.

PREFERRED PRACTICE
(a)

(b)

Fig. 9.27.   Drilled Flanges.

BOLT CIRCLE (B.C.)

Fig. 9.28.   Revolution of a Portion of an
Object.

THEORETICAL
CUTTING PLANE   (b)

USUALLY SHOWN
THROUGH RIB

(a)

Fig. 9.29.   Conventional Treatment of Ribs
in Section.

Rib

Fig. 9.30.   Alternate Treatment of Ribs in
Section.

9.14. Ribs in section. When a machine part has a rib cut by a plane of section (Fig. 9.29), a "true" sectional view taken through the rib would prove to be false and misleading, because the crosshatching on the rib would cause the object to appear "solid." The preferred treatment is to omit arbitrarily the section lines from the rib, as illustrated by Fig. 9.29(*a*). The resulting sectional view may be considered the view that would be obtained if the plane were offset to pass just in front of the rib (*b*).

An alternate conventional method, approved but not used as frequently, is illustrated in Fig. 9.30. This practice of omitting alternate

CAST IRON
IN GENERAL USE FOR ALL
MATERIALS ON DETAIL DRAWINGS

STEEL

BRASS, BRONZE, AND
COPPER

BABBITT, LEAD, ZINC,
AND ALLOYS

MAGNESIUM,
ALUMINUM, AND
ALUMINUM ALLOYS

RUBBER, PLASTIC
ELECTRICAL INSULATION

ELECTRIC WINDINGS,
ELECTRO-MAGNETS,
RESISTANCE, ETC.

CORK, FELT, FABRIC,
ASBESTOS, INSULATION,
LEATHER, AND FIBRE

FIREBRICK AND
REFRACTORY MATERIAL

BRICK AND STONE
MASONRY

MARBLE, SLATE, GLASS,
PORCELAIN, ETC.

CONCRETE

EARTH

ROCK

WATER AND LIQUIDS

ACROSS
GRAIN

WITH
GRAIN

WOOD

FOR OTHER SYMBOLS FOR MATERIALS IN SECTION AND ELEVATION SEE ARCHITECTURAL DRAWING CHAPTER

Fig. 9.31. Material Symbols.

section lines sometimes is adopted when it is necessary to emphasize a rib that might otherwise be overlooked.

9.15. Material symbols. The section-line symbols recommended by the American Standards Association for indicating various materials are shown in Fig. 9.31. Code section lining ordinarily is not used on a working (detail) drawing of a separate part. It is considered unnecessary to indicate a material symbolically when its exact specification must also be given as a note. For this reason, and in order to save time as well, the easily drawn symbol for cast iron is commonly used on detail drawings for all materials. Contrary to this general practice, however, some few chief draftsmen insist that symbolic section lining be used on all detail drawings prepared under their supervision.

Code section lining usually is employed on an assembly section showing the various parts of a unit in position, because a distinction between the materials causes the parts to "stand out" to better advantage. Furthermore, a knowledge of the type of material of which an individual part is composed often helps the reader to identify it more quickly and understand its function.

Symbols and conventions which are commonly used to represent materials and manufactured items on the working drawings of a structure are shown in Fig. 23.15.

9.16. Problems. The following problems were designed to emphasize the principles of sectioning. It is not recommended that a great amount of time be spent on them, as more practice in applying the fundamentals of sectioning is offered the student by problems at the end of the chapter on working drawings. Those orthographic drawings that are prepared from the pictorials of objects may be dimensioned if the elementary principles of dimensioning (Chapter 15) are carefully studied.

1. (Fig. 9.32.) Reproduce the top and side views and change the front view into a sectional view that will be in accordance with the indicated cutting plane.

Fig. 9.32. Mutilated Block.

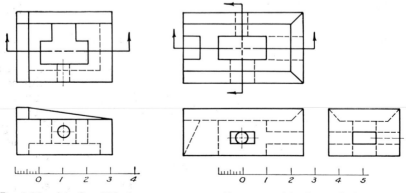

Fig. 9.33. Mutilated Block.   Fig. 9.34. Mutilated Block.

2. (Fig. 9.33.) Reproduce the top view and change the front view into a full section view in accordance with the indicated cutting plane.

3. (Fig. 9.34.) Reproduce the top view and change the front and side views into sectional views that will be in accordance with the indicated cutting planes.

4. (Fig. 9.35.) Draw a front view of the pulley (circular view) and a side view in full section.

5. (Fig. 9.36.) Reproduce the top view of the rod support and draw the front view in full section. Read Sec. 10.5 before starting to draw.

6. (Fig. 9.37.) Draw a front view of the "V" pulley (circular view) and a side view in full section.

Fig. 9.35. Pulley.   Fig. 9.36. Rod Support.   Fig. 9.37. "V" Pulley.

7. (Fig. 9.38.) Draw a full sectional view of the fluted column. Reproduce the circular view.

Fig. 9.38. Fluted Column.

8. (Fig. 9.39.)   Make a full sectional view of the "rectangular view" of the piston head.   Reproduce the circular view.

Fig. 9.39.   Piston Head.

9. (Fig. 9.40.)   Reproduce the two views of the hand wheel and change the right-side view into a full section.

Fig. 9.40.   Hand Wheel.

10. (Fig. 9.41.) Reproduce the circular front view of the pump cover and convert the right-side view to a full section.

Fig. 9.41. Pump Cover.

11. (Fig. 9.42.) Reproduce the top view of the control housing cover and convert the front view to a full section.

Fig. 9.42. Control Housing Cover.

12. (Fig. 9.43.)   Draw the necessary views of the link and use a revolved or detail section to show the cross section through the rib.

Fig. 9.43.   Link.

13–22. (Figs. 9.44–9.53.)   These problems may be dimensioned, as are working drawings.   For each object, the student should draw all the views necessary for a working drawing of the part.   Good judgment should be exercised in deciding whether the sectional view should be a full section, half section, revolved section, or detail section.   After the student has made his decision, he should consult his class instructor.

    The end guide has five ribs (Fig. 9.53).

Fig. 9.44.   Cover.   **Fig. 9.45.   Radiator Outlet.**

Fig. 9.46. Rod Yoke.

Fig. 9.47. End Cap.

Fig. 9.48. Attachment Guide.

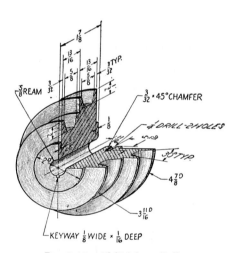

Fig. 9.49. "V" Motor Pulley.

Fig. 9.50.   Cone Pulley.

Fig. 9.51.   Flanged Pulley.

Fig. 9.52.   Cover.

Fig. 9.53.   End Guide.

23. (Fig. 9.54.)   Reproduce the front and top views of the steady brace. Complete the top view and draw the required side view and auxiliary section. Since this is a structural drawing, the figure giving the value of a distance appears above an unbroken dimension line in accordance with the custom in this field of engineering. (See Chapter 22.)   The slope (45°) of the inclined member to which the plates are welded is indicated by a slope triangle with 12-inch legs.

This problem has been designed to make it necessary for the student to test his power of visualization if he is to determine the shape of the inclined structural member.   Good judgment must be exercised in determining the location of the third hole in each plate.   All hidden object lines are to be shown.

Fig. 9.54.   Steady Brace.

10

Conventional Practices and Representations

10.1. In commercial drafting, certain conventional practices have been adopted in order to obtain added clearness. Many of them eliminate particularly awkward conditions that arise from strict adherence to the rules of projection. These idioms of drawing have slowly developed with the graphic language until at the present time they are universally recognized and observed.

Fig. 10.1. Conventional Practice of Representing Unimportant Intersections, Ribs, and Lugs.

10.2. The treatment of unimportant intersections. The conventional methods of treating various unimportant intersections are shown in Fig. 10.1. To show the true line of intersection in each case would add little to the value of the drawing. Therefore, in the views designated as preferred, true projection has been ignored in the interest of simplicity. On the front views, in (a) and (b) for example, there is so little difference between the descriptive values of the true and approximate representations of the hole that the extra labor necessary to draw the true representation is unwarranted.

10.3. Aligned views. Pieces that have arms, ribs, lugs, or other parts at an angle are often shown aligned or "straightened out" in one view, as illustrated in Fig. 10.2.   By this method, it is possible to show the true shape as well as the true position of such features.

10.4. Developed views.   Bent pieces, similar to the piece shown in Fig. 10.3, are often drawn so that one view is a developed view of the blank from which the piece is to be formed, and the other is a true view showing the character- istic contour.

In laying out the developed view, extra metal must be allowed for bends.   The empirical formula used for computing the bend allow- ance (arc length) for a bend is shown in (b).

Fig. 10.2.   Aligned Views.

10.5. Conventional treatment of radially arranged features. Many objects that have radially arranged features may be shown more clearly if true projection is violated (Fig. 10.4).   Violation of true projec- tion in such cases consists of intentionally showing such features swung out of position in one view so as to present the idea of symmetry and show

Fig. 10.3.   Developed Views.

the true relationship of the features at the same time.   For example, while the radially arranged holes in a flange (see Fig. 10.5) should always be shown in their true position in the circular view, they should be shown in a revolved position in the other view in order to show their true relation- ship with the rim.   The conventional treatment for drilled flanges in section is explained in Sec. 9.13.

Radial ribs and radial spokes are similarly treated.   The true projec- tion of such features may create representations that are unsymmetrical and misleading.   The preferred conventional method of treatment, by preserving symmetry, produces representations that are more easily understood and that at the same time are much simpler to draw.   Figure 10.6 illustrates the preferred treatment for radial ribs.   The proper method for treating radial ribs and radial spokes in sectioned views is explained in Secs. 9.13 and 9.14.

10.6. Representation of fillets and rounds.   Interior corners, which are formed on a casting by unfinished surfaces, always are filled in

Fig. 10.4. Symmetry.

Fig. 10.5. Radially Arranged Holes.

HOLE SHOWN IN A
REVOLVED POSITION

GOOD PRACTICE

HOLE DRAWN IN
TRUE PROJECTION

POOR PRACTICE

FILLET

ROUND

**Fig. 10.6. Conventional Treatment of
Radially Arranged Ribs.**

Fig. 10.7. Fillets and Rounds.

(filleted) at the intersection, in order to avoid possible fracture at that point. Sharp corners are also difficult to obtain and are avoided for this reason as well (Fig. 10.7). Exterior corners are rounded for appearance and for the comfort of persons who must handle the part when assembling or repairing the machine on which the part is used. A rounded internal corner is known as a "fillet"; a rounded external corner is known as a "round."

When two intersecting surfaces are machined, however, their intersection will become a sharp corner. For this reason, all corners formed by unfinished surfaces should be shown "broken" by small rounds, and all corners formed by two finished surfaces or one finished surface and one unfinished surface should be shown "sharp." Although in the past it has been the practice to allow pattern makers to use their judgment about the size of fillets and rounds, many present-day companies require their designers and draftsmen to specify their size even though their exact size may not be important.

Since fillets and rounds eliminate the intersection lines of intersecting surfaces, they create a special problem in orthographic representation. To treat them in the same manner as they would be treated if they had large radii results in views that are misleading. For example, the true

Fig. 10.8.   Conventional Practice of Representing Nonexisting Lines of Intersection.

projection view in Fig. 10.8(a) confuses the reader, because at a first glance it does not convey the idea that there are abrupt changes in direction. To prevent such a probable first impression and to improve the descriptive value of the view, it is necessary to represent these theoretically nonexisting lines. These characteristic lines are projected from the approximate intersections of the surfaces, with the fillets disregarded.

Figure 10.9 illustrates the accepted conventional method of representing the "run-out" intersection of a fillet in cases where a plane surface is tangent to a cylindrical surface. Although run-out arcs such as these are usually drawn freehand, a french curve or a bow instrument may be used. If they are drawn with the latter type of instrument, a radius should be used that is equal to the radius of the fillet, and the completed arc should form approximately one-eighth of a circle.

The generally accepted methods of representing intersecting fillets and rounds are illustrated in Fig. 10.10.   The treatment, in each of the cases shown, is determined by the relationship existing between the sizes of the intersecting fillets and rounds.   Figure 10.10 shows several illustrations of accepted conventional methods used to represent run-outs.

10.7. Accepted violations of true projection in the representation of boltheads, slots, and holes for pins.   Another departure from

POINT OF TANGENCY

POINT OF TANGENCY

APPROX. ⅛ CIRCLE
ENDING ON ℄

APPROX. ⅛ CIRCLE
(FREEHAND OR WITH A
BOW INSTRUMENT)

(a)   (b)

Fig. 10.9.   The Conventional Treatment for Fillets.

POINT OF TANGENCY

(a)   (b)   (c)

Fig. 10.10.   The Approximate Methods of Representing Intersecting Fillets and Rounds.

true projection is encountered in representing a bolthead.   For example, on a working drawing, it is considered to be the best practice to show the head across corners in both views, regardless of the fact that in true projection one view would show "across flats." (See Fig. 10.11.)   This method of treatment eliminates the possibility of a reader interpreting a hexagonal head to be a square head.   Furthermore, the showing of a head the "long way" in both views clearly reveals the space needed for proper clearance.

Figure 10.11 also shows several illustrations of the correct method of representing slots and holes for pins. In the case of the slotted head fasteners the slots are shown at 45° in the end views in order to avoid placing a slot on a center line where it is usually difficult to draw so that the center line passes accurately through the center. This practice does not affect the descriptive value of the drawing, because the true size and

Fig. 10.11. Treatment of Boltheads, Slots, and Holes for Pins.

Fig. 10.12. A Half View.

shape of the slot is shown in the front view. The hole for a pin is shown at 45° for the same reason. In such a position it may be more quickly observed.

10.8. Half views. When the space available is insufficient to allow a satisfactory scale to be used for the representation of a symmetrical piece, it is considered good practice to make one view a half view, as shown in Fig. 10.12. The half view, however, must be the top or side view and not the front view, which shows the characteristic contour. When the front view is an exterior view, the half view should be the front half of the top or side view; when the front view is a sectional view, it should be the rear half.

10.9. Conventional breaks.   A relatively long piece of uniform section may be shown to a larger scale, if a portion is broken out so that

Fig. 10.13.   A Broken-Out View.

the ends can be drawn closer together (Fig. 10.13).   When such a scheme is employed, a conventional break is used to indicate that the length of the representation is not to scale.   The American Standard conventional breaks, shown in Fig. 10.14, are used on either detail or assembly drawings. The breaks representation for indicating the broken ends of rods, shafts,

Fig. 10.14.   Conventional Breaks.

tubes, and so forth, are designed to reveal the characteristic shape of the cross section in each case.   Although break lines for round sections may be drawn freehand, particularly on small views, it is better practice to draw them with either an irregular curve or a bow instrument.   The breaks for wood sections, however, always should be drawn freehand.

Figure 10.15 shows the steps for drawing the break lines for the broken end of a solid round section.   The small connecting curves may be drawn freehand.

10.10. Ditto lines.   When it is desirable to minimize labor in order to save time, ditto lines may be used to indicate a series of identical

Fig. 10.15.   Steps in Drawing Break Lines for a Round Section.

Fig. 10.16.   Ditto Lines.

features.   For example, the threads on the shaft shown in Fig. 10.16 are just as effectively indicated by ditto lines as by a completed profile representation.   When ditto lines are used, a long shaft of this type may be shortened without actually showing a conventional break.

10.11. A conventional method for showing a part in alternate positions. A method frequently used for indicating an alternate position of a part or a limiting position of a moving part is shown in Fig. 10.17.   The long and short dashes forming the object lines of the view showing the alternate position should be thin.   The

Fig. 10.17.   Alternate Positions.

phantom line shown in Fig. 3.71 as recommended in both the SAE and ASA Standards should be used for representing the alternate position of a part.

10.12. Conventional representation.   Conventional representations are used by engineers of all fields to represent many of the details that occur repeatedly on their drawings.   Symbols are used on topographic drawings, architectural drawings, electrical drawings, and machine drawings.   No draftsman or engineer can very well escape their use.   (See Figs. 10.18 and 10.19.)

The conventionalized symbolic methods for representing screw threads, springs, pipe fittings, welding, and topographic features may be found in the chapters covering these subjects.   Symbols for electrical apparatus are given in the Appendix.

From Marcus and Marcus, Elements of Radio, *3rd ed., Prentice-Hall, Inc.*

Fig. 10.18.   An Electrical Diagram.

Fig. 10.19.   Welding Symbols.

Most of the illustrations that are shown in Fig. 10.20 should be easily understood. However, the crossed-lines (diagonals) symbol has two distinct and different meanings. First, this symbol may be used on a drawing of a shaft to indicate the position of a surface for a bearing, or, second, it may indicate that a surface perpendicular to the line of sight is flat. These usages are illustrated with separate examples.

Fig. 10.20.   Conventional Symbols.

11 | Pictorial Drawing

11.1 An orthographic drawing of two or more views describes an object accurately in form and size, but, since each of the views shows only two dimensions without any suggestion of depth, such a drawing can convey information only to those who are familiar with graphic representation. For this reason, multiview drawings are used mainly by engineers, draftsmen, contractors, and shopmen.

Frequently, however, engineers and draftsmen find they must use conventional picture drawings to convey specific information to persons who do not possess the trained imagination necessary to construct mentally an object from views. To make such drawings, several special schemes of one-plane pictorial drawing have been devised that combine the pictorial effect of perspective with the advantage of having the principal dimensions to scale. But pictorial drawings, in spite of certain advantages, have disadvantages that limit their use. A few of these are as follows:

1. Some drawings frequently have a distorted, unreal appearance that is disagreeable.

2. The time required for execution is, in many cases, greater than for an orthographic drawing.

3. They are difficult to dimension.

4. Some of the lines cannot be measured.

Even with these limitations, pictorial drawings are used extensively for catalogs, Patent Office records, piping diagrams, and furniture designs. Occasionally they are used, in one form or another, to supplement and clarify machine and structural details which would be difficult to visualize. (See Fig. 11.1.)

11.2. Divisions of pictorial drawing. Single-plane pictorial drawings are classified in three general divisions: (1) axonometric projection, (2) oblique projection, and (3) perspective projection. (See Fig. 11.2.)

Perspective methods produce the most realistic drawings, but the necessary construction is more difficult and tedious than the construction required for the conventional methods classified under the other two divisions. For this reason, engineers customarily use some form of either axonometric or oblique projection. Modified methods, which are not theoretically correct, are often used to produce desired effects.

11.3. Divisions of axonometric projection. Theoretically, axonometric projection is a form of orthographic projection. The distinguish-

229

ing difference is that only one plane is used instead of two or more, and the object is turned from its customary position so that three faces are displayed (Fig. 11.3). Since an object may be placed in a countless number of positions relative to the picture plane, an infinite number of views may

Courtesy North American Aviation Corp.

Fig. 11.1. Pictorial Presentation for a Manual.

AXONOMETRIC   *OBLIQUE*   *PERSPECTIVE*

Fig. 11.2. Axonometric, Oblique, and Perspective Projection.

be drawn which will vary in general proportions, lengths of edges, and sizes of angles. For practical reasons, a few of these possible positions have been classified in such a manner as to give the recognized divisions of axonometric projection: (1) isometric, (2) dimetric, and (3) trimetric.

Isometric projection is the simplest of these, because the principal axes make equal angles with the plane of projection and the edges are therefore foreshortened equally.

11.4. Isometric projection. If the cube in Fig. 11.3 were revolved through an angle of 45 degrees about an imaginary vertical axis, as shown in II, and is then tilted forward until its body diagonal is perpendicular to the vertical plane, the edges would be foreshortened equally and the cube would be in the correct position to produce an isometric projection.

The three front edges, called isometric axes, make angles of approximately 35° 16′ with the vertical plane of projection or picture plane. In this form of pictorial, the angles between the projections of these axes are 120°, and the projected lengths of the edges of an object, along and parallel to these axes, are approximately 81 per cent of their true lengths. It

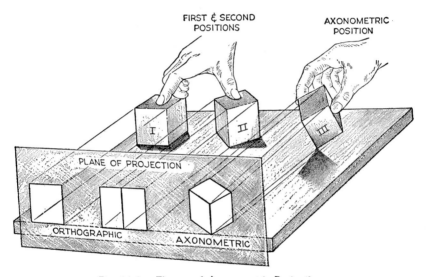

Fig. 11.3. Theory of Axonometric Projection.

should be observed that the 90° angles of the cube appear in the isometric projection as either 120° or 60°.

It was stated in Sec. 8.1 (Chapter 8) that the distinguishing difference between revolution projection and auxiliary projection is that, in the procedure of revolution, the observer turns the object with respect to himself, while in auxiliary projection he shifts his position in relation to it. Therefore, since axonometric projection is a form of orthographic projection, both methods will produce the same final pictorial representation when applied to axonometric projection.

In Fig. 11.3, the object (cube) was turned and tilted until the body diagonal was in a position perpendicular to the plane of projection. Now, if instead of turning and tilting the object in relation to a principal plane of projection, an auxiliary plane is used that will be perpendicular to the body diagonal, the view projected on the plane will be an axonometric projection. Since the auxiliary plane will be inclined to the principal planes upon which the front, top, and side views would be projected, the auxiliary view, taken in a position perpendicular to the body diagonal, will be a secondary auxiliary view, as shown in Fig. 11.4.

11.5. Isometric scale. An isometric scale (proportional scale) for laying off distances parallel to isometric axes may be made by the simple graphical method shown in Fig. 11.5. Usually, the scale is drawn along the edge of a strip of paper or cardboard. Its use is illustrated in Fig. 11.6.

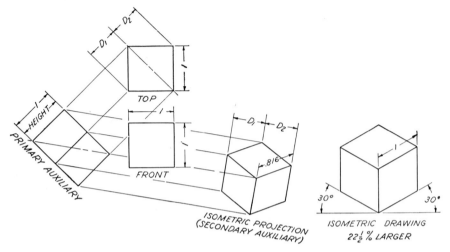

Fig. 11.4. Comparison of Isometric Projection and Isometric Drawing.

Fig. 11.5. Isometric Scale.

Fig. 11.6. Use of an Isometric Scale.

11.6. Isometric drawing. Objects seldom are drawn in true isometric projection, the use of an isometric scale being inconvenient and impractical. Instead, a conventional method is used in which all foreshortening is ignored, and actual true lengths are laid off along isometric axes and isometric lines. To avoid confusion and to set this method apart from true isometric projection, it is called isometric drawing.

The isometric drawing of a figure is slightly larger (approximately $22\frac{1}{2}$ per cent) than the isometric projection, but, since the proportions are the same, the increased size does not affect the pictorial value of the representation. (See Fig. 11.4.) The use of a regular scale makes it possible for a draftsman to produce a satisfactory drawing with a minimum expenditure of time and effort.

In isometric drawing, lines that are parallel to the isometric axes are called *isometric lines.*

11.7. To make an isometric drawing of a rectangular object. The procedure followed in making an isometric drawing of a rectangular block is illustrated in Fig. 11.7. The three axes that establish the front edges, as shown in (*b*), should be drawn through point *A* so that one extends vertically downward and the other two upward to the right and

Fig. 11.7. Procedure for Constructing an Isometric Drawing.

left at an angle of 30° from the horizontal. Then the actual lengths of the edges may be set off, as shown in (*c*) and (*d*), and the remainder of the view completed by drawing lines parallel to the axes through the corners thus located, as in (*e*) and (*f*).

Hidden lines, unless absolutely necessary for clearness, always should be omitted on a pictorial representation.

The same object may be drawn by starting with point *B*. (See Fig. 11.8.) Often it is more convenient to start at a lower corner.

11.8. Nonisometric lines. In a pictorial view, the lines that are oblique to the isometric axes are called nonisometric lines. Since a line of this type does not appear in its true length and cannot be measured directly, its position and projected length must be established by locating its extremities. In Fig. 11.9, *AB* and *CD*, which represent the edges of the block, are nonisometric lines. The location of *AB* is established in the pictorial view by locating points *A* and *B*. Point *A* is on the top edge, *X* distance from the left side surface. Point *B* is on the upper edge of the base, *Y* distance from the right side surface. All other lines coincide with or are parallel to the axes and, therefore, may be measured off with the scale.

The pictorial representation of an irregular solid containing a number of nonisometric lines may be conveniently constructed by the box method; that is, the object may be enclosed in a rectangular box so that both

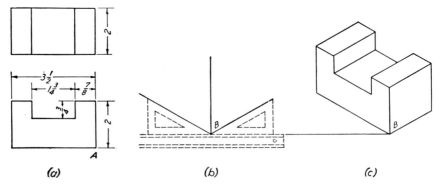

Fig. 11.8.   Alternate Procedure Construction.

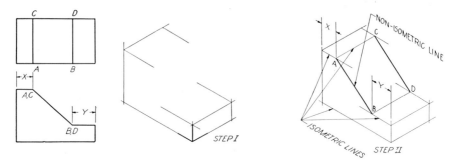

Fig. 11.9.   Nonisometric Lines.

isometric and nonisometric lines may be located by points of contact with its surfaces and edges.   (See Fig. 11.10.)

A study of Figs. 11.9 and 11.10 reveals the important fact that lines that are parallel on an object are parallel in the pictorial view, and, conversely, lines that are not parallel on the object are not parallel on the view.   It is often possible to eliminate much tedious construction work by the practical application of this principle of parallel lines.

11.9. Co-ordinate construction method.   When an object contains a number of inclined surfaces, such as the one shown in Fig. 11.11, the use of the co-ordinate construction method is desirable.   In this method, the end points of the edges are located in relation to an assumed isometric base line located upon an isometric reference plane.   For example, the line *RL* is used as a base line from which measurements are made along isometric lines, as shown.   The distances required to locate point *A* are taken directly from the orthographic views.

Irregular curved edges are most easily drawn in isometric by the offset method, which is a modification of the co-ordinate construction method

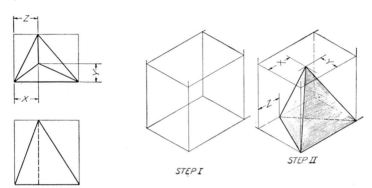

STEP I   STEP II

Fig. 11.10.   Box Construction.

Fig. 11.11.   Co-ordinate Construction.

STEP I   STEP II   STEP III

Fig. 11.12.   Offset Construction.

(Fig. 11.12).   The position of the curve readily can be established by plotted points that may be located by measuring along isometric lines.

11.10. Angles in isometric drawing.   When nonisometric lines are located by angular measurements (Fig. 11.13), it is necessary to draw at least a partial orthographic view of the object and take off the dimensions. The scale should be the same as that of the pictorial view (*a*).   A practical application of this principle, to the construction of an isometric drawing of a 60° angle, is shown in (*b*). By making this construction at the place where the angle is to appear on the isometric drawing, the position of the required line is obtained graphically.

11.11. Circle and circle arcs in isometric drawing. In isometric drawing, a circle appears as an ellipse. The tedious construction required for plotting an ellipse accurately (Figs. 11.14 and 11.15) often is avoided by using some approximate method of drawing. The representation thus

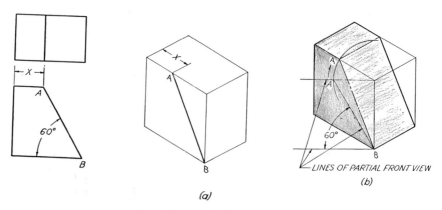

Fig. 11.13.   Angles in Isometric.

Fig. 11.14.   Pictorial Ellipses.   Fig. 11.15.   To Plot an Isometric Circle.

obtained is accurate enough for most work, although the true ellipse, which is slightly narrower and longer, is more pleasing in shape (Fig. 11.14). For an approximate construction, a four-center method is generally used.

To draw an ellipse representing a pictorial circle, a square is conceived to be circumscribed about the circle in the orthographic projection. When transferred to the isometric plane in the pictorial view, the square becomes a rhombus (isometric square) and the circle an ellipse tangent to the rhombus at the mid-points of its sides. If the ellipse is to be drawn by the four-center method (Fig. 11.16), the points of intersection of the perpendicular bisectors of the sides of the rhombus will be centers for the four arcs forming the approximate ellipse. The two intersections that lie on the corners of the rhombus are centers for the two large arcs, while the remaining intersections are centers for the two small arcs. Furthermore, the length along the perpendicular from the center of each arc to

Fig. 11.16.   Four-Center Approximation.

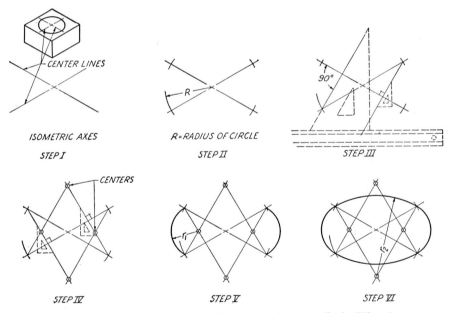

Fig. 11.17.   Steps in Drawing a Four-Center Isometric Circle (Ellipse).

the point at which the arc is tangent to the rhombus (mid-point) will be the radius. All construction lines required by this method may be made with a T-square and a 30 × 60° triangle.

The amount of work may be still further shortened, and the accuracy of the construction improved, by following the procedure shown in Fig. 11.17. The steps in this method are:

Step I.   Draw the isometric center lines of the required circle.

Step II. Using a radius equal to the radius of the circle, strike arcs across the isometric center lines.

Steps III–IV. Through each of these points of intersection erect a perpendicular to the other isometric center line.

Steps V–VI. Using the intersection points of the perpendiculars as centers and the lengths of the perpendiculars as radii, draw the four arcs that form the ellipse.

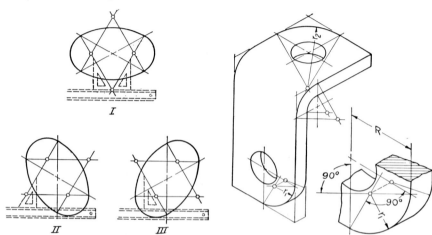

Fig. 11.18. Isometric Circles.　　　　Fig. 11.19. Isometric Circle Arcs.

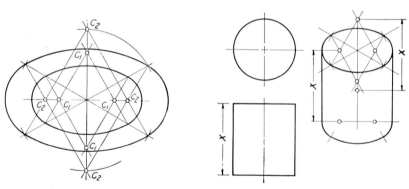

Fig. 11.20. Isometric Concentric Circles.　　Fig. 11.21. Isometric Parallel Circles.

A circle arc will appear in pictorial representation as a segment of an ellipse. Therefore, it may be drawn by using as much of the four-center method as is required to locate the needed centers. (See Fig. 11.19.) For example, to draw a quarter circle, it is only necessary to lay off the true radius of the arc along isometric lines drawn through the center and to draw intersecting perpendiculars through these points.

To draw isometric concentric circles by the four-center method, a set of centers must be located for each circle (Fig. 11.20).

When several circles of the same diameter occur in parallel planes, the construction may be simplified. Figure 11.21 shows two views of a

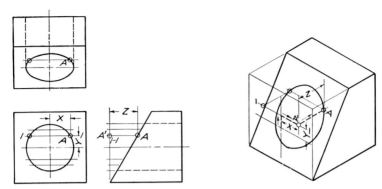

Fig. 11.22.   Circles in Nonisometric Planes.

cylinder and its corresponding isometric drawing.   The centers for the
ellipse representing the upper base are found in the usual way, while the
four centers for the lower base are located by moving the centers for the
upper base downward a distance equal to the height of the cylinder.   It

should be noted that corresponding
centers lie along an isometric line parallel to the axis of the cylinder.

Circles and circle arcs in nonisometric planes are plotted by using the offset
or co-ordinate method (Fig. 11.22).
Sufficient points for establishing a curve
are located by transferring measurements from the orthographic views to
isometric lines in the pictorial view, as
illustrated for point A.

The pictorial representation of a
sphere is the envelope of all of the great
circles which could be drawn on the surface.   In isometric drawing, the great
circles appear as ellipses and a circle is
their envelope.   In practice it is necessary to draw only one ellipse, using the

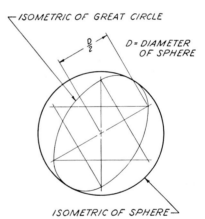

Fig. 11.23.   Isometric Drawing of a
Sphere.

true radius of the sphere and the four-center method of construction.
The diameter of the circle is the long diameter of the ellipse (Fig. 11.23).

11.12. Positions of isometric axes.   It sometimes is desirable to
place the principal isometric axes so that an object will be in position to
reveal certain faces to a better advantage (Fig. 11.24).

(a)

(b)

(c)

(d)

Fig. 11.24.   Convenient Positions of Axes.

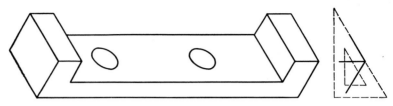

Fig. 11.25.   Main Axis Horizontal—Long Objects.

The difference in direction should cause no confusion, since the angle between the axes and the procedure followed in constructing the view are the same for any position.   The choice of the direction may depend upon the construction of the object, but usually this is determined by the position from which the object ordinarily is viewed.

(a)

ISOMETRIC HALF SECTION
(b)

Fig. 11.26.   Isometric Half Section.

Reversed axes are used in architectural work to show a feature as it would be seen from a natural position below (b).

Sometimes, long objects are drawn with the long axis horizontal, as shown in Fig. 11.25.

11.13. Isometric sectional views (Fig. 11.26).   Generally, an isometric sectional view is used for showing the inner construction of an object, when there is a complicated interior to be explained or when it is desirable to emphasize features that would not appear in a usual outside view.   Sectioning in isometric drawing is based upon the same principles as sectioning in orthographic drawing.   Isometric planes are used for cutting an object, and the general procedure followed in constructing the representation is the same as for an exterior view.

Figure 11.26 shows an isometric half section.   It is easier, in this case, to outline the outside view of the object in full and then remove a front quarter with isometric planes.

Figure 11.27 illustrates a full section in isometric. The accepted procedure for constructing this form of sectional view is to draw the cut face and then add the portion that lies behind.

Section lines should be sloped at an angle that produces the best effect, but they should never be drawn parallel to object lines.   In Fig. 11.28, (a) illustrates the slope that is correct for most drawings, while (b), (c), and (d) show the poor effect produced when this phase of

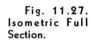

Fig. 11.27. Isometric Full Section.

section lining is ignored.   Ordinarily, isometric section lines are drawn at 60°.

11.14. Dimetric projection.   The view of an object that has been so placed that two of its axes make equal angles with the plane of projection is called a *dimetric projection*.   The third axis may make either a smaller or larger angle. All of the edges along or parallel to the first two axes are foreshortened equally, while those parallel to the third axis are foreshortened a different amount. It might be said that dimetric projection, a division of axonometric projection, is like isometric projection in that the object must be placed to satisfy specific conditions. Similarly

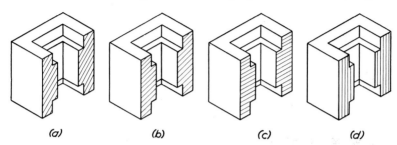

(a)   *(b)*   *(c)*   *(d)*

Fig. 11.28.   Section Lining.

Fig. 11.29.   Dimetric Projection.

a dimetric projection may be drawn by using the auxiliary view method. Figure 11.29 shows the front, top, primary auxiliary, and secondary auxiliary view of a part. The secondary auxiliary view is the dimetric projection. The procedure is the same as for an isometric projection (see Fig. 11.4), except that the line of sight is taken in the direction necessary to obtain the desired dimetric projection. Obviously, an infinite number of dimetric projections are possible.

In practical application, dimetric projection is sometimes modified so that regular scales can be used to lay off measurements to assumed ratios. This is called dimetric drawing (Fig. 11.30a).

The angles and scales may be worked out* for any ratios such as $1:1:\frac{1}{2}$ (Full size: Full size: Half size), $1:1:\frac{3}{4}$ (Full size: Full size: Three-fourths size). For example, the angles for the ratios $1:1:\frac{1}{2}$ are $7°$ $11'$ and $41°$ $25'$. After the scales have been assumed and the angles computed, an enclosing box may be drawn in conformity to the angles and the view completed by following the general procedure used in isometric drawing, except that two scales must be used. The positions commonly used, along with the scale ratios and corresponding angles, are shown in Fig. 11.30(b). The first scale given in each ratio is for the vertical axis. Since obviously two of the axes are foreshortened equally, while the third is foreshortened in different ratio, two scales must be used. This is an effective method of representation.

DIMETRIC DRAWING (APPROX.)

(a)

DIMETRIC AXES

(b)

Fig. 11.30. Approximate Dimetric Drawing.

11.15. Trimetric projection. A trimetric projection of an object is the view obtained when each of the three axes makes a different angle with the plane of projection. Figure 11.31 illustrates the application of the auxiliary view method to the construction of a trimetric projection. It must be noted that the object shown in Fig. 11.31 is rectangular and that the line of sight for the primary auxiliary view was not taken perpendicular to the body diagonal of a cube as in the case of the dimetric projection illustrated in Fig. 11.29. This form of pictorial representation has been used to some extent by certain aircraft companies for the preparation of production illustrations.

11.16. Oblique projection. In oblique projection, the view is produced by using parallel projectors that make some angle other than 90° with the plane of projection. Generally, one face is placed parallel to the picture plane and the projection lines are taken at 45°. This gives a view that is pictorial in appearance, as it shows the front and one or

---

* Formula: $\cos \alpha = -\dfrac{\sqrt{2s_1{}^2 s_2{}^2 - s_2{}^4}}{2s_1 s_2}$. In this formula, α is one of the equal angles; s_1 is one of the equal scales; s_2 is the third scale.

more additional faces of an object. In Fig. 11.32, the orthographic and oblique projections of a cube are shown. When the angle is 45°, as in this illustration, the representation is sometimes called cavalier projection. It is generally known, however, as an oblique projection or an oblique drawing.

11.17. Principle of oblique projection. The theory of oblique projection can be explained by imagining a vertical plane of projection in front of a cube parallel to one of its faces (Fig. 11.32). When the projectors make an angle of 45° in any direction with the picture plane, the

Fig. 11.31. Trimetric Projection.

length of any oblique projection $A'B'$ of the edge AB is equal to the true length of AB. Note that the projectors could be parallel to any element of a 45° cone having its base in the plane of projection. With projectors at this particular angle (45°), the face parallel to the plane is projected in its true size and shape and the edges perpendicular to the picture plane are projected in their true length. If the projectors make a greater angle, the oblique projection will be shorter, while if the angle is less, the projection will be longer.

11.18. Oblique drawing. This form of drawing is based upon three mutually perpendicular axes along which, or parallel to which, the necessary measurements are made for constructing the representation. Oblique drawing differs from isometric drawing principally in that two axes are always perpendicular to each other while the third (receding axis) is at some convenient angle, such as 30°, 45°, or 60° with the horizontal. (See Fig. 11.34.) It is somewhat more flexible and has the following advantages over isometric drawing: (1) circular or irregular outlines on the front face show in their true shape; (2) distortion can be reduced by foreshortening along the receding axis; and (3) a greater

Fig. 11.32. Theory of Oblique Projection.

(a)   (b)   (c)   (d)

Fig. 11.33. Various Positions of the Receding Axis.

choice is permitted in the selection of the positions of the axes. A few of the various views that can be obtained by varying the inclination of the receding axis are illustrated in Fig. 11.33. Usually, the selection of the position is governed by the character of the object.

11.19. To make an oblique drawing. The procedure followed in constructing an oblique drawing of an adjustable guide is illustrated in Fig. 11.34. The three axes that establish the perpendicular edges in (b) are drawn through point O representing the front corner. OA and OB are perpendicular to each other and *OC* is at any desired angle (say 45°) with the horizontal. After the length, height, and depth have been set off, as in (*c*), the front face may be laid out in its true size and shape and the view can be completed by drawing lines parallel to the receding axes through the established corners. The circle and semicircle are shown parallel to the picture plane in order to avoid distortion and because, from the draftsman's standpoint, it is easier to draw a circle than to construct an ellipse.

In general, the procedure for constructing an oblique drawing is the same as for an isometric drawing.

Fig. 11.34. Procedure for Constructing an Oblique Drawing.

11.20. Rules for placing an object. Generally, the most irregular face, or the one containing the most circular outlines, should be placed parallel to the picture plane, in order to minimize distortion and simplify construction. By following this practice, all or most of the circles and circle arcs can be drawn with a compass, and the tedious construction that would be required to draw their elliptical representations in a receding plane is eliminated. In selecting the position of an object, two rules should be followed. The first is to place the face having the most irregular contour, or the most circular outlines, parallel to the picture plane. Note in Fig. 11.35 the advantage of following this rule.

When the longest face of an object is used as the front face, the pictorial view will be distorted to a lesser degree and, therefore, will have a more realistic and pleasing appearance. Hence, the second rule is to place the longest face parallel to the picture plane. Compare the views shown in Fig. 11.36 and note the greater distortion in (*a*) over (*b*).

POOR PRACTICE   GOOD PRACTICE

(*a*)   (*b*)

Fig. 11.35.   Irregular Contour Parallel to Picture Plane.

If these two rules clash, the first should govern. It is more desirable to have the irregular face show its true shape than it is to lessen the distortion in the direction of the receding axis.

11.21. Use of a basic plane. If the front face of an object is in one plane, it will appear in the oblique drawing exactly the same as in orthographic drawing. Note this fact in Fig. 11.34. But the front of many objects is composed of two or more parallel planes whose relationship

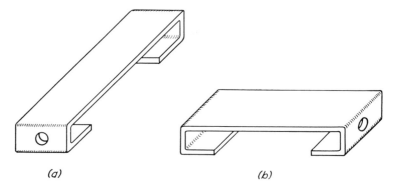

(*a*)   (*b*)

Fig. 11.36.   Long Axis Parallel to Picture Plane.

must be carefully established. The convenient way to accomplish this is to use one of the planes as a basic (starting) plane and work from it in the direction of the receding axis, as illustrated in Fig. 11.37. Since the front surface *A* presents the contour shape, it should be selected as the basic plane and drawn first as the front of the oblique projection, as shown in (*c*). The center *P* of the circles for surface *B* may be located easily by measuring along the axis of the hole from *O*, in plane *A*, a distance *X* equal to the distance between the planes. The measurement must be made forward along the axis from *O*, because surface *B* is in front of *A*. The centers of the arcs on the surface *C* are located in a similar manner, except that the direction of making the measurements is from the basic plane toward the back.

When an object has an inclined front surface with a curved outline, it may be drawn by constructing a right section and making offset measurements as shown in Fig. 11.38.

11.22. Angles, circles, and circle arcs in oblique. As previously stated, angles, circles, and irregular outlines on surfaces parallel to the plane of projection show in true size and shape. When located on receding faces, the construction methods used in isometric drawing usually may be applied. Figure 11.39 shows the method of drawing the elliptical representation of a circle on an oblique face. Note that the method is identical with that used for constructing isometric circles, except for the slight change in the position of the axes.

11.23. Reduction of measurements in the direction of the receding axis. An oblique drawing often presents a distorted appearance that is unnatural and disagreeable to the eye. In some cases the view constructed by this scheme is so misleading in appearance that it is unsatisfactory for any practical purpose. As a matter of interest, the effect of distortion is due to the fact that the receding lines are parallel and do not appear to converge as the eye is accustomed to anticipating. Note the comparison between oblique and perspective drawing in Fig. 11.40. The perspective view in (b) has a natural appearance because the receding lines appear to converge.

The appearance of excessive thickness can be overcome somewhat by reducing the length of the receding lines. For practical purposes, measurements usually are reduced one-half, but any scale of reduction may be arbitrarily adopted if the view obtained will be more realistic in appearance. When the receding lines are drawn one-half their actual length, the resulting pictorial view is called a cabinet drawing. Figure 11.41 shows an oblique drawing (a) and a cabinet drawing (c) of the same object, for the purpose of comparison.

Fig. 11.37. Basic Plane Theory of Construction.

Fig. 11.38. Curved Outlines on an Inclined Plane.

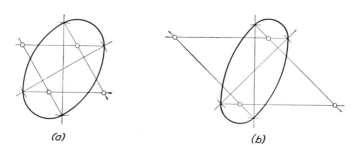

(a)   (b)

Fig. 11.39. Oblique Circles.

OBLIQUE   PERSPECTIVE
(a)   (b)

Fig. 11.40. Comparison of Oblique and Perspective.

OBLIQUE   CABINET
(a)   (b)   (c)

Fig. 11.41. Foreshortening in the Direction of the Receding Axis.

11.24. Oblique sectional views. Oblique sectional views are drawn to show the interior construction of objects. The construction procedure is the same as for an isometric sectional view, except that oblique planes are used for cutting the object. An oblique half section is illustrated in Fig. 11.42.

11.25. Pictorial dimensioning. The dimensioning of isometric and other forms of pictorial working drawings is done in accordance with the following rules:

1. Draw extension and dimension lines (except those dimension lines applying to cylindrical features) parallel to the pictorial axes in the plane of the surface to which they apply (Fig. 11.43).

Fig. 11.42.   Oblique Half Section.

2. If possible, apply dimensions to visible surfaces.

3. Place dimensions on the object, if, by so doing, better appearance, added clearness, and easy readings result.

4. Notes may be lettered either in pictorial or as on ordinary drawings. When lettered as on ordinary drawings the difficulties encountered in forming pictorial letters are avoided (Fig. 11.43).

Fig. 11.43.   Extension and Dimension Lines in Isometric (Left); Numerals, Fractions, and Notes in Oblique (Right).

5. Make the figures of a dimension appear to be lying in the plane of the surface whose dimension it indicates, by using vertical figures drawn in pictorial (Fig. 11.43). (Note: Guide lines and slope lines are drawn parallel to the pictorial axes.)

11.26. Conventional treatment of pictorial drawings. When it is desirable for an isometric or an oblique drawing of a casting to present a somewhat more or less realistic appearance, it becomes necessary to represent the fillets and rounds on the unfinished surfaces.   One method, commonly used by draftsmen, is shown in Fig. 11.44(*b*).   On the drawing in (*a*), all of the edges have been treated as if they were sharp.   The conventional treatment for threads in pictorial is illustrated in (*b*).

Figure 11.45 shows a pictorial diagram.

Fig. 11.44.   Conventional Treatment of Fillets, Rounds, and Threads in Pictorial.

Courtesy Allied Radio Corp.

Fig. 11.45.   Pictorial Diagram.

11.27. Perspective.   In perspective projection, an object is shown much as the human eye or camera would see it at a particular point. Actually, it is a geometrical method by which a picture can be projected upon a picture plane in much the same way as in photography.   Perspective drawing differs from the methods previously discussed in that,

STD. NON-ADJUSTABLE
FOOT – STD. A-6-18

STD. YOKE

STD. ADJUSTABLE FOOT-STD. A-6-18

STD. FLOOR PLATE

DIAPHRAGM

EXTRA ANGLES (ITEM 3) MAY BE PLACED
ACROSS BETWEEN DIAPHRAGMS TO
SUPPORT MINOR JIG PARTS

NOTE –
FOR DETAILS OF CONSTRUCTION AND
METHOD OF ASSEMBLY REFER TO STD. A-71
SHEET S '2 TO '6.

Prepared by Victory Aircraft Limited
Courtesy Craftint Mfg. Co.

Fig. 11.46.   A Production Illustration.

although the projectors or visual rays are oblique to the picture plane, they intersect at a common point known as the station point. (See Fig. 11.49.)

Since perspective shows an object as it appears instead of showing its true shape and size, it is rarely used by engineers. It is more extensively employed by architects to show the appearance of proposed buildings, by artist-draftsmen for production illustrations, and by illustrators in preparing advertising drawings.

Figure 11.1 shows a type of production illustration that has been widely used in assembly departments as an aid to those persons who find it difficult to read an orthographic assembly. This form of presentation, which shows the mechanism both exploded and assembled, has made it possible for industrial concerns to employ semitrained personnel. Figure 11.46 shows a type of industrial drawing made in perspective that has proved useful in aircraft plants. Because of the growing importance of this type of drawing, and also because engineers frequently will find perspective desirable for other purposes, its elementary principles should be discussed logically in this text. Other books on the subject, some of which are listed in the bibliography, should be studied by architectural students and those interested in a more thorough discussion of the various methods.

The fundamental concepts of perspective can be explained best if the reader will imagine himself looking through a picture plane at a formal garden with a small pool flanked by lamp posts, as shown in Fig. 11.47. The point of observation, at which the rays from the eye to the objects in the scene meet, is called the *station point*, and the plane upon which the view is formed by the piercing points of the visual rays is known as the *picture plane* (*PP*). The piercing points reproduce the scene, the size of which depends upon the location of the picture plane.

It should be noted that objects of the same height intercept a greater distance on the picture plane when close to it than when farther away. For example, rays from the lamp post at 2 intercept a distance 1–2 on the picture plane, while the rays from the pole at 4, which actually is the same height, intercept the lesser distance 3–4. From this fact it should be observed that the farther away an object is, the smaller it will appear, until a point is reached at which there will be no distance intercepted at all. This happens at the horizon.

Figure 11.48 shows the scene observed by the man in Fig. 11.47 as it would be formed on the picture plane. The posts farther from the picture plane diminish in height, as each one has a height on the picture plane equal to the distance it intercepts, as shown in Fig. 11.47. The lines of the pool and hedge converge to the center of vision or vanishing point, which is located directly in front of the observer, on the horizon.

11.28. Perspective nomenclature. Figure 11.49 illustrates pictorially the accepted nomenclature of perspective drawing. The horizon line is the line of intersection of the horizontal plane through the observation point (eye of the observer) and the picture plane. The horizontal plane is known as the *plane of the horizon*. The ground line is the line of intersection of the ground plane and the picture plane. The *CV* point

Fig. 11.47.   The Picture Plane.

Fig. 11.48.   The Picture (Perspective).

is the center of vision of the observer. It is located directly in front of the eye in the plane of the horizon on the horizon line.

11.29. Location of picture plane. The picture plane is usually placed between the object and the *SP* (station point). In parallel perspective (Sec. 11.34) it may be passed through a face of the object in order to show the true size and shape of the face.

11.30. Location of the station point. Care must be exercised in selecting the location for the station point, for its position has much to do with the appearance of the finished perspective drawing. A poor choice of position may result in a distorted perspective that will be decidedly displeasing to the eye.

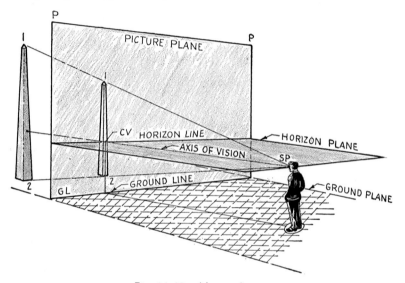

Fig. 11.49. Nomenclature.

In general, the station point should be offset slightly to one side and should be located above or below the exact center of the object. However, it must be remembered that the center of vision must be near the center of interest for the viewer.

One should always think of the station point as the viewing point, and its location should be where the object can be viewed to the best advantage. It is desirable that it be at a distance from the picture plane equal to at least twice the maximum dimension (length, height, or depth) of the object, for at such a distance, or greater, the entire object can be viewed naturally, as a whole, without turning the head.

A wide angle of view is to be avoided in the interest of good picturization. It has been determined that best results are obtained when the visual rays from the station point (*SP*) to the object are kept within a cone having an angle of not more than 30° between diametrically opposing elements. (See Fig. 11.50.)

In locating an object in relation to the picture plane, it is advisable to place it so that both of the side faces do not make the same angle with the picture plane and thus will not be equally visible. It is common practice to choose angles of 30° and 60° for rectangular objects.

11.31. Position of the object in relation to the horizon. When making a perspective of a tall object, such as a building, the horizon usually is assumed to be at a height above the ground plane equal to the standing height of a man's eye, normally about 5'6".

A small object may be placed either above or below the horizon (eye level), depending upon the view desired. If an object is above the horizon, it will be seen looking up from below as shown in Fig. 11.51. Should the object be below the horizon line, it will be seen from above.

11.32. Lines. The following facts should be recognized concerning the perspective of lines:

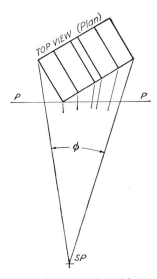

Fig. 11.50.   Angle of Vision.

1. Parallel horizontal lines vanish at a single *VP* (vanishing point). Usually the *VP* is at the point where a line parallel to the system through the *SP* pierces the *PP* (picture plane).

2. A system of horizontal lines has its *VP* on the horizon.

3. Vertical lines, since they pierce the picture plane at infinity, will appear vertical in perspective.

4. When a line lies in the picture plane, it will show its true length because it will be its own perspective.

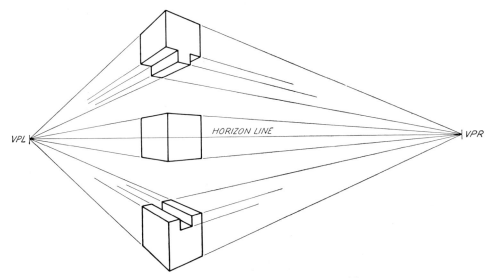

Fig. 11.51.   Objects On, Above, or Below the Horizon.

5. When a line lies behind the picture plane, its perspective will be shorter than the line.

11.33. Types of perspective. In general, there are two types of perspective: *parallel perspective* and *angular perspective*. In parallel perspective, one of the principal faces is parallel to the picture plane and is its own perspective. All vertical lines are vertical, and the receding horizontal lines converge to a single vanishing point. In angular perspective, the object is placed so that the principal faces are at an angle with the picture plane. The horizontal lines converge at two vanishing points.

11.34. Parallel perspective. Figure 11.52 shows the parallel perspective of a rectangular block. The *PP* line is the top view of the

Fig. 11.52. Parallel Perspective.   Fig. 11.53. Circles in Parallel Perspective.

picture plane, SP_H is the top view of the station point, and CV is the center of vision. The receding horizontal lines vanish at CV. The front face, since it lies in the picture plane, is its own perspective and shows in its true size. The lines representing the edges back of the picture plane are found by projecting downward from the points at which the visual rays pierce the picture plane, as shown by the top views of the rays. Figure 11.53 shows a parallel perspective of a cylindrical machine part.

11.35. Angular perspective. Figure 11.54 shows pictorially the graphical method for the preparation of a two-point perspective drawing of a cube. To visualize the true layout on the surface of a sheet of drawing paper, it is necessary to revolve mentally the horizontal plane downward into the vertical or picture plane. Upon completion of Sec. 11.35, it is suggested that the reader turn back and endeavor to associate the development of the perspective in Fig. 11.55 with the

Fig. 11.54.   Angular Perspective.

Fig. 11.55.   Angular Perspective.

pictorial presentation in Fig. 11.54. For a full understanding of the construction in Fig. 11.55, it is necessary to differentiate between the lines that belong to the horizontal plane and those that are on the vertical or picture plane. In addition, it must be fully realized that there is a top view for the perspective that is a line, and that in this line view lie the points that must be projected downward to the perspective representation (front view).

Figure 11.55 shows an angular perspective of a mutilated block. The block has been placed so that one vertical edge lies in the picture plane. The other vertical edges are parallel to the plane, while all of the horizontal lines are inclined to it so that they vanish at the two vanishing points, *VPL* and *VPR*, respectively.

In constructing the perspective shown in this illustration, an orthographic top view was drawn in such a position that the visible vertical faces made angles of 30° and 60° with the picture plane. Next, the location of the observer was assumed and the horizon line was established. The vanishing points *VPL* and *VPR* were found by drawing a 30° line and a 60° line through the *SP*. Since these lines are parallel to the two systems of receding horizontal lines, each will establish a required vanishing point at its intersection with the picture plane. The vertical line located in the picture plane, which is its own perspective, was selected as a measuring line on which to project vertical measurements from the orthographic front view. The lines shown from these division points along this line to the vanishing points (*VPL-VPR*) established the direction of the receding horizontal edge lines in the perspective. The position of the back edges was determined by projecting downward from the points at which the projectors from the station point (*SP*) to the corners of the object pierced the picture plane, as shown by the top view of the object and projectors.

11.36. Use of measuring lines. Whenever the vertical front edge of an object lies in the picture plane, it can be laid off full length in the perspective, because, theoretically, it will be in true length in the picture formed on the plane by the visual rays. (See Fig. 11.55.) Should the near vertical edge lie behind the picture plane, as is the case with the edge line *AB* in Fig. 11.56, the use of a measuring line becomes desirable. The measuring line *a'b'* is the vertical edge *AB* moved forward to the picture plane where it will appear in its true height. Some prefer to think of the vertical side as being extended to the picture plane so that the true height of the side is revealed. The length and position of *AB* is established in the perspective picture by first drawing vanishing lines from *a'* and *b'* to *VPR*; then, the top view of the edge in the picture plane (point *X*) is projected downward to the front view picturization. Points *A* and *B* must fall on the vanishing lines from *a'* and *b'* to *VPR* respectively.

A measuring line may be used to establish the "picture height" of any feature of an object. For example, in Fig. 11.56 the vertical measuring line through *c'* was used as needed to locate point *C* and the top line of the object in the perspective.

11.37. Vanishing points for inclined lines. In general, the perspective of any inclined straight line can be found by locating the end points of the line perspectively.   By this method, an end point may be located by drawing the perspective representations of any two horizontal lines intersecting at the end point.   Where several parallel inclined lines vanish to the same vanishing point, it may prove to be worth while to locate the *VP* for the system in order to conserve time and achieve a higher degree of accuracy.

Just as in the case of other lines, the vanishing point for any inclined line may be established by finding the piercing point in the picture plane (*PP*) of a line through *SP* parallel to the given inclined line.

Fig. 11.56.   Use of Measuring Lines.

In Fig. 11.57 the inclined lines are *AB* and *CD*.   If one is to understand the construction shown for locating vanishing point *VPI*, he must recognize that vertical planes vanish in vertical lines and that a line in a vertical plane will vanish at a point on the vanishing line of the plane. The preceding statements being true, the vanishing point *VPI* for line *CD* must lie at some point on a vertical line through *VPR*, since *CD* and *CE* lie in the same vertical plane.   *VPI* is the point at which a line drawn parallel (in space) to *CD* through *SP* pierces the picture plane.

On the drawing, the distance *D* that *VPI* is above *VPR* may be found easily through the construction of a right triangle with *SP–Q* as a base. Angle *β* is the slope angle for line *CD* (see side view).   The needed distance *D* is the line *QR* or the short leg of the triangle.

11.38. Use of measuring points. Frequently, it is desirable to use measuring points in preparing a perspective drawing, because their use permits the laying off of a series of direct measurements that can be transferred quickly and accurately to the perspective. Measuring points are, in reality, special vanishing points that are used to establish distances in perspective along perspective lines.

To understand the measuring point method, one must realize that, in theory, a vertical face is rotated into the picture plane so that direct

Fig. 11.57.   Vanishing Point for Inclined Lines.

measurements may be made along the horizontal ground line to the same scale as the top view. In Fig. 11.58 the vertical face containing line AB was revolved into the picture plane to position ab_r. The vanishing point of the line bb_r is MPR. The position of MPR was established by first drawing a line from SP parallel to bb_r to a piercing point in the picture plane and, then, projecting to the horizon line.

Another method for determining the location of measuring points is included in this same illustration. By this second method, the location of a measuring point can be readily found by swinging an arc with the plan view of the vanishing point as a center and using a radius equal to the distance from this center to the SP. For example, the location of MPR on the horizon was determined by swinging an arc from Y using the distance from Y to SP as a radius. The point of intersection of this arc and picture plane (in plan) projected to the horizon established the position of *MPR* for use in preparing the perspective drawing shown. *MPL* was similarly located.

The scaled lengths (D_1, D_2 and D_3) laid off along ab_r, when vanished to *MPR*, established the desired lengths along the line *AB*, which represents the perspective of the lower edge of the object. Height distances were laid off along the measuring line through the vertical edge lying in the picture plane at *a*. With length, height, and depth distances

Fig. 11.58. Use of Measuring Points.

established, the perspective drawing was completed by following the procedure given in Sec. 11.35.

11.39. Circles in perspective. If a circle is on a surface that is inclined to the picture plane (*PP*), its perspective will be an ellipse. It is the usual practice to construct the representation within an enclosing square by finding selected points along the curve in the perspective as shown in Fig. 11.59. Any points might be used, but it is recommended that points be located on 30°, 45°, and 60° lines.

11.40. Problems. The student will find that a preliminary sketch will facilitate the preparation of isometric and oblique drawings of the problems of this chapter. On such a sketch he may plan the procedure

Fig. 11.59.   Circles in Perspective.

of construction.   Since many engineers frequently find it necessary to
prepare pictorial sketches during discussions with untrained persons who
cannot read orthographic views, it is recommended that some problems
be sketched freehand on either plain or pictorial grid paper.   (See Fig.
13.18.)   Additional problems may be found at the end of Chapter 13.

1–18.   (Figs. 11.60–11.77.)   Prepare instrumental isometric drawings or freehand sketches of the objects as assigned.

Fig. 11.60.   **Fig. 11.61.**   **Fig. 11.62.**

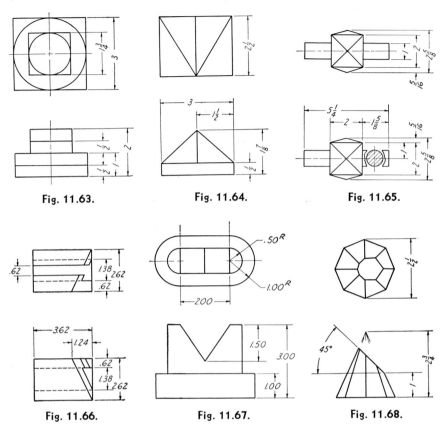

Fig. 11.63.   Fig. 11.64.   Fig. 11.65.

Fig. 11.66.   Fig. 11.67.   Fig. 11.68.

19–27. (Figs. 11.69–11.77.) Prepare instrumental oblique drawings or freehand sketches of the objects as assigned.

Fig. 11.69.   Fig. 11.70.   Fig. 11.71.

Fig. 11.72.   Fig. 11.73.   Fig. 11.74.

Fig. 11.75.

Fig. 11.76.

(Do not show fillets and rounds)

Fig. 11.77.

28. (Fig. 11.78.)   Make an isometric drawing of the sawhorse.   Select a suitable scale.

Fig. 11.78.   Sawhorse.   **Fig. 11.79.   Locomotive Driver Nut.**

29. (Fig. 11.79.)   Make an oblique drawing of the locomotive driver nut.

30. (Fig. 11.80.)   Make an oblique drawing of the adjustment cone.

Fig. 11.80.   Adjustment Cone.   **Fig. 11.81.   Fork.**

31. (Fig. 11.81.)   Make an oblique drawing of the fork.

32. (Fig. 11.82.)   Make an oblique drawing of the feeder guide.

Fig. 11.82.   Feeder Guide.   **Fig. 11.83.   Hinge Bracket.**

33. (Fig. 11.83.)   Make an isometric drawing of the hinge bracket.

34. (Fig. 11.84.)   Make an isometric drawing of the alignment bracket.

Fig. 11.84.   Alignment Bracket.   Fig. 11.85.   Stop Block.

35. (Fig. 11.85.)   Make an isometric drawing of the stop block.

36. (Figs. 11.80–11.82.)   Make a parallel perspective drawing as assigned.

37. (Figs. 11.83–11.85.)   Make an angular perspective drawing as assigned.

38. (Fig. 11.86.)   Make a pictorial drawing (oblique, isometric, or perspective) of the slotted bell crank.

(Do not show fillets and rounds)

Fig. 11.86.   Slotted Bell Crank.   Fig. 11.87.   Control Guide.

39. (Fig. 11.87.)   Make a pictorial drawing (oblique, isometric, or perspective) of the control guide.

40. (Fig. 11.88.)   Make an isometric drawing of the stepladder.   Select a suitable scale.

Fig. 11.88.   Stepladder.

41. (Fig. 11.89.)   Make an isometric drawing of the differential spider.

Fig. 11.89.   Differential Spider.

12 | Freehand Drafting

12.1. Value of freehand drafting. Freehand technical drafting is primarily the language of those in responsible charge of the development of technical designs
and plans. Chief engineers, chief draftsmen, designers, and squad bosses
have found that the best way to present their ideas for either a simple or
complex design is through the medium of sketches (Fig. 12.1). Sketches
may be schematic, as are those that are original expressions of new ideas,
or they may be instructional, their purpose being to convey ideas to
draftsmen or shopmen. Some sketches, especially those prepared for
the manufacture of parts that are to replace worn or broken parts on
existing machines, may resemble complete working drawings.

Courtesy Teleflex, Inc.

Fig. 12.1. A Design Sketch for a Connector of a Remote Control Unit.

Since the importance of freehand drafting very often is underesti-
mated, the purpose of this discussion is to amplify training in this phase.
The young prospective engineer should understand, when beginning his
studies, that sketching and not mechanical drafting will be his ultimate
form of expression and that he must be able to prepare complete sketches
that will present his ideas and decisions to subordinates in an understandable manner. Figure 12.2 is an example of a working sketch.

12.2. Sketching materials. For the type of sketching discussed
here, the required materials are an F pencil, a soft eraser, and some paper.
In the industrial field, men who have been improperly trained in sketching
often use straightedges and cheap pocket compasses that they could well

268

dispense with if they would adopt the correct technique. Preparing sketches with instruments consumes much unnecessary time.

For the person who cannot produce a satisfactory sketch without guide lines, cross-section paper is helpful. Ordinarily, the ruling on this paper forms one-inch squares which are subdivided into one-eighth or one-tenth inch squares. Such paper is especially useful when sketching to scale is desirable (Fig. 12.3).

THUMBNAIL PICTORIAL

FORK
STEEL PLATE I REQ'D
JUNE 6, 1951

Fig. 12.2. Working Sketch.

12.3. Projections. Although freehand drafting lacks the refinement given by mechanical instruments, it is based upon the same principles of projection and conventional practices that apply to multiview, pictorial, and the other divisions of mechanical drawing. For this reason, one must be thoroughly familiar with projection, in all of its many forms, before he is adequately trained to prepare sketches.

12.4. Technique of lines. Freehand lines quite naturally will differ in their appearance from mechanical ones. A well-executed freehand line will never be perfectly straight and absolutely uniform in weight, but an effort should be made to approach *exacting uniformity.* As in the case of mechanical lines, they should be black and clear and not broad and fuzzy. (See Fig. 12.4.)

Fig. 12.3. Sketches on Cross-Section Paper.

12.5. Sharpening the sketching pencil. A sketching pencil should be sharpened, on a file or piece of sandpaper, to a conical point. The point then should be rounded slightly, on the back of the sketch pad or on another sheet of paper, to the correct degree of dullness. When rounding the point, the pencil should be rotated to prevent the formation of sharp edges.

Fig. 12.4.   Sketch Lines.

Fig. 12.5.   Steps in Sketching a Straight Line.

12.6. Straight lines.   The pencil should rest on the second finger and be held loosely by the thumb and index finger about 1 to $1\frac{1}{2}$ inches above the point.

Horizontal lines are sketched from left to right with an easy arm motion that is pivoted about the muscle of the forearm.   The straight line thus becomes an arc of infinite radius.

When sketching a straight line, it is advisable first to mark the end points with light dots or small crosses (Fig. 12.5).   The complete procedure for sketching a straight line is as follows:

1. Mark the end points.

2. Make a few trial motions between the marked points to adjust the eye and hand to the contemplated line.

3. Sketch a *very* light line between the points by moving the pencil in two or three sweeps. When sketching the trial line, the eye should be on the point toward which the movement is directed. With each stroke, an attempt should be made to correct the most obvious defects of the stroke preceding, so that the finished trial line will be relatively straight.

Fig. 12.6. Sketching Horizontal Lines.

Fig. 12.7. Sketching Vertical Lines.

4. Darken the finished line, keeping the eye on the pencil point on the trial line.

The final line, replacing the trial line, should be distinct, black, uniform, and straight.

It is helpful to turn the paper through a *convenient angle* so that the horizontal and vertical lines assume a slight inclination (Fig. 12.6). A horizontal line, when the paper is in this position, is sketched to the right and upward, thus allowing the arm to be held slightly away from the body and making possible a free arm motion.

Short vertical lines may be sketched either downward or upward, without changing the position of the paper. When sketching downward, the arm is held slightly away from the body and the movement is toward the sketcher (see Fig. 12.7). To sketch vertical lines upward, the arm is held well away from the body.

By turning the paper, a long vertical line may be made to assume the position of a horizontal line and can be sketched with the same general movements used for the latter.

Inclined lines running upward from lower left to upper right may be sketched upward with the same movements used for horizontal lines, but those running downward from upper left to lower right are sketched with the general movements used for either horizontal or vertical ones, depending upon their inclination (Fig. 12.8). Inclined lines may be more easily sketched by turning the paper to make them conform to the direction of horizontal lines.

12.7. Circles. Small circles may be sketched by marking radial distances on perpendicular center lines (Fig. 12.9). These distances can be marked off either by eye or by measuring with a marked strip of paper

Fig. 12.8.   Sketching Inclined Lines.

(see Fig. 12.10). Larger circles may be constructed more accurately by sketching two or more diagonals, in addition to the center lines, and by sketching short construction lines perpendicular to each, equidistant from the center. Tangent to these lines, short arcs are drawn perpendicular to the radii. The circle is completed with a light construction line, and all defects are corrected before darkening (Fig. 12.11).

12.8. Ellipses. An ellipse of good proportion may be sketched within an enclosing rectangle. The rectangle, since it is used merely as an aid in forming the ellipse, should be drawn with very light lines, and the required ellipse should be sketched tangent to the sides.

12.9. Making a sketch. When making orthographic working sketches, a systematic order should be followed and all the rules and conventional practices used in making working drawings should be applied. The following procedure is recommended:

1. Examine the object, giving particular attention to detail.
2. Determine which views are necessary.

Fig. 12.9. Sketching Small Circles.

Fig. 12.10. Marking Off Radial Distances.

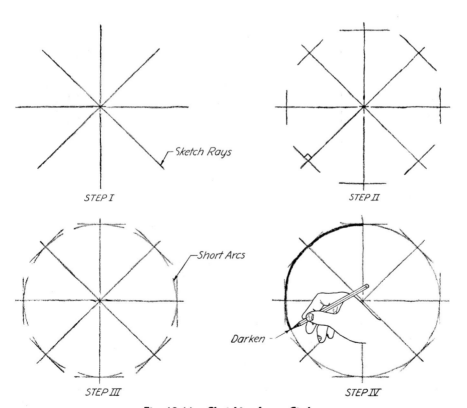

Fig. 12.11. Sketching Large Circles.

3. "Block in" the views, using light construction lines.

4. Complete the detail and darken the object lines.

5. Sketch extension lines and dimension lines, including arrowheads.

6. Complete the sketch by adding dimensions, notes, title, date, sketcher's name or initials, and so on.

7. Check the entire sketch carefully to see that no dimensions have been omitted.

The progressive steps in making a sketch of an object are shown in Fig. 12.12.

Fig. 12.12.   Steps in Sketching.

12.10. Proportions.   The beginner must recognize the importance of being able to estimate comparative relationship between the length, height, and depth of an object being sketched.   The complete problem of proportioning a sketch also involves relating the estimated dimensions for any component parts such as slots, holes, and projections to the over-all dimensions of the object.   It is not the practice to attempt to estimate actual dimensions, for sketches are not usually made to scale.   Rather one must decide, for example, that the length of the object is twice its height, that the width of a given slot is equal to one-half the length of the object, and that its depth is approximately one-fourth of the over-all height.

To become proficient at sketching one must learn to recognize proportions and be able to compare dimensions "by eye."   Until he is able to do so, he can not really "think with his pencil." Some can develop a keen eye for proportion with only a limited amount of practice and can maintain these estimated proportions when making the views of the sketch. Others have alternatingly discouraging and encouraging experiences. Discouragement comes when one's knowledge of sketching is ahead of his ability and he has not had as much practice as he needs. The many who find it difficult to make the completed views of a sketch agree with the estimated proportions of the object may at the start use the graphical method shown in Fig. 12.13(a), (b), and (c). This method is based on the fact that a rectangle (enclosing a view) may be divided to obtain intermediate distances along any side that are in such proportion of the total length as one-half, one-fourth, one-third, and so forth. Those who start with this rectangle method as an aid in proportioning must realize that they should abandon its use when they have developed their eye and sketching skill so that it is no longer needed.

Fig. 12.13.   Methods of Proportioning a Rectangle Representing the Outline of a View.

Sketching must be done rapidly and the addition of unnecessary lines consumes much valuable time. Furthermore, the addition of construction lines distracts the reader, and it is certain that they do not contribute to the neatness of the sketch.

The mid-point of a rectangle is the point of intersection of the diagonals, as shown in Fig. 12.13(a). A line sketched through this point that is perpendicular to any side will establish the mid-point of that side. Should it be necessary to determine a distance that is equal to one-fourth the length of a side, say AC, the quarter-point may be located by repeating this procedure for the small rectangle representing the upper left-hand quarter of $ABCD$.

With the mid-point J located by the intersecting diagonals of the small rectangle representing one-fourth of the larger rectangle $EFGH$ as in (b), the one-third point along FH may be located by sketching a line from point G through J and extending it to line FH. The point K at the intersection of these lines establishes the needed one-third distance.

To determine one-sixth of the length of a side of a rectangle as in (c), sketch a line from N through point P as was done in (b) to determine a one-third distance. Point Q at which the line NP crosses the centerline of the rectangle establishes the one-sixth distance along the centerline.

Figure 12.14 shows how this method for dividing the sides of a rectangle might be used to proportion an orthographic sketch.

The square may be used to proportion a view after one dimension for the view has been assumed. In using this method, additional squares are added to the initial one having the assumed length as one side (Fig. 12.15). As an example, suppose that it has been estimated that the front view of an object should be three times as long as it is high. In Fig. 12.15 the height of the view has been represented by the line *AB* sketched to an assumed length. The first step in making the construction is to sketch the initial square *ABCD* and extend *AC* and *BD* to indefinite length, being certain that the over-all length from *A* and *B* will be slightly greater than

Fig. 12.14. The Rectangle Method Applied in Making an Orthographic Sketch.

Fig. 12.15. The Build-Up Method.

three times the length of *AB*. Then the center line must be sketched through the intersection of *AD* and *BC*. Now *BX* extended to *E* locates *EF* to form the second square, and *DY* extended to point *G* locates the line *GH*. Line *AG* will be three times the length of *AB*.

12.11. Use of an overlay sheet. An overlay sheet may be used to an advantage in making any sketch that is complicated with details (Fig. 12.16). In this case, a quick sketch showing the general outline of the principal parts is made first in a rather rough form. Then an overlay sheet is placed over this outline sketch and the lines are retraced. In doing so, slight corrections can be made for any known errors existing in the proportions of the parts or in the position of any of the lines of the original rough sketch. When this has been done, the representation of the related minor parts are added. If at any time one becomes dis-

USE OF AN OVERLAY SHEET

A VIEW FROM THE ROUGH SKETCH   A VIEW FROM THE FINISHED SKETCH
                                    ON OVERLAY SHEET

Fig. 12.16. Use of an Overlay Sheet for Creating a Final and Complete Sketch of a Mechanism.

couraged with a sketch that he is making and feels that a new start is needed, an overlay sheet should be used, for there are usually many features on his existing sketch that may be retraced with a great saving of time.

Fig. 12.17.   A, Steel Scale; B, Protractor; C, Micrometer Calipers; D, Thread-Pitch Gage.

12.12. Making sketches of parts for the purpose of replacement and repair.   It quite frequently is necessary to make working-drawing sketches of broken or worn parts.   Such sketches are used instead of mechanical drawings because they can be made and sent to the shop in a much shorter time.   The procedure given in Sec. 12.9 should be followed carefully when making sketches to be used by workmen in the shops.

12.13. Measurements and measuring instruments.   If a sketch is to serve as a working drawing, it must contain all the necessary dimensions and instructional notes needed by the workmen.   If a sketch is for the manufacture of a part that is to replace a worn or broken part in an existing machine, measurements must be taken from the original part with the same general types of measuring devices to be used in manufacturing the new part (Fig. 12.17).   The instrument selected for each particular detail should be of a type that will allow measurements to be made with the correct degree of accuracy.   For most machine parts, a steel scale and a set of inside and outside calipers will prove sufficient.

Fig. 12.18.   Outside Calipers.

Fig. 12.19.   Inside Calipers.

When more accurate measurements are necessary, a micrometer must be used.   In any case, the selection of the instrument for a measurement should be determined by exercising good judgment backed by practical shop experience.   Figure 12.18 shows how the outside calipers are used to take measurements from an object.   Figure 12.19 shows the use of the inside calipers for measuring the diameter of a hole.

When taking measurements, certain practices are recommended.   For example, to obtain the distance between holes (shown on the sketch as between centers), measure the distance between corresponding edges.   To locate other features and to take off size dimensions, measure from a finished surface whenever possible, for a finished surface is usually a mating surface.   The man in the shop must work from such a surface if he is to produce a part accurate enough to function in the existing machine.

12.14. The title.   A title is far more important on a sketch than many persons realize.   It serves to identify the sketch and usually contains additional valuable information such as (1) the type of material, (2) the number required, (3) the name or initials of the sketcher, and (4) the date.

12.15. Problems.   The following practical one-view working sketches were selected to provide practice in lettering and sketching.   The pictorial representations of practical machine parts offer the opportunity for practice in sketching and further study of multiview projection.

1–6. (Figs. 12.20–12.25.)   Reproduce an assigned one-view sketch on a sheet of sketching paper.

PLATE
#16(.0625) GAGE STEEL PLATE

Fig. 12.20.

GASKET,
PUNCH FROM 1/16 CORK

Fig. 12.21.

SHIM
#10(.1019) GAGE BRASS

Fig. 12.22.

STAMPING
#24(.0201) BRASS

Fig. 12.23.

GUIDE PLATE
#11 (.1250) GAGE STEEL PLATE

Fig. 12.24.

GASKET,
PUNCH FROM 1/16 CORK

Fig. 12.25.

7–26. (Figs. 12.26–12.45.) Make a multiview sketch of an assigned machine part. Show only the necessary views. For convenience, important distances have been marked off in units. The selected length for the unit in each case will determine the size dimensions of the part.

Fig. 12.26.　　　　　　　　　　　　Fig. 12.27.

Fig. 12.28.　　　　　　　　　　　　Fig. 12.29.

Fig. 12.30.　　　　　　　　　　　　Fig. 12.31.

Fig. 12.32.　　　　　　　　　　　　Fig. 12.33.

Fig. 12.34.

Fig. 12.35.

Fig. 12.36.

Fig. 12.37.

Fig. 12.38.

Fig. 12.39.

Fig. 12.40.   Bearing Block.

Fig. 12.41.   Corner Block.

Fig. 12.42.   Feeder Cone.

Fig. 12.43.   Bracket.

Fig. 12.44.   Link.

Fig. 12.45.   Bearing Bracket.

13 | Pictorial Sketching

13.1. Pictorial sketching. Often an engineer or draftsman must sketch an object pictorially, freehand, in order to present an idea to another who has not been trained to read a multiview (orthographic) drawing. In design work, a pictorial view frequently is placed on a preliminary sketch along with the dimensioned views, so that anyone assisting in the development of the design may be able quickly to grasp an idea of the pictorial form visualized by the designer.

The engineer is a creative person living in a world where all that he creates must exist in space. He must visualize space conditions, space distances, and movement in space. In addition he must be able to retain as well as alter the image of his idea, which will at the very start exist only in his mind.

In developing a design, the engineer nearly always resorts to sketching to organize his thoughts quickly and to visualize more clearly the problems that appear. The first ideas may be sketched in pictorial form as they are visualized. Later, a combination of orthographic design sketches and pictorial sketches may quickly pile upon his desk as problems are recognized and possible solutions are recorded for reference and for conferences with others (Fig. 13.1).

Design sketches may be done in the quiet of the engineer's office or amid the confusion of the conference table. To meet the requirement of speed of preparation, one must resist all temptation to use instruments of any type and rely on the pencil alone, for the true measure of the quality of a finished sketch is neatness and good proportion rather than the straightness of the lines. A pictorial sketch need not be an artistic masterpiece to be useful.

Students may employ pictorial sketches to advantage as an aid in visualizing and organizing problems. Sales engineers may frequently include pictorial sketches with orthographic sketches when preparing field reports on the needs and suggestions of the firm's customers.

With some training anyone can prepare pictorial sketches that will be satisfactory for all practical purposes. Artistic ability is not needed. This fact is important, for many persons lack only the necessary confidence to start making pictorial sketches.

13.2. Mechanical methods of sketching. Many engineers have found that they can produce satisfactory pictorial sketches by using one of the so-called mechanical methods. They rely on these methods

284

because of their familiarity with the procedures used in making pictorial drawings with instruments.

It has been assumed that the student has read Chapter 12 covering "Freehand Drafting," for the techniques discussed there apply to pictorial sketching.

The practices presented in Chapter 11 for the mechanical methods, axonometric, oblique, and perspective, are followed generally in pictorial

Courtesy General Electric Co.

Fig. 13.1. A Pictorial Design Sketch.

sketching, except that angles are assumed and lengths are estimated. For this reason, one must develop an eye for good proportion before he will be able to create a satisfactory pictorial sketch that will be in no way misleading.

A student having difficulty in interpreting a multiview drawing usually will find that a pictorial sketch, prepared as illustrated in Fig. 13.2, will clarify the form that he is trying to visualize, even before the last lines of the sketch have been drawn.

13.3. Isometric sketching. Isometric sketching starts with three isometric lines, called axes, which represent three mutually perpendicular lines. One of these axes is sketched vertically, the other two at 30° with the horizontal.   In Fig. 13.2 (step I), the near front corner of the enclosing box lies along the vertical axis, while the two visible receding edges of the base lie along the axes receding to the left and to the right.

If the object is of simple rectangular form, as in Fig. 13.2, it may be sketched by drawing an enclosing isometric box (step I) upon the surfaces of which the orthographic views may be sketched (step II).   Care must be taken in assuming lengths and distances so that the finished view (step III) will have relatively correct proportions.   In constructing the enclosing box (step I), the vertical edges are parallel to the vertical axis, and edges receding to the right and to the left are parallel to the right and left axes, respectively.

Fig. 13.2.   Steps in Isometric Sketching.

Objects of more complicated construction may be "blocked in" as shown in Fig. 13.3.   Note that the projecting cylindrical features are enclosed in "isometric" prisms, and that the circles are sketched within isometric squares.   The procedure in Fig. 13.3 is the same as in Fig. 13.2, except that three enclosing isometric boxes are needed in the formation of the final representation instead of one.

In sketching an ellipse to represent a circle pictorially, an enclosing "isometric square" (rhombus) is drawn having sides equal approximately to the diameter of the true circle (step I, Fig. 13.4).   The ellipse is formed by first drawing arcs tangent to the mid-points of the sides of the isometric square in light sketchy pencil lines (step II).   In finishing the ellipse (step III) with a dark heavy line, care must be taken to obtain a nearly elliptical shape.

Fig. 13.3. Blocking In an Isometric Sketch.

SKETCH "ISOMETRIC SQUARE"   SKETCH SHORT ARCS   COMPLETE ELLIPSE

STEP I   STEP II   STEP III

Fig. 13.4. Isometric Circles.

I   II   III

Fig. 13.5. Isometric Circles.

Figure 13.5 shows the three positions for an isometric circle. Note that the major axis is horizontal for an ellipse on a horizontal plane (I).

13.4. Proportioning. As stated in the previous chapter, one should eventually be able to judge lengths and recognize proportions. Until this ultimate goal has been reached, the graphical method presented in Fig. 12.13 may be used with pictorial sketching (Fig. 13.6). The procedures as used are identical, the only recognizable difference being that the rectangle in the first case now becomes a rhomboid.   Figure 13.7 illustrates how the method might be applied in making a sketch of a simple object. The enclosing box was sketched first with light lines, and then the graphical method was applied as shown to locate the points at one-quarter and one-half of the height.   To establish the line of the top surface that is at a distance equal to one-third of the length from the end, a construction line was sketched from A to the mid-point B to locate C at the point of intersection of AB with the diagonal.   Point C will fall on the required line.

13.5. Sketches in isometric.   In making a sketch in isometric, an experienced person frequently foreshortens the distances in the direction of each of the receding axes until the proportions satisfy the eye.   In addition, some who are a little more confident will make the receding lines

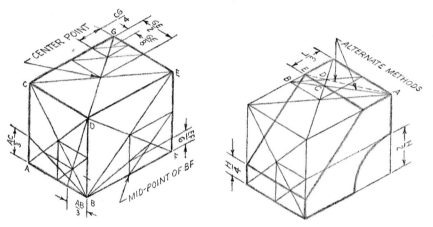

**Fig. 13.6.   Methods for Proportioning a   Fig. 13.7.   Proportioning Method Applied.
Rhomboid.**

converge slightly.   A pictorial sketch treated in this manner is said to be in pseudoperspective.

A sketch giving the parts of a simple mechanism arranged for assembly is shown in Fig. 13.8.   An idea sketch showing parts assembled is shown in Fig. 13.9.

13.6. Oblique projection.   A sketch in oblique shows the front face without distortion, in its true shape.   It has this one advantage over axonometric projection, even though the final result usually will not present so pleasing an appearance.   It is not recommended for objects having circular or irregularly curved features on any but the front plane or in a plane parallel to it.

The beginner who is familiar with axonometric sketching will have very little difficulty in preparing a sketch in oblique, for, in general, the methods of preparation presented in the previous sections apply to both. The principal difference between these two forms of sketching is in the position of the axes, oblique sketching being unlike the axonometric in

that two of the axes are at right angles to each other.   The third axis
may be at any convenient angle as indicated in Fig. 13.11.

Figure 13.10 shows the steps in making an oblique sketch using the
proportioning methods previously explained for dividing a rectangle and a
rhomboid.   The receding lines are made parallel when a sketch is made
in oblique projection.

The distortion and illusion of extreme elongation in the direction of
the receding axis may be minimized by foreshortening to obtain propor-

Fig. 13.8.   A Sketch of a Simple Mechanism.

Fig. 13.9.   An Idea Sketch in Isometric.

tions that are more realistic to the eye and by making the receding lines
converge slightly.   The resulting sketch will then be in a form of pseudoperspective, which resembles parallel perspective to some extent.

13.7. Perspective sketching.   A sketch that has been prepared in
accordance with the concepts of perspective will present a somewhat
more pleasing and realistic effect than one in oblique or isometric projection.   A perspective sketch actually presents an object as it would
appear when observed from a particular point.   The recognition of this
fact, along with an understanding of the concepts that an object will
appear smaller at a distance than when it is close, and that horizontal

lines converge as they recede until they meet at a vanishing point, should enable one to produce sketches having a perspective appearance. In sketching an actual object, a position should be selected that will show it to the best advantage. When the object exists only in one's mind or on paper in orthographic form, then the object must be visualized and the viewing position assumed.

At the start, the principal lines should be sketched in lightly, extending each line for some length toward its vanishing point. After this has

Sketch Box	Block-in Outline	Complete Pictorial
STEP I	STEP II	STEP III

Fig. 13.10.   Steps in Oblique Sketching.

Fig. 13.11.   Blocking In an Oblique Sketch.

been accomplished, the enclosing perspective squares for circles should be blocked in and the outline for minor details added. When the object lines have been darkened, the construction lines extending beyond the figure may be erased.

Figure 13.12 shows a parallel or one-point perspective that bears some resemblance to an oblique sketch. All faces in planes parallel to the front show their true shape. All receding lines should meet at a single vanishing point. Figure 13.13 is an angular or two point perspective.

As stated previously, a two point perspective sketch shows an object as it would appear to the human eye at a fixed point in space and not as it actually exists. All parallel receding lines converge (Fig. 13.15).

Fig. 13.12. A Sketch in Parallel Perspec-   Fig. 13.13.   A Sketch in Angular Perspective.   tive.

Fig. 13.14.   Obtaining Proportions by Means of a Pencil.

Should these receding lines be horizontal, they will converge at a vanishing point on the eye-line.   Those lines extending towards the right converge to a vanishing point to the right (VP_R); and those to the left
converge to the left (VP_L).   These vanishing points are at the level of
the observer's eye (Fig. 13.15).   A system of lines that is neither perpendicular nor horizontal will converge to a VP for inclined lines.

In one point perspective one of the principal faces is parallel to the
picture plane.   All of the vertical lines will appear as vertical, and the
receding horizontal lines converge to a single vanishing point (Fig. 13.16).

Those interested in a complete discussion of the geometry of perspective drawing should read Secs. 11.27 through 11.39.   The beginner should make two or three mechanically drawn perspectives at the start to fix the fundamentals of the methods of perspective projection in his mind, even though there is some difference between sketching what one sees or imagines and true geometrical perspective.

In making a sketch in artist's perspective, several fundamental concepts must be recognized.

First, a circle sketched in perspective will appear as an ellipse (Fig. 13.15).   The long diameter of an ellipse representing a circle on a horizontal plane is always in a horizontal direction (Fig. 13.17).

Fig. 13.15.   Preparing a Perspective Sketch.

Second, if an object or a component part of an object is above the eye-line, it will be seen from below.   Should the object be below the eye-line, it will be seen from above (Fig. 13.15).   The farther the object is removed below or above the eye-line, the more one can see of the top or the bottom surface.

Third, the nearest vertical edge of an object will be the longest vertical line of the view as shown in Fig. 13.15.   When two or more objects of the same actual height appear in a perspective sketch, their represented heights will decrease in the view as they near the vanishing point.

13.8. Determining proportions.   When an object exists only as an image in one's mind, all proportions can be assumed.   However, when sketching by eye an object that already exists, it becomes necessary to be able to compare the relationship between the length, width, and height dimensions as they are seen. That is, some sort of a measuring stick is needed to compare these lengths in the proportions that they are being seen, at the fixed position of the observer, who is at some distance from the object itself. To satisfy this need most sketchers use the most convenient thing that is available—their sketching pencil. Apparent lengths can be determined along the body of the pencil held at arms length in a plane perpendicular to the line of sight, as shown in Fig. 13.14. One marks with the tip of the thumbnail the length on the object that is covered from the top of the pencil downward. With this basic distance established, the arm is rotated until the pencil coincides with another edge of the object and then an estimate is made as to whether the second line is to be made one-fifth, one-fourth, one-half, or three-fourths as long as the first. To make an estimate of a proportion in terms closer than in fifths is impractical and unnecessary.

13.9. To make a perspective sketch. The application of proportioning methods to the construction and division of an enclosing box is shown in Fig. 13.15. Read sections 12.10 and 13.4. The construction of a required perspective by steps is as follows:

Step I. Sketch the eye-line. This line should be well towards the top of the sheet of sketch paper.

Step II. Locate *VPL* and *VPR* on the eye-line. These vanishing points should be placed as far apart as possible.

Step III. Assume the position and length for the near front edge *AB*. The length of this line, along with the spacing of the vanishing points, establishes the size of the finished sketch. The position of *AB* determines how the visible surfaces are to appear. For instance, if the line *AB* had been moved downward from the position shown in (*a*), much more of the top surface would be seen in (*b*) and (*c*). Should *AB* have been moved to the right from its position shown in (*a*), the left side would have become more prominent. If *AB* were placed midway between the two vanishing points, then both the front and left side surfaces would be at 45 degrees with the picture plane for the perspective. As it has been placed in (*a*), the side face is at 60 degrees to the picture plane while the front face is at 30 degrees. Before establishing the position for the near front edge, one must decide which surfaces are the most important surfaces and how they may best be displayed in the sketch.

Step IV. Sketch light construction lines from points *A* and *B* to each vanishing point.

Step V. Determine the proportions for the enclosing box, in this case $4\frac{1}{2}$, 2, and $1\frac{1}{2}$, and mark off two equal units along *AB*.

Step VI. Sketch perspective squares, representing the faces of one-unit cubes, starting at *AB* and working towards each vanishing point. In cases where an over-all length must be completed with a partial unit, a full perspective square must be sketched at the end.

Step VII. Subdivide any of the end squares if necessary and sketch-in the enclosing box (*a*).

Step VIII.   Locate and block-in the details, subdividing the perspective squares as is required to establish the location of any detail.   When circles are to be sketched in perspective by a beginner, it is advisable to sketch the enclosing box first using light lines (b).

Step IX.   Darken the object lines of the sketch.   Construction lines may be removed and some shading added to the surfaces as shown in (c), if desired.

A sketch in one-point perspective might be made as shown in Fig. 13.16.   For this particular sketch the enclosing box was made to the assumed over-all proportions for the part.   Then the location of the details was established by subdividing the regular rectangle of the front face of the enclosing box and the perspective rectangle of the right side.

EYE-LINE   VP

Fig. 13.16.   A Sketch Made in One-Point Perspective.

13.10. Conventional treatment of fillets, rounds, and screw threads.   Sketches that are not given full pencil shading may be given a more or less realistic appearance by representing the fillets and rounds of the unfinished surfaces as shown in Fig. 11.44.   The conventional treatment for screw threads is shown in (b) of the same illustration.

13.11. Illustration sketches showing mechanisms exploded.   A sketch of a mechanism showing the parts in exploded positions along the principal axes is shown in Fig. 13.17.   Through the use of such sketches those who have not been trained to read multiview drawings may readily understand how a mechanism should be assembled, for both the shapes of the parts and their order of assembly, as denoted by their space relationship, is shown in pictorial form.

Many persons find that it is desirable, when preparing sketches of exploded mechanisms, first to block in the complete mechanism with all of the parts in position.   At this initial stage of construction, the parts are sketched in perspective in rough outline and the principal axes and object lines are extended part way towards their vanishing points.

Horizon Line

TO VPL

TO VPR

TO VPL ←

→ TO VPR

Block-in assembly in outline

OVERLAY
SHEET

Retrace parts on overlay sheet in
exploded positions from assembly sketch

Fig. 13.17.   A Sketch Showing the Parts of a Mechanism in Exploded Positions.

When the rough layout has been completed to the satisfaction of the person preparing the sketch, an overlay sheet is placed over the original sketch and the parts are traced directly from the sketch beneath in exploded positions along the principal axes and along the axes of holes. Frequently some persons make a traced sketch of each individual part and place the sketches in exploded positions before preparing the finished sketch. Others with more experience accomplish the same results by first tracing the major part along with the principal axes and then moving the overlay sheet as required to trace off the remaining parts in their correct positions along the axes.

It should be recognized that in preparing sketches of exploded mechanisms in this manner the parts are not shown perspectively reduced although they are removed from their original place in the pictorial assembly outward and towards the vanishing points. To prepare a sketch of this type with all of the parts shown in true geometrical perspective would result in a general picture which would be misleading and one that would be apt to confuse the non-technical person because some parts would appear much too large or too small to be mating parts.

Fig. 13.18.   Sketches on Isometric Paper.

13.12. Materials—technique. For pictorial sketching, the materials needed are an HB or F pencil, a soft eraser, and some paper. Although one should become proficient in sketching on plain white bond paper, a specially ruled paper, shown in Fig. 13.18, can be used by those who need the help of guide lines.

13.13. Problems. The problems presented in this chapter were selected to give practice in preparing pictorial sketches—axonometric, oblique, or perspective. Additional problems that are suitable for pictorial sketching may be found in Chapters 11 and 20.

1–9. (Figs. 13.19–13.27.)   Make freehand isometric sketches of the objects as assigned.

10–18. (Figs. 13.19–13.27.)   Make freehand oblique sketches of the objects as assigned.

19–27. (Figs. 13.19–13.27.)   Make freehand perspective sketches of the objects as assigned.

28. (Fig. 20.60.)   Make a pictorial sketch of a part from the pipe stand as assigned.

29. (Fig. 20.61.)   Make a pictorial sketch of a part from the flexible joint as assigned.

30. (Fig. 20.62.)   Make a pictorial sketch of the base of the tool holder.

31. (Fig. 20.63.)   Make a pictorial sketch of the base of the self-aligning shaft support.

32. (Fig. 20.70.)   Make a pictorial sketch of the bracket of the shaft support.

33. (Fig. 20.70.)   Make a pictorial sketch of the shaft support showing the unit assembled.

34. (Fig. 20.70.)   Make an exploded perspective sketch of the shaft support. See Fig. 13.17.

Fig. 13.19.   Fig. 13.20.   Fig. 13.21.

Fig. 13.22.   Fig. 13.23.   Fig. 13.24.

Fig. 13.25.   Fig. 13.26.   Fig. 13.27.

14 | Developments and Intersections

14.1. A comprehensive study of intersections and developments is logically a part of the subject of Descriptive Geometry. A few of the many practical applications that can be handled without advanced study in projection, however, are presented in this chapter. Desired lines of intersection between geometrical surfaces may be obtained by applying the principles of orthographic projection with which the student is already familiar. Although developments are laid out and are not drawn by actual projection in the manner of exterior views, their construction nevertheless requires the application of orthographic projection in finding the true lengths of elements and edges.

14.2. Geometric surfaces. A geometric surface is generated by the motion of a geometric line, either straight or curved. Surfaces that are generated by a moving straight line are known as *ruled surfaces*, and those generated by a curved line are known as *double curved surfaces*. Any position of the generating line, known as a generatrix, is called an *element of the surface*.

Ruled surfaces include planes, single curved surfaces, and warped surfaces.

A *plane* is generated by a straight line moving in such a manner that one point touches another straight line as it moves parallel to its original position.

A *single curved surface* is generated by a straight line moving so that in any two of its near positions it is in the same plane.

A *warped surface* is generated by a straight line moving so that it does not lie in the same plane in any two near positions.

Double curved surfaces include surfaces that are generated by a curved line moving in accordance with some mathematical law.

14.3. Geometric objects. Geometric solids are bounded by geometric surfaces. They may be classified as follows:

1. Solids bounded by plane surfaces:
   Tetrahedron, cube, prism, pyramid, and others.
2. Solids bounded by single curved surfaces:
   Cone and cylinder (generated by a moving straight line).
3. Solids bounded by warped surfaces:
   Conoid, cylindroid, hyperboloid of one nappe, and warped cone.
4. Solids bounded by double curved surfaces:
   Sphere, spheroid, torus, paraboloid, hyperboloid, and so on (surfaces of revolution generated by curved lines).

298

DEVELOPMENTS

14.4. A layout of the complete surface of an object is called a development or pattern. The development of an object bounded by plane surfaces may be thought of as being obtained by turning the object, as illustrated in Figs. 14.1 and 14.2, so as to unroll the imaginary enclosing surface upon a plane. Practically, the drawing operation consists of drawing the successive surfaces in their true size with their common edges joined.

The surfaces of cones and cylinders also may be unrolled upon a plane. The development of a right cylinder (Fig. 14.3) is a rectangle having a width equal to the altitude of the cylinder and a length equal to the cylinder's computed circumference (πd). The development of a right circular

Fig. 14.1. The Development of a Prism.

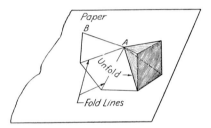

Fig. 14.2. The Development of a Pyramid.

Fig. 14.3. The Development of a Cylinder.

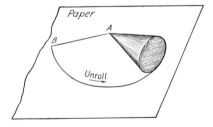

Fig. 14.4. The Development of a Cone.

cone (Fig. 14.4) is a sector of a circle having a radius equal to the slant height of the cone and an arc length equal to the circumference of its base.

Warped and double curved surfaces cannot be developed accurately, but they may be developed by some approximate method. Ordinarily, an approximate pattern will prove to be sufficiently accurate for practical purposes if the material of which the piece is to be made is somewhat flexible.

Plane and single curved surfaces (prisms, pyramids, cylinders, and cones), which can be accurately developed, are said to be developable. Warped and double curved surfaces, which can be only approximately developed, are said to be nondevelopable.

14.5. Practical developments. On many industrial drawings, a development must be shown to furnish the necessary information for making a pattern to facilitate the cutting of a desired shape from sheet metal. Present-day draftsmen must have a broad knowledge of the methods of constructing varied types of developments, because of the rapid advance of the art of manufacturing an ever-increasing number of pieces by fold-ing, rolling, or pressing cut sheet-metal shapes.   Patterns also are used in stone cutting as guides for shaping irregular faces.

A development of a surface should be drawn with the inside face up, as it theoretically would be if the surface were unrolled or unfolded as illus-trated in Figs. 14.1–14.4.   In commercial drafting, this practice is further justified by the fact that sheet-metal workers must make the necessary punch marks for folding on the inside surface.

Although in actual sheet-metal work extra metal must be allowed for lap at seams, no allowance will be shown on the developments in this

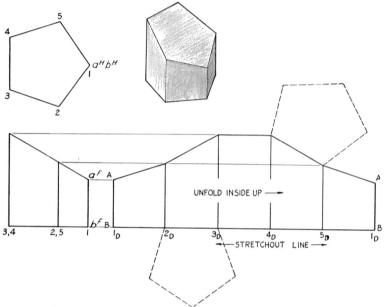

Fig. 14.5. The Standard Method of Developing the Lateral Surface of a Right Prism.

chapter.   Many other practical considerations have been purposely ignored, as well, in order to avoid confusing the beginner.

14.6. To develop a right truncated prism.   Before the develop-ment of the lateral surface of a prism can be drawn, the true lengths of the edges and the true size of a right section must be determined.   In the right truncated prism, shown in Fig. 14.5, the true lengths of the prism edges are shown in the front view and the true size of the right section is shown in the top view.

The lateral surface is "unfolded" by first drawing a "stretch-out line" and marking off the widths of the faces (distances 1-2, 2-3, 3-4, and so on, from the top view) along it in succession.   Through these points light con-struction lines are then drawn perpendicular to the line 1_D-1_D, and the length of the respective edge is set off on each by projecting from the front view.   When projecting edge lengths to the development, the points should be taken in a clockwise order around the perimeter as indicated

by the order of the figures in the top view.   The outline of the development is completed by joining these points.   Thus far, nothing has been
said about the lower base or the inclined upper face.   These may be
joined to the development of the lateral surface, if so desired.

In sheet-metal work, it is the usual practice to make the seam on the
shortest element in order to save time and conserve solder or rivets.

14.7. To develop an oblique prism.   The lateral surface of an
oblique prism, such as the one shown in Fig. 14.6, is developed by the same
general method used for a right prism.   Similarly, the true lengths of the
edges are shown in the front view, but it is necessary to find the true size

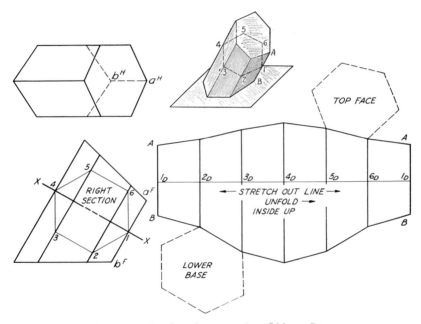

Fig. 14.6.   The Development of an Oblique Prism.

of the right section by auxiliary plane construction.   The widths of the
faces, as taken from the auxiliary right section, are set off along the stretch-
out line, and perpendicular construction lines representing the edges are
drawn through the division points.   The lengths of the portions of each
respective edge, above and below plane X-X, are transferred to the corresponding line in development.   Distances above plane X-X are laid off
above the stretch-out line, and distances below X-X are laid off below it.
The development of the lateral surface is then completed by joining the
end points of the edges by straight lines.   Since an actual fold will be
made at each edge line when the prism is formed, it is the usual practice
to heavy these edge (fold) lines on the development.

The stretch-out line might well have been drawn in a position perpendicular to the edges of the front view (see Fig. 14.7), so that the length
of each edge might be projected to the development (as in the case of the

right prism).   Much better balance of the views usually is obtained, however, when the stretch-out line is drawn in a horizontal position.

14.8. To develop a right cylinder.   When the lateral surface of a
right cylinder is rolled out upon a plane, the base develops into a straight
line (Fig. 14.8).   The length of this line, which is equal to the circumference of a right section ($\pi \times$ dia.), may be calculated and laid off as the
stretch-out line 1_D-1_D.

Since the cylinder can be thought of as being a many-sided prism, the
development may be constructed in a manner similar to the method illustrated in Fig. 14.5.   The elements drawn on the surface of the cylinder
serve as edges of the many-sided prism.   Twelve or twenty-four of these

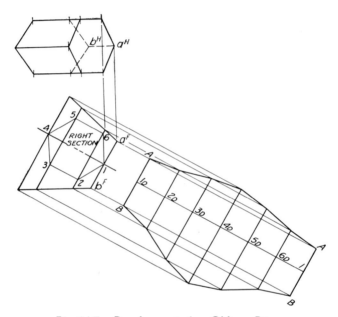

Fig. 14.7. Development of an Oblique Prism.

elements ordinarily are used, the number depending upon the size of the
cylinder.   Usually they are spaced by dividing the circumference of the
base, as shown by the circle in the top view, into an equal number of
parts.   The stretch-out line is divided into the same number of equal
parts, and perpendicular elements are drawn through each division point.
Then the true length of each element is projected to its respective representation on the development, and the development is completed by
joining the points with a smooth curve.   In joining the points, it is advisable to sketch the curve in lightly, freehand, before using the french
curve.   Since the surface of the finished cylindrical piece forms a continuous curve, the elements on the development are not heavied.   When the
development is symmetrical, as in this case, only one-half need be drawn.

A piece of this type might form a part of a two-piece, three-piece, or
four-piece elbow.   The pieces are usually developed as illustrated in Fig.

14.9.   The stretch-out line of each section is equal in length to the computed perimeter of a right section.

14.9. To develop an oblique cylinder.   Since an oblique cylinder theoretically may be thought of as enclosing a regular oblique prism hav-

Fig. 14.8.   Development of a Right Circular Cylinder.

Fig. 14.9.   Two-Piece Elbow.

ing an infinite number of sides, the development of the lateral surface of the cylinder shown in Fig. 14.10 may be constructed by using a method similar to the method illustrated in Fig. 14.6.   The circumference of the right section becomes stretch-out line 1_D-1_D for the development.

14.10. To determine the true length of a line.   In order to construct the development of the lateral surface of some objects, it frequently is necessary to determine the true lengths of oblique lines that represent the edges. The general method for determining the true lengths of lines inclined to all of the co-ordinate planes of projection has been explained in detail in Sec. 8.8. This article should be reviewed before reading the discussion that follows.

If a line is oblique to each of the three planes of projection, none of its

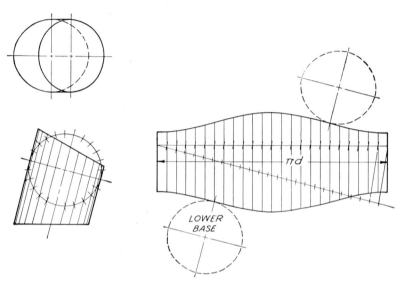

Fig. 14.10.   Development of an Oblique Cylinder.

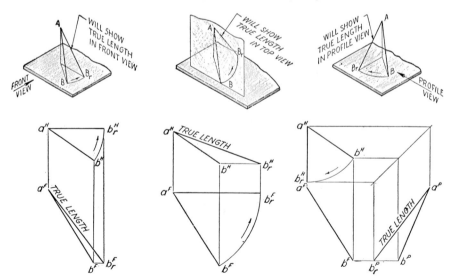

Fig. 14.11.
Revolution to Position Parallel to Frontal Plane.

Fig. 14.12.   Revolution to Position Parallel to Horizontal Plane.

Fig. 14.13.   Revolution to Position Parallel to Profile Plane.

principal projections will show its true length. Note in Fig. 14.11 that the principal projections of the edge AB are inclined. To determine the true length of AB, it may be revolved into a position parallel to either the H, F, or P co-ordinate planes, as shown in Figs. 14.11, 14.12, and 14.13. In Fig. 14.11, AB has been revolved into a position parallel to the F (frontal) plane. The view of AB revolved, $a^F b_r^F$ shows the true length. In Fig. 14.12, AB was revolved parallel to the H (horizontal) plane, and $a^H b_r^H$ shows the true length. In Fig. 14.13, the edge is shown revolved parallel to the P (profile) co-ordinate plane.

14.11. True-length diagrams. When it is necessary, in developing a surface, to find the true lengths of a number of edges or elements, some confusion may be avoided by constructing a true-length diagram adjacent to the orthographic view as shown in Fig. 14.14. The elements were

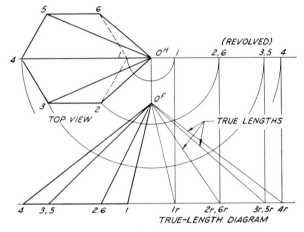

Fig. 14.14. A True-Length Diagram (the Revolution Method).

revolved into a position parallel to the F (frontal) plane so that their true lengths show in the diagram. This practice prevents the front view in the illustration from being cluttered with lines, some of which would represent elements and others their true lengths.

Figure 14.15 shows a diagram that gives the true lengths of the edges of the pyramid. Each line representing the true length of an edge is the hypotenuse of a right triangle whose altitude is the altitude of the edge in the front view and whose base is equal to the length of the projection of the edge in the top view. The lengths of the top projections of the edges of the pyramid are laid off horizontally from the vertical line $o^F X$, which could have been drawn at any distance from the front view. Since all the edges have the same altitude, this line is a common vertical leg for all the right triangles in the diagram. For example, $o^F X 1'$ is a true-length triangle having the line $o^F X$ as a vertical leg and $X 1'$, which is equal in length to $o^H 1$ in the top view, as a base. Other triangles are $o^F X 2'$, $o^F X 3'$, $o^F X 4'$, and so on. The true-length diagram shown in Fig. 14.14 could very well have been constructed by this method.

14.12. To develop a right pyramid. To develop (unfold) the lateral surface of a right pyramid, it is first necessary to determine the true lengths of the edges and the true size of the base. With this information, the development can be constructed by laying out the faces in successive order with their common edges joined. If the surface is imagined to be unfolded by turning the pyramid, as shown in Fig. 14.2, each triangular

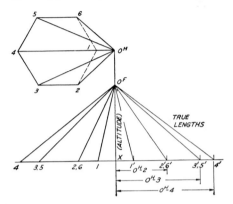

Fig. 14.15.   True-Length Diagram (Right Triangle Method).

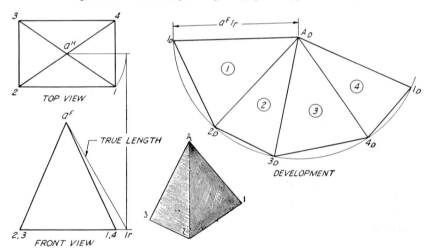

Fig. 14.16.   The Development of a Rectangular Right Pyramid.

face is revolved into the plane of the paper about the edge that is common to it and the preceding face.

Since the edges of the pyramid shown in Fig. 14.16 are all equal in length, it is necessary only to find the length of the one edge $A1$ by revolving it into the position $a^F 1_r$. The edges of the base, 1-2, 2-3, and so on, are parallel to the horizontal plane of projection and consequently show in their true length in the top view. With this information, the development is easily completed by constructing the four triangular surfaces. In practice, this construction can be simplified by adhering to the following procedure.   First, draw an arc of radius a^F1_r with some convenient point A_D as a center.   Second, step off the perimeter of the base along the arc.   Third, join the end points of the edges of the base (1_D, 2_D, 3_D, and 4_D) with the vertex A_D and draw the lines of the base to complete the development.   The base may be attached to the development, if so desired.

14.13. To develop the surface of a frustum of a pyramid.   To develop the lateral surface of the frustum of a pyramid (Fig. 14.17), it is necessary to determine the true lengths of edges of the complete pyramid as well as the true lengths of edges of the frustum.   The desired development is obtained by first constructing the development of the complete pyramid and then laying off the true lengths of the edges of the frustum on the corresponding lines of the development.

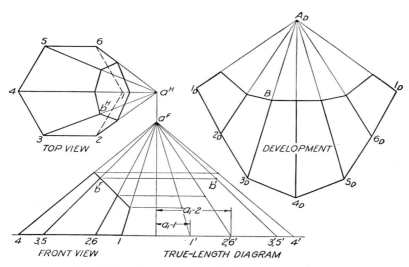

Fig. 14.17.   Development of the Frustum of a Pyramid.

It may be noted with interest that the true length of the edge $B3$ is equal to the length $b'3'$ on the true-length line a^F3', and that the location of point b' can be established by the short-cut method of projecting horizontally from point b^F.   Point b' on a^F3' is the true revolved position of point B, because the path of point B is in a horizontal plane that projects as a line in the front view.

14.14. To develop a right cone.   As previously explained in Sec. 14.4, the development of a regular right circular cone is a sector of a circle. The development will have a radius equal to the slant height of the cone and an included angle at the center equal to $r/s \times 360°$ (Fig. 14.18).   In this equation, r is the radius of the base and s is the slant height.

14.15. To develop a right truncated cone.   The development of a right truncated cone must be constructed by a modified method of triangulation, in order to develop the outline of the elliptical inclined surface. This commonly used method is based upon the theoretical assumption that a cone is a pyramid having an infinite number of sides.   The development of the incomplete right cone shown in Fig. 14.19 is constructed upon a layout of the whole cone by a method similar to the standard method illustrated for the frustum of a pyramid in Fig. 14.17.

Elements are drawn on the surface of the cone to serve as edges of the many-sided pyramid. Either twelve or twenty-four are used, depending

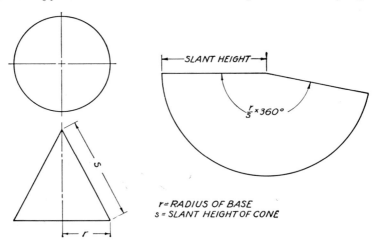

Fig. 14.18.   Development of a Right Cone.

Fig. 14.19.   Development of a Truncated Cone.

upon the size of the cone. Their location is established upon the developed sector by dividing the arc representing the unrolled base into the same number of equal divisions, into which the top view of the base has been divided. At this point in the procedure, it is necessary to determine the true lengths of the elements of the frustum in the same manner that the true lengths of the edges of the frustum of a pyramid were obtained in Fig. 14.17. With this information, the desired development can be completed by setting off the true lengths on the corresponding lines of the development and joining the points thus obtained with a smooth curve.

14.16. The triangulation method of developing approximately developable surfaces. A nondevelopable surface may be developed approximately if the surface is assumed to be composed of a number of small developable surfaces (Fig. 14.21). The particular method ordinarily used for warped surfaces and the surfaces of oblique cones is known as the triangulation method. The procedure consists of completely covering the lateral surface with numerous small triangles that will lie approximately on the surface (Fig. 14.20). These triangles, when laid out in their true size with their common edges joined, produce an approximate development that is accurate enough for most practical purposes.

Fig. 14.20. Triangulation of an Oblique Cone.

Fig. 14.21. Triangulation of a Surface.

Although this method of triangulation is sometimes used to develop the lateral surface of a right circular cone, it is not recommended for such purpose. The resulting development is not as accurate as it would be if constructed by one of the standard methods (see Secs. 14.14 and 14.15).

14.17. To develop an oblique cone using the triangulation method. A development of the lateral surface of an oblique cone is constructed by a method similar to that used for an oblique pyramid. The surface is divided into a number of unequal triangles having sides that are elements on the cone and bases that are the chords of short arcs of the base.

The first step in developing an oblique cone (Fig. 14.22) is to divide the circle representing the base into a convenient number of equal parts and draw elements on the surface of the cone through the division points (1, 2, 3, 4, 5, and so on). To construct the triangles forming the development, it is necessary to know the true lengths of the elements (sides of the triangles) and chords. In the illustration, all the chords are equal. Their true lengths are shown in the top view. The true lengths of the oblique elements may be determined by one of the standard methods explained in Sec. 14.11.

Since the seam should be made along the shortest element, $A1$ will lie on the selected starting line for the development and $A7$ will be on the center line. To obtain the development, the triangles are constructed in order, starting with the triangle A-1-2 and proceeding around the cone in a clockwise direction (as shown by the arrow in the top view). The first step in constructing triangle A-1-2 is to set off the true length a^F1' along the starting line. With point A_D of the development as a center, and with a radius equal to a^F2', strike an arc; then, with point 1_D as a center, and with a radius equal to the chord 1-2, strike an arc across the first arc to locate point 2_D. The triangle $A_D2_D3_D$ and the remaining

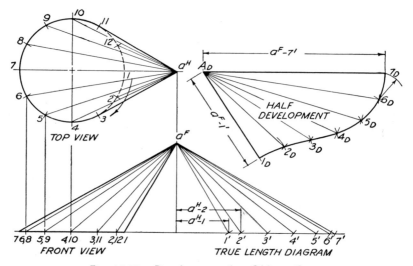

Fig. 14.22.   Development of an Oblique Cone.

triangles are formed in exactly the same manner. When all the triangles have been laid out, the development of the whole conical surface is completed by drawing a smooth curve through the end points of the elements.

After the beginner has constructed a few such developments, he will find that much time can be saved by drawing all the long arcs before striking off any of the short ones. To offset any errors in judgment about their approximate correct location, the long arcs may be made fairly long.

14.18. Transition pieces. A few of the many types of transition pieces used for connecting pipes and openings of different shapes and sizes are illustrated pictorially in Fig. 14.23. The transition at (a), which is composed of triangular and conical surfaces, connects a square opening with a round one. The transition at (b) serves similarly. At (c), the transition piece is the frustum of a pyramid. The transition shown at (d) is formed of cylinders. The ones at (e) and (f) are special types that are not frequently encountered.

14.19. To develop a transition piece connecting rectangular pipes. The transition piece shown in Fig. 14.24 is designed to connect two rectangular pipes of different sizes on different axes.   Since the piece is a frustum of a pyramid, it can be accurately developed by the method explained in Sec. 14.13.

14.20. To develop a transition piece connecting two circular pipes.   The transition piece shown in Fig. 14.25 connects two circular

(a)   *(b)*   *(c)*

(d)   *(e)*   *(f)*

Fig. 14.23.   Transition Pieces.

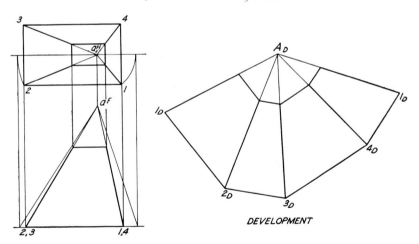

DEVELOPMENT

Fig. 14.24.   Transition Piece.

pipes on different axes.   Since the piece is a frustum of an oblique cone, the surface must be triangulated, as explained in Sec. 14.17, and the development must be constructed by laying out the triangles in their true size in regular order.   The general procedure is the same as that illustrated in Fig. 14.22.   In this case, however, since the true size of the base is not shown in the top view, it is necessary to construct a partial auxiliary

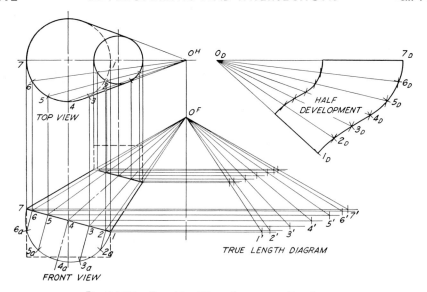

Fig. 14.25.   Transition Piece Connecting Two Pipes.

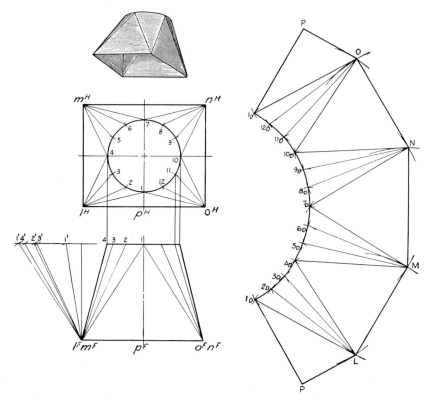

Fig. 14.26.   Transition Piece Connecting a Circular and Square Pipe.

view to find the true lengths of chords between the end points of the elements.

14.21. To develop a transition piece connecting a circular and a square pipe. A detailed analysis of the transition piece shown in Fig. 14.26 reveals the fact that it is composed of four isosceles triangles whose bases form the square base of the piece and four conical surfaces that are parts of oblique cones. It is not difficult to develop this type of transition piece, because, since the whole surface may be "broken up" into component surfaces, the development may be constructed by developing the

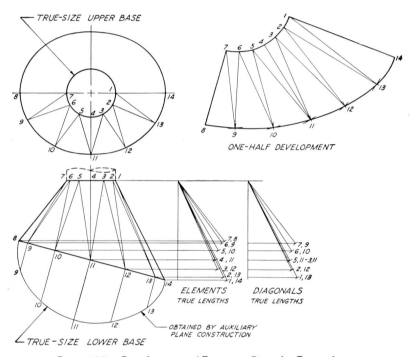

Fig. 14.27. Development of Transition Piece by Triangulation.

first and then each succeeding component surface separately (Fig. 14.21). The surfaces are developed around the piece, in a clockwise direction, in such a manner that each successive surface is joined to the preceding surface at their common element. In the illustration, the triangles $1LO$, $4LM$, $7MN$, and $10NO$ are clearly shown in top view. Two of these, $1LO$ and $10NO$, are visible on the pictorial drawing. The apexes of the conical surfaces are located at the corners of the base.

Before starting the development, it is necessary to determine the true lengths of the elements by constructing a true-length diagram as explained in Sec. 14.11. The true lengths of the edges of the lower base (LM, MN, NO, and OL) and the true lengths of the chords (1-2, 2-3, 3-4, and so on) of the short arcs of the upper base are shown in the top view. The development is constructed in the following manner: First, the triangle 1_DPL is constructed, using the length $p^H l^H$, taken from the top view, and true lengths from the diagram. Next, using the method explained in Sec. 14.17, the conical surface whose apex is at L is developed in an attached position. Triangle $4_D L M$ is then added, and so on, until all component surfaces have been drawn.

14.22. To develop a transition piece having an approximately developable surface by the triangulation method. Figure 14.27 shows a half development of a transition piece that has a warped surface instead of a partially conical one like that discussed in Sec. 14.21. The

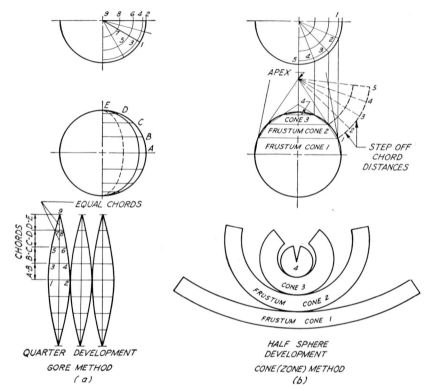

QUARTER DEVELOPMENT

GORE METHOD

(a)

HALF SPHERE
DEVELOPMENT

CONE (ZONE) METHOD

(b)

Fig. 14.28.   The Approximate Development of a Sphere.

method of constructing the development is somewhat similar, however, in that it is formed by laying out, in true size, a number of small triangles that approximate the surface. The true size of the circular intersection is shown in the top view, and the true size of the elliptical intersection is shown in the auxiliary view, which was constructed for that purpose.

The front half of the circle in the top view should be divided into the same number of equal parts as the half-auxiliary view. By joining the division points, the lateral surface may be initially divided into narrow quadrilaterals. These in turn may be subdivided into triangles, by drawing diagonals which, though theoretically they are curved lines, are assumed to be straight. The true lengths of the elements and the diagonals are found by constructing two separate true-length diagrams by the method illustrated in Fig. 14.15.

14.23. To develop a sphere.   The surface of a sphere is a double curved surface that can be developed only by some approximate method. The standard methods commonly used are illustrated in Fig. 14.28.

In (*a*) the surface is divided into a number of equal meridian sections of cylinders.   The developed surfaces of these form an approximate development of the sphere.   In drawing the development, it is necessary to develop the surface of only one section, for this can be used as a pattern for the developed surface of each of the others.

In (*b*) the sphere is cut by parallel planes which divide it into a number of horizontal sections, the surfaces of which approximate the surface of the sphere.   Each of these sections may be considered the frustum of a right cone whose apex is located at the intersection of the chords extended.

INTERSECTIONS

14.24. Lines of intersection of geometric surfaces.   The line of intersection of two surfaces is a line that is common to both.   It may be considered the line that would contain the points in which the elements of one surface would pierce the other.   Almost every line on a practical orthographic representation is a line of intersection; therefore, the following discussion may be deemed an extended study of the same subject. The methods presented in this chapter are the recognized easy procedures for finding the more complicated lines of intersection created by intersecting geometric surfaces.

Commercial draftsmen, in order to complete a view of a working drawing or a view necessary for developing the surfaces of intersecting geometric shapes, frequently must find the line of intersection between surfaces.   On an ordinary working drawing, the line of intersection may be "faked in" through a few critical points.   On a sheet-metal drawing, however, a sufficient number of points must be located to obtain an accurate line of intersection and an ultimately accurate development.

The line of intersection of two surfaces is found by determining a number of points common to both surfaces and drawing a line or lines through these points in correct order.   The resulting line of intersection may be straight, curved, or straight and curved.   The problem of finding such a line may be solved by one of two general methods, depending upon the type of surfaces involved.

For the purpose of simplifying this discussion of intersections, it should be assumed that all problems are divided into these two general groups:

Group I.   Problems involving two surfaces, both of which are composed of plane surfaces.

Group II.   Problems involving two surfaces which are either single curved or double curved.

For instance, the procedure for finding the line of intersection of two prisms is the same as that for finding the line of intersection of a prism and a pyramid; hence, both problems belong in the same group (Group I). Since the problem of finding the line of intersection of two cylinders and the problem of finding the line of intersection of a cylinder and a cone both involve single curved surfaces, these two also belong in the same group (Group II).

Problems of the first group are solved by locating the points through which the edges of each of two geometrical shapes pierce the other. These points are vertices of the line of intersection. Whenever one of two intersecting plane surfaces appears as a line in one view, the points through which the lines of the other surfaces penetrate it usually may be found by inspecting that view.

Problems of the second group may be solved by drawing elements on the lateral surface of one geometrical shape in the region of the line of intersection. The points at which these elements intersect the surface of the other geometrical shape are points that are common to both surfaces

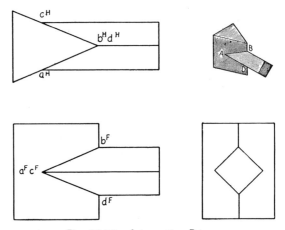

Fig. 14.29. Intersecting Prisms.

and consequently lie on their line of intersection. A curve, traced through these points with the aid of a french curve, will be a representation of the required intersection. To obtain accurate results, some of the elements must be drawn through certain critical points at which the curve changes sharply in direction. These points usually are located on contour elements. Hence, the usual practice is to space the elements equally around the surface, starting with a contour element.

A thorough knowledge of descriptive geometry is necessary to solve the more difficult problems of this second group, but, since these do not logically form a part of the subject of engineering drawing, the following discussions will concern only problems of a type that can be solved by means of elements cut by imaginary planes that would be perpendicular to at least one of the co-ordinate planes of projection.

14.25. To find the intersection of two prisms. In Fig. 14.29 (see pictorial), points A, B, C, and D, through which the edges of the horizontal prism pierce the faces of the triangular prism, are the critical points or vertices of the closed intersection. The location of these piercing points may be found in the top view by inspection. Then they may be projected to the front view, to establish their location there. For example, the top view shows that the front edge of the horizontal prism pierces the near face of the vertical triangular prism at point a^H. Point a^H, projected downward to the line representing that edge in the front view, locates point a^F in the front view. After the piercing points B, C, and D have been found and projected to the front view in a similar manner, the intersection is completed by joining, in order, the projected points a^F, b^F, c^F, and d^F with straight lines.

14.26. To establish the location of the piercing point of an edge intersecting an inclined surface. In Fig. 14.30, points A, C, and D, through which the edges of the horizontal prism pierce the vertical prism, are first found in the top view and are then projected downward to the

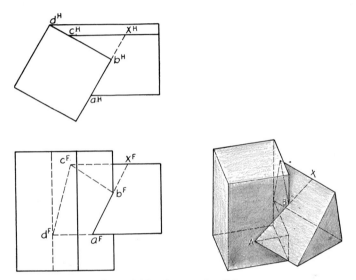

Fig. 14.30. Intersecting Prisms.

corresponding edges in the front view. Point B, through which the edge of the vertical prism pierces the near face of the triangular prism, cannot be found in this manner because the side view from which it could be projected to the front view is not shown. Its location, however, can be established in the front view without even drawing a partial side view, if some scheme like the one illustrated in the pictorial drawing is used. In this scheme, the intersection line AB, whose direction is shown in the top view as line $a^H b^H$, is extended on the triangular face to point X on the top edge. Point x^H is projected to the corresponding edge in the front view and a light construction line is drawn between the points a^F and x^F. Since point B is located on line AX (see pictorial) at the point where the edge of the prism pierces the line, its location in the front view is at point b^F where the edge cuts the line $a^F x^F$.

14.27. To find the intersection of a pyramid and a prism. The intersection of a right pyramid and a prism (see Fig. 14.31) may be found by the same general method used for finding the intersection of two prisms (see Sec. 14.25).

14.28. To find the intersection of two cylinders. If a series of elements are drawn on the surface of the small horizontal cylinder, as in

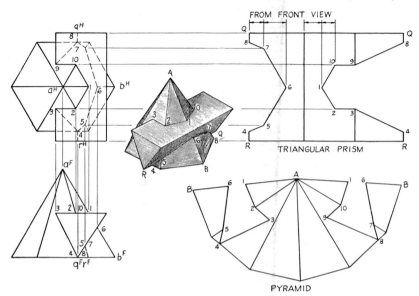

Fig. 14.31.   Intersecting Pyramid and Prism.

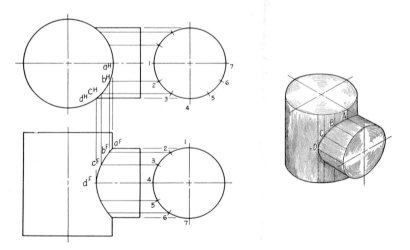

Fig. 14.32.   Intersecting Cylinders.

Fig. 14.32, the points A, B, C, and D in which they intersect the vertical cylinder will be points on the line of intersection (see pictorial). These points, which are shown as a^H, b^H, c^H, and d^H in the top view, may be located in the front view by projecting them downward to the corresponding elements in the front view where they are shown as points a^F, b^F, c^F, and d^F.   The desired intersection is represented by a smooth curve drawn through these points.

14.29. To find the intersection of two cylinders oblique to each other.   The first step in finding the line of intersection of two cylinders that are oblique to each other (see Fig. 14.33) is to draw a revolved right section of the oblique cylinder directly on the front view of that cylinder. If the circumference of the right section then is divided into a number of equal divisions and elements are drawn through the division points, the points A, B, C, and D in which the elements intersect the surface of the vertical cylinder will be points on the line of intersection (see pictorial). In the case of the above illustration, these points are found first in the

Fig. 14.33.   Intersecting Cylinders.

top view and then are projected downward to the corresponding elements in the front view.   The line of intersection in the front view is represented by a smooth curve drawn through these points.

14.30. To find the intersection of a cylinder and a cone.   The intersection of a cylinder and a cone may be found by assuming a number of elements upon the surface of the cone.   The points at which these elements cut the cylinder are on the line of intersection (see pictorial drawings in Figs. 14.34 and 14.35).   In selecting the elements, it is the usual practice to divide the circumference of the base into a number of equal parts and draw elements through the division points.   To obtain needed points at locations where the intersection line will change suddenly in curvature, however, there should be additional elements.

In Fig. 14.34, the points at which the elements pierce the cylinder are first found in the top view and are then projected to the corresponding elements in the front view.   A smooth curve through these points forms the figure of the intersection.

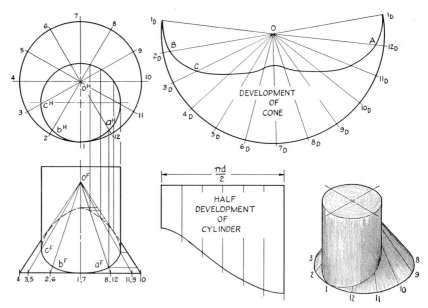

Fig. 14.34.   Intersecting Cylinder and Cone.

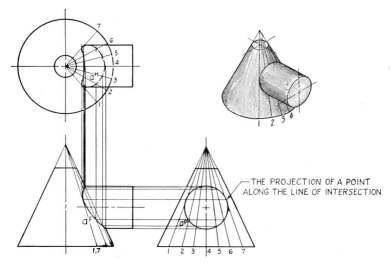

Fig. 14.35.   Intersecting Cylinder and Cone.

In Fig. 14.35, the intersection points are first found in the side view.
An alternate method for finding the line of intersection of a cylinder
and a right cone is illustrated in Fig. 14.36.   Here horizontal cutting
planes are passed through both geometrical shapes in the region of their
line of intersection.   In each cutting plane, the circle cut on the surface
of the cone will intersect elements cut on the cylinder at two points common to both surfaces (see pictorial).   A curved line traced through a

number of such points in different planes is a line common to both surfaces and is therefore the line of intersection.

14.31. To find the intersection of a prism and a cone. The complete line of intersection may be found by drawing elements on the

Fig. 14.36.   Intersecting Cylinder and Cone.   Fig. 14.37.   Intersecting Cone and Prism.

Fig. 14.38.   Cone and Hexagonal Prism.

surface of the cone (see Fig. 14.37) to locate points on the intersection as explained in Sec. 14.30.   To obtain an accurate curve, however, some thought must be given to the placing of these elements.   For instance, although most of the elements may be equally spaced on the cone to facilitate the construction of its development, additional ones should be drawn through the critical points and in regions where the line of intersection changes sharply in curvature.   The elements are drawn on the view that will reveal points on the intersection; then, the determined points are projected to the corresponding elements in the other view or views. In this particular illustration a part of the line of intersection in the top view is a portion of the arc of a circle that would be cut by a horizontal plane containing the bottom surface of the prism.

If the surfaces of the prism are parallel to the axis of the cone, as in Fig. 14.38, the line of intersection will be made up of the tips of a series of hyperbolas.   The intersection may be found by passing planes that will cut circles on the surface of the cone.   The points at which these cutting circles pierce the faces of the prism are points common to the lateral surfaces of both shapes and are therefore points on the required line of intersection.   It should be noted that the resulting solution represents a chamfered bolthead.

14.32. Problems.   The problems of this chapter have been designed to offer an opportunity to apply the principles of intersections and developments and to provide further drill in projection.

1. (Fig. 14.39.)   Develop the lateral surface of one or more of the prisms as assigned.

Fig. 14.39. Prisms.

2. (Fig. 14.40.)   Develop the lateral surface of one or more of the prisms as assigned.

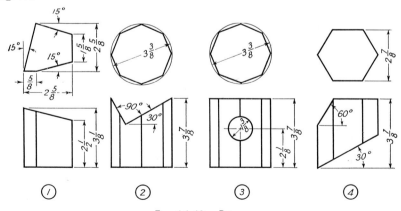

Fig. 14.40. Prisms.

3. (Fig. 14.41.)   Develop the lateral surface of one or more of the pyramids as assigned.   Make construction lines light.   Show construction for finding the true lengths of the lines.

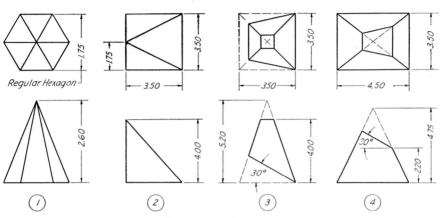

Fig. 14.41. Pyramids.

4. (Fig. 14.42.)   Develop the lateral surface of one or more of the pyramids as assigned.   With a hard pencil, show the construction for finding the true lengths of the lines.

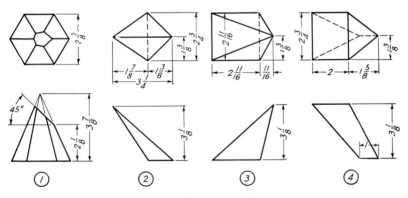

Fig. 14.42. Pyramids.

5. (Fig. 14.43.)   Develop the lateral surface of one or more of the cylinders as assigned.   Use a hard pencil for construction lines and make them light.

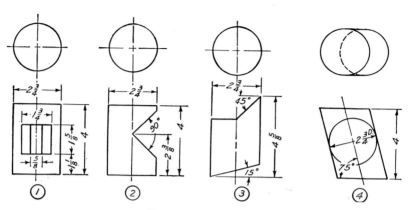

Fig. 14.43.   Cylinders.

6. (Fig. 14.44.)   Develop the lateral surface of one or more of the cones as assigned.   Show all construction. Use a hard pencil for construction lines and make them light.   In each case start with the shortest element and unroll, inside up.   It is suggested that 12 elements be used, in order to secure a reasonably accurate development.

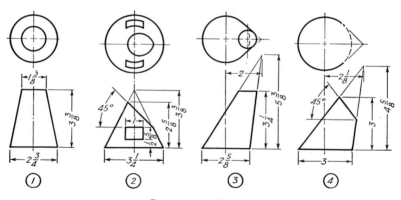

Fig. 14.44.   Cones.

7. (Fig. 14.45.) Develop the lateral surface of one or more of the transition pieces as assigned. Show all construction lines in light sharp pencil lines. Use a sufficient number of elements on the curved surfaces to assure an accurate development.

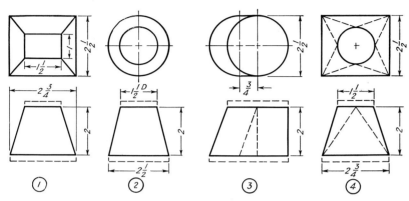

Fig. 14.45. Transition Pieces.

8. (Fig. 14.46.) Develop the sheet-metal connections. On pieces 3 and 4, use a sufficient number of elements to obtain a smooth curve and an accurate development.

Fig. 14.46. Sheet-Metal Connections (Transitions).

9–10. (Figs. 14.47 and 14.48.)   Draw the line of intersection of the intersecting geometrical shapes as assigned.   Show the invisible portions of the lines of intersection as well as the visible.   Consider that the interior is open.

Fig. 14.47.   Intersecting Surfaces.

Fig. 14.48.   Intersecting Surfaces.

11–12. (Figs. 14.49 and 14.50.)   Draw the line of intersection of the intersecting geometrical shapes as assigned.   It is suggested that the elements that are used to find points along the intersection be spaced 15 degrees apart.   Do not erase the construction lines.   One shape does not pass through the other.

Fig. 14.49.   Intersecting Surfaces.

Fig. 14.50.   Intersecting Surfaces.

13. (Fig. 14.51.)   Draw the line of intersection of the intersecting geometrical shapes as assigned.   Show the invisible portions of the line of intersection as well as the visible.   The interior of the combination is hollow.   One shape does not pass through the other.   Show construction with light sharp lines drawn with a hard pencil.

Fig. 14.51.   Intersecting Surfaces.

15 Dimensioning

FUNDAMENTALS AND TECHNIQUES

15.1. A detail drawing, in addition to giving the shape of a part, must furnish the workman with information on the distances between surfaces, locations of holes, kind of finish, type of material, number required, and so forth. The expression of this information on a drawing by the use of lines, symbols, figures, and notes is known as dimensioning.

Intelligent dimensioning requires engineering judgment and a thorough knowledge of the practices of pattern making, forging, and machining. It should be remembered that the shopman must be able to produce the part exactly as it is designed and shown on the blueprint. He should not be required to seek additional information, add or subtract dimensions, or use his judgment about a class of fit. The dimensions given are not those used in the design or in making the drawing. Instead, they are the ones required by the shopman and should be placed with that in mind.

In order to satisfy each craftsman's demands, the draftsman must first review the object represented and decide upon the production procedures necessary to create the part. Then, he mentally should follow it through all of these processes in order to determine the required dimensions, being careful to locate each dimension where the machinist or pattern maker will expect to find it. In brief, a drawing should be so dimensioned that the work may be done as economically and conveniently as possible.

15.2. Theory of dimensioning. Any part may be dimensioned easily and systematically by dividing it into simple geometrical solids. Even complicated parts, when analyzed, usually are found to be composed principally of cylinders and prisms and, frequently, frustums of pyramids and cones. The dimensioning of an object may be accomplished by dimensioning each elemental form to indicate its size and relative location from a center line, base line, or finished surface. A machine drawing requires two types of dimensions: *size dimensions* and *location dimensions*.

15.3. Size dimensions (Figs. 15.1 and 15.2). Size dimensions give the size of a piece, component part, hole, or slot.

Figure 15.1 should be carefully analyzed, as the placement of dimensions shown is applicable to the elemental parts of almost every piece.

The rule for placing the three principal dimensions (length, height, and depth) on the drawing of a prism or modification of a prism is: *Give two dimensions on the principal view and one dimension on one of the other views.*

The circular cylinder, which appears as a boss or shaft, requires only *the diameter and length, both of which are shown preferably on the rectangular view.* It is better practice to dimension a hole (negative cylinder) by giving the diameter and operation as a note on the contour view with a leader to the circle (Figs. 15.5 and 15.8).

Cones are dimensioned by giving the diameter of the base and the altitude on the same view. A taper is one example of a conical shape found on machine parts (Fig. 15.58).

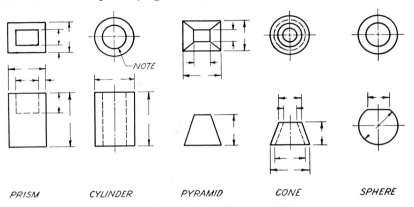

PRISM   CYLINDER   PYRAMID   CONE   SPHERE

Fig. 15.1.   Dimensioning Geometrical Shapes.

Fig. 15.2.   Size Dimensions.   Fig. 15.3.   Location Dimensions.

Pyramids, which frequently form a part of a structure, are dimensioned by giving two dimensions on the view showing the shape of the base.

A sphere requires only the diameter.

15.4. Location dimensions (Fig. 15.3). Location dimensions fix the relationship of the component parts (projections, holes, slots, and other significant forms) of a piece or structure. Particular care must be exercised in their selection and placing, because upon them depend the accuracy of the operations in making a piece and the proper mating of the piece with other parts. To select location dimensions intelligently, the draftsman should determine the contact surfaces, finished surfaces, and center lines of the elementary geometrical forms and, with the accuracy demanded and the method of production in mind, decide from what other surface or center line each should be located. Mating location dimensions must be given from the same center line or finished surface on both pieces.

Location dimensions are given center to center, surface to center, or surface to surface. Figure 15.4 illustrates each of these cases.

15.5. Procedure in dimensioning. The theory of dimensioning may be applied in six steps, as follows:

1. Mentally divide the object into its component geometrical shapes.

2. Place the size dimensions on each form.

3. Select the locating center lines and surfaces after giving careful consideration to mating parts and to the processes of manufacture.

4. Place the location dimensions so that each geometrical form is located from a center line or finished surface.

5. Add the over-all dimensions.

6. Complete the dimensioning by adding the necessary notes.

L_1 - CENTER TO CENTER
L_2 - SURFACE TO CENTER
L_3 - SURFACE TO SURFACE

Fig. 15.4. Types of Location Dimensions.

If the foregoing procedure is followed in the order stated, all required dimensions will have been given. Its application to the *rod support* (Fig. 15.5) gives the following results:

1. The piece is analyzed as a positive cylinder, three negative cylinders, and three positive prisms.

2. The size dimensions required on the component geometrical forms are designated by the letter S. Observe that a note serves as the size dimension for the hole (negative cylinder).

3. The finished surface of the base was selected as a locating surface.

4. From this surface, a location dimension designated by the letter L is placed as shown, in order to locate accurately the axis of the hole in relation to this contact surface.

5. Over-all dimensions and size dimensions (length and depth) are the same for the piece. Since the top of the object is cylindrical, no over-all height dimension should be shown. (See rule 16, Sec. 15.10.)

6. The notes complete the dimensioning of the drawing.

15.6. Placing dimensions. Dimensions must be placed where they will be most easily understood—in the locations where the shopman will expect to find them. They generally are attached to the view that shows the contour of the features to which they apply, and a majority of them usually will appear on the principal view (Fig. 15.6). Except in cases where special convenience and ease in reading are desired, or when a dimension would be so far from the form to which it referred that it might

Fig. 15.5. Dimensioning Component Shapes.

be misinterpreted, dimensions should be placed outside a view. They should appear directly on a view only when clarity demands.

All extensions and dimension lines should be drawn before the arrowheads have been filled in or the dimensions, notes, and titles have been lettered. Spacing dimension lines $\frac{1}{2}''$ from the view and $\frac{3}{8}''$ from each other provides an ample distance to satisfy the one rule to which there is no exception: *Never crowd dimensions*. Although it sometimes may be necessary to reduce the distance between dimension lines to a minimum of $\frac{1}{4}''$, the spacing should be uniform throughout. If the location of a dimension forces a poor location on other dimensions, its shifting may allow all to be placed more advantageously without sacrificing clearness. Important location dimensions should be given where they will be conspicuous, even if a size dimension must be moved.

15.7. Terms and dimensioning motion. A generally recognized system of lines, symbols, figures, and notes is used to indicate size and location. Figure 15.8 illustrates dimensioning terms and notation.

A *dimension line* is a light-weight line that is terminated at each end by an arrowhead. A numerical value, given along the dimension line, specifies the number of units for the measurement that is indicated

Visualizing Geometrical Forms
(a)

A Dimensioned Drawing
(b)

Fig. 15.6.   Placing Dimensions.

Break line for numeral and fraction
(a) Fractional Dimension

Break line for numerals in a single line
(b) Decimal Dimension

Do *not* break line for numerals in two lines
(c) Toleranced Dimensions

Fig. 15.7.   A Dimension Line.

(Fig. 15.7). When the numerals are in a single line, the dimension line is broken near the center as shown in (a) and (b). Under no circumstances should the line pass through the numerals. When the numerals are in two lines the dimension line is not broken and one line of numerals is placed above the dimension line and the other below as in (c).

Extension lines are light continuous lines extending from a view to indicate the extent of a measurement given by a dimension line that is located outside of a view. They start $\frac{1}{16}''$ from the view and extend $\frac{1}{8}''$ beyond the dimension line (Fig. 15.8).

Arrowheads are drawn for each dimension line, before the figures are lettered. They are made with the same pen or pencil used for the lettering. The size of an arrowhead, although it may vary with the size of a drawing, should be uniform on any one drawing. To have the proper proportions, the length of an arrowhead must be approximately three times its spread (American Standard). This length for average work is usually $\frac{1}{8}''$. Figure 15.9 shows enlarged drawings of both correct and incorrect heads. Use of any one of the incorrect shapes should be

Fig. 15.8.   Terms and Dimensioning Notation.

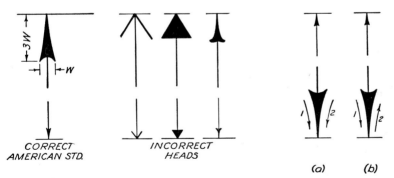

Fig. 15.9.   Arrowheads.   Fig. 15.10.   Formation of Arrowheads.

avoided, for it may ruin what otherwise would be a well-executed drawing. Although many draftsmen draw an arrowhead with one stroke, the beginner will get better results by using two slightly concaved strokes drawn toward the point (Fig. 15.10a) or, as shown in Fig. 15.10(b), one stroke drawn to the point and one away from it.

A *leader* or *pointer* is a light continuous line (terminated by an arrowhead) that extends from a note to the feature of a piece to which the note applies (Fig. 15.11). It should be made with a straightedge and should not be curved or made freehand (American Standard's recommendation).

A leader pointing to a curve should be a radial, and the first $\frac{1}{8}''$ of it should be in line with the note (Fig. 15.11).

Fig. 15.11.   A Leader.

Finish marks indicate the particular surfaces of a rough casting or forging that are to be machined or "finished." They are placed in all views, across the visible or invisible lines that are the edge views of surfaces to be machined (Fig. 15.13).

The modified italic *f*, shown in Fig. 15.12(*a*), is the form of finish mark that is preferred for general use. The student will find that careful adherence to the dimensions shown will improve the appearance of the *f* marks on his drawing.

Figure 15.12(*b*) shows the 60 degree V style of mark with its point touching the line view of the surface to be machined. In commercial

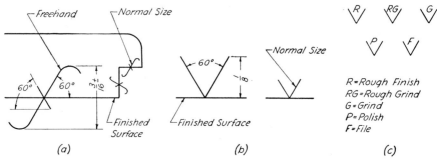

R=Rough Finish
RG=Rough Grind
G=Grind
P=Polish
F=File

(a)   (b)   (c)

Fig. 15.12.   Finish Marks.

Fig. 15.13.   Placing *f* Marks.

practice a code letter oftentimes is used to indicate the type of machining required. The code letter or letters are placed in the V as shown in (*c*).

It is not necessary to show finish marks on drilled or reamed holes, when the finish is specified as an operation in a note, such as $\frac{3}{4}''$ DRILL or

1″ REAM. They are also omitted, and a title note, "finish all over," is substituted, if the piece is to be completely machined. Finish marks are not required when limit dimensions are used.

Dimension figures should be lettered either horizontal or vertical with the whole numbers equal in height to the capital letters in the notes. Guide lines and slope lines must be used and should be drawn with the Braddock Triangle, as shown in Fig. 2.9. The holes illustrated in this figure give $\frac{1}{8}$″ whole numbers and $\frac{1}{4}$″ fractions, the usual heights for ordinary working drawings. Figures must be legible; otherwise, they might be misinterpreted in the shop and cause errors which would be embarrassing to the draftsman.

15.8. Fractional dimensioning. For ordinary work, where accuracy is relatively unimportant, shopmen work to nominal dimensions given as common fractions of an inch, as $\frac{1}{2}, \frac{1}{4}, \frac{1}{8}, \frac{1}{16}, \frac{1}{32}, \frac{1}{64}$. When dimensions are given in this way, many large corporations specify the required accuracy through a note on the drawing that reads as follows: *Permissible variations on common fraction dimensions to machined surfaces to be plus or minus .010 unless otherwise specified.* It should be understood that the allowable variations will differ among manufacturing concerns because of the varying degrees of accuracy required for different types of work.

15.9. Decimal system. Since the use of the decimal system for expressing dimensional values has made rapid gains in American industry and is now accepted in the aircraft and automotive fields, many of the examples in this chapter will show decimal dimensions. (Read Sec. 3.11.) At present, the fractional system, which dominated the whole of American industry until the Ford Motor Company adopted the decimal-inch some twenty-five years ago, is still used widely in those fields that are not under the direct influence of the automotive and aircraft companies. How long the present co-existence of the two systems will last cannot be foretold. It could be only a few years or it could be many years before the decimal system completely replaces the fractional system.

However, this need not be of great concern to the student, for he should be primarily interested in the selection and placement of dimensions. At a later time he will find it easy to use either the fractional or decimal systems as is required in his field of employment.

DET. 15 RIVET SET
I-TYPE CC" STEEL
STK. 1⅜ WT .84 LBS.
HEAT IN CYANIDE TO 1525°F
QUENCH IN OIL
DRAW AT 350°F
ROCKWELL 54-59C

Courtesy Ford Motor Co.

Fig. 15.14. Decimal Dimensioning.

To assist one to use either system, a Standard Conversion Table has been provided in the Appendix (Table I).

In Fig. 15.14 a drawing is shown that was obtained from the Ford Motor Co.

The ASA recommendation for decimal dimensioning, as given in the standard ASA Y14.5–1957, reads as follows:

Optionally, decimals may be used to replace common fractions altogether. The elimination of common fractions simplifies computations; decimals can be added, subtracted, multiplied or divided more easily than fractions. . . . The following conventions are generally observed by those who have adopted the decimal system. However, the advantages of using decimals can be gained, whether or not all of these rules are followed.

(a) Two-place decimals are used for dimensions where tolerance limits of ±.01 or more can be allowed. [See Fig. 15.14.]

(b) Decimals to three or more places must be used for tolerance limits less than ±.010. [See Fig. 15.7b and c.]

(c) The second decimal place in a two-place decimal should preferably be an even digit (.02, .04, .06 are preferred to .01, .03, .05, etc.), so that when divided by two, as in obtaining a radius from a diameter, the result will remain a two-place decimal. Odd two-place decimals are used where necessary for design reasons; as, to provide clearance, strength, smooth curves, etc.

(d) Common fractions may be used to indicate standard nominal sizes of materials, punched holes, drilled holes, threads, keyways and other features produced by tools that are so designated. Example: $\frac{1}{4}$-20UNC-2A; $\frac{5}{16}$ Drill; Stock $\frac{5}{8} \times \frac{7}{8}$.

(e) Where it is desired to use decimals exclusively, nominal sizes of materials, threads and other features produced by commercial tools may be expressed in decimal equivalents of commercial sizes; as, .625 HEX.

GENERAL DIMENSIONING PRACTICES

15.10. Selection and placement of dimensions and notes. The reasonable application of the selected dimensioning practices that follow should enable a student to dimension acceptably. The practices in bold-face type should never be violated. In fact, these have been so definitely established by practice that they might be called rules.

1. Place dimensions using either of two recognized methods—aligned or unidirectional.

Fig. 15.15. Reading Dimensions Aligned.

a. Aligned method. Place the numerals for the dimension values so that they are readable from the bottom and right side of the drawing. An aligned expression is placed along and in the direction of the dimension line. (See Fig. 15.15.) Make the values for oblique dimensions readable from the directions shown in Fig. 15.16.

Fig. 15.16. Reading Oblique Dimensions-Aligned.

All dimension values read from bottom

Fig. 15.17. Reading Dimensions-Unidirectional.

GOOD PRACTICE

(a)

POOR PRACTICE

(b)

Fig. 15.18. Placing Dimensions.

b. Unidirectional method. Place the numerals for the dimension values so that they can be read from the bottom of the drawing. (See Fig. 15.17.) The fraction bar for a common fraction should be parallel to the bottom of the drawing (Fig. 15.23).

2. Place dimensions outside a view, unless they will be more easily and quickly understood if shown on it. (See Figs. 15.18 and 15.19.)

3. Place dimensions between views unless the rules, such as the contour rule, the rule against crowding, and so forth, prevent their being so placed.

4. Do not use an object line or a center line as a dimension line.

5. Locate dimension lines so that they will not cross extension lines.

6. If possible, avoid crossing two dimension lines.

Some dimensions may be placed on a view for added clearness and ease of reading

Keep area around numerical values free of section lines

Fig. 15.19. Dimensions on the View.

Fig. 15.20.   Extended Center Line.

Fig. 15.21.   Spacing Dimension Lines.

7. A center line may be extended to serve as an extension line (Fig. 15.20).

8. Keep parallel dimensions equally spaced (usually $\frac{3}{8}''$ apart) and the figures staggered (see Fig. 15.21).

9. Always give locating dimensions to the centers of circles that represent holes, cylindrical projections, or bosses (Fig. 15.22).

Fig. 15.22.   Locating Holes.

Fig. 15.23.   Contour Principle of Dimensioning.

10. If possible, attach the location dimensions for holes to the view upon which they appear as circles (Fig. 15.23).

11. Group related dimensions on the view showing the contour of a feature (Fig. 15.23).

12. Arrange a series of dimensions in a continuous line (Fig. 15.24).

13. Dimension from a finished surface, center line, or base line that can be readily established (Fig. 15.25).

14. Stagger the figures in a series of parallel dimension lines to allow sufficient space for the figures and to prevent confusion (Fig. 15.26).

15. Place longer dimensions outside shorter ones so that extension lines will not cross dimension lines (Fig. 15.27).

16. Give three over-all dimensions located outside any other dimensions (unless the piece has cylindrical ends).

Fig. 15.24.   **Consecutive Dimensions.**

ALL FILLETS & ROUNDS $\frac{1}{8}^R$ UNLESS OTHERWISE SPECIFIED

Fig. 15.25.   **Dimensioning a Bracket.**

Fig. 15.26.   **Parallel Dimensions.**   Fig. 15.27.   **Long and Short Dimensions.**

Fig. 15.28. Omit Unnecessary Dimensions.

Fig. 15.29. Dimension Figures on a Section View.

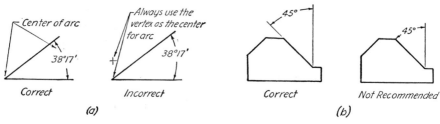

Fig. 15.30. To Dimension an Angle.

17. When an over-all is given, one intermediate distance should be omitted unless noted (REF.) as being given for reference (Fig. 15.28).

18. Do not repeat a dimension. One of the duplicated dimensions may be missed if a change is made. Give only those dimensions that are necessary to produce or inspect the part.

19. Make decimal points of a sufficient size so that dimensions cannot be misread.

20. When dimension figures appear on a sectional view, show them in a small uncrosshatched portion so that they may be easily read. This may be accomplished by doing the section lining after the dimensioning has been completed (Fig. 15.29).

21. When an arc is used as a dimension line for an angular measurement, use the vertex of the angle as the center (Fig. 15.30a). It is usually undesirable to terminate the dimension line for an angle at lines that represent surfaces. It is better practice to use an extension line (Fig. 15.30b).

Fig. 15.31. Angular Dimensions.

22. Place the figures of angular dimensions so they will read from the bottom of a drawing, except in the case of large angles (Fig. 15.31).

23. Always dimension an arc by giving its radius followed by the abbreviation R, and indicate the center with a small cross. (Note that the arrowhead is omitted at the center (Fig. 15.32).)

Fig. 15.32. Dimensioning Radii.   Fig. 15.33.   Dimensioning a Cylindrical Piece.

24. Show the diameter of a circle, never the radius. If it is not clear that the dimension is a diameter, the figures should be followed by the abbreviation D or DIA (Figs. 15.33 and 15.35). Often this will allow the elimination of one view.

25. When dimensioning a portion of a sphere with a radius the term SPHER. R is added (Fig. 15.34).

26. Letter all notes horizontally.

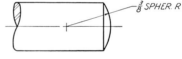

Fig. 15.34. Dimensioning a Piece with a Spherical End.

27. Make dimensioning complete, so that it will not be necessary for a workman to add or subtract to obtain a desired dimension or to scale the drawing.

Fig. 15.35. Dimensioning Machined Cylinders.

Fig. 15.36. Dimensioning Cored and Bored Holes.

28. Letter the word *bore* or *core* with the diameter of bored or cored holes (Fig. 15.36).

29. Give the diameter of a circular hole, never the radius, because all hole-forming tools are specified by diameter. If the hole does not go through the piece, the depth may be given as a note (Fig. 15.37).

Fig. 15.37.   Dimensioning Holes.

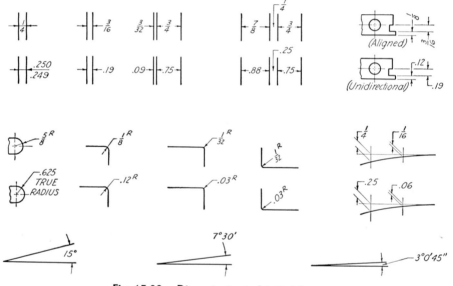

Fig. 15.38.   Dimensioning in Limited Spaces.

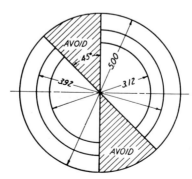

Fig. 15.39.   Areas to Avoid.

30. Never crowd dimensions into small spaces. Use the practical methods suggested in Fig. 15.38.

31. Avoid placing inclined dimensions in the shaded areas shown in Fig. 15.39. Place them so that they may be conveniently read from the right side of the drawing. If this is not desirable, make the figures read from the left in the direction of the dimension line (Fig. 15.40a). The unidirectional method is shown in (b).

32. Omit superfluous dimensions. Do not supply dimensional information for the same feature in two different ways.

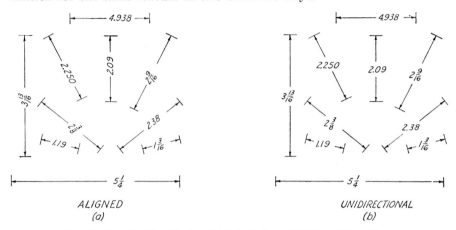

ALIGNED
(a)

UNIDIRECTIONAL
(b)

Fig. 15.40.   Reading Horizontal, Vertical, and Oblique Dimensions.

Fig. 15.41.   Dimension Values.

33. Give dimensions up to 72″ in inches, except on structural and architectural drawings (Fig. 15.41). Omit the inch marks when all dimensions are in inches.

34. Show dimensions in feet and inches as illustrated in Fig. 15.42. Note that the use of the hyphen in (a) and (b), and the cipher in (b), eliminates any chance of uncertainty and misinterpretation.

(a)

(b)

Fig. 15.42.   Feet and Inches.

35. If feasible, design a piece and its elemental parts to such dimensions as $\frac{3}{8}''$, $\frac{1}{2}''$, $\frac{5}{8}''$ or .40 and .50. Avoid such fractions as $\frac{17}{32}''$ and $\frac{19}{64}''$ and decimals as .19 and .53.

36. Dimension a chamfer by giving the angle and length as shown in Fig. 15.43. For a 45° angle only, it is permissible to give the needed information as a note. The word chamfer may be omitted in the note form.

Fig. 15.43.   Dimensioning a Chamfer.

37. Equally spaced holes in a circular flange may be dimensioned by giving the diameter of the bolt circle, across the circular center line, and the size and number of holes, in a note (Fig. 15.44).

Fig. 15.44.   Equally Spaced Holes.*

38. When holes are unequally spaced on a circular center line, give the angles as illustrated in Fig. 15.45.

39. Holes that must be accurately located should have their location established by the co-ordinate method. Holes arranged in a circle may be located as shown in Fig. 15.46 rather than through the use of angular measurements. Figure 15.47 shows the application of the co-ordinate method to the location of holes arranged in a general rectangular form. The method with all dimensions referred to datum lines is sometimes called base-line dimensioning.

40. Dimension a curved line by giving offsets or radii.

a. A non-circular curve may be dimensioned by the co-ordinate method illustrated in Fig. 15.48. Offset measurements are given from datum lines.

Fig. 15.45.   Locating Holes on a Circle by Polar Co-ordinates.*   Fig. 15.46.   Accurate Location Dimensioning of Holes.*

* ASA Y14.5–1957.

Fig. 15.47.   Location Dimensioning of Holes.

Fractions of an inch
replace the two-place
decimals when the fractional
system is used

Fig. 15.48.   Dimensioning Curves by Offsets.

b. A curved line, which is composed of circular arcs, should be dimensioned by giving the radii and locations of either the centers or points of tangency.   (See Fig. 15.49.)

Fig. 15.49.   Dimensioning Curves by Radii.

41. Show an offset dimension line for an arc having an inaccessible center (Fig. 15.49). Locate with true dimensions the point placed in a convenient location that represents the true center.

42. Dimension, as required by the method of production, a piece with rounded ends. (See Figs. 15.50–15.53.)

a. Give radii and center-to-center distance on parts that would be laid out by using centers and radii. Do not show an over-all dimension. It is not required. (See Fig. 15.50.)

Fig. 15.50. Dimensioning a Piece with Rounded Ends.

Fig. 15.51. Slot to Provide for Adjustment.

Fig. 15.52. Slots Performing a Mechanical Function.

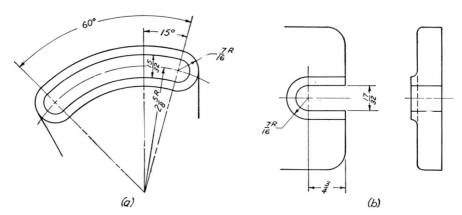

(a)

(b)

Fig. 15.53. Dimensioning Semicircular Features.

b. Slots that are to provide for adjustment are dimensioned by over-all length and width dimensions and are located by dimensions given to their center lines. (See Fig. 15.51.)

c. Slots that are to perform a mechanical function are dimensioned from center-to-center as two partial holes. The R is given to indicate a true radius. Slots of this type are subject to gage inspection. (See Fig. 15.52.)

d. Give the width and over-all length for Pratt and Whitney keyways because this is the manner in which the keys are specified.

43. A keyway on a shaft or hub should be dimensioned as shown in Fig. 15.54. Woodruff keyslots are dimensioned as shown in (*b*).

44. When knurls are to provide a rough surface for better grip, it is necessary to specify the pitch and kind of knurl as shown in Fig. 15.55(*a*)

and (b).   When specifying knurling for a press fit, it is the best practice to give the diameter before knurling with a tolerance and include the minimum diameter after knurling in the note that gives the pitch and type of knurl as shown in (c).

(a) Keyways for Stock Keys

(b) Woodruff Keyslots

Fig. 15.54.   Dimensioning Keyways and Keyslots. *

Fig. 15.55.   Dimensioning Knurls.

Fig. 15.56.   Dimensioning a Dovetail Slot and Tongue.

Fig. 15.57.   Profile Dimensioning. †

45. Snug fitting dovetailed parts should be dimensioned with tolerances as shown in Fig. 15.56.   Dimensions are given to sharp corners. Flats may be substituted for rounded corners if desired.

46. In sheet-metal work mold lines are used in dimensioning instead of the centers of the arcs.   (See Fig. 15.57.)   A mold line (construction

* ASA Y14.5–1957.
† ASA Z14.1–1946.

line) is the line at the intersection of the plane surfaces adjoining a bend. The formula for bend allowance is given in Fig. 10.3.

47. Dimension standard and special tapers as illustrated in Fig. 15.58. Standard tapers require one diameter, the length, and a note specifying the taper by number. The usual practice is to give the diameter at the large end.

Fig. 15.58. Dimensioning Tapers.

Special conical tapers may be dimensioned in different ways, as illustrated in (b), (c), and (d). The recommendation given in ASA Y14.5–1957 reads as follows:

Conical tapers. The following dimensions may be given in different combinations, to specify the size and form of tapered conical surfaces:

   (a) the diameter at each end of the taper;
   (b) the length of the taper;
   (c) the diameter at a selected cross-sectional plane; this plane may or may not be within the length of the tapered piece;
   (d) the distance locating a cross-sectional plane at which a diameter is specified;
   (e) the rate of taper;
   (f) the included angle.

The dimensioning of non-critical tapers is shown in (b) and (c). The dimensions and notes given in (d) are considered adequate for tapers which engage one another permanently or intermittently.

Flat tapers may be dimensioned as shown in (*e*).

When given in a note, taper may be specified either in inches per foot or inches per inch.   (See *d* and *e*.)

48. A half section may be dimensioned through the use of hidden lines on the external portion of the view (Fig. 15.59).

49. The fact that a dimension is out of scale may be indicated either by a wavy line placed underneath the dimension value or by the use of the abbreviation NTS with the dimension figures.   (See Fig. 15.60.)

Fig. 15.59. Dimensioning a Half-Section.

15.11. Dimensions from datum.   When it is necessary to locate the holes and surfaces of a part with a considerable degree of accuracy, it is the usual practice to specify their position by dimensions given from a datum (Fig. 15.61) in order to avoid cumulative tolerances.   By this method the different features of a part are located with respect to carefully selected datums and not with respect to each other (Fig. 15.47). Lines and surfaces that are selected to serve as datums must be easily recognizable and accessible during production.   Corresponding datum points, lines, or surfaces must be used as datums on mating parts.

15.12. Notes (Fig. 15.62).   The use of properly composed notes often adds clarity to the presentation of dimensional information involv-

Fig. 15.60.   Dimension Out of Scale.

Fig. 15.61.   Dimensions from Datum Lines.*

ing specific operations.   Notes also are used to convey supplementary instructions about the kind of material, kind of fit, degree of finish, and so forth.   It is good practice to specify a dimension representing a tool operation or a series of tool operations by a note rather than by figured dimensions.   Brevity in form is desirable for notes of general information or specific instruction.

RULES FOR THE FORMULATION AND PLACEMENT OF SHOP NOTES

1. Give the size first, then the machining operation.
EXAMPLE: $\frac{17}{32}$ DRILL.

2. In the case of threaded parts, use the terminology recommended by the ASA for the American-British unified thread.
EXAMPLE: $\frac{1}{2}$-13UNC-2A.

3. Where there are several holes alike in a group, use one note and indicate the number of holes.
EXAMPLE: $\frac{1}{2}$ DRILL-4 HOLES.

4. Where there are two or more similar groups, repeat the entire note for each group.

_____
* ASA Y14.5–1957.

$\frac{3}{4}$ DRILL - $\frac{3}{4}$ DEEP

$\frac{55}{64}$ DRILL
.875 / .877 REAM

$\frac{19}{32}$ DRILL - 82° C'SK TO $1\frac{1}{32}$ D

$\frac{17}{32}$ DRILL
$1\frac{1}{16}$ SPOTFACE - 4 HOLES

$\frac{21}{32}$ DRILL - $\frac{29}{32}$ C'BORE
$\frac{3}{8}$ DEEP - 4 HOLES

(a)   (b)   (c)   (d)   (e)

WOODRUFF KEYSEAT #606

KEYSEAT .188 WIDE × .188 DEEP

1.250

NECK $\frac{1}{8}$ WIDE × $\frac{1}{16}$ DEEP

$\frac{5}{8}$ - 11 UNC-2A

SPOT FOR SET SCREW WITH
PC #10 IN POSITION

.06 × 45° CHAMFER

33 P. DIAMOND KNURL $\frac{1}{4}$ DEEP

Pitch

35° $^{-0°}_{+5°}$ CHAMFER TO
DEPTH OF THD.

(f)   (g)

KEYWAY .188 WIDE × .109 DEEP

DRILL & REAM FOR
#1 TAPER PIN WITH
PC #5 IN POSITION

$\frac{11}{32}$ DRILL $\frac{1}{8}$ - NPT

.250-20 UNC-2B
(S.A.E. Standard)

.06 SAWCUT

(h)   (j)   (k)   (m)

FILLETS AND ROUNDS $\frac{1}{8}$ R EXCEPT AS SHOWN

FINISH ALL OVER

SANDBLAST

PEEN OVER IN ASSEMBLY

POLISH TO REMOVE ALL TOOL MARKS

$\frac{3}{8}$ DRILL - 3 HOLES EQUALLY SPACED

BREAK ALL SHARP EDGES

ALL DRAFT ANGLES 7° UNLESS
                    OTHERWISE SPECIFIED

GRIND

2 REQ'D

UNDERCUT $\frac{1}{4}$ WIDE × $\frac{1}{8}$ DEEP

BROACH

HEAT-TREAT

PICKLE

TUMBLE

(n)

Fig. 15.62. Shop Notes.

5. For drilled holes and reamed holes, give the diameter, the operation required, and the depth.   If the hole goes all the way through the piece, the depth should be omitted.

6. For a tapped (threaded) hole, give the tap-drill size, the diameter of the screw, the number of threads per inch, the kind of thread, and the thread class. (See Fig. 16.20.) The depth is omitted if the hole goes all the way through the piece. Depth measurements for drilled and tapped holes are shown in Fig. 15.63.

Fig. 15.63.   Depth of Drilled and Tapped Holes.

7. Locate the notes for a piece in such a way that they will not overlap the adjacent views of another piece on the same drawing.

8. Notes should not be placed on views or near the lines of a drawing. Use leaders to clarify their purpose.

9. When putting a shop note for a hole on a drawing, if possible, make the leader point to the circular view.

10. If a single note is applicable to similar holes on two adjacent pieces on the same drawing, it should not be used as a common reference but should be repeated for each piece.

11. *Good practice.*   In the formulation of shop notes, it is good practice to supply all necessary information.   For example, although 5-40NC-2 is considered by many to be a satisfactory note, it is much better to add the tap-drill size thus: #38(.1015) DRILL, 5-40NC-2.

In the case of reamed holes, the drill should accompany the note, as for example: $\frac{31}{64}$ DRILL $\frac{.5000}{.5010}$ REAM.   This will relieve the engineering department of any responsibility in case the wrong drill should be used.

LIMIT DIMENSIONING AND GEOMETRIC TOLERANCING

15.13. Limit dimensions.   Present-day competitive manufacturing requires quantity production and interchangeability for many closely mating parts.   The production of each of these mating parts to an exact decimal dimension, although theoretically possible, is economically unfeasible, since the cost of a part rapidly increases as an absolute correct size is approached.   For this reason, the commercial draftsman specifies an allowable error (tolerance) between decimal limits (Fig. 15.64).   The determination of these limits depends upon the accuracy and clearance required for the moving parts to function satisfactorily in the machine. Although manufacturing experience is often used to determine the proper limits for the parts of a mechanism, it is better and safer practice to adhere to the fits recommended by the American Standards Association in ASA B4.1–1955.   This standard applies to fits between plain cylindrical parts. Recommendations are made for preferred sizes, allowances, tolerances, and fits for use where applicable.   Up to a diameter of 20 inches the standard is in accordance with ABC (American-British-Canadian) conference agreements.

There are many factors that a designer must take into consideration when selecting fits for a particular application. These factors might be the bearing load, speed, lubrication, materials, and length of engagement. Frequently temperature and humidity must be taken into account. Considerable practical experience is necessary to make a selection of fits or to make the subsequent adjustments that might be needed to satisfy critical functional requirements. In addition, manufacturing economy must never be overlooked.

Those interested in the selection of fits should consult texts on machine design and technical publications, for coverage of this phase of the dimensioning of cylindrical parts is not within the scope of this book. However, since it is desirable to be able to determine limits of size following the selection of a fit, attention in this section will be directed to the use of

Fig. 15.64. Limit Dimensioning.

Table XXX. Whenever the fit to be used for a particular application has not been specified in the instructions for a problem or has not been given on the drawing, the student should consult his instructor after a tentative choice has been made based on the brief descriptions of fits as given in this section.

To compute limit dimensions it is necessary to understand the following associated terms.*

Nominal Size. The nominal size is the designation which is used for the purpose of general identification.

Basic Size. The basic size is that size from which the limits of size are derived by the application of allowances and tolerances.

Allowance. An allowance is an intentional difference between the maximum material limits of mating parts. It is a minimum clearance (positive allowance) or maximum interference (negative allowance) between mating parts.

---

* Extracted from American Standard Preferred Limits and Fits for Cylindrical Parts (ASA B4.1–1955) with permission of the publisher, The American Society of Mechanical Engineers, 29 W. 39th St., New York 18, N.Y.

Tolerance. A tolerance is the total permissible variation of a size. The tolerance is the difference between the limits of size.

Limits of Size. The limits of size are the applicable maximum and minimum sizes.

Fit. Fit is the general term used to signify the range of tightness which may result from the application of a specific combination of allowances and tolerances in the design of mating parts.

Clearance Fit. A clearance fit is one having limits of size so prescribed that a clearance always results when mating parts are assembled.

Interference Fit. An interference fit is one having limits of size so prescribed that an interference always results when mating parts are assembled.

Transition Fit. A transition fit is one having limits of size so prescribed that either a clearance or an interference may result when mating parts are assembled.

Basic Hole System. A basic hole system is a system of fits in which the design size of the hole is the basic size and the allowance is applied to the shaft.

Basic Shaft System. A basic shaft system is a system of fits in which the design size of the shaft is the basic size and the allowance is applied to the hole.

Tables XXX-A, B, C, D, and E cover three general types of fits: running fits, locational fits, and force fits. For educational purposes standard fits may be designated by means of letter symbols as follows:

    RC—Running or Sliding Fit
    LC—Locational Clearance Fit
    LT—Transition Fit
    LN—Locational Interference Fit
    FN—Force or Shrink Fit

It should be understood that these letters are not to appear on working drawings. Only the limits for sizes are shown.

When a number is added to these letter symbols a complete fit is represented. For example FN4 specifies symbolically a class 4 force fit for which the limits of size for mating parts may be determined from use of Table XXX-E. The minimum and maximum limits of clearance or interference for a particular application may be read directly from this table.

Classes of fits as given in these tables are as follows:

    Running and sliding fits—Classes RC1 through RC9
    Clearance locational fits—Classes LC1 through LC11
    Transition locational fits—Classes LT1 through LT7
    Interference locational fits—Classes LN2 and LN3
    Force and Shrink fits—Classes FN1 through FN5

*Running and Sliding Fits.** Running and sliding fits are intended to provide a similar running performance, with suitable lubrication allowance, throughout the range of sizes. The clearances for the first two classes, used chiefy as slide fits, increase more slowly with diameter than the other classes, so that accurate location is maintained even at the expense of free relative motion.

A brief description of the fits is given here. For a more complete understanding one should read and study the standard.

* Extracted from American Standard Preferred Limits and Fits for Cylindrical Parts (ASA B4.1–1955).

RC1—Close sliding fits are intended for accurate location of parts which must assemble without perceptible play.

RC2—Sliding fits are intended for accurate location but with greater maximum clearance than Class RC1.

RC3—Precision running fits are about the closest fits which can be expected to run freely and are intended for precision work at slow speeds and light journal pressures, ...

RC4—Close running fits are intended chiefly for running fits on accurate machinery with moderate surface speeds and journal pressures, ...

RC5⎱ Medium running fits are intended for higher running speeds, or heavy
RC6⎰ journal pressures, or both.

RC7—Free running fits are intended for use where accuracy is not essential or where large temperature variations are likely to be encountered, ...

RC8⎱ Loose running fits are intended for use where materials such as cold-
RC9⎰ rolled shafting and tubing, made to commercial tolerances, are involved.

*Locational Fits.** Locational fits are divided into three groups: clearance fits (LC), transition fits (LT), and interference fits (LN).

LC. Locational clearance fits are intended for parts which are normally stationary, but which can be freely assembled or disassembled. They run from snug fits for parts requiring accuracy of location, through the medium clearance fits for parts such as spigots, to the closer fastener fits where freedom of assembly is of prime importance.

LT. Transition fits are a compromise between clearance and interference fits, for application where accuracy of location is important, but either a small amount of clearance or interference is permissible.

LN. Locational interference fits are used where accuracy of location is of prime importance, and for parts requiring rigidity and alignment with no special requirements for bore pressure.

*Force Fits.** Force or shrink fits constitute a special type of interference fit, normally characterized by maintenance of constant bore pressures throughout the range of sizes.

FN1—Light drive fits are those requiring light assembly pressures, and produce more or less permanent assemblies.

FN2—Medium drive fits are suitable for ordinary steel parts, or for shrink fits on light sections.

FN3—Heavy drive fits are suitable for heavier steel parts, or for shrink fits in medium sections.

FN4⎱ Force fits are suitable for parts which can be highly stressed, or for
FN5⎰ shrink fits where the heavy pressing forces required are impractical.

15.14. Computation of limits of size for cylindrical parts. To obtain the correct fit between two engaging parts, compute limit dimensions that modify the nominal size of both. Numerical values of the modifications necessary to obtain the proper allowance and tolerances for various diameters for all fits mentioned previously are given in Tables XXX-A, B, C, D, and E in the Appendix.

---

*Extracted from American Standard Preferred Limits and Fits for Cylindrical Parts (ASA B4.1–1955).

The two systems in common use for computing limit dimensions are (1) the basic hole system, and (2) the basic shaft system. The same American Standard tables may be used conveniently for both systems.

15.15. Basic hole system. Because most limit dimensions are computed on the basic hole system, the illustrated example shown in Fig. 15.65 involves the use of this system. If, as is the usual case, the nominal size is known, all that is necessary to determine the limits is to convert the

LIMITS FOR HOLE

0.5000 + 0.0000 = 0.5000
0.5000 + 0.0010 = 0.5010

LIMITS FOR SHAFT

0.5000 − 0.0012 = 0.4988
0.5000 − 0.0022 = 0.4978

HOLE   SHAFT   HOLE   SHAFT

NOMINAL SIZE   COMPUTATIONS   LIMITS
(a)   (b)   (c)

Fig. 15.65.   Computation of Limits (Basic Hole System).

nominal size to the basic hole size and apply the figures given under "standard limits," adding or subtracting (according to their signs) to or from the basic size to obtain the limits for both the hole and the shaft.

EXAMPLE:

Suppose that a $\frac{1}{2}''$ shaft is to have a class RC6 fit in a $\frac{1}{2}''$ hole (Fig. 15.65a). The nominal size of the hole is $\frac{1}{2}''$. The basic hole size is the exact theoretical size 0.5000.

From Table XXX it is found that the hole may vary between plus 0.0000 and plus 0.0010, and the shaft between −0.0012 and −0.0022. The tolerance on both mating parts is 0.0010, and the allowance (minimum clearance) is 0.0012 as given in the table.

The limits on the hole are: $\dfrac{(0.5000 \text{ plus } 0.0000)}{(0.5000 \text{ plus } 0.0010)} = \dfrac{0.5000}{0.5010}$

The limits on the shaft are: $\dfrac{(0.5000 - 0.0012)}{(0.5000 - 0.0022)} = \dfrac{0.4988}{0.4978}$

The limits are placed in the order in which they will be approached when the part is machined (Fig. 15.65c). The minimum limit should appear above the line for an internal dimension, and the maximum limit above for an external dimension.

15.16. Basic shaft system. When a number of parts requiring different fits but having the same nominal size must be mounted upon a shaft, the basic shaft system is used because it is much easier to adjust the limits for the holes than to machine a shaft of one nominal diameter to a number of different sets of limits required by different fits.

For basic shaft fits the maximum size of the shaft is basic. The limits of clearance or interference are the same as those shown in Tables XXX-A, B, C, D and E for the corresponding fits. The symbols for basic shaft fits are identical with those used for the standard fits with a letter S added.

For example, LC4S specifies a clearance locational fit, class 4, as determined on a basic shaft basis.

To determine the limits for size under this system, the limits for hole and shaft as given in Tables XXXA-E are increased for clearance fits, or decreased for transition or interference fits by the value shown for the upper shaft limit which is the amount required to change the maximum shaft to basic size.

15.17. Tolerances. Necessary tolerances may be expressed by general notes printed on a drawing form or they may be given with definite values for specific dimensions (Fig. 15.64). When expressed in the form of a printed note, the wording might be as follows: ALLOWABLE VARIATION ON ALL FRACTIONAL DIMENSIONS IS ± 0.10 UNLESS OTHERWISE SPECIFIED. A general note for tolerance on decimal dimensions might read: ALLOWABLE VARIATION ON DECIMAL DIMENSIONS IS $\pm .001$. This general note would apply to all decimal dimensions where limits were not given.

The general notes on tolerances should be allowed to apply to all dimensions where it is not necessary to use specific tolerances.

15.18. Unilateral tolerances. Unilateral tolerances may be expressed in any one of several ways as shown in Fig. 15.66.

Fig. 15.66.   Unilateral Tolerances.

Two limits may be given as in (a) or the basic size can be shown to the required number of decimal places, followed by a plus tolerance above a minus tolerance as in (b). Another method illustrated in (c) gives the preferred dimension with a tolerance that may be plus or minus but not both. When the dimension is given as a fraction the zero tolerance is expressed by a 0 (cipher).

Fig. 15.67.   Bilateral Tolerances.

15.19. Bilateral tolerances. Bilateral tolerances are expressed with a divided tolerance (Fig. 15.67). Whenever the plus and minus values are unequal as in (c) the plus value is placed above the dimension line.

15.20. Cumulative tolerances. An undesirable condition may result when either the location of a surface or an over-all dimension is affected by more than one tolerance dimension. When this condition exists as illustrated in Fig. 15.68(a) the tolerances are said to be cumulative. It can be noted in (a) where the dimensions are continuous from surface-to-surface that there is a permissible variation of only 0.005 in the over-all length of the piece while at the same time it is not unreasonable to expect all dimensions to vary between either the extreme high or low limits. If minimum tolerances are obtained between all surfaces, the length of the part could be 3.980 as against a minimum specified length of 3.995. If it is necessary to maintain the over-all dimension within the specified limits, the allowable variation of 0.005 must be distributed among the four dimensions. This would increase manufacturing costs because the machinist would find it necessary to work to limits closer than

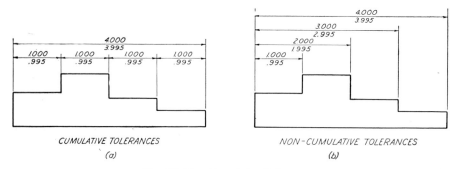

CUMULATIVE TOLERANCES
(a)

NON-CUMULATIVE TOLERANCES
(b)

Fig. 15.68. Cumulative Tolerances.

THESE SURFACES MUST BE
PARALLEL WITHIN .002

ALL DIAMETERS MARKED ₵ TO BE
CONCENTRIC WITHIN .002
FULL INDICATOR READING

THIS SURFACE TO BE FINISHED TO MAXIMUM OF
4 MICRO-INCHES ROOT MEAN SQUARE

Fig. 15.69. Tolerance of Concentricity and Parallelism.

those that are specified. In order to avoid this situation, it is the preferred practice to locate the surfaces from a datum plane as shown in (b), so that each surface is affected by only one dimension. The use of a datum plane makes it possible to take full advantage of permissible variations in size and still satisfy all requirements for the proper functioning of the part.

15.21. Production tolerances. Whenever extreme accuracy is required for the production of parts it becomes necessary to specify tolerances for concentricity, squareness, parallelism, and flatness. The tolerances for these features are usually expressed in notes. See Figs. 15.64 and 15.69.

15.22. Specification of angular tolerances. Angular tolerances may be expressed in degrees, minutes, or seconds. (See Fig. 15.70.) If desired, an angle may be given in degrees and decimal parts of a degree with the tolerance in decimal parts of a degree.

15.23. Geometrical tolerancing. Geometrical tolerances specify the maximum variation that can be allowed in form or position from true geometry. Actually, a geometrical tolerance is either the width or diameter of a tolerance zone within which a surface or axis of a hole or cylinder can lie with the resulting part satisfying the necessary standards of accuracy for proper functioning and interchangeability. Whenever tolerances of form are not specified on a drawing for a part, it is understood that the

Fig. 15.70. Angular Tolerances.

Fig. 15.71. Specification for Straightness.

Fig. 15.72. Specification for Flatness.

part as produced will be acceptable regardless of form variations. Expressions of tolerances of form control straightness, flatness, parallelism, squareness, concentricity, roundness, angular displacement, and so forth.

15.24. Tolerance specification for straightness. Straightness is specified by a note that is lettered on the drawing in the form shown at the left in Fig. 15.71. The significance of the note is illustrated by the drawing at the right.

15.25. Tolerance specification for flatness. The note used to control flatness requires that all points of the actual surface must lie between two parallel planes that are a distance apart equal to the specified tolerance. (See Fig. 15.72.) The expressions MUST NOT BE CONCAVE or MUST NOT BE CONVEX may be added to the specification note if desired.

15.26. Tolerance specification for squareness. The notes used to govern squareness and their significance are shown in Figures 15.73 and

15.74. It should be noted that for the condition illustrated in Fig. 15.73, the tolerance zone is cylindrical.

15.27. Tolerance specification for parallelism. The form of note to be used to control parallelism is shown in Fig. 15.75. In using this

Fig. 15.73. Specification for Squareness.

Fig. 15.74. Specification for Squareness.

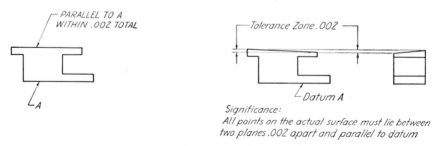

Fig. 15.75. Specification for Parallelism.

method, the datum is considered as a plane established by the high points of surface A. All points of the other surface must lie between two planes that are parallel to the datum.

15.28. Tolerance specification for concentricity. When the cylindrical or conical features of a part must be basically concentric, it is the usual practice to specify the permissible eccentricity in terms of the

maximum permissible deviation from concentricity.   The form of note
that is commonly used is shown in Fig. 15.76.

15.29. Tolerance specification for angularity.   The note that is
commonly used to specify the tolerance for control of angularity is shown
in Fig. 15.77.   The term angularity is used to define the relation of such
features as surfaces, axes, and so forth, to each other when they are not
perpendicular.

15.30. True position dimensioning.   In the past, it has been the
usual practice to locate points by means of rectangular dimensions given
with tolerances.   A point located in this manner lies within a square or

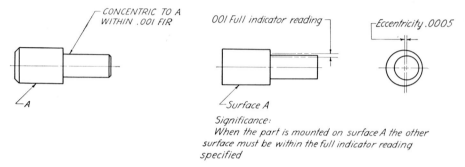

Fig. 15.76.   Specification for Concentricity.

Fig. 15.77.   Specification for Angularity.

rectangular area.   However, this method frequently does not convey the
engineering intent nor does it take full account of the relations that must
be maintained for the interchangeable assembly of mating parts.   True
position dimensioning locates the point within a circular area.

Positional tolerancing can be used for specific features of a machine
part.   When the part contains a number of features arranged in groups,
positional tolerances can be used to relate each of the groups to one
another as necessary and to tolerance the position of the features within
a group independently of the features of the other groups.

The term "true position" denotes the theoretically exact position for
a feature.   In practice, the basic (exact) location is given with untoler-
anced dimensions as shown in Fig. 15.78.   Then, an expression such as
LOCATED AT TRUE POSITION WITHIN .XXX DIA. or LOCATED
WITHIN .XXXR OF TRUE POSITION is added to the normal note

specifying the size of the feature to be located.   When the alignment
between mating parts depends upon some functional feature, this feature
is selected as a datum, and the datum is identified in the note.   Such a
note might read: XX HOLES LOCATED WITHIN .XXXR OF TRUE
POSITION IN RELATION TO DATUM A.

The requirement of true position dimensioning for a cylindrical feature
is illustrated in Fig. 15.79(a).   As must be understood, the axis of the

Fig. 15.78.   True Position Dimensioning.

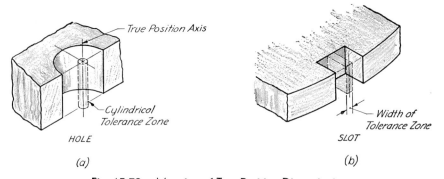

Fig. 15.79.   Meaning of True Position Dimensioning.

hole at all points must lie within the specified cylindrical tolerance zone
having its center located at true position.   This cylindrical tolerance zone
also defines the limits within which variations in the squareness of the
axis of the hole in relation to the flat surface must be confined.

In applying true position dimensioning to noncylindrical features,
such as slots, dovetails, serrations, and so forth, it will be found that the
principal difference is in the geometrical form of the tolerance zone.   The
note specifying slots might read: 6 SLOTS EQUALLY SPACED AND
LOCATED WITHIN .005 EACH SIDE OF TRUE POSITION.   The
expression .005 EACH SIDE OF TRUE POSITION specifies that the
axis of the slot must fall within a rectangular tolerance zone as shown in

Fig. 15.79(b). The tolerance zone must be symmetrically disposed on each side of true position by the amount of the true position tolerance.

The illustrations used with this discussion have been presented with the sole idea of showing briefly what is meant by true position dimensioning. They are not to be thought of as being practical examples. Dotted circles have been added to each illustration to call attention to the imaginary tolerance zones. Those who may have the need for the use of this method of tolerancing should consult Section 5, American Drafting Standards Manual (ASA Y14.5–1957) so as to acquire a full understanding of true position dimensioning.

15.31. Maximum material condition. Although, in general, tolerances of position are determined by the maximum metal condition of mating features, and limits of location must be strictly observed at times regardless of the actual finished size of mating components, there are situations in which the limits of center distance may be exceeded and acceptable parts produced when the finished sizes of mating features are away from maximum material conditions. With this latter condition permissible, it is desirable to indicate the fact that limits of center distance need be observed only under maximum material conditions. This is accomplished by a note reading as follows: $\frac{.500}{.502}$ 2 HOLES LOCATED AT TRUE POSITION WITHIN .010 DIA AT MMC. The letters MMC denote maximum material condition.

When maximum material condition is not used, and the exact positional tolerance applies regardless of the size of the feature, this fact should be indicated by a note. Such a note might read: 6 HOLES LOCATED AT TRUE POSITION WITHIN .010 DIA REGARDLESS OF HOLE SIZE or 6 HOLES LOCATED WITHIN .005R OF TRUE POSITION REGARDLESS OF HOLE SIZE.

Additional information concerning the meaning of MMC as related to positional tolerances may be found in the Appendix of ASA Y14.5–1957.

15.32. Surface quality. The improvement in machining methods within recent years coupled with a strong demand for increased life for machined parts has caused engineers to give more attention to the quality of the surface finish. Not only the service life but also the proper functioning of the part as well may depend upon obtaining the needed smoothness quality for contact surfaces.

On an engineering drawing a surface may be represented by line if shown in profile or it may appear as a bounded area in a related view. Machined and ground surfaces, however, do not have the perfect smoothness represented on a drawing. Actually a surface has three dimensions, namely, length, breadth, and curvature (waviness) as illustrated in Fig. 15.80(a). In addition there will be innumerable peaks and valleys of differing lengths, widths, and heights. An exaggerated profile of surface roughness is shown in (b). Combined waviness and roughness is illustrated in (c).

The following terms must be understood before the surface symbol shown in Fig. 15.81(a) can be properly applied.

Roughness. Roughness is the relatively finely spaced surface irregularities that are produced by the cutting action of tool edges and abrasive grains on surfaces that are machined.

Waviness. Waviness is the surface undulations that are of much greater magnitude than the roughness irregularities. Waviness may result from machine or work deflections, vibrations, warping, strains, or similar causes.

Lay. Lay is the predominate direction of the tool marks of the surface pattern. See Fig. 15.81(*b*).

Fig. 15.80. Surface Definitions Illustrated.

Fig. 15.81. Surface Quality Symbols.

Fig. 15.82. Application of Surface Finish Symbols.

Microinch. A microinch is one millionth (0.000001) of an inch.

The following was abstracted from the American Standard Publication "Drawings and Drafting Room Practice" (ASA Z14.1–1946):

A surface whose finish is to be specified should be marked with the finish mark having the general form of a check mark ($\checkmark$) so that the point of the symbol is

    (a) On the line indicating the surface,

    (b) On a leader pointing to the surface (Fig. 15.82).

Where it is desired to specify only the surface roughness height, and the width of roughness or direction of tool marks is not important, the simplest form of the symbol should be used. See Fig. 15.64. This height may be either maximum peak to valley height, average peak to valley height, or average deviation from the mean (RMS or arithmetical). The numerical value is placed in the $\checkmark$ as shown.

Where it is desired to specify waviness height in addition to roughness height a straight horizontal line should be added to the top of the simple symbol. See Fig. 15.81(*a*). The numerical value of height of waviness would be shown above this line.

Then, if the nature of the preferred lay is to be shown in addition to these two characteristics, it will be indicated by the addition of a combination of lines as shown in Fig. 15.81(*a*) and (*b*). The parallel and perpendicular part of the symbol indicates that the dominant lines on the surface are parallel or perpendicular to the boundary line of the surface in contact with the symbol.

The complete symbol, including the roughness width placed to the right of the lay symbol, is shown in Fig. 15.81(*a*).

The use of only one number to specify the height or width of roughness or waviness shall indicate the maximum value. Any lesser degree of roughness will be satisfactory. When two numbers are used separated by a dash, they indicate the maximum and minimum permissible values.

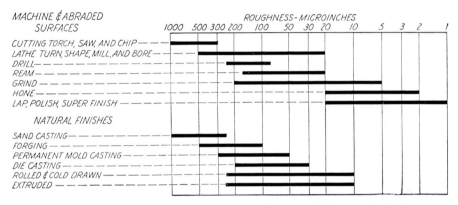

Fig. 15.83.   Surface Finishes Expected from Common Production Methods.

Surface finish should be specified only by experienced personnel because the function of many parts does not depend upon the smoothness quality of a surface or surfaces. In addition, surface quality need not be necessarily indicated for many parts that are produced to close dimensional tolerances because a satisfactory surface finish may result from the required machining processes. It should be remembered that the cost of producing a part will generally become progressively greater as the specification of surface finish becomes more exacting.

The chart in Fig. 15.83 shows the expected surface roughness in microinches for surfaces produced by common production methods.

The surface-quality symbol, which is used only when it is desirable to specify surface smoothness, should not be confused with a finish mark that indicates the removal of material. A surface-quality symbol might be used for a surface on a die-casting, forging, or extruded shape where the surface is to have a natural finish and no material is to be removed.

15.33. Problems. The following problems offer the student the opportunity to apply the rules of dimensioning given in this chapter.

1–2. (Figs. 15.84–15.85.) Reproduce the given views of an assigned part. Determine the dimensions by transferring them from the drawing to the open-

divided scale by means of the dividers.   Decimal-inch dimensioning is to be
used for the parts given in Fig. 15.85.

Fig. 15.84.   Dimensioning Problems.

Fig. 15.85.   Dimensioning Problems.

Representation and Specification of Threads and Fastenings

16

SCREW THREADS

16.1. In the commercial field, where the practical application of engineering drawing takes the form of working drawings, knowledge of screw threads and fasteners is important. There is always the necessity for assembling parts together either with permanent fastenings, such as rivets, or with bolts, screws, and so forth, which may be removed quite easily.

Fig. 16.1. Screw Thread Nomenclature.

Engineers, detailers, and draftsmen must be completely familiar with the common types of threads and fastenings, as well as with their use and correct methods of representation, because of the frequency of their occurrence in structures and machines. Information concerning special types of fasteners may be obtained from manufacturers' catalogues.

The beginner should study Fig. 16.1 to acquaint himself with the terms commonly associated with screw threads.

16.2. Threads. The principal uses of threads are: (1) for fastening, (2) for adjusting, and (3) for transmitting power. To satisfy most of the requirements of the engineering profession, the different forms of threads shown in Fig. 16.2 are used.

The American Standard form (National Form N) thread which is being replaced by the new unified thread form is still widely used in the United States. The sharp V is used to some extent where adjustment and holding power are essential.

For the transmission of power and motion, the modified square, Acme, and Brown and Sharpe worm threads have been adopted. The modified square thread, which is now rarely used, transmits power parallel to its axis. A still further modification of the square thread is the stronger Acme, which is easier to cut and more readily disengages split nuts (as lead screws on lathes). The Brown and Sharpe worm thread, with similar proportions but with longer teeth, is used for transmitting power to a worm wheel.

The knuckle thread, commonly found on incandescent lamps, plugs, and so on, can be cast or rolled.

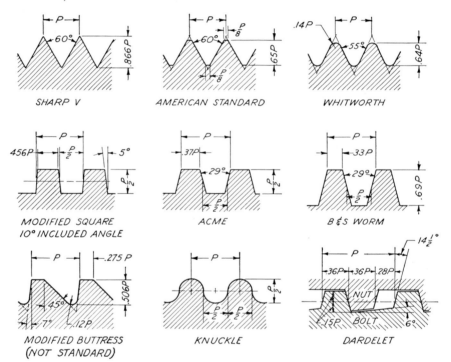

Fig. 16.2. Screw Threads.

The Whitworth and buttress threads are not often encountered by the average engineer. The former, which fulfills the same purpose as the American Standard thread, is used in England but is also frequently found in this country. The buttress or breech-block thread, which is designed to take pressure in one direction, is used for breech mechanisms of large guns and for airplane propeller hubs. The thread form has not been standardized and appears in different modified forms.

The Dardelet thread is self-locking in assembly.

16.3. American-British unified thread. The Unified Thread Standards (ASA B1.1–1949) came into existence after the representatives of the United States, Great Britain, and Canada signed a unification agreement on Nov. 18, 1948, in Washington, D.C. This accord, which made possible the interchangeability of threads for these countries, created a new thread form (Fig. 16.3) that is a compromise between our own American Standard design and the British Whitworth. The external thread of the new form has a rounded root and may have either a flat or rounded crest.

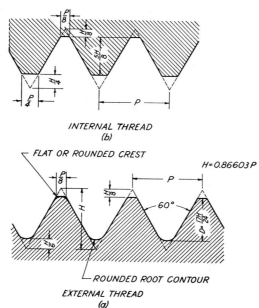

INTERNAL THREAD
(b)

EXTERNAL THREAD
(a)

Fig. 16.3. American-British Unified Thread (American Standard).

RIGHT-HAND   LEFT-HAND

Fig. 16.4. Right-Hand and Left-Hand Threads.

16.4. Right-hand and left-hand threads. A right-hand thread advances into a threaded hole when turned clockwise; a left-hand thread advances when turned counterclockwise. They can be easily distinguished by the thread slant. A right-hand thread on a horizontal shank always slants upward to the left $\diagdown$ and a left-hand upward to the right $\diagup$ (Fig. 16.4). A thread is always considered to be right-hand if it is not otherwise specified. A left-hand thread is always marked L.H. on a drawing.

16.5. Multiple threads. Whenever a quick advance is desired, as on fountain pens, valves, and so on, two or more threads are cut side by side. Two threads form a double thread, three a triple thread, and so on. A thread that is not otherwise designated is understood to be a single thread.

Figure 16.5 shows heavy strings wound around a rod for the purpose of demonstrating single and double threads. The center line of the single string, representing the single thread, assumes the form of a helix. In the case of the double thread, it should be noted that there are two strings side-by-side that are shaded differently for clarity. On a double thread, each thread starts diametrically opposite the other one.

16.6. Pitch. The pitch of a thread is the distance from any point on a thread to the corresponding point on the adjacent thread, measured parallel to the axis as shown in Fig. 16.1.

SINGLE   DOUBLE

Fig. 16.5.   Demonstration of a Helix as Related to a Single and Double Screw Thread.

16.7. Lead. The lead of a screw may be defined as the distance advanced parallel to the axis when the screw is turned one revolution. (See Fig. 16.6.) For a single thread, the lead is equal to the pitch; for a double thread, the lead is twice the pitch; for a triple thread, the lead is three times the pitch, and so on.

16.8. Detailed screw thread representation. The true representation of screw threads by helical curves, requiring unnecessary time and laborious drafting, is rarely used. The detailed representation, closely approximating the actual appearance, is preferred in commercial practice, for it is much easier to represent the helices with slanting lines and the truncated roots and crest with sharp "V's" (Fig. 16.7). Since detailed rendering is also time consuming, its use is justified only in those few cases where appearance and permanency are important factors, and when it is necessary to avoid the possibility that confusion might result from the use of one of the symbolic methods. The preparation of a detailed representation is a task that belongs primarily to a draftsman, the engineer being concerned only with specifying that this form be used.

The steps in drawing a sharp V-thread are shown in Figs. 16.8 and 16.9.

Fig. 16.6. Single, Double, and Triple Threads.

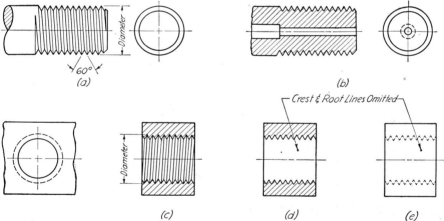

Fig. 16.7. Detailed Representation.

The flattened roots and crests are disregarded in the representation of Unified-American threads and they are drawn as sharp V's. An effective relief and finish is given by drawing all lines fine except root lines.

In drawing a single, triple, or an odd-number multiple thread, a crest is always diametrically opposite a root; in a double or even-number multiple thread, a crest is opposite a crest and a root opposite a root (Fig. 16.6).

The stages in drawing the detailed representation of modified square and Acme threads are shown in Figs. 16.11, 16.12, and 16.13. All lines of the finished square thread are made the same weight. The root lines of the Acme thread are made heavier than the other lines.

$$P = \frac{1}{\text{NUMBER OF THREADS PER INCH}}$$

Fig. 16.8.   Detailed Representation of Unified and American and Sharp V-Threads (External).

Fig. 16.9.   Detailed Representation of Unified and American and Sharp V-Threads (Internal).

Fig. 16.10.   Simplified Representation of a Square Thread.

Fig. 16.10 shows a simplified method of representation for square threads.

16.9. American Standard Conventional thread symbols. Recognizing the necessity for saving time and expense in the preparation of drawings, the American Standards Association has adopted the "sche-

Fig. 16.11. Detailed Representation of Square Threads (Modified).

Fig. 16.12. Detailed Representation of Square Threads (Internal).

matic" and "simplified" representations to be used for threads having a diameter of one inch or less (Figs. 16.14 and 16.15).

The simplified representation was adopted to simplify drafting on drawings.   The root of the thread is represented by invisible lines drawn parallel to the axis.

The schematic representation consists of alternate long and short

Fig. 16.13. Detailed Representation of Acme Thread.

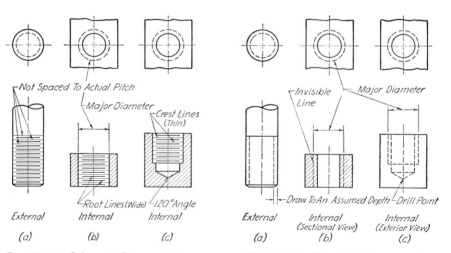

Fig. 16.14. Schematic Representation.   Fig. 16.15. Simplified Representation.

lines perpendicular to the axis. Although these lines, representing the crests and roots of the thread, are not spaced to actual pitch, their spacing should indicate noticeable differences in the number of threads per inch of different threads on the same working drawing or group of drawings. The root lines are made heavier than the crest lines.

Before a hole can be tapped (threaded), it must be drilled to permit the tap to enter. See Table II for tap drill sizes for standard threads. Since the last of the thread cut is not well formed or usable, the hole must be shown drilled and tapped deeper than the screw will enter. (See Figs. 16.18d, e, f.) To show the threaded portion extending to the bottom of the drilled hole indicates the use of a bottoming tap to cut full threads at the bottom. This is an extra and expensive operation not justified except in cases where the depth of the hole and the distance the screw must enter are limited. (See Figs. 16.18g, h, i.)

SCHEMATIC   SIMPLIFIED

(a)   (b)

Fig. 16.16. External Thread Representation.

Fig. 16.17. Drawing Conventional Threads.

16.10. Threads in section. The detailed representation of threads in section, which is used for large diameters only, is shown in Fig. 16.9. Since the far side of an internal thread in section is visible, the crest and root lines incline in the opposite direction to those of an external thread having the same specifications.

The schematic and simplified representations for threads of small diameter are shown in Figs. 16.16 and 16.18.

A sectioned assembly drawing is shown in Fig. 16.19. When assembled pieces are both sectioned, the detailed representation is used, and the thread form is drawn. Simplified representation could have been used for the thread on the cap screw instead of the schematic representation shown. (See Fig. 16.26.)

16.11. Unified and American screw thread series. The Unified and American screw thread series as given in ASA B1.1–1949 consists of six series and a selection of special threads that cover special combinations of diameter and pitch. Each series differs from the other by the number

(a) ELEVATION   (b) SECTION   (c) SECTION

TAPPED THROUGH

(d)   (e)   (f)

Thread Depth   Drill Depth

TAP DRILL SHOWN

(g)   (h)   (i)

Depth

BOTTOM TAPPED

Fig. 16.18. Representation of Internal Threads.

of threads per inch for a specific diameter. See Tables II and III, Appendix.

The coarse thread series (UNC and NC) is designated UNC for sizes above $\frac{1}{4}''$ in diameter. This series is recommended for general industrial use.

The fine thread series (UNF and NF), designated UNF for sizes above $\frac{1}{4}''$, was prepared for use when a fine thread is required and for general use in the automotive and aircraft fields.

Fig. 16.19. Threads in Section.*

The extra-fine thread series, designated NEF is used for automotive and aircraft work when a maximum number of threads is required for a given length. A few specific sizes of this series are designated UN.

The 8 thread series (8N) is a uniform pitch series for large diameters. It is sometimes used in place of the coarse thread series for diameters greater than $1''$. This series was originally intended for high pressure joints.

The 12 thread series (12UN or 12N) is a uniform pitch series intended for use with large diameters requiring threads of medium-fine pitch. This series is used as a continuation of the fine thread series for diameters greater than $1\frac{1}{2}$ inches.

* ASA Y14.6–1957.

The 16 thread series (16UN or 16N) is a uniform pitch series for large diameters requiring a fine pitch thread. This series is used as a continuation of the extra-fine thread series for diameters greater than 2 inches.

16.12. Unified and American screw thread classes. Classes of thread are determined by the amounts of tolerance and allowance specified.

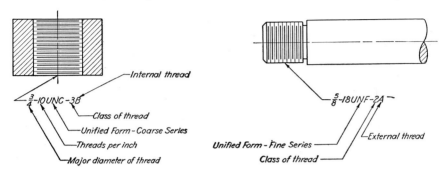

Fig. 16.20.   Unified Thread Identification Symbols.

Fig. 16.21.   Thread Identification Symbols.

Under the new unified system classes 1A, 2A, and 3A apply only to external threads; classes 1B, 2B, and 3B apply to internal threads. Classes 2 and 3 from the former American Standard have been retained without change in the new Unified and American Thread Standard for use in the United States only, but they are not among the Unified classes even though the thread forms are identical. These classes are used with the American thread series (NC, NF, and N series) which covers sizes from size 0 (.060) to 6″.

Class 1A and Class 1B replace class 1 of the old American Standard.

Class 2A and Class 2B were adopted as the recognized standards for screws, bolts, and nuts.

Class 3A and class 3B invoke new classes of tolerance. These classes along with class 2A and class 2B should eventually replace class 2 and class 3 now retained from the American Standard. Class 2 and class 3 are defined in the former standard ASA B1.1–1935 as follows:

Class 2 fit. Represents a high quality of commercial thread product and is recommended for the great bulk of interchangeable screw-thread work.

Class 3 fit. Represents an exceptionally high quality of commercially threaded product and is recommended only in cases where the high cost of precision tools and continual checking is warranted.

16.13. Identification symbols for Unified screw threads. Threads are specified under the new unified system by giving the diameter, number of threads per inch, initial letters (UNC, UNF, etc.), and class of thread (1A, 2A, and 3A; or 1B, 2B, and 3B). (See Fig. 16.20.)

16.14. Identification symbols for American Standard, Square, and Acme Threads. American Standard, Square, and Acme threads are specified on drawings, in specifications, and in stock lists by thread information given as shown in Fig. 16.21.

FASTENERS

16.15. American Standard bolts and nuts (Fig. 16.22). Commercial producers of bolts and fasteners manufacture their products in

Fig. 16.22. American Standard Bolts and Nuts.

accordance with the standard specifications given in the American Standard entitled "Square and Hexagon Bolts and Nuts" (Revised 1955).*
See Table VI in Appendix

The ASA has approved the specification for three series of bolts and nuts:

1. *Regular series.* The regular series was adopted for general use.
2. *Heavy series.* Heavy boltheads and nuts are designed to satisfy the special commercial need for greater bearing surface.
3. *Light series nuts.* Light nuts are used under conditions requiring a sub-

* ASA B18.2–1955.

stantial savings in weight and material. They are usually supplied with a fine thread.

The amount of machining is the basis for further classification of hexagonal bolts and nuts in both the regular and heavy series as unfinished and semifinished.

Square-head bolts and nuts are standardized as unfinished only.

Unfinished heads and nuts are not washer-faced, nor are they machined on any surface.

Semifinished boltheads and nuts are machined or treated on the bearing surface so as to provide a washer face for boltheads and either a washer face or a circular bearing surface for nuts. Nuts, not washer-faced, have the circular bearing surface formed by chamfering the edges.

Bolts and nuts are *always* drawn across corners in all views. This recognized commercial practice, which violates the principles of true projection, prevents confusion of square and hexagonal forms on drawings.

The chamfer angle on the tops of heads and nuts is 30 degrees on hexagons and 25 degrees on squares, but both are drawn at 30 degrees on bolts greater than $1''$ in diameter.

Bolts are specified in parts lists and elsewhere by giving the diameter, number of threads per inch, series, class of thread, length, finish, and type of head.

EXAMPLE: $\frac{1}{2}$-13UNC-2A $\times$ $1\frac{3}{4}$ SEMI-FIN. HEX. HD. BOLT.

Frequently it is advantageous and practical to abbreviate the specification thus:

EXAMPLE: $\frac{1}{2}$ $\times$ $1\frac{3}{4}$ UNC SEMI-FIN. HEX. HD. BOLT.

Although bolt lengths have not been standardized in construction practice, because of the varied requirements in engineering design, length increments for length under the head to the end of a hexagonal bolt can be considered as: $\frac{1}{8}''$ for bolts $\frac{1}{4}''$ to $\frac{3}{4}''$ in length, $\frac{1}{4}''$ for bolts $\frac{3}{4}''$ to $3''$ in length, and $\frac{1}{2}''$ for bolts $3''$ to $6''$ in length. Length increments for square head bolts are: $\frac{1}{8}''$ for bolts $\frac{1}{4}''$ to $\frac{3}{4}''$ in length, and $\frac{1}{4}''$ for bolts $\frac{3}{4}''$ to $4\frac{3}{4}''$ in length.

The minimum thread length for bolts up to and including 6 inches in length shall be twice the diameter plus $\frac{1}{4}$ inch. For lengths over 6 inches the minimum thread length shall be twice the diameter of the bolt plus $\frac{1}{2}$ inch (ASA B18.2–1955).

16.16. To draw boltheads and nuts. Using the dimension taken from the tables, draw the lines representing the top and contact surfaces of the head or nut and the diameter of the bolt. Lay out a hexagon about an inscribed chamfer circle having a diameter equal to the distance across the flats (Fig. 16.23) and project the necessary lines to block in the view. Draw in the arcs after finding the centers as shown in Fig. 16.23.

A square-head bolt or nut may be drawn by following the steps indicated in Fig. 16.24.

16.17. Studs. A stud, or stud bolt, which is threaded on both ends, is shown in Fig. 16.25. Studs are used where bolts would be impractical and for parts that must be frequently removed (cylinder heads, steam chest covers, pumps, and so on). They are first screwed permanently into the tapped holes in one part before the removable member with its corresponding clearance holes is placed in position. Nuts are used on the projecting ends to hold the parts together.

WIDTH ACROSS FLATS HEIGHT OF HEAD T-SQUARE
SEE TABLE SEE TABLE

Fig. 16.23. Steps in Drawing a Hexagonal Bolthead.

WIDTH ACROSS FLATS HEIGHT OF HEAD T-SQUARE
SEE TABLE SEE TABLE

Fig. 16.24. Steps in Drawing a Square Bolthead.

Fig. 16.25. Stud Bolt.   **Fig. 16.26. Hexagonal-Head Cap Screw.**

Since studs are not standard they must be produced from specifications given on a detail drawing. In dimensioning a stud, the length of thread must be given for both the stud end and nut end along with an over-all dimension. The thread information is given by note.

In a bill of material, studs may be specified as follows:

EXAMPLE: $\frac{1}{2}$-13UNC-2A × $2\frac{3}{4}$ STUD.

It is good practice to abbreviate the specification thus:

EXAMPLE: $\frac{1}{2}$ × $2\frac{3}{4}$ STUD.

16.18. Cap screws (Fig. 16.27). Cap screws are similar to machine screws. They are available in four standard heads, usually in finished form. When parts are assembled, the cap screws pass through clear holes in one member and screw into threaded holes in the other (Fig. 16.26). Hexagonal cap screws have a washer face $\frac{1}{64}''$ thick with a diameter equal to the distance across flats. Short cap screws are threaded to as near the head as practicable (usually three pitches).

Fig. 16.27. Cap Screws.

SOCKET HEAD *(Hexagonal)*   SOCKET HEAD *(Fluted)*   FILLISTER HEAD *(Slotted)*   HEXAGONAL HEAD   ROUND HEAD *(Slotted)*   FLAT HEAD *(Slotted)*

Cap screws are specified by giving the diameter, number of threads per inch, series, class of thread, length, and type of head.

EXAMPLE: $\frac{5}{8}$-11UNC-2A × 2 FIL. HD. CAP SC.

It is good practice to abbreviate the specification thus:

EXAMPLE: $\frac{5}{8}$ × 2UNC FIL. HD. CAP SC.

16.19. Machine screws. Machine screws, which fulfill the same purpose as cap screws, are used chiefly for small work having thin sections (Fig. 16.28). Under the approved American Standard, they range from

Fig. 16.28. Use of a Machine Screw.

FLAT HD.   ROUND HD.   FILLISTER HD.   OVAL HD.

Fig. 16.29. Types of Machine Screws.

No. 0 (0.060″ dia.) to $\frac{3}{4}''$ (0.750 dia.) and are available in either the American Standard Coarse or Fine-Thread Series. The four forms of heads shown in Fig. 16.29 have been standardized. A machine screw $1\frac{1}{4}''$ or less in length is threaded to the underneath side of the head.

To specify machine screws, give the diameter, threads per inch, thread series, class, length, and type of head.

EXAMPLE: No. 12-24NC-3 × $\frac{3}{4}''$ FIL. HD. MACH. SC.

It is good practice to abbreviate by omitting the thread series and class.

EXAMPLE: No. 12-24 × $\frac{3}{4}''$ FIL. HD. MACH. SC.

16.20. Commercial lengths: studs, cap screws, machine screws. Unless a fastening of any of these types carries a constant and appreciable fatigue stress, the usual practice is to have it enter a distance related to its nominal diameter (Fig. 16.30).   If the depth of the hole is not limited, it should be drilled to a depth of 1 diameter beyond the end of the fastener to permit tapping to a distance of $\frac{1}{2}$ diameter below the fastener.

The length of the fastening should be determined to the nearest commercial length that will allow it to fulfill minimum conditions.   In the

DRILLED
(a)
A = *Minimum distance fastener*
must enter threaded hole
B = *Standard length of fastener*
D = *Major diameter of fastener*
C + E = $\frac{1}{2}$ *D (Minimum)*

TAPPED
(b)

FASTENER IN POSITION
(c)
A (MINIMUM)
STEEL – A = D
CAST IRON, BRASS, BRONZE – A = $1\frac{1}{2}$ D
ALUMINUM – A = 2D

Fig. 16.30.   Threaded Hole and Fastener.

case of a stud, care should be taken that the length allows for a full engagement of the nut.   Commercial lengths for fasteners increase by the following increments:

> *Standard length increments:*
> For fastener lengths $\frac{1}{4}''$ to $1'' = \frac{1}{8}''$
> For fastener lengths $1''$ to $4'' = \frac{1}{4}''$

16.21. Set screws.   Set screws are used principally to prevent rotary motion between two parts, such as that which tends to occur in the case of a rotating member mounted on a shaft.   A set screw is screwed through one part until the point presses firmly against the other part (Fig. 16.31).

The several forms of safety heads shown in Fig. 16.32 are available in combination with any of the points.   Headless set screws comply with safety codes and should be used on all revolving parts.   The many serious injuries that have been caused by the projecting heads of square-head set screws have led to legislation prohibiting their use in some states.

Set screws are specified by giving the diameter, number of threads per inch, series, class of thread, length, type of head, and type of point.

EXAMPLE: $\frac{1}{4}$-20UNC-2A $\times$ $\frac{1}{2}$ SLOTTED CONE PT. SET SC.

The preferred abbreviated form gives the diameter, number of threads per inch, length, type of head, and type of point.

EXAMPLE $\frac{1}{4}$ 20 $\times$ $\frac{1}{2}$ HEX. SOCKET CONE PT. SET SC.

16.22. Application of set screws. Fig. 16.33 illustrates the method of milling a flat surface on a shaft to provide a seat for a set screw. This practice prevents the formation of a burr on the rounded surface and creates a more resistant pressure between the set-screw point and the shaft.

HEADLESS SET SCREW
(a)

AMERICAN STD. SET SCREW
(b)

Fig. 16.31. Use of Set Screws.

SLOTTED   HEXAGONAL SOCKET   FLUTED SOCKET

CONE POINT   FLAT POINT   OVAL POINT   CUP POINT   FULL DOG POINT   HALF DOG POINT

Fig. 16.32. Set Screws.

The cone point which fits into a conical spot in the shaft (Fig. 16.34) is sometimes used to prevent both rotary and longitudinal axial motion.

16.23. Keys. Keys are used in the assembling of machine parts to secure them against relative motion, generally rotary, as is the case between shafts, cranks, wheels, and so on. When the relative forces are not great, a round key, saddle key, or flat key is used (Fig. 16.35). For heavier duty, rectangular keys are more suitable.

The square key (Fig. 16.36) and the Pratt and Whitney key (Fig.

Fig. 16.33.   Treatment of Shaft for Flat Point Set Screw.

Fig. 16.34.   Treatment of Shaft for Cone Point Set Screw.

SADDLE   FLAT   ROUND

LIGHT DUTY KEYS

KENNEDY   BARTH   LEWIS

HEAVY DUTY KEYS

Fig. 16.35.   Special Light- and Heavy-Duty Keys.

SQUARE KEY

Fig. 16.36.   A Square Key.

P&W KEY

Fig. 16.37.   A Pratt and Whitney Key.

GIB HEAD KEY

Fig. 16.38.   A Gib-Head Key.

16.37) are the two keys most frequently used in machine design. A plain milling cutter is used to cut the keyway for the square key, while an end mill is used for the Pratt and Whitney keyway. Both keys fit tightly in the shaft and in the part mounted upon it.

The gib-head key (Fig. 16.38) is designed so that the head remains far enough from the hub to allow a drift pin to be driven to remove the key. The hub side of the key is tapered $\frac{1}{8}''$ per foot to insure a fit tight enough to prevent both axial and rotary motion. For this type of key, the keyway must be cut to one end of the shaft.

16.24. Woodruff keys. A Woodruff key is a flat segmental disc with either a flat or a round bottom (Fig. 16.39). It is always specified by a number, the last two digits of which indicate the nominal diameter in eighths of an inch, while the digits preceding the last two give the nominal width in thirty-seconds of an inch.

CUTTER

WOODRUFF KEY

KEY

(a)   (b)

Fig. 16.39. A Woodruff Key.

A practical rule for selecting a Woodruff key for a given shaft is: Choose a standard key that has a width approximately equal to one-fourth of the diameter of the shaft, and a radius nearly equal (plus or minus) to the radius of the shaft. Table XXI in the Appendix gives the dimensions for American Standard Woodruff keys.

When Woodruff keys are drawn, it should be remembered that the center of the arc is placed above the top of the key at a distance shown in column E in the table.

16.25. Locking devices. A few of the many types of locking devices that prevent nuts from becoming loose under vibration are shown in Figs. 16.40–16.47.

Figure 16.40 shows six forms of patented spring washers. The ones shown in D, E, and F have internal and external teeth. Although the external tooth type is used more often than the internal tooth design, the latter is desirable where a smooth outside edge is to be preferred.

A fastener and washer combination that can be purchased preassembled is shown in Fig. 16.41. The shank-locking screw (Fig. 16.42), having a slot cut in the thread, is spread to a slight "bulge" so that there will be a friction contact against the thread in the tapped hole.

Fig. 16.40.   Special Lock Washers.

Fig. 16.41. Shake-Proof Preassembled Fastener and Washer.

Fig. 16.42. Shank-Locking Screw.

Fig. 16.43. Bolt, Nut, and Palnut.

Fig. 16.44. Shake-Proof Preassembled Nut and Lock Washer.

Fig. 16.45. Elastic Stop Nut.

Fig. 16.46. Castellated Nut.

Figure 16.43 shows a bolt and nut combination along with a Palnut. The Palnut is, in reality, a single-thread lock nut having a slotted cone-shaped thread-engaging portion.   When tightened down, the outside of the nut is forced securely against the regular nut.   The locking action (due to the design) is produced by a spring action upward against the thread and downward against the regular nut.

Figure 16.44 shows a preassembled nut and washer combination.

Secured in the top of the elastic stop nut shown in Fig. 16.45 is a red fiber locking collar slightly smaller than the diameter of the bolt.   Because this collar is plastic in character, it forms to the bolt thread and grips securely enough to prevent the nut from coming loose under strong vibration.

In common use is the castellated nut (Fig. 16.47a) with a spring cotter pin that passes through the shaft and the slots in the top.   This type is used extensively in automotive and aeronautical work.

Figure 16.47(b) shows a regular nut that is prevented from loosening by an American Standard jam nut.   A jam nut has the same across-flats dimension as a regular nut of the same diameter (Table VI Appendix).

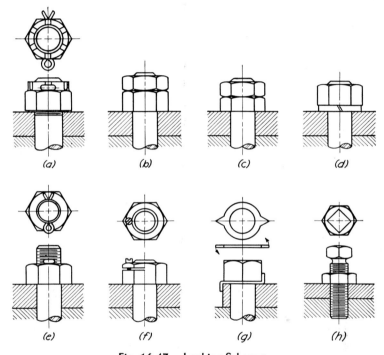

(a)   *(b)*   *(c)*   *(d)*

(e)   *(f)*   *(g)*   *(h)*

Fig. 16.47.   Locking Schemes.

In Fig. 16.47(c) the use of two jam nuts is illustrated.

A regular nut with a spring-lock washer is shown in Fig. 16.47(d). The reaction provided by the lock washer tends to prevent the nut from turning.

A regular nut with a spring cotter pin through the shaft, to prevent the nut from backing off, is shown in Fig. 16.47(e).

Special devices for locking nuts are illustrated in Fig. 16.47(f) and (g).   A set screw may be held in position with a jam nut as in (h).

16.26. Areo thread.   The Areo-thread screw-thread system allows the use of high-strength cap screws and studs in light soft metals such as aluminum and magnesium, through the use of a phosphor bronze or stainless steel coilspring lining in the tapped hole, as shown in Fig. 16.48. This coil (screw bushing) is formed to fit a modified American Standard

Fig. 16.48. Areo Thread.

thread. Special inserting and extracting tools are needed for inserting the coil in the tapped hole.

16.27. Parker-Kalon self-tapping screws and nails (Fig. 16.49). Parker-Kalon self-tapping screws are unique in that they have a specially hardened thread that makes it possible for the screws to form their own internal thread as they are driven into a hole. The use of self-tapping screws eliminates costly tapping operations and the time-consuming task of assembling and tightening nuts and bolts.

Type "A" fasteners, known as the original sheet-metal screws, are used extensively for sheet-metal work in the manufacture of signs, furnaces, automobiles, and aircraft.

Type "Z" fasteners are suitable for assembling both light and heavy sheet metal, aluminum, and die castings, and parts made of plastics.

When using self-tapping fasteners and screw nails detailed information should be obtained from data sheets furnished by the Parker-Kalon Corporation.

16.28. Miscellaneous bolts, screws, and nuts. Other types of bolts and screws that have been adopted for commercial use are illustrated in Fig. 16.50.

TYPE "A" SELF-TAPPING SCREW   TYPE "Z" SELF-TAPPING SCREW

TYPE "F"   TYPE F-Z   SHEET METAL SCREW   METALLIC DRIVE SCREW   SHEET METAL DRIVE SCREW

SCREW NAIL   MASONRY NAIL

Fig. 16.49. Parker-Kalon Self-Tapping Screws.

Fig. 16.50.　Miscellaneous Bolts, Screws, and Nuts.

Wood screws have threads proportioned for the holding strength of wood. They are available with different forms of heads (flat, round, and oval).

The Phillips head, shown in Fig. 16.51 for a wood screw, is one of various types of recessed heads. Although special drivers are usually employed for installation, an ordinary screw driver can be used. Machine screws, cap screws, and many special types of fasteners are available with Phillips heads.

A few of the fastenings shown in Fig. 16.50 have been standardized by the American Standards Association.

16.29. Rivets. Rivets are permanent fasteners used chiefly for connecting members in such structures as buildings and bridges and for assembling steel sheets and plates for tanks, boilers, and ships. They are cylindrical rods of wrought iron or soft steel, with one head formed when

Fig. 16.51. Phillips Head Screw.

manufactured. A head is formed on the other end after the rivet has been put in place through the drilled or punched holes of the mating parts.

A hole for a rivet is generally drilled, punched, or punched and reamed $\frac{1}{16}''$ larger than the diameter of the shank of the rivet.   Figure 16.52(a) illustrates a rivet in position, before heading, with enough of a shank projecting to fill the hole completely and form the head.   Figure 16.52(b) shows the fastening completed.   Small rivets, less than $\frac{1}{2}''$ in diameter, may be driven cold, but the larger sizes are driven hot.   For specialized types of engineering work, rivets are manufactured of chrome-iron, nickel,

(a)   *(b)*

Fig. 16.52.   Riveting Procedure.

SINGLE-RIVETED   DOUBLE-RIVETED   SINGLE-RIVETED   SINGLE-RIVETED
LAP JOINT   LAP JOINT   SINGLE STRAP   DOUBLE STRAP
                                                                          BUTT JOINT   BUTT JOINT

DOUBLE-RIVETED   DOUBLE-RIVETED
SINGLE STRAP BUTT JOINT   DOUBLE STRAP BUTT JOINT

Fig. 16.53.   Forms of Riveted Joints.

brass, copper, and so on.   Dimensions for American Standard small-head rivets are given in Table XVIII, Appendix.

16.30. Riveted joints.   Joints on boilers, tanks, and so on, are classified as either lap joints or butt joints (Fig. 16.53).   Lap joints are generally used for seams around the circumference.   Butt joints are used for longitudinal seams, except on small tanks where the pressure is to be less than 100 pounds per square inch.

16.31. Springs.   In production work, a spring is largely a matter of mathematical calculation rather than drawing, and it is usually purchased from a spring manufacturer, with the understanding that it will fulfill specified conditions.   For experimental work and when only one is needed, it may be formed by winding oil-tempered spring wire or music wire around a cylindrical bar. As it is wound, the wire follows the helical path of the screw thread. For this reason the steps in the layout of the representation for a spring are similar to the screw thread as shown in Figs. 16.54 and 16.55. Pitch distances are marked off, and the coils are given a slope of one-half of the pitch. Figure 16.54(a) shows a partial layout of a tension spring. Other types of ends are shown in (b). A

SPRING LAYOUT – FULL LOOP- CLOSED   OTHER TYPES OF ENDS

(a)   (b)

Fig. 16.54.   Tension Springs.

SPRING LAYOUT–PLAIN END   OTHER TYPES OF ENDS

(a)   (b)

Fig. 16.55.   Compression Springs.

COMPRESSION SPRING   TORSION SPRING   TENSION SPRING

Fig. 16.56.   Single Line Representation of Springs.*

compression spring layout, with various types of ends, is illustrated in Fig. 16.55.

When making a detail working drawing of a spring, it should be shown to its free length. On either an assembly or detail drawing, a fairly accurate representation, neatly drawn, will satisfy all requirements.

Single line symbols for the representation of springs are shown in Fig. 16.56.

* ASA Z14.1–1946.

392   **THREADS AND FASTENINGS**   •Ch. 16

The length and controlling diameter must be given along with the size and number of turns of the wire on a detail working drawing of a spring. The type of end must always be shown even though the spring is standard and is not designed to suit some special condition.

16.32. Problems. Excellent practice in drawing threads, threaded fasteners, keys, and rivets is provided through the making of some of the assembly drawings given in Chapter 20. A few of the typical situations are offered here, however, in order to familiarize the student with the approved methods of representation before he is required to use them on a working drawing.

1. Draw a detailed representation of a V-thread (Fig. 16.8). Make the diameter of the thread 2″, the pitch $\frac{1}{4}$″, and the length 3″.

2. Draw a detailed representation of a square thread. Make the diameter of the thread $2\frac{1}{4}$″, the pitch $\frac{1}{2}$″, and the length 3″.

3. Draw a detailed representation of an Acme thread. Make the diameter $2\frac{1}{4}$″, the pitch $\frac{1}{2}$″, and the length 3″.

4. Same as problem 3, but show a B & S worm thread.

5. Draw an American Standard hexagonal-head bolt and nut. The diameter of the bolt is to be 1″; the thread is to be UNC. The bolt is to be semifinished and have a length of 5″. Use the detailed representation. The length of the thread should be $1\frac{1}{2}$ D plus $\frac{1}{4}$″.

6. Using schematic representation, as shown in Fig. 16.16, draw the following fasteners in the order given: (1) a $\frac{3}{4}$″ × 3″ hexagonal-head cap screw, (2) a $\frac{5}{8}$″ × 3″ fillister-head cap screw, (3) a $\frac{3}{4}$″ × 3″ flat-head cap screw. Balance the three drawings on an $8\frac{1}{2}$″ × 11″ or a 9″ × 12″ sheet of drawing paper.

7. Draw the threads shown in Fig. 16.57.

$1\frac{3}{4}$ - ?UNC-2A $1\frac{1}{2}$ -2 SQ.-L.H. DOUBLE

Fig. 16.57.

8. Draw the layout shown in Fig. 16.58, and on it show the following fasteners: (1) On center line *A-A* draw a $\frac{3}{4}$″ unfinished hexagonal-head bolt and nut. (2) On center line *B-B* draw a $\frac{7}{8}$″ square-head bolt and nut. (3) On center line *C-C* draw a $\frac{3}{4}$″ fillister-head cap screw. (4) On center line *D-D* draw a $\frac{5}{8}$″ hexagonal head cap screw. Determine the measurements for the layout by using the given scale. Make each fastener a standard length. Use schematic representation for the threads.

9. Reproduce the three layouts shown in Fig. 16.59 to full size, using the given scale to determine the measurements. On layout (1), complete the drawing to show a suitable fastener on center line *A-A*. On layout (2), show a $\frac{1}{2}$″ hexagonal-head cap screw on center line *B-B*. On layout (3), show a $\frac{3}{8}$″ button-head rivet on center line *C-C* and a No. 608 Woodruff key on center line *D-D*. Use schematic representation for the threads.

Fig. 16.58.

Fig. 16.59.

10. (Fig. 16.60.)   Reproduce the views of the assembly of the alignment bearing.   On C. L.'s A show $\frac{1}{4}''$ button-head rivets (4 required).   On C. L. B show a $\frac{5}{16}'' \times \frac{1}{2}''$ Am. Std. square-head set screw.   Do not dimension the views.

11. (Fig. 16.61.)   Reproduce the views of the assembly of the impeller drive. On C. L.'s A show $\frac{1}{4}''$-20UNC $\times \frac{1}{2}''$ round-head machine screws and regular lock

Fig. 16.60.   Alignment Bearing.

Fig. 16.61.   Impeller Drive.

washers.   On C. L. *B* show a No. 406 Woodruff key.   On C. L. *C* show a standard No. 2 × 1½″ taper pin.

12. (Fig. 16.62.)   Reproduce the views of the assembly of the bearing head. On C. L.'s *A* show ½″-UNC studs with regular lock washers and regular semifinished hexagonal nuts (4 required).   On C. L.'s *B* show ⅜″-UNC × 1¼″ hexagonal-head cap screws (2 required).   On C. L. *C* drill through the tap ⅛″ pipe thread.

13. (Fig. 16.63.)   Reproduce the views of the assembly of the air cylinder. On C. L. *A-A* at the left end of the shaft show a 1″-UNF semifinished hexagonal nut.   At the right end show a hole tapped ¾″-UNF × 1½″ deep.   Between the

Fig. 16.62.   Bearing Head.

Fig. 16.63.   Air Cylinder.

piston and the (right) end plate draw a spring $3''$ O.D., 5 full coils, $\frac{1}{4}''$ wire.   On C. L.'s B show $\frac{3}{8}''$-UNC $\times 1\frac{1}{4}''$ hexagonal-head cap screws.   On C. L.'s C draw $\frac{1}{4}''$-UNC $\times \frac{3}{4}''$ flat-head cap screws with heads to the left.   On C. L. D show a $\frac{1}{4}''$ standard pipe thread.   On C. L.'s E show $\frac{1}{2}''$-UNC $\times 1\frac{3}{4}''$ semifinished hexagonal-head bolts.   Use semifinished hexagonal nuts.   Show visible fasteners on the end view.

17 | Welding Drawings

17.1. Welding processes. For convenience, the various welding processes used in commercial production may be classified into three types: pressure processes, nonpressure processes, and casting processes. The nonpressure processes are arc welding and gas welding. Metallic arc welding is the joining of two pieces of metal through the use of a sustained arc formed between the work and a metal rod held in a holder. The intense heat melts the metal of the work and at the same time heats the end of the electrode, causing small globules to form and cross the arc to the weld. In gas welding, the heat is produced by a burning mixture of two gases, which ordinarily are oxygen and acetylene. The weld is formed by melting a filler rod with the torch flame, along the line of contact, after the metal of the work has been preheated to a molten state. This method is essentially a puddling process, in that the weld is produced by a small moving molten pool that is maintained by the flame constantly directed upon it. Resistance welding is a pressure process, the fusion being made through heat and mechanical pressure. The work is heated by a strong electrical current that passes through it until fusion temperature is reached; then pressure is applied to create the weld.

The forms of resistance welding are: projection welding, seam welding, spot welding, and flash welding. In spot welding, the parts are overlapped and welds are made at successive single spots. A seam weld is similar to a spot weld, except that a continuous weld is produced. In projection welding, one part is embossed and welds are made at the successive projections. In making a flash weld, the two pieces to be joined are held end to end in jaws and act as electrodes. At the right instant, after the facing metal has been heated by the arc across the gap, the power is shut off and the two ends are forced together to cool in a fused position.

Thermit welding can be considered a casting process, in that molten iron is run into a mold built around the parts at the point at which they are to be connected. The liquid metal is obtained from a mixture of finely divided iron oxide and aluminum, which is ignited in a crucible. In the chemical reaction that takes place, the oxygen passes from the iron oxide to the aluminum, leaving free molten iron that flows into the mold around to the preheated parts forming the joint. The metal of the members being welded fuses with the liquid metal and forms a weld when the joint is cool.

396

17.2. Types of welds.   Figure 17.1 illustrates in pictorial some of the various types of welds.   Cross sectional views of the fundamental welds which are commonly encountered are shown in Fig. 17.2.

17.3. Classification of welded joints.   Welded joints are classified in accordance with the method of assembly of the parts at a joint.   See Fig. 17.3.

Fig. 17.1.   Types of Welds.

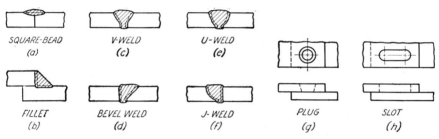

Fig. 17.2.   Types of Welds.

Fig. 17.3.   Types of Welded Joints.

17.4. Working drawings of welded parts.   Figure 17.4 shows a part that is to be constructed by welding rolled shapes.   It should be noted that each joint is completely specified through the use of a welding symbol.   A careful study will show that the drawing, except for the absence of fillets and rounds and the fact that properly composed welding symbols are directed to the necessary joints, is very much like a casting drawing.

A satisfactory welding design may be produced by a competent designer who possesses a fair amount of ingenuity, and the necessary drawing can be made by any draftsman who has a thorough understanding of the use of the symbols recommended in ASA Z32.2.1–1949.

17.5. Arrow-side and other-side welds (Fig. 17.5). "The use of the words 'far side' and 'near side' in the past has led to confusion, because when joints are shown in section, all welds are equally distant from the reader, and the words 'near' and 'far' are meaningless. In the present system the joint is the basis of reference. Any joint the welding of which is indicated by a symbol will always have an 'arrow side' and an 'other side.'"*   Read Sec. 1, General Provisions.

Courtesy Lincoln Electric Co.

Fig. 17.4.   A Welding Drawing.

Fig. 17.5.   Arrow-Side and Other-Side Welds.

17.6. Welding symbols. An enlarged drawing of the approved welding symbol is shown in Fig. 17.6, along with explanatory notes that indicate the proper locations of the marks and size dimensions necessary for a complete description of a weld.

The arrow is the basic portion of the symbol, as shown in Fig. 17.7(*a*). It points toward the joint where the required weld is to be made, as in Fig. 17.7(*b*).

If the weld is on the arrow-side, the symbol indicating the type of weld is placed below or to the right of the base line, depending upon

---

* Extracted from ASA Z32.2.1–1949.

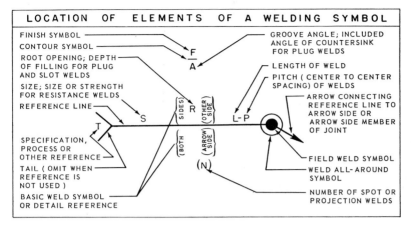

Fig. 17.6. The Basic Welding Symbol.*

(a)   (b)

Fig. 17.7. Welding Arrow.

whether that line is horizontal or vertical (Fig. 17.8). If the weld is located on the other-side, the symbol should be above or to the left.

To indicate that a weld is to be made all around a connection, as is necessary when a piece of tubing must be welded to a plate, a weld-all-around symbol, a circle, is placed as shown in Fig. 17.9.

The size of a weld is given along the base of the arrow, at the side of the symbol, as shown in Fig. 17.10. If the welds on the arrow-side and the other-side of a lap joint are the same size, only one dimension should be given (Fig. 17.11). If they are not the same size, each dimension should be placed beside its associated symbol (Fig. 17.12).

The welding terms associated with the specification of the size of welds are illustrated in Fig. 17.13.

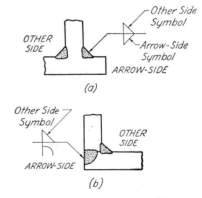

Fig. 17.8. Location of Welding Symbols.

Figure 17.14 shows the common types of single-groove welds and the related symbol for each. The symbols for double-groove welds are illustrated in Fig. 17.15.

* ASA Z32.2.1–1949.

Fig. 17.9.   Weld-All-Around Symbol.

Fig. 17.10.   Method of Specifying the Size of Weld.

Fig. 17.11.   Dimensioning a Weld.   Fig. 17.12.   Dimensioning a Weld.

Fig. 17.13.   Welding Terms

Fig. 17.14.   Single-Groove Welds and Symbols.

Fig. 17.15.   Double-Groove Welds and Symbols.

17.7. Gas and arc welding symbols.   In order to satisfy the need for a standard group of symbols that could be understood in all manufacturing plants, the American Welding Society recommended in 1940 a set of conventional symbols so designed that each symbol resembled in a general way the type of weld it represented.   Figure 17.16 shows a

Fig. 17.16. Arc and Gas Welding Symbols.*

Fig. 17.17. Supplementary Symbols.*

Fig. 17.18. Resistance Welding Symbols.*

condensed table of symbols taken from ASA Z32.2.1–1949. The symbols shown are the same as those first proposed by the American Welding Society. Supplementary symbols are shown in Fig. 17.17.

17.8. Resistance welding. Figure 17.18 shows the symbols for the four principal types of resistance welding. The method of specifying

---

* ASA Z32.2.1–1949.

resistance welds differs from the methods used for arc and gas welds.   In the former, the strength of a weld is given in units instead of size, and the symbols do not show the form of the weld.   The strength of spot and projection welds is given in units of pounds per weld.   The strength for seam welds is given in units of pounds per linear inch.

17.9. Welded machine parts. Many machine parts often can be constructed of welded rolled shapes at a much lower cost than if they were cast.   This is due to the fact that the cost of the preparation of patterns is completely eliminated, less material is required, and labor costs are lower.   A welded part is sometimes more desirable for a particular mechanism, because steel is stiffer, stronger in tension, and more resistant to fatigue stresses and sudden impact.   Also, aside from the production of new parts, welding can be used to make a machine part to replace a broken cast part when it

Fig. 17.19.   Bracket-Welded Design.

is necessary to place a machine back in operation in the shortest possible time.   Figure 17.19 shows a part that is constructed of plates.   Figure 17.20 shows the construction of a link using plates and round bar stock.

Fig. 17.20.   Link-Welded Design.

As previously stated, a designer is limited only by his own ingenuity. Parts of all shapes and sizes may be produced of readily available rolled forms.   Simple bearings, levers, cranks, clevises, gear arms, and even cams can be quickly and easily made.

17.10. Instructions for use of welding symbols. The general instructions that follow were extracted from the American Standards publication ASA Z32.2.1–1949, which was reaffirmed in 1953.

SECTION I—GENERAL PROVISIONS

1. Location significance of arrow. *a.* In the case of groove, fillet, and flash or upset welding symbols, the arrow shall connect the welding symbol reference line to one side of the joint, and this side shall be considered the *arrow side* of the joint. The side opposite the arrow side of the joint shall be considered the *other side* of the joint.

b. In the case of plug, slot, spot, seam and projection welding symbols, the arrow shall connect the welding symbol reference line to the outer surface of one of the members of the joint at the center line of the desired weld. The member to which the arrow points shall be considered the *arrow-side* member. The other member of the joint shall be considered the *other-side* member.

c. When a joint is depicted by a single line on the drawing and the arrow of a welding symbol is directed to this line, the arrow side of the joint shall be considered as the near side of the joint in accordance with the usual conventions of drafting.

d. When a joint is depicted as an area parallel to the plane of projection in a drawing and the arrow of a welding symbol is directed to near area, the *arrow-side* member of the joint shall be considered as the near side of the joint in accordance with the usual conventions of drafting.

2. Location of weld with respect to joint. *a.* Welds on the arrow side of the joint shall be shown by placing the weld symbol on the side of the reference line toward the reader, thus:

Fig. 17.21.

b. Welds on the other side of the joint shall be shown by placing the weld symbol on the side of the reference line away from the reader, thus:

Fig. 17.22.

c. Welds on both sides of the joint shall be shown by placing weld symbols on both sides of the reference line, toward and away from the reader, thus:

Fig. 17.23.

d. Spot, seam, flash and upset weld symbols have no arrow-side or other-side significance in themselves, although supplementary symbols used in conjunction therewith may have such significance. Spot, seam, flash and upset weld symbols shall be centered on the reference line, thus:

Fig. 17.24.

3. Method of drawing symbols. Symbols may be drawn mechanically or freehand, as desired.

4. Use of inch, degree, and pound marks. Inch, degree and pound marks may be used on welding symbols or not, as desired, except that inch marks shall be used for indicating the diameter of spot and projection welds and the width of seam weld, when such welds are specified by linear dimension.

5. Location of specification, process, or other references. When a specification, process or other reference is used with a welding symbol, the reference shall be placed in the tail, thus:

Fig. 17.25.

6. Use of symbols without references. When desired, symbols may be used without specification, process or other references in the following instances:

a. When a note such as the following appears on the drawing: "Unless otherwise designated, all welds are to be made in accordance with Specification No. —."

b. When the welding procedure to be used is prescribed elsewhere.

7. Use of general notes. When desired, general notes such as the following may be placed on a drawing to provide detailed information pertaining to the predominating welds, and this information need not be repeated on the symbols.

"Unless otherwise indicated, all fillet welds are $\frac{5}{16}$ inch size."

"Unless otherwise indicated, root openings for all groove welds are $\frac{3}{16}$ inch."

8. Use of weld-all-around symbol. Welds extending completely around a joint shall be indicated by means of the weld-all-around symbol, thus:

Fig. 17.26.

9. Use of field weld symbol. Field welds (welds not made in a shop or at the place of initial construction) shall be indicated by means of the field weld symbol, thus:

Fig. 17.27.

10. Extent of welding denoted by symbols. Symbols apply between abrupt changes in the direction of the welding or to the extent of hatching or dimension lines, except when the weld-all-around symbol is used.

11. Weld proportions. All welds shall be continuous and of user's standard proportions unless otherwise indicated.

12. Finishing of welds. Finishing of welds, other than cleaning, shall be indicated by suitable contour and finish symbols. (See Sec. II-9.)

13. Location of weld symbols. *a.* Weld symbols, except spot and seam, shall be shown only on the welding symbol reference line and not on the lines of the drawing.

b. Spot and seam weld symbols may be placed directly on drawings at the locations of the desired welds, thus:

Fig. 17.28.

14. Construction of fillet and bevel- and J-groove welding symbols.
Fillet and bevel- and J-groove weld symbols shall be shown with the perpendicular leg *always* to the left, thus:

Fig. 17.29.

15. Use of break in arrow of bevel- and J-groove welding symbols.
When a bevel- or J-groove weld symbol is used, the arrow shall point with a definite break toward the member which is to be chamfered, thus: (In cases where the member to be chamfered is obvious, the break in the arrow may be omitted.)

Fig. 17.30.

16. Reading of information on welding symbols. Information on welding symbols shall be placed to read from left to right along the reference line in accordance with the usual conventions of drafting, thus:

Fig. 17.31.

17. Combined weld symbols. For joints having more than one weld, a symbol shall be shown for each weld, thus:

Fig. 17.32.

18. Designation of special types of welds. When the basic weld symbols are inadequate to indicate the desired weld, the weld shall be shown by a cross section, detail or other data, with a reference thereto on the welding symbol, observing the usual location significance, thus:

Fig. 17.33.

SECTION II—FILLET WELDS

1. General. *a.* Dimensions of fillet welds shall be shown on the same side of reference line as the weld symbol, thus:

Fig. 17.34.

b. When no general note governing the dimensions of fillet welds appears on the drawing, the dimensions of fillet welds on both sides of the joint shall be shown as follows:

(1) When both welds have the same dimensions, one or both may be dimensioned, thus:

Fig. 17.35.

(2) When the welds differ in dimensions, both shall be dimensioned, thus:

Fig. 17.36.

c. When there appears on the drawing a general note governing the dimensions of fillet welds, such as "All fillet welds $\frac{5}{16}$ in. size unless otherwise noted," the dimensions of fillet welds on both sides of the joint shall be indicated as follows:

(1) When both welds have dimensions governed by the note, neither need be dimensioned, thus:

Fig. 17.37.

(2) When the dimensions of one or both welds differ from the dimensions given in the general note, both welds shall be dimensioned, thus:

Fig. 17.38.

2. Size of fillet welds.   *a.* The size of a fillet weld shall be shown to the left of the weld symbol, thus:

Fig. 17.39.

b. The size of a fillet weld with unequal legs shall be shown in parentheses to the left of the weld symbol, as shown below.   Weld orientation is not shown by the symbol and shall be shown on the drawing when necessary.

Fig. 17.40.

3. Length of fillet welds. *a.* The length of a fillet weld, when indicated on the welding symbol, shall be shown to the right of the weld symbol, thus:

Fig. 17.41.

b. When fillet welding extends for the full distance between abrupt changes in the direction of the welding (See Sec. I-10), no length dimension need be shown on the welding symbol.

c. Specific lengths of fillet welding may be indicated by symbols in conjunction with dimension lines, thus:

Fig. 17.42.

4. Extent of fillet welding. *a.* When it is desired to show the extent of fillet welding graphically, one type of hatching with definite end lines shall be used, thus:

Fig. 17.43.

b. Fillet welding extending beyond abrupt changes in the direction of the welding shall be indicated by means of additional arrows pointing to each section of the joint to be welded, except when the weld-all-around symbol is used.

5. Dimensioning of intermittent fillet welding. *a.* The pitch (center-to-center spacing) of intermittent fillet welding shall be shown as the distance between centers of increments on *one* side of the joint.

b. The pitch (center-to-center spacing) of intermittent fillet welding shall be shown to the right of the length dimension, thus:

Fig. 17.44.

c. Chain intermittent fillet welding shall be shown thus:

Fig. 17.45.

d. Staggered intermittent fillet welding shall be shown thus:

Fig. 17.46.

6. Termination of intermittent fillet welding. *a.* When intermittent fillet welding is used by itself, the symbol indicates that increments shall be located at the ends of the dimensioned length.

b. When intermittent fillet welding is used between continuous fillet welding the symbol indicates that spaces equal to the pitch minus the length of one increment shall be left at the ends of the dimensioned length.

7. Combination of intermittent and continuous fillet welding. Separate symbols shall be used for intermittent and continuous fillet welding when the two are used in combination.

8. Fillet welds in holes and slots. Fillet welds in holes and slots shall be shown by means of fillet weld symbols.

9. Surface contour of fillet welds. *a.* Fillet welds that are to be welded approximately flat-faced without recourse to any method of finishing shall be shown by adding the flush-contour symbol to the weld symbol, observing the usual location significance, thus:

Fig. 17.47.

b. Fillet welds that are to be made flat-faced by mechanical means, shall be shown by adding both the flush-contour symbol and the user's standard finish symbol* to the weld symbol, observing the usual location significance, thus:

Fig. 17.48.

c. Fillet welds that are to be mechanically finished to a convex contour, shall be shown by adding both the convex-contour symbol and the user's standard finish symbol* to the weld symbol, observing the usual location significance, thus:

Fig. 17.49.

SECTION III—GROOVE WELDS

1. General. *a.* Dimensions of groove welds shall be shown on the same side of the reference line as the weld symbol, thus:

Fig. 17.50.

b. When no general note governing the dimensions of groove welds appears on the drawing, the dimensions of double-groove welds shall be shown as follows:

---

* Finish symbols used herein indicate the method of finishing (C = chipping; G = grinding; M = machining) and not the degree of finish.

(1) When both welds have the same dimensions, one or both may be dimensioned, thus:

Fig. 17.51.

(2) When the welds differ in dimensions, both shall be dimensioned, thus:

Fig. 17.52.

c. When there appears on the drawing a general note governing the dimensions of groove welds, such as "All V-groove welds shall have a 60° groove angle unless otherwise noted," the dimensions of double-groove welds shall be indicated as follows:

(1) When both welds have dimensions governed by the note, neither need be dimensioned, thus:

Fig. 17.53.

(2) When the dimensions of one or both welds differ from the dimensions given in the general note, both welds shall be dimensioned, thus:

Fig. 17.54.

2. Size of groove welds.   *a.* The size of groove welds shall be shown to the left of the weld symbol, thus:

Fig. 17.55.

b. The size of groove welds with no specified root penetration shall be shown as follows:

(1) The size of single-groove and symmetrical double-groove welds which extend completely through the member or members being joined need not be shown on the welding symbol.
(2) The size of groove welds which extend only partly through the member or members being joined shall be shown on the welding symbol.

c. The size of groove welds with specified root penetration shall be indicated by showing both the depth of chamfering and the root penetration, separated by a plus mark and placed to the left of the weld symbol.   The depth of chamfering and the root penetration shall read in that order from left to right along the reference line, thus:

Fig. 17.56.

3. Groove dimensions. *a.* Root opening of groove welds shall be the user's standard unless otherwise indicated. Root opening of groove welds, when not the user's standard, shall be shown inside the weld symbol, thus:

Fig. 17.57.

b. Groove angle of groove welds shall be the user's standard, unless otherwise indicated. Groove angle of groove welds, when not the user's standard, shall be shown thus:

Fig. 17.58.

c. Groove radii and root faces of U- and J-groove welds shall be the user's standard unless otherwise indicated. When groove radii and root faces of U- and J-groove welds are not the user's standard, the weld shall be shown by a cross section, detail or other data, with a reference thereto on the welding symbol, observing the usual location significance, thus:

Fig. 17.59.

4. Designation of back and backing welds. Bead-type back and backing welds of single-groove welds shall be shown by means of the bead weld symbol. (See Sec. IV-2.)

5. Surface contour of groove welds. *a.* Groove welds that are to be welded approximately flush without recourse to any method of finishing shall be shown by adding the flush-contour symbol to the weld symbol, observing the usual location significance, thus:

Fig. 17.60.

b. Groove welds that are to be made flush by mechanical means shall be shown by adding both the flush-contour symbol and the user's standard finish symbol* to the weld symbol, observing the usual location significance, thus:

Fig. 17.61.

---

* Finish symbols used herein indicate the method of finishing (C = chipping; G = grinding; M = machining) and not the degree of finish.

c. Groove welds that are to be mechanically finished to a convex contour shall be shown by adding both the convex-contour symbol and the user's standard finish symbol* to the weld symbol, observing the usual location significance, thus:

Fig. 17.62.

SECTION IV—BEAD WELDS

1. General. *a.* The single bead weld symbol shall be used to indicate bead-type back or backing welds of single-groove welds.

b. The dual bead weld symbol shall be used to indicate surfaces built up by welding.

2. Use of bead weld symbol to indicate bead-type back or backing welds. *a.* Bead welds used as back or backing welds of single-groove welds shall be shown by placing a single bead weld symbol on the side of the reference line opposite the groove weld symbol, thus:

Fig. 17.63.

b. Dimensions of bead welds used as back or backing welds shall not be shown on the welding symbol.   If it is desired to specify these dimensions, they shall be shown on the drawing.

3. Surface contour of back or backing welds. *a.* Back or backing welds that are to be welded approximately flush without recourse to any method of finishing shall be shown by adding the flush-contour symbol to the bead weld symbol, thus:

Fig. 17.64.

b. Back or backing welds that are to be made flush by mechanical means shall be shown by adding both the flush-contour symbol and the user's standard finish symbol* to the bead weld symbol, thus:

Fig. 17.65.

c. Back or backing welds that are to be mechanically finished to a convex contour shall be shown by adding both the convex-contour symbol and the user's standard finish symbol* to the bead weld symbol, thus:

Fig. 17.66.

---

* Finish symbols used herein indicate the method of finishing (C = chipping; G = grinding; M = machining) and not the degree of finish.

4. Use of bead weld symbol to indicate surfaces built up by welding.
a. Surfaces built up by welding, whether by single- or multiple-pass bead welds, shall be shown by the dual bead weld symbol, thus:

Fig. 17.67.

b. The dual bead weld symbol does not indicate the welding of a joint, and hence has no arrow- or other-side significance. This symbol shall be drawn on the side of the reference line toward the reader and the arrow shall point clearly to the surface on which the weld is to be deposited.
c. Dimensions used in conjunction with the dual bead weld symbol shall be shown on the same side of the reference line as the weld symbol, thus:

Fig. 17.68.

5. Size (height) of surfaces built up by welding. *a.* The size of a surface built up by welding shall be indicated by showing the minimum height of the weld deposit to the left of the weld symbol, thus:

Fig. 17.69.

b. When no specific height of weld deposit is desired, no size dimension need be shown on the welding symbol.
6. Extent, location, and orientation of surfaces built up by welding.
a. When the entire area of a plane or curved surface is to be built up by welding, no dimension other than size (height of deposit) need be shown on the welding symbol.
b. When a portion of the area of a plane or curved surface is to be built up by welding, the extent, location and orientation of the area to be built up shall be indicated on the drawing.

SECTION V—PLUG WELDS

1. General. *a.* Holes in the arrow-side member of a joint for plug welding shall be indicated by placing the weld symbol on the side of the reference line toward the reader, thus:

DESIRED   SECTION OR   PLAN OR
                 END VIEW   ELEVATION

Fig. 17.70.

b. Holes in the other-side member of a joint for plug welding shall be indicated by placing the weld symbol on the side of the reference line away from the reader, thus:

DESIRED   SECTION OR   PLAN OR
                 END VIEW   ELEVATION

Fig. 17.71.

c. Dimensions of plug welds shall be shown on the same side of the reference line as the weld symbol, thus:

Fig. 17.72.

d. The plug weld symbol shall not be used to designate fillet welds in holes. (See Sec. II-8.)

2. Size of plug welds. The size of a plug weld shall be shown to the left of the weld symbol, thus:

Fig. 17.73.

3. Angle of countersink. Included angle of countersink of plug welds shall be the user's standard unless otherwise indicated. Included angle of countersink, when not the user's standard, shall be shown thus:

Fig. 17.74.

4. Depth of filling. Depth of filling of plug welds shall be complete unless otherwise indicated. When the depth of filling is less than complete, the depth of filling, in inches, shall be shown inside the weld symbol, thus:

Fig. 17.75.

5. Spacing of plug welds. Pitch (center-to-center spacing) of plug welds shall be shown to the right of the weld symbol, thus:

Fig. 17.76.

6. Surface contour of plug welds. *a.* Plug welds that are to be welded approximately flush without recourse to any method of finishing shall be shown by adding the flush-contour symbol to the weld symbol, thus:

Fig. 17.77.

b. Plug welds that are to be made flush by mechanical means shall be shown by adding both the flush-contour symbol and the user's standard finish symbol* to the weld symbol, thus:

Fig. 17.78.

SECTION VI—SLOT WELDS

1. General.   *a.* Slots in the arrow-side member of a joint for slot welding shall be indicated by placing the weld symbol on the side of the reference line toward the reader, thus:

Fig. 17.79.

b. Slots in the other-side member of a joint for slot welding shall be indicated by placing the weld symbol on the side of the reference line away from the reader, thus:

Fig. 17.80.

c. Dimensions of slot welds shall be shown on the same side of the reference line as the weld symbol, thus:

Fig. 17.81.

d. The slot weld symbol shall not be used to designate fillet welds in slots.

2. Depth of filling.   Depth of filling of slot welds shall be complete unless otherwise indicated.   When the depth of filling is less than complete, the depth of filling, in inches, shall be shown inside the weld symbol, thus:

Fig. 17.82.

---

* Finish symbols used herein indicate the method of finishing (C = chipping; G = grinding; M = machining) and not the degree of finish.

3. Details of slot welds. Length, width, spacing, included angle of countersink, orientation and location of slot welds cannot be shown on the welding symbol. These data shall be shown on the drawing or by a detail with a reference thereto on the welding symbol, observing the usual location significance, thus:

Fig. 17.83.

4. Surface contour of slot welds. *a.* Slot welds that are to be welded approximately flush without recourse to any method of finishing shall be shown by adding the flush-contour symbol to the weld symbol, thus:

Fig. 17.84.

b. Slot welds that are to be made flush by mechanical means shall be shown by adding both the flush-contour symbol and the user's standard finish symbol* to the weld symbol, thus:

Fig. 17.85.

SECTION VII—SPOT WELDS

1. General. *a.* Spot weld symbols have no arrow- or other-side significance in themselves, although supplementary symbols used in conjunction therewith may have such significance (see Sec. VII-6). Spot weld symbols shall be centered on the reference line.

b. Dimensions of spot welds may be shown on either side of the reference line.

2. Size of spot welds. Spot welds shall be dimensioned by either size or strength, as follows:

(1) The size of spot welds shall be designated as the diameter of the weld expressed decimally in hundredths of an inch, and shall be shown, with inch marks, to the left of the weld symbol, thus:

Fig. 17.86.

(2) The strength of spot welds shall be designated as the minimum acceptable shear strength in pounds per spot, and shall be shown to the left of the weld symbol, thus:

Fig. 17.87.

---

* Finish symbols used herein indicate the method of finishing (C = chipping; G = grinding; M = machining) and not the degree of finish.

3. Spacing of spot welds. *a.* The pitch (center-to-center spacing) of spot welds shall be shown to the right of the weld symbol, thus:

Fig. 17.88.

b. When spot weld symbols are shown directly on the drawing, spacing shall be shown by dimensions.

4. Extent of spot welding. When spot welding extends less than the distance between abrupt changes in the direction of the welding, or less than the full length of the joint (see Sec. I-10), the extent shall be dimensioned, thus:

Fig. 17.89.

5. Number of spot welds. When a definite number of spot welds is desired in a certain joint, the number shall be shown in parentheses either above or below the weld symbol, thus:

Fig. 17.90.

6. Flush spot-welded joints. When the exposed surface of one member of a spot-welded joint is to be flush, that surface shall be indicated by adding the flush-contour symbol to the weld symbol, observing the usual location significance, thus:

Fig. 17.91.

SECTION VIII—SEAM WELDS

1. General. *a.* Seam weld symbols have no arrow- or other-side significance in themselves, although supplementary symbols used in conjunction therewith may have such significance. (See Sec. VIII-7.) Seam weld symbols shall be centered on the reference line.

b. Dimensions of seam welds may be shown on either side of the reference line.

2. Size of seam welds. Seam welds shall be dimensioned by either size or strength as follows:

(1) The size of seam welds shall be designated as the width of the weld expressed decimally in hundredths of an inch, and shall be shown, with inch marks, to the left of the weld symbol, thus:

Fig. 17.92.

(2) The strength of seam welds shall be designated as the minimum acceptable shear strength in pounds per linear inch, and shall be shown to the left of the weld symbol, thus:

Fig. 17.93.

3. Length of seam welds.   *a.* The length of a seam weld, when indicated on the welding symbol, shall be shown to the right of the weld symbol, thus:

Fig. 17.94.

b. When seam welding extends for the full distance between abrupt changes in the direction of the welding (see Sec. I-10), no length dimension need be shown on the welding symbol.

c. When seam welding extends less than the distance between abrupt changes in the direction of the welding, or less than the full length of the joint, the extent shall be dimensioned, thus:

Fig. 17.95.

4. Dimensioning of intermittent seam welding.   *a.* The pitch (center-to-center spacing) of intermittent seam welding shall be shown as the distance between centers of the weld increments.

b. The pitch (center-to-center spacing) of intermittent seam welding shall be shown to the right of the length dimension, thus:

Fig. 17.96.

5. Termination of intermittent seam welding.   *a.* When intermittent seam welding is used by itself, the symbol indicates that increments shall be located at the ends of the dimensioned length.

b. When intermittent seam welding is used between continuous seam welding, the symbol indicates that spaces equal to the pitch minus the length of one increment shall be left at the ends of the dimensioned length.

6. Combination of intermittent and continuous seam welding. Separate symbols shall be used for intermittent and continuous seam welding when the two are used in combination.

7. Flush seam-welded joints.   When the exposed surface of one member of a seam-welded joint is to be flush, that surface shall be indicated by adding the flush-contour symbol to the weld symbol, observing the usual location significance, thus:

Fig. 17.97.

SECTION IX—PROJECTION WELDS

1. General.   *a.* Embossments on the arrow-side member of a joint for projection welding shall be indicated by placing the weld symbol on the side of the reference line toward the reader, thus:

SECTION OR   PLAN OR
END VIEW   . ELEVATION
DESIRED   SYMBOLS

Fig. 17.98.

b. Embossments on the other-side member of a joint for projection welding shall be indicated by placing the weld-symbol on the side of the reference line away from the reader, thus:

SECTION OR   PLAN OR
END VIEW   ELEVATION
DESIRED   SYMBOLS

Fig. 17.99.

c. Proportions of projections shall be shown by a detail or other suitable means.

d. Dimensions of projection welds shall be shown on the same side of the reference line as the weld symbol, thus:

Fig. 17.100.

2. Size of projection welds.   Projection welds shall be dimensioned by either size or strength, as follows:

(1) The size of projection welds shall be designated as the diameter of the weld expressed decimally in hundredths of an inch, and shall be shown, with inch marks, to the left of the weld symbol, thus:

Fig. 17.101.

(2) The strength of projection welds shall be designated as the minimum acceptable shear strength in pounds per weld, and shall be shown to the left of the weld symbol, thus:

Fig. 17.102.

3. Spacing of projection welds. The pitch (center-to-center spacing) of projection welds shall be shown to the right of the weld symbol, thus:

Fig. 17.103.

4. Extent of projection welding. When projection welding extends less than the distance between abrupt changes in the direction of the welding, or less than the full length of the joint, the extent shall be dimensioned, thus:

Fig. 17.104.

5. Number of projection welds. When a definite number of projection welds is desired in a certain joint, the number shall be shown in parentheses, thus:

Fig. 17.105.

6. Flush projection-welded joints. When the exposed surface of one member of a projection-welded joint is to be made flush, that surface shall be indicated by adding the flush-contour symbol to the weld symbol, observing the usual location significance, thus:

Fig. 17.106.

SECTION X—FLASH AND UPSET WELDS

1. General. *a.* Flash and upset weld symbols have no arrow-side or other-side significance in themselves although supplementary symbols used in conjunction therewith may have such significance (see Sec. X-2). Flash or upset weld symbols shall be centered in the reference line.

b. Dimensions of flash and upset welds shall not be shown on the welding symbol.

2. Surface contour of flash and upset welds. *a.* Flash and upset welds that are to be made flush by mechanical means shall be shown by adding both the flush-contour symbol and the user's standard finish symbol* to the weld symbol, observing the usual location significance, thus:

Fig. 17.107.

---

* Finish symbols used herein indicate the method of finishing (C = chipping; G = grinding; M = machining) and not the degree of finish.

b. Flash and upset welds that are to be mechanically finished to a convex contour shall be shown by adding both the convex-contour symbol and the user's standard finish symbol* to the weld symbol, observing the usual location significance, thus:

Fig. 17.108.

17.11. Problems. Two problems offering experience in the preparation of welding drawings are given in Figs. 17.109 and 17.110. Others may be had by redesigning many of the cast parts, given at the end of the chapter on multiview drawing and in some of the other chapters, in such a way that they may be made of welded steel shapes. The student will find in these problems an opportunity to exercise some of his own ingenuity.

1. Prepare a welding drawing of the bracket shown in Fig. 17.109.

Fig. 17.109.   Bracket.   **Fig. 17.110.   Caster Bracket.**

2. Prepare a welding drawing of the caster bracket shown in Fig. 17.110. The length of the tubing is $2\frac{11}{16}''$.

3. Make a two-view orthographic drawing of the object shown in Fig. 17.1. The dimensions are to be assumed. The plates are $\frac{3}{8}''$ thick. Show the correct specification for each type of weld.

4. Make a three-view detail drawing of the bracket shown in Fig. 17.19. The dimensions are to be assumed. Show the correct specification for the welds.

5. Make a two-view detail drawing of the link shown in Fig. 17.20. The dimensions are to be assumed. Show correct specifications for the welds.

---

* Finish symbols used herein indicate the method of finishing (C = chipping; G = grinding; M = machining) and not the degree of finish.

18

Piping Drawings

18.1. Since piping is used in all types of construction for conveying fluids and gases such as oil, water, steam, and chemicals, some knowledge of it is essential not only for the draftsman making drawings but for the engineer who must select and use pipe in the design of machines, power plants, water systems, and so on. There are so many types of fittings and materials used for various purposes that only the most common can be discussed briefly in this chapter. Additional information may be obtained from publications of research associations and from the catalogs of manufacturers.

18.2. Pipe materials. The Greeks and Romans used pipes made of wood or lead, but the quick deterioration of wood and the poisoning brought about by lead made both types unsatisfactory. Not until about 1660 was iron pipe cast in a foundry; this was for the fountains at Versailles, France. Before the year 1834, when the first foundry was established at Millville, New Jersey, all cast-iron pipe used in this country was purchased in England. Pipe made of bored pine and spruce log was used in many Eastern cities.* Even today water pipes composed of wood staves and steel hoops can be seen in the mountain regions of the West. For all general purposes, however, cast-iron, wrought-iron, and steel pipes are now used.

Cast-iron pipe is suitable for underground gas and water mains, plumbing lines, and low-pressure steam systems.

Steel pipe is used chiefly where high temperatures and high pressures are encountered. The addition of such alloys as nickel, chromium, and the like makes the steel pipe more resistant to corrosion at high temperatures.

Seamless brass pipe is the most satisfactory type for hot-water lines, condenser tubes, and so on, but it is expensive and, therefore, is used only when conditions justify the extra cost.

For lines having turns and bends in accessible locations, copper tubing is frequently used. But copper pipe, even though it is flexible and can resist the corrosive action of chemicals, is not always practical. It cannot be used in any system subject to high temperatures and repeated stress.

Lead and lead-lined pipe is widely used for chemical work, particularly where piping is subject to the action of acids.

Galvanized pipe (ordinary iron pipe that has been dipped in molten zinc to prevent rust) is suitable for lines conveying drinking water.

---

* Information from a publication of the Cast Iron Pipe Research Association.

421

18.3. American Standard pipe thread. The American Standard pipe taper thread, illustrated in Fig. 18.1, is similar to the ordinary American Standard thread and has the same thread angle; but it is tapered $\frac{1}{16}''$ per inch, to insure a tight joint at a fitting. The crest is flattened and the root is filled in so that the depth of the thread is 0.80P. The number of threads per inch for any given nominal diameter can be obtained from Table XXV in the Appendix.

The distance a pipe enters a fitting is fixed for any nominal diameter. Numerical values for this distance may be determined from Table XXV.

An American National straight pipe thread, having the same number of threads per inch as the taper thread, is in use for pressure-tight joints for couplings, for pressure-tight joints for grease and oil fittings, and for hose couplings and nipples. This thread may also be used for free-fitting mechanical joints. Usually a taper external thread is used with a straight

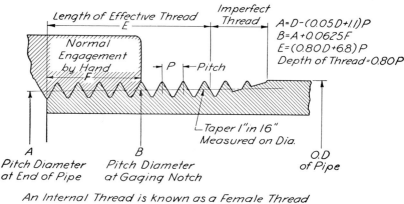

Fig. 18.1. American Standard Pipe Thread.

internal thread, as pipe material is sufficiently ductile for an adjustment of the threads.

In specifying pipe threads, the ASA recommends that the note be formulated using symbolic letters as illustrated in Fig. 18.2. For example, the specification for a 1″ standard pipe thread should read, 1″-NPT. The letters NPT, following the nominal diameter, indicate that the thread is American National (N), pipe (P), taper (T) thread. Continuing with the same scheme of using letters, the specification for a 1″ straight pipe thread would read, 1″-NPS [National (N)—pipe (P)—straight (S)]. The form of note given in (a), reading 1″ AM. STD. PIPE THD, is quite commonly used in practice. Identification symbols and dimensions of American National pipe threads are given in the American Standard for Pipe Threads (ASA B2.1–1945).

18.4. Drawing pipe threads. The taper on a pipe thread is so slight that it will not attract attention on a drawing unless it is exaggerated. If it is shown at all, it is usually magnified to $\frac{1}{8}''$ per inch.

Pipe threads are generally represented by the same conventional symbols used for ordinary American Standard thread.   (See Fig. 18.2.)

18.5. Specification of wrought-iron and steel pipe.   The standardized weights commonly used are the standard, extra strong, and double extra strong.   All are specified by the nominal inside diameter.

Fig. 18.2.   American Standard Representation of Pipe Threads.

The nominal inside diameter of standard pipe is less than the actual diameter, because early manufacturers made the wall thickness greater than necessary and, in correcting, took all of the excess from the inside to avoid altering the size of openings in fittings.   Metal was added to the inside to increase wall thicknesses for the extra strong and double extra strong.   As a result, all three weights of pipe for any given nominal diameter have the same outside diameter and can be used with the same fittings.

Wrought-iron or steel pipe greater than 12″ in diameter is specified by giving the outside diameter and the thickness of the wall.

Fig. 18.3 illustrates the relative wall thickness of 1″ standard, extra strong, and double extra strong pipe.

Fig. 18.3. Comparison of Different Weights of 1″ Wrought-Iron Pipe.[*]

18.6. Sizes of wrought-iron, steel, and cast-iron pipe.   The standard-weight pipe is used for normal pressures.   It may be purchased in sizes ranging from $\frac{1}{8}$″ to 12″ (nominal diameter).   Pipe is received threaded on both ends with a plain coupling attached.

---

[*] ASA B36.10–1950.

Extra strong pipe, designed for steam and hydraulic pressures over 125 pounds per square inch, also is manufactured in sizes $\frac{1}{8}''$ to 12''.

Double extra strong pipe, designed for extremely high pressures, is furnished in nominal diameters from $\frac{1}{2}''$ to 8'' in the same lengths as the extra strong.

Cast-iron pipe, in sizes ranging up to 48'', can be used for pressures up to 350 pounds per square inch.

| TEE | SERVICE TEE | 90° ELBOW | 45° ELBOW | REDUCING ELBOW | 90° STREET ELBOW |

| 45° Y-BRANCH | CROSS | CAP | R & L COUPLING | REDUCER | HEX. BUSHING |

| BUSHING | CLOSE NIPPLE | SHORT NIPPLE | LONG NIPPLE | PLUG | BEND |

Fig. 18.4.   Screwed Fittings.

Fig. 18.5.   Flanged Fittings.

TEE   90° ELBOW   45° ELBOW

Fig. 18.6.   Welded Fittings.

18.7. Pipe fittings.   Fittings are parts, such as elbows, tees, crosses, couplings, nipples, flanges, and so on, which are used to make turns and connections. They fall into three general classes: screwed, welded, and flanged.

In small piping systems and for house plumbing, screwed fittings are generally used (Fig. 18.4).

Welded fittings are used where connections are to be permanent. They are manufactured of forged seamless steel, having the same thickness as the pipe. In this type of construction, the weld is depended upon to seal the joint and to carry the pipe-line stresses. Many miles of line having welded fittings are giving satisfactory service to pipe-line corporations.

Flanged fittings are used in large piping systems where pressures are high and the connection must be strong enough to carry the weight of large pipes. Table XXIX in the Appendix gives the dimensions for American Standard 125-pound cast-iron flange fittings. Several types of flanges and flanged joints are shown in Figs. 18.7 and 18.8.

18.8. Screwed fittings (Fig. 18.4). Straight sections of pipe are connected by a short cylindrical fitting (threaded on the inside), which is known as a *coupling*. A *right and left coupling*, which can be recognized by the ribs on the outside, is often used to close a system. A *union* is preferable, however, where pipe must be frequently disconnected.

(a)   (b)   (c)

Fig. 18.7. Flanges.

(a)   (b)

Fig. 18.8. Flanges.

A *cap* is screwed on the end of a pipe to close it.

A *plug* is used to close an opening in a fitting.

A *nipple* is a short piece of pipe that has been threaded on both ends. If it is threaded the entire length, it is called a *close nipple;* if not, it is called a *short* or *long nipple.* Extra long nipples may be purchased.

A *bushing* is used to reduce the size of an opening in a fitting when it would be inconvenient to use a reducing fitting.

Tees, crosses, and *laterals* form the connections for lines and branches in a piping system.

By standardizing the screwed fittings, the American Standards Association has eliminated many difficulties that would arise if each manufacturer produced the varied sizes of elbows, tees, laterals, and so on, according to his own specifications. The adopted dimensions, now recognized by all manufacturers, will be found in Tables XXVI, XXVII, and XXVIII in the Appendix.

18.9. Specification of fittings. A fitting is specified by giving the nominal inside diameter of the pipe for which the openings are threaded, the type of fitting, and the material. If it connects more than one size of pipe, it is called a reducing fitting, and the largest opening of the through run is given first, followed in order by the opposite end and the outlet. Figure 18.9 illustrates the order of specifying reducing fittings. If all of the openings are for the same size of pipe, the fitting is known as a straight tee, cross, and so on. A straight fitting is specified by the size of the openings followed by the name of the fitting (2″ tee, 4″ cross, etc.).

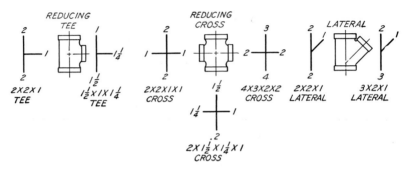

Fig. 18.9. Specification of Fittings.

Fig. 18.10. Unions.

18.10. Unions. Screwed or flanged unions connect pipes that must be frequently disconnected for the purpose of making repairs. In many cases, screwed unions are used for making the final closing connection in a line. The union illustrated in Fig. 18.10(a) is made up of three separate pieces. The mating parts, A and B, are screwed on the ends of the two pipes. The third part, the nut, draws them together so that A and B will be against the gasket, D, to insure a tight joint. In systems having pipes over 2″ in diameter, screwed unions are not generally used, because the stronger and more substantial flange unions, such as the one shown at (c), become desirable. A screwed union with a ground metal seat is shown at (b).

18.11. Valves. Valves are used in piping systems to stop or control the movement of fluids and gases. A few of the many forms are illustrated in Fig. 18.11. Of these, the globe valve and gate valve are the two types most frequently used.

Globe valves are used for throttling steam, in both high- and low-pressure steam lines, and to regulate the passage of other fluids. Their design, however, creates a slight retardation to the flow, because the

GLOBE VALVE   SWING CHECK VALVE   GATE VALVE

BALL CHECK VALVE   HORIZONTAL LIFT CHECK VALVE   FOUR-WAY STEAM COCK

Courtesy Crane Co.

Fig. 18.11. Valves.

fluid is forced to make a double turn and pass through the opening at 90° to the axis of the pipe. The valve disc is raised or lowered to stop or regulate the flow through a circular opening.

A gate valve allows a straight-line movement of a fluid and offers only slight resistance to the flow. Since the disc moves completely out of the passage and leaves a full opening, this type of valve is particularly suitable for water lines, oil lines, and the like.

A swing-type check valve permits movement in one direction only and prevents any back flow. It will be noted from a study of this valve that the design makes the action automatic. Such valves are used in feed-water lines to boilers. The ball-check valve is preferred for heavy liquids.

Fig. 18.12.   Single-Line Drawing.

Fig. 18.13.   Double-Line Drawing.

Fig. 18.14.   Pictorial Line Diagram.

The dimensions of the valves given in Fig. 18.11, as well as those for many special types, may be found in the catalogs of manufacturers.

18.12. Piping drawings.   Since standard pipe and fittings can be purchased for almost any purpose, a piping drawing usually shows only the arrangement of a system in some conventional form, and gives the size and location of fittings.   The drawing may be a freehand sketch, single-line diagram, double-line diagram, or pictorial diagram.   Occasionally, when conditions necessitate the design of special valves or the redesign of an existing type, complete working drawings are made.

GRAPHICAL SYMBOLS FOR PIPE FITTINGS

	FLANGED	SCREWED	BELL & SPIGOT	WELDED	SOLDERED
1) BUSHING		⊐▷	∈	✕	⊣⊢
2) CAP		⊐⌐	⌐		
3) CROSS-STRAIGHT SIZE					
4) ELBOW — 45 DEGREE					
— 90 DEGREE					
— TURNED DOWN					
— TURNED UP					
5) LATERAL					
6) PLUG		◁	⊏		
7) TEE — STRAIGHT SIZE					
— OUTLET UP					
— OUTLET DOWN					
8) UNION					
9) REDUCER — CONCENTRIC					
— ECCENTRIC					
10) CHECK VALVE — STRAIGHT WAY					
11) GATE VALVE					
12) GLOBE VALVE					
13) ANGLE VALVE GLOBE — ELEVATION					
GLOBE — PLAN					

ASA Z 32.2.3 — 1949

Fig. 18.15. Conventional Symbols for Fittings.

Single-line drawings or sketches are made in orthographic projection or are drawn as if the entire system were swung into one plane (Fig. 18.12). On these drawings, single lines represent the runs of pipe, regardless of variations in diameters; conventional symbols are used for the fittings. A developed single-line sketch is frequently used for repair work, small jobs, and for making studies and calculations. For more complicated small-scale layouts, a single-line diagram drawn in orthographic projection is more suitable.

Double-line diagrams are drawn when many similar installations are to be made at the plants of various purchasers of pumps, manufacturing equipment, heating equipment, and so on (Fig. 18.13).

A conventional pictorial diagram (Fig. 18.14), showing a piping layout in space, reveals the changes in direction and the difference in levels more clearly than does any other type of line diagram. Pictorial diagrams are often used for preliminary layouts.

18.13. Dimensions on piping drawings. The rules for dimensioning working drawings apply to piping drawings. Fittings and pipes are always located by giving center-to-center distances, because the determination of pipe lengths is generally left to the pipe fitter. Notes should be used to specify the nominal size and type of each fitting and the nominal size of the pipe in each run. In addition, it is good practice to indicate, on a flanged valve, the diameter of the handwheel and its distance above the center of the fitting when wide open. It may be necessary to give over-all dimensions for other apparatus, if the maximum space to be allowed is important.

The date and a descriptive title should be given on all piping sketches and drawings.

18.14. Conventional symbols. Figure 18.15 shows a few of the conventional symbols for fittings that have been approved by the American Standards Association.

18.15. Problems.

1. Make a freehand sketch (on $\frac{1}{8}''$ grid paper, if it is available) of a $1''$ nipple connecting, a $1''$ cast-iron elbow, and a $2'' \times 2'' \times 1''$ malleable-iron tee. The distance between centers of fittings is to be $6''$. Enter neatly, in draftsman's style, the length of the nipple to the nearest $\frac{1}{8}''$.

2. Make a freehand sketch (on $\frac{1}{8}''$ grid paper) of a $1'' \times 1'' \times 1''$ malleable-iron tee and a $1''$ cast-iron elbow joined by a length of pipe. The distance between centers of fittings is $4''$. Enter the length of the connecting pipe to the nearest $\frac{1}{8}''$.

3. Make a single-line multiview sketch of the portion of a piping system shown in Fig. 18.14.

4. Make a double-line developed drawing of the portion of a piping system shown in Fig. 18.14. Use $2''$ pipe and screwed fittings. Select a suitable scale. Determine the measurements by transferring distances from the drawing to the open-divided scale in the figure.

5. Dimension the drawing of problem 4.

19 | Shop Processes

19.1. Shop processes. An engineering draftsman must be thoroughly familiar with the fundamental shop processes before he is qualified to prepare drawings that will fulfill the requirements of the production shops. In preparing working drawings, he must consider each and every individual process involved in the production of a piece, and then specify the processes in terms that the shopman will understand. All too frequently, drawings that specify impractical methods and impossible operations are sent to the shops. Most of these impractical specifications are the result of a lack of knowledge, on the draftsman's part, of what can or cannot be done by skilled craftsmen using modern machines and tools.

Although an accurate knowledge of the shop processes can be acquired only through actual experience in the various shops, it is possible for an apprentice draftsman to obtain a working knowledge of the fundamental operations through study and observation. This chapter presents and explains the principal operations in the pattern shop, foundry, forge shop, and machine shop.

19.2. Castings. Castings are formed by pouring molten metal into a mold or cavity. In sand molding, the molten metal assumes the shape of the cavity that has been formed in a sand mold by ramming a prepared moist sand around a pattern and then removing the pattern. Although a casting shrinks somewhat in cooling, the metal hardens in the exact shape of the pattern used (Fig. 19.1).

A sand mold consists of at least two sections. The upper section, called the *cope*, and the lower section, called the *drag*, together form a box-shaped structure called a *flask*.

When large holes ($\frac{3}{4}''$ and over) or interior passageways and openings are needed in a casting, dry sand cores are placed in the cavity. Cores exclude the metal from the space they occupy and thus form desired openings. Large holes are cored in order to avoid an unnecessary shop operation. A dry sand core is formed by ramming a mixture of sand and a binding material into a core box that has been made in the pattern shop. To make a finished core rigid, the coremaker places it in a core oven where it is baked until it is hard.

The molder when making a mold inserts in the sand a sprue stick that he removes after the cope has been rammed. This resulting hole, known as the *sprue*, conducts the molten metal to the *gate*, which is a passageway

431

cut to the cavity.   The adjacent hole called the *riser* provides an outlet
for excess metal.

19.3. The pattern shop.   The pattern shop prepares patterns of all
pieces that the foundry is to cast.   Although special pattern drawings
are frequently submitted, the pattern maker ordinarily uses a drawing of
the finished piece that the draftsman has prepared for both the pattern
shop and the machine shop.   The finish marks on such a drawing are just
as important to him as to the machinist, for he must allow, on each surface
to be finished, extra metal, the amount of which depends upon the method

Fig. 19.1. Sand Mold.

of machining and the size of the casting.   In general, this amount varies
from $\frac{1}{16}''$, in very small castings, to as much as $\frac{3}{4}''$, in large castings.

It is not necessary for the draftsman to specify on his drawing the
amount to be allowed for shrinkage, for the pattern maker has available a
"shrink rule," which is sufficiently oversize (approximately $\frac{1}{8}''$ per foot) to
take care of the shrinkage.

A pattern usually is first constructed of light strong wood, such as
white pine or mahogany, which, if only a few castings are required, may
be used in making sand molds.   In quantity production, however, where
a pattern must be used repeatedly, the wooden one will not hold up, so a
metal pattern (aluminum, brass, and so on) is made from it and is used in
its place.

Every pattern must be constructed in such a way that it can be withdrawn from each section of the sand mold.   If the pattern consists of two

halves (split), the plane of separation should be so located that it will coincide with the plane of separation of the cope and the drag (Fig. 19.1). Each portion of the pattern must be slightly tapered, so that it can be withdrawn without leaving a damaged cavity. The line of intersection, where the dividing plane cuts the pattern, is called the *parting line*. Although this line is rarely shown on a drawing, the draftsman should make certain that his design will allow the pattern maker to establish it. Ordinarily, it is not necessary to specify the slight taper, known as *draft*, on each side of the parting line, for the pattern maker assumes such responsibility when constructing the pattern.

Fig. 19.2.   **Fillets and Rounds on a Casting.**

A "filled-in" interior angle on a casting is called a *fillet*, to distinguish it from a rounded exterior angle, which is known as a *round* (Fig. 19.2). Sharp interior angles are avoided for two reasons: They are difficult to cast; and they are likely to be potential points of failure because the crystals of the cooling metal arrange themselves at a sharp corner in a weak pattern. Fillets are formed by nailing quarter rounds of wood or strips of leather into the sharp angles, or by filling the angles with wax.

19.4. The foundry. Although a draftsman is not directly concerned with the foundry, since the pattern maker takes his drawing and prepares all patterns and core boxes for the molder, it is most important that he be familiar with the operations in making a sand mold and a casting. Otherwise, he will find it difficult to prepare an economical design, the cost of which depends upon how simple it is to mold and cast.

19.5. Die casting. Die casting is an inexpensive method for producing certain types of machine parts, particularly those needing no great strength, in mass production. The castings are made by forcing molten metal or molten alloy into a cavity between metal dies in a die-casting machine. Parts thus produced usually require little or no finishing.

19.6. The forge shop. Many machine parts, especially those that must have strength and yet be light, are forged into shape, the heated metal being forced into dies with a drop hammer. Drop forging, since heated metal is made to conform to the shape of a cavity, might be considered a form of casting. However, because dies are difficult to make and are expensive, this method of production is used principally to make parts having an irregular shape that would be costly to machine and could not be made from casting material. Forgings are made of a high-grade steel. Dies are made by expert craftsmen who are known simply as diemakers.

Generally, special drawings, giving only the dimensions needed, are made for the forge shop.

19.7. Standard stock forms. Many types of metal shapes, along with other materials that are used in the shops for making parts for structures, are purchased from manufacturers in stock sizes. They are made available from the stock department, where rough stock, such as rods, bars, plates, sheet metal, and so on, is cut into sizes desired by the machine shop.

19.8. The machine shop. In general, the draftsman is more concerned with machine-shop processes than with the processes in other shops, as all castings and forgings that have been prepared in accordance with his drawings must receive their final machining in the machine shop. Since all machining operations must be considered in the design and then properly specified, a draftsman must be thoroughly familiar with the limitations as well as the possibilities of such common machines as the lathe, drill press, boring machine, shaper, planer, milling machine, and grinder. An explanation of the operation and capabilities of each machine will be given in the following sections.

19.9. The lathe. Many common operations, such as turning, facing, boring, reaming, knurling, threading, and so on, may be performed with this widely used machine. In general, however, it is used principally

Fig. 19.3. Lathe Operation—Turning.

for machining (roughing-out) cylindrical surfaces to be finished on a grinding machine. Removing metal from the exterior surfaces of cylindrical objects is known as turning and is accomplished by a sharp cutting tool that removes a thin layer of metal each time it travels the length of a cylindrical surface on the revolving work (Fig. 19.3). The piece, which is supported in the machine between two aligned centers, known as the *dead center* and the *live center*, is caused to rotate about an axis by power transmitted through a lathe dog, chuck, or a face plate. The work revolves against the cutting tool, held in a tool post, as the tool moves parallel to the longitudinal axis of the piece being turned. Cutting an interior surface is known as *boring* (Fig. 19.4). A note is not necessary on a drawing to indicate that a surface is to be turned on a lathe.

When a hole is reamed, it is finished very accurately with a fluted reamer of the exact required diameter. If the operation is performed on a lathe, the work revolves as the nonrotating reamer is fed into the hole by turning the handwheel on the tail stock. (See Fig. 19.5.)

Screw threads may be cut on a lathe by a cutting tool that has been ground to the shape required for the desired thread. The thread is cut as the tool travels parallel to the axis of the revolving work at a fixed speed (Fig. 19.6).

Knurling is the process of roughening or embossing a cylindrical surface. This is accomplished by means of a knurling tool containing knurl rollers that press into the surface of the work as it is fed across them (Fig. 19.7).

Fig. 19.4.   Boring on a Lathe.

Fig. 19.5.   Reaming on a Lathe.

19.10. The drill press. A drill press is a necessary piece of equipment in any shop because, although it is used principally for drilling, as the name implies (Fig. 19.8), other operations, such as reaming, counterboring, countersinking, and so on, may be performed on it by merely using the proper type of cutting tool. The cutting tool is held in position in a chuck and is made to revolve, through power from a motor or line shafting, at a particular speed suitable for the type of metal being drilled. The most flexible drill press, especially for large work, is the radial type, which is so designed that the spindle is mounted on a movable arm that

Fig. 19.6.   Cutting Threads on a Lathe.

Fig. 19.7.   Knurling.

Fig. 19.8.   A Drill Press.

Fig. 19.9.   Counterboring on a Drill Press.

can be revolved into any desired position for drilling.   With this machine,
holes may be drilled at various angles and locations without shifting the
work, which may be either clamped to the horizontal table or held in a
drill vise or drill jig.   The ordinary type of drill press without a movable
arm is usually found in most shops along with the radial type.   A multi-
spindle drill is used for drilling a number of holes at the same time.

Figure 19.9 shows a setup on a drill press for performing the operation
of counterboring.   A counterbore is used to enlarge a hole to a depth that

will allow the head of a fastener, such as a fillister-head cap screw, to be brought to the level of the surface of the piece through which it passes. A counterbore has a piloted end having approximately the same diameter as the drilled hole.

Figure 19.10 shows a setup for the operation of countersinking. A countersink is used to form a tapering depression that will fit the head of a flat-head machine screw or cap screw and allow it to be brought to the level of the surface of the piece through which it passes.

A plug tap is used to cut threads in a drilled hole (Fig. 19.11).

A spotfacer is used to finish a round spot that will provide a good seat for the head of a screw or bolt on the unfinished surface of a casting. Figure 19.12 shows various cutting tools commonly used for forming holes and cutting threads.

Fig. 19.10.   Countersinking on a Drill Press.

Fig. 19.11.   Tapping on a Drill Press.

19.11. Hand reaming.   A hole may be finished to an accurate size by hand reaming, as shown in Fig. 19.13.   The reamer in this illustration is of a special type known as a *line reamer*.

19.12. Boring (Fig. 19.14).   Boring is the operation of enlarging a circular hole for accuracy in roundness or straightness, and may be accomplished on a lathe, drill press, milling machine, or boring mill.   When the hole is small and of considerable length, the operation may be performed on a lathe.   If the hole is large, the work is usually done on a boring mill, of which there are two types—the vertical and the horizontal.   On a vertical boring machine, the work is fastened on a horizontal revolving table, and the cutting tool or tools, which are stationary, advance vertically into it as the table revolves.   On a horizontal boring machine, the tool revolves and the work is stationary.

19.13. The milling machine.   A milling machine is used for finishing plane surfaces and for milling gear teeth, slots, keyways, and so on. In finishing a plane surface, a rotating circular cutter removes the metal for a desired cut as the work, fastened to a moving horizontal bed, is auto-

PLUG TAP

BOTTOMING TAP

STRAIGHT REAMER

TAPER REAMER

COUNTERSINK   COUNTERSINK

COUNTERBORE   TWIST DRILL

THREAD DIE

Fig. 19.12.   Various Cutting Tools.

Fig. 19.13.   Hand Reaming.

matically fed against it.   Several types of milling cutters are shown in Fig. 19.15.

Figure 19.16 shows a setup for milling gear teeth in a gear blank. Note the form of this particular type of cutter.

19.14. The shaper (Fig. 19.17). A shaper is used for finishing small plane surfaces and for cutting slots and grooves. In action, a fast-moving reciprocating ram carries a tool across the surface of the work, which is fastened to an adjustable horizontal table. The tool cuts only on the forward stroke.

19.15. The planer. The planer is a machine particularly designed for cutting down and finishing large flat surfaces. The work is fastened to a long horizontal table that moves back and forth under the cutting tool. In action, the tool cuts as the table moves the surface against it. Unlike the

Fig. 19.14.   Boring on a Boring Mill.

cutter on the shaper, it is stationary except for a slight movement laterally for successive cuts.

19.16. The grinding machine. A grinding machine has a rotating grinding wheel that, ordinarily, is either an emery wheel (fine or coarse)

(a)

(b)

(c)

(d)

Fig. 19.15.   Milling Cutters and Operations.

or some type of high-speed wheel made of carborundum.   Grinding consists in bringing the surface to be ground into contact with the wheel. Although grinding machines are often used for "roughing" and for grinding down projections and surfaces on castings, their principal use, as far as a draftsman is concerned, is for the final finishing operation to bring a

Fig. 19.16.   Cutting Gear Teeth on a Milling Machine.

Fig. 19.17.   Shaper.

piece of work down to accurate dimensions.   Internal grinders are available for various purposes.

19.17. Polishing.   Polishing consists of bringing a ground surface into contact with a revolving disc of leather or cloth, thus producing a lustrous smoothness that would be impossible to obtain by using even the finest grinding wheel.   The operation is specified on a drawing by a note, "polish" or "grind and polish."

Quick Reading with Decimal Equivalents

Fig. 19.18.   The Steel Rule.

Dividers   Outside Calipers   Inside Calipers

Fig. 19.19.   Calipers.

Fig. 19.20.   Micrometers.

19.18. Broaching. A broach is a tool used to cut keyways and to form square, rectangular, hexagonal, or irregular-shaped holes. It is a hard, tempered steel shaft with serrated cutting edges that enlarge a drilled, punched, or cored hole to a required shape. Broaches are either pushed or pulled through the work. A special broaching machine is used for pulling broaches. Some form of press, hydraulic or otherwise, is required for push broaches.

19.19. Jigs and fixtures. Often, when an operation must be performed many times in making a part in quantities on a general machine, one of two devices, a *jig* or a *fixture*, may be used to facilitate production and insure accuracy without making repeated measurements. Although both jigs and fixtures fulfill the same general purpose, there is a distinguishing difference between them. A jig, for example, holds the work as it guides the tool and, ordinarily, is not fixed to the machine. A fixture, on the other hand, is rigidly fastened to a machine and holds the work in position without acting as a guide for the cutting tools.

Since most large manufacturing concerns have special departments for designing jigs and fixtures, the ordinary draftsman is not directly concerned with these auxiliary devices when he is preparing working drawings.

19.20. Special production machines. In large industrial concerns, most mechanical parts are made on specialized machines by semiskilled operators. A discussion of even a few of these, however, is beyond the scope of a general drawing text in which each subject is limited to a few pages. Since most specialized mass-production machines operate on the same general principles as the general-purpose machines, a young engineering draftsman should be able to determine their limitations and capabilities through observation, if he has a general knowledge of such machines as the lathe, shaper, drill press, milling machine, and so on. No prospective designer or draftsman should ever forego an opportunity to observe special production machines. He must have a thorough understanding of all shop machines and methods, if his drawings are to be satisfactory for the shops.

19.21. Measuring tools. Figures 19.18, 19.19, and 19.20 show a few of the measuring tools commonly available in shops. When great accuracy is not required, calipers are used (Fig. 19.19). The outside calipers are suited for taking external measurements, as for example from a shaft. They are adjusted to fit the piece, and then the setting is applied to a rule to make a reading. The inside calipers have out-turned toes, which fits them for taking internal measurements, as for example in measuring either a cylindrical or a rectangular hole. When extreme accuracy is required, some form of micrometer calipers may be used (Fig. 19.20).

20 Working Drawings

20.1. A working drawing is prepared for the purpose of furnishing all necessary information to those persons who must manufacture and assemble the machine or structure represented. It is a technical record that must be so complete and accurate that no supplementary verbal or written explanations will be necessary. The information must be conveyed in the most understandable manner, in accordance with good drafting-room conventions and practices. Since these conventions and practices vary somewhat among different concerns, the practices presented in this text are those given in the approved standards of the American Standards Association and the Society of Automotive Engineers.*

20.2. Sketches and design drawings. The first stage in the development of an idea for a structure or machine is to prepare freehand sketches and to make the necessary calculations required to determine the feasibility of the design. From these sketches the designer prepares a layout, on which an accurate analysis of the design is worked out. It is usually drawn full size and is executed with instruments in pencil. The layout should be sufficiently complete to allow a survey of the location of parts (to avoid interference), the accessibility for maintenance, the requirements for lubrication, and the method of assembly.

Usually, only center distances and certain fixed dimensions are given. The general dimensioning, as well as the determination of material and degree of finish of individual parts, is left for the draftsman who makes the detail drawings.

Design layouts require both empirical and scientific design. Empirical design involves the use of charts, formulas, tables, and so forth, which have been derived from experimental studies and scientific computations. Scientific design, which requires a broad knowledge of the allied fields such as mechanics, metallurgy, and mathematics, is used when a new machine is designed to operate under special specified conditions for which data are not available in any handbook.

20.3. Classes of working drawings. There are two recognized classes of working drawings: detail drawings and assembly drawings.

20.4. Set of working drawings. A complete set of working drawings for a machine consists of detail sheets, giving all necessary shop information for the production of individual pieces, and an assembly

---

* ASA Y14–1957 (Sections 1–6).
SAE Automotive Drafting Standards.

443

drawing showing the location of each piece in the finished machine. In addition, the set may include drawings showing a foundation plan, piping diagram, oiling diagram, and so on.

20.5. Detail drawings. A detail drawing should give complete information for the manufacture of a part, describing with adequate dimensions the part's size. Finished surfaces should be indicated and all necessary shop operations shown. The title should give the material of which the part is to be made and should state the number of the parts that are required for the production of an assembled unit of which the part is a member. Commercial examples of detail workings are shown in Figs. 20.1 and 20.2.

Courtesy Warner & Swasey Co.

Fig. 20.1. A Detail Drawing.

Since a machinist will ordinarily make one part at a time, it is advisable to detail each piece, regardless of its size, on a separate individual sheet. In some shops, however, custom dictates that related parts be grouped on the same sheet, particularly when the parts form a unit in themselves. Other concerns sometimes group small parts of the same material together thus: castings on one sheet, forgings on another, special fasteners on still another, and so on.

20.6. Making a detail drawing. With a design layout or original sketches as a guide, the procedure for making a detail drawing is as follows:

1. Select the views, remembering that, aside from the view showing the characteristic shape of the object, there should be as many additional views as are necessary to complete the shape description. These may be

Courtesy International Harvester Co.

Fig. 20.2. A Detail Drawing.

sectional views that reveal a complicated interior construction, or auxiliary views of surfaces not fully described in any of the principal views.

2. Decide upon a scale that will allow, without crowding, a balanced
arrangement of all necessary views and the location of dimensions and
notes. Although very small parts should be drawn double size or larger,
to show detail and to allow for dimensions, a full-size scale should be used
when possible. In general, the same scale should be used for pieces of
the same size.

3. Draw the main center lines and block in the general outline of the
views with light, sharp 6H pencil lines. (See Fig. 20.3.)

4. Draw main circles and arcs in finished weight.

Fig. 20.3.   Steps in Making a Detail Drawing.

5. Starting with the characteristic view, work back and forth from view to view until the shape of the object is completed.   Lines whose definite location and length are known may be drawn in their finished weight.

6. Put in fillets and rounds.

7. Complete the views by darkening the object lines.

8. Draw extension and dimension lines.

9. Add arrowheads, dimensions, and notes.

10. Complete the title.

11. Check the entire drawing carefully.

20.7. One-view drawings.   Many parts, such as shafts, bolts, studs, and washers, may require only one properly dimensioned view.   In the case of each of these parts, a note can imply the complete shape of the piece without sacrificing clearness.   Most engineering departments, however, deem it better practice to show two views.

20.8. Detail titles.   Every detail drawing must give information not conveyed by the notes and dimensions, such as the name of the part, part

number, material, number required, and so on.   The method of recording
and the location of this information on the drawing varies somewhat in
different drafting rooms.   It may be lettered either in the record strip or
directly below the views.   (See Figs. 20.2 and 20.4.)

If all surfaces on a part are machined, finish marks are omitted and a
title note, "Finish all over," is added to the detail title.

20.9. Title blocks and record strips.   The purpose of a title or
record strip is to present in an orderly manner the name of the machine,
name of the manufacturer, date, scale, drawing number, and other
drafting-room information.

Fig. 20.4.   A Working Drawing.

Every commercial drafting room has developed its own standard title
forms, whose features depend upon the processes of manufacture, the
peculiarities of the plant organization, and the established customs of
particular types of manufacturing.   In large organizations, the blank
form, along with the border line, is printed on standard sizes of drawing
or tracing paper.

A record strip is a form of title extending almost the entire distance
across the bottom of the sheet.   In addition to the usual title information,
it may contain a section for recording revisions, changes, and so on, with
the dates on which they were adopted.

20.10. Contents of the title (Figs. 20.2 and 20.10).   The title on a
machine drawing generally contains the following information:

1. Name of the part.

DET. NO.	AMT.	MAT'L	STOCK SIZE OR PATTERN NO.

FAIRFIELD MANUFACTURING CO.
LAFAYETTE, IND.

TOOL NAME

ALL LOOSE DETAILS TO BE STAMPED WITH THEIR RESPECTIVE NUMBERS   BREAK ALL CORNERS EXCEPT CUTTING EDGES.

SCALE	DO NOT SCALE. REPORT ERRORS	
DRWN.	SHEETS	SHEET No.
STAMP PART No.	STAMP TOOL No.	

Courtesy Fairfield Mfg. Co.

Fig. 20.5.   A Printed Title Block.

REFERENCE	LET.	BY	DATE	REVISIONS	INTERNATIONAL HARVESTER COMPANY		

Courtesy International Harvester Co.

Fig. 20.6.   A Printed Record Strip.

Courtesy The Hoover Co.

Fig. 20.7.   A Record Strip.

2. Name of the machine or structure.   (This is given in the main title and is usually followed by one of two words: *details* or *assembly*.)

3. Name and location of the manufacturing firm.

4. Name and address of the purchasing firm, if the structure has been designed for a particular company.

5. Scale.

6. Date. (Often spaces are provided for the date of completion of each operation in the preparation of the drawing. If only one date is given, it is usually the date of completion of the drawing.)

7. Initials or name of the draftsman who made the pencil drawing.

8. Initials of the checker.

9. Initials or signature of the chief draftsman, chief engineer, or another in authority who approved the drawing.

10. Initials of the tracer (if drawing has been traced).

11. Drawing number. This generally serves as a filing number and may furnish information in code form. Letters and numbers may be so combined to indicate departments, plants, model, type, order number, filing number, and so on. The drawing number is sometimes repeated in the upper left-hand corner (in an upside-down position), so that the drawing may be quickly identified if it should become reversed in the file.

Some titles furnish information such as material, part number, pattern number, finish, treatment, estimated weight, superseded drawing number, and so on.

20.11. Corrections and alterations. Alterations on working drawings are made either by cancellation or by erasure. Cancellations are indicated by parallel inclined lines drawn through the views, lines, notes, or dimensions to be changed.

Superseding dimensions should be placed above or near the original ones. If alterations are made by erasure, the changed dimensions are often underlined.

All changes on a completed or approved drawing should be recorded in a revision record that may be located either adjacent to the title block (Fig. 20.10) or at one corner of the drawing (Fig. 20.8). This note should contain the identification symbol, date, authorization number, character of the revision, and the initials of the draftsman and checker who made the change. The identification symbol is a letter or numeral placed in a small circle near the alteration on the body of the drawing. (See Fig. 20.8.)

If changes are made by complete erasure, record prints should be made for the file before the original is altered. Many companies make record prints whenever changes are extensive.

Since revisions on completed drawings are usually necessitated by unsatisfactory methods of production or by a customer's request, they should never be made by a draftsman unless an order has been issued with the approval of the chief engineer's office.

20.12. Pattern-shop drawings. Sometimes special pattern-shop drawings, giving information needed for making a pattern, are required for large and complicated castings. If the pattern maker receives a drawing that shows finished dimensions, he provides for the draft necessary to draw the pattern and for the extra metal for machining. He allows for shrinkage by making the pattern oversize. When, however, the draft and allowances for finish are determined by the engineering department, no finish marks appear on the drawing. The allowances are included in the dimensions.

20.13. Forge-shop drawings. If a forging is to be machined, separate detail drawings usually are made for the forge and machine shops. A forging drawing gives all the nominal dimensions required by the forge shop for a completed rough forging.

20.14. Machine-shop drawings. Rough castings and forgings are sent to the machine shop to be finished. Since the machinist is not interested in the dimensions and information for the previous stages, a machine-shop drawing frequently gives only the information necessary for machining.

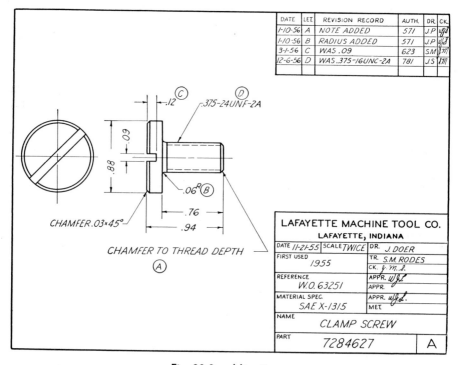

Fig. 20.8. Alterations.

20.15. Assembly drawings. A drawing that shows the parts of a machine or machine unit assembled in their relative working positions is an assembly drawing. There are several types of such drawings: design assembly drawings, working assembly drawings, unit assembly drawings, installation diagrams, and so on, each of which will be described separately (Figs. 20.9–20.14).

20.16. Working assembly drawings. A working assembly drawing, showing each piece completely dimensioned, is sometimes made for a simple mechanism or unit of related parts. No additional detail drawings of parts are required.

20.17. Sub-assembly (unit) drawings. A unit assembly is an assembly drawing of a group of related parts that form a unit in a more complicated machine. Such a drawing would be made for the tail stock

8	WING NUT		1
7	LOCK PIN		1
6	ALIGNMENT PIN		1
5	GUIDE ROD	C.R.S.	1
4	VISE SCREW	C.R.S.	1
3	HANDLE	C.R.S.	1
2	L.H VISE JAW–PAT. 19991–1	M. I.	1
1	R. H. VISE JAW–PAT. 19991–1	M. I.	1
PART NO.	NAME OF PART	MATERIAL	NO. REQ.

_ _ _ _ _ _ UNIVERSITY
DEPT. OF GENERAL ENGINEERING

HAND   VISE   ASSEMBLY

DATE 11·1·'42	SCALE. FULL	DRAWING NUMBER
DR. C.R.H.	TR. R.A.C.	
CH. *L.Z.R*	APP. *J.C.M.*	19991

Fig. 20.9.   An Assembly Drawing.

Courtesy Studebaker-Packard Corp.

Fig. 20.10.   A Unit Assembly Drawing.

INDEXING MECHANISM
PRESS DIAL TABLE

12 STATIONS AS SHOWN EQUALLY SPACED

REAM IN ASSEMBLY FOR
*2"×4 TAPER PIN

*6 PITCH-30 TOOTH GEAR

*6 PRESS FIT IN LEVER
*3 RUNNING FIT IN BEARING

SECTION A-A

PC NO	NAME	MAT
1	BASE	CI
2	FLYWHEEL	CI
3	GEAR	CI
4	CONNECTING ROD	CI
5	LEVER	CS
6	CAM	SAE 1315
7	CAM FOLLOWER	SAE 1315
8	SHAFT	CRS
9	CROSSHEAD	SAE 1345
10	PAWL	CRS
11	CROSSHEAD SHOULDER SC	HEX CRS
12	PAWL SHOULDER SC	HEX CRS
13	FLYWHEEL SHOULDER SC	CRS
14	LEVER PIN	CRS
15	PAWL PIN	CRS
16	PAWL SPRING PIN	CRS
17	⅜-NC STD HEX NUT	
18	*2"×4 STD TAPER PIN	
19	*304 WDRF KEY	
20	*404 WDRF KEY	
21	PAWL SPRING	MUSIC WIRE

Fig. 20.11. Indexing Mechanism—Assembly Drawing.

NO	NAME	SYMBOL	REQ
1	CYLINDER	A404C	1
2	HEAD	B404A	1
3	ROTOR	C404E	3
4	BUCKET	I404A	1
9	PACKNUT	J202	1
12	PACKING	3/8 X 11	1
14	CRANK	L404A	1
15	HANDLE	U409A	1
22	HEAD CAPSCREWS	3/8 X 3/4	7
27	HANDLE PIN	P409	1
28	LOCK NUT	1/4 JAM	1
75	CRANK THUMBSCW	3/8 X 3/4	1
59	BUCKET SPRING	Y404	3

UNLESS SPECIFIED, TOLERANCE TO FINISHED SURFACES IS ± .010			
			PART SYMBOL
			WH404
WH			PART NAME
8-29-40	8-29-40	10-4-40	HAND PUMP ASSEMBLY
DRAFTSMAN	CHECKER	ENGR. CH. ENGR.	DWG. NUMBER
			WH404A

BLACKMER PUMP CO.
INCORPORATED
GRAND RAPIDS, MICHIGAN

G				
F				
E				
D				
C				
B				
A				
LET.	DCF.NO.		DATE	CH. ENG
	REVISION			

DISCHARGE
INTAKE

2-1/2" HOLES

Courtesy Blackmer Pump Co.

Fig. 20.12. An Assembly Drawing.

Fig. 20.13.   An Outline Assembly Drawing.

of a lathe, the clutch of an automobile, or the carburetor of an airplane. A set of assembly drawings thus takes the place of a complete assembly of a complex machine (Fig. 20.10).

20.18. Installation assembly drawings. An installation drawing gives useful information for putting a machine or structure together. The names of parts, order of assembling parts, location dimensions, and special instructions for operating may also be shown.

20.19. Outline assembly drawings. Outline assembly drawings are most frequently made for illustrative purposes in catalogs. Usually

Courtesy Instruments Magazine.

Fig. 20.14. A Diagram Assembly Drawing.

they show merely over-all and principal dimensions. (See Fig. 20.13.) Their appearance may be improved by the use of line shading.

20.20. Diagram assembly drawings. Diagram drawings may be grouped into two general classes: (1) those composed of single lines and conventional symbols, such as piping diagrams, wiring diagrams, and so on (see Fig. 20.14), and (2) those drawn in regular projection, such as an erection drawing, which may be shown in either orthographic or pictorial projection.

Piping diagrams give the size of pipe, location of fittings, and so on. To draw an assembly of a piping system in true orthographic projection would add no information and merely entail needless work.

A large portion of electrical drawing is composed of diagrammatic sketches using conventional electrical symbols. Electrical engineers therefore need to know the American Standard wiring symbols given in the Appendix.

20.21. Bill of material. A bill of material is a list of parts placed on an assembly drawing just above the title block, or, in the case of quantity production, on a separate sheet. The bill contains the part number, descriptive name, material, quantity (number) required, and so on, of each piece. Additional information, such as stock size, pattern number (castings), and so forth, is sometimes listed.

Suggested dimensions for ruling are shown in Fig. 20.15. For $\frac{1}{8}''$ letters, the lines should never be spaced closer than $\frac{5}{16}''$. Fractions are made slightly less than full height and are centered between the lines.

When listing standard parts in a bill of material, the general practice is to omit the name of the materials and to use abbreviated descriptive titles. A pattern number may be composed of the commercial job number

ITEM	NAME	NO PER UNIT	MATERIAL
9	$\frac{1}{2} \times 1\frac{1}{6}$ PLAIN WASHER	1	
8	$\frac{3}{8}$-24×$\frac{1}{2}$ SLOTTED DOG PT. SET SC.	1	
7	#10-24×$\frac{3}{4}$ FLAT HD. MACH. SC.	6	
6	BALL	2	C.R.S.
5	HANDLE	1	C.R.S.
4	VISE SCREW	1	C.R.S.
3	JAW PLATE	2	C.R.S.
2	JAW PATT. NO. 19742-2	1	C.I.
1	BASE PATT. NO. 19742-1	1	C.I.

VISE ASSEMBLY — SCALE FULL SIZE — APPROVED WJL — TRACED BY J.H.D — CHECKED BY J.H.P — DATE 12-10-51 — DRAWN BY DOE, JOHN H. — CODE WJL-E-15 — DRAWING NO. 19742

Fig. 20.15. A Bill of Material.

followed by the assigned number one, two, three, and so on. It is suggested that parts be listed in the following order: (a) castings, (b) forgings, (c) parts made from bar stock, (d) standard parts.

Sometimes bills of material are first typed on thin paper and then blueprinted. The form may be ruled or printed.

20.22. Title. The title strip on an assembly drawing usually is the same as that used on a detail drawing. It will be noted, when lettering in the block, that the title of the drawing is generally composed of the name of the machine followed by the word *assembly*. (See Figs. 20.9, 20.10, and 20.12.)

20.23. Making the assembly drawing. The final assembly may be traced from the design assembly drawing, but more often it is redrawn to a smaller scale on a separate sheet. Since the redrawing, being done from both the design and detail drawings, furnishes a check that frequently reveals errors, the assembly always should be drawn before the details are accepted as finished and the blueprints are made. The assembly of a simple machine or unit is sometimes shown on the same sheet with the details.

Accepted practices to be observed on assemblies are:

1. *Sectioning.*   Parts should be sectioned using the American Standard symbols shown in Fig. 9.31.   The practices of sectioning apply to assemblies.

2. *Views.*   The main view, which is usually in full section, should show to the best advantage nearly all the individual parts and their locations.   Additional views are shown only when they add necessary information that should be conveyed by the drawing.

3. *Hidden lines.*   Hidden lines should be omitted from an assembly drawing, for they tend merely to overload it and create confusion.   Complete shape description is unnecessary, since parts are either standard or are shown on detail drawings.

4. *Dimensions.*   Over-all dimensions and center-to-center distances indicating the relationship of parts in the machine as a whole are sometimes given.   Detail dimensions are omitted, except on working assembly drawings.

5. *Identification of parts.*   Parts in a machine or structure are identified on the assembly drawing by numbers that are used on the details and in the bill of material.   These should be made at least $\frac{3}{16}''$ high and enclosed in a $\frac{3}{8}''$ circle (Fig. 20.16). The centers of the circles are located not less than $\frac{3}{4}''$ from the nearest line of the drawing.   Leaders, terminated by arrowheads touching the parts, are drawn radial with a straightedge. The numbers, in order to be centered in the circles, should be made first and the circles drawn around them. An alternate method used in commercial practice is to letter the name and descriptive information for each part and draw a leader pointing to it in the main view.

Fig. 20.16.   Identification (Part) Numbers.

20.24. Checking drawings.   Checking, the final assurance that the machine is correctly designed, should be done by a person (checker or squad foreman) who has not prepared the drawings but who is thoroughly familiar with the principles of the design.   He must have a broad knowledge of shop practices and assembly methods.   In commercial drafting rooms, the most experienced men are assigned to this type of work.   The assembly drawing is checked against the detail drawings and corrections are indicated with either a soft or colored pencil.   The checker should:

1. Survey the machine as a whole from the standpoint of operation, ease of assembly, and accessibility for repair work.   He should consider the type, strength, and suitability of the materials.

2. Check each part with the parts adjacent to it, to make certain that proper clearances are maintained.   (To determine whether or not all

positions are free of interference, it may be necessary to lay out the extreme travel of moving parts to an enlarged scale.)

3. Study the drawing to see that each piece has been illustrated correctly and that all necessary views, types of views, treatments of views, and scales have been shown.

4. Check dimensions by scaling; calculate and check size and location dimensions that affect mating parts; determine the suitability of dimensions from the standpoint of the various departments' needs, such as pattern, forge, machine, assembly shop, and so on; examine views for proper dimensioning and mark unnecessary, repeated, or omitted dimensions.

5. Check tolerances, making sure the computations are correct and that proper fits have been used, so that there will be no unnecessary production costs.

6. See that finishes and such operations as drilling, reaming, boring, tapping, and grinding are properly specified.

7. Check specifications for material.

8. Examine notes for correctness and location.

9. See that stock sizes have been used for standard parts such as bolts, screws, keys, and so on. (Stock sizes may be determined from catalogs.)

10. Add any additional explanatory notes that should supply necessary information.

11. Check the bill of material to see that each part is completely and correctly specified.

12. Check items in the title block.

13. Make a final survey of the drawing in its entirety, making certain there is either a check or correction for each dimension, note, and specification.

20.25. Chemical engineering drawings. In general, the chemical engineer is concerned with plant layouts and equipment design. He must be well informed on the types of machinery used in grinding, drying, mixing, evaporation, sedimentation, and distillation, and must be able to design or select conveying machinery.

It is obvious that the determining of the sequence of operations, selecting of machinery, arranging of piping, and so on, must be done by a trained chemical engineer who can speak the basic language of the mechanical, electrical, or civil engineer with whom he must co-operate. To be able to do this, he must have a thorough knowledge of the principles of engineering drawing.

Plant layout drawings, the satisfactory development of which requires numerous preliminary sketches (layouts, scale diagram, flow sheets, and so on), show the location of machines, equipment, and the like. Often, if the machinery and apparatus are used in the manufacturing of chemicals and are of a specialized nature, a chemical engineer is called upon to do the designing. It even may be necessary for him to build experimental apparatus.

20.26. Electrical engineering drawings. Electrical engineering drawings are of two types, working drawings and diagrammatic assemblies

(Fig. 20.17). Working drawings, which are made for electrical machinery, involve all of the principles and conventions of the working drawings of the mechanical engineer. Diagrammatic drawings have been discussed in Sec. 20.20.

20.27. Floor-plan drawings. An engineer usually is not an architect nor is an architect usually an engineer; therefore, when a new factory is to be built or an addition is to be added to an existing one, both architect and engineer are needed and both must co-operate in the design. In this partnership, it becomes the job of the engineer to prepare the floor plans, so that the highest possible production efficiency can be obtained. He must study carefully the necessary steps of production and then decide

From Marcus and Horton, Elements of Radio, *Prentice-Hall, Inc.*

Fig. 20.17. A Schematic Diagram.

upon the locations for the offices, supply rooms, storage rooms, shops, and finally the production machines. The design becomes a recorded study of the flow of materials and parts through the plant. Frequently, it may be necessary to show a conveyor system or a piping system on the plan. In the case of small plants, circumstances may be such that the engineer must assume full responsibility for the design of the entire building.

20.28. Problems. The four general types of problems presented in this chapter have been designed to furnish practice in the preparation of working drawings. The first type is composed of dimensioned pictorial drawings of individual pieces taken from a wide variety of mechanisms. The student should prepare complete working detail drawings of these pieces as they are assigned by his instructor. It should be recognized that dimensions are not necessarily placed the same on orthographic views as they are on pictorial drawings. In order to make it possible for the student to apply the principles presented in the previous chapters, no special effort has been made to place dimensions in accordance with the rules of good practice. Furthermore there are many cases where dimensions cannot be placed on pictorial drawings in the same locations as on the orthographic views.

The second type of problem is one that shows in pictorial all the parts of a unit mechanism. This gives the student an opportunity to prepare a complete set of working drawings of a simple unit. It is suggested that the detail drawings be prepared before the assembly is drawn.

The third and fourth types provide practice in both reading and preparing drawings, the third requiring the preparation of detail drawings from given assembly drawings, and the fourth requiring the making of assembly drawings from the details.

All the problems have been designed to fit an $8\frac{1}{2}'' \times 11''$ or an $11'' \times 17''$ sheet of drawing paper if the proper scale is selected. The scale may be either suggested by the instructor or left to the student's judgment. Although working drawings may be drawn in pencil and later traced in ink on tracing paper or cloth, it is suggested that most of the drawings be prepared in pencil on lightweight bond paper as is done extensively in industrial drawing rooms. Some drawings may be prepared as sketches.

Thread specifications containing the series identification UNC or UNF refer to the Unified Thread Standard now common to American-British-Canadian practice. Other thread specifications having a series identification of NC, NF, or N are considered to refer to the American Standard (ASA B1.1–1949) having the Unified thread form. If desired, all thread specifications on a finished drawing may be specified as required under the Unified Standard.

1–29. (Figs. 20.18–20.46.) Make a detail drawing of an assigned machine part. Draw all necessary views. Give a detail title with suitable notes concerning material, number required, etc.

Fig. 20.18. End Plate.

Fig. 20.19.   Guide Bracket.

Fig. 20.20.   Hanger Bracket.

Fig. 20.21.   Adjustment Block.

Fig. 20.22.   Control Bracket.

Fig. 20.23.   Corner Bracket.

Fig. 20.24.   Pipe Support.

Fig. 20.25.   Flange.

Fig. 20.26.   Lathe Leg.

Fig. 20.27.   Bent Angle.

Fig. 20.28.   Idler Lever.

Fig. 20.29.   Guide Bracket.

Fig. 20.30.   Link.

Fig. 20.31.   Handle Block.

Fig. 20.32.   Auxiliary Fork.

Fig. 20.33.   Elevator Bracket.

Fig. 20.34.   Link.

Fig. 20.35.   Sound Drum Bracket.

Fig. 20.36.   Valve Seat.

Fig. 20.37.   Angle Bracket.

FILLETS & ROUNDS $\frac{1}{8}$R

$1\frac{1}{8}$ REAM

$\frac{1}{4}$-20UNC-2B

$\frac{3}{4}$ BORE

$\frac{11}{32}$ DRILL
2 HOLES

$\frac{3}{8}$R

$\frac{5}{16}$-18UNC-2B

Fig. 20.38.   Torch Holder.

FILLETS & ROUNDS $\frac{1}{16}$R EXCEPT AS SHOWN

$1\frac{1}{8}$ REAM

$\frac{1}{4}$R

$\frac{1}{4}$-20UNC-2B

Fig. 20.39.   Gear Shifting Fork.

FILLETS & ROUNDS .12R
EXCEPT AS SHOWN

1.81

3.62

2.24

1.12

.500 $^{+.0005}_{-.0000}$ REAM

.50^R

2.24^D

.50^R

.015^R

.999 $^{+.000}_{-.002}$

.06^R

.312 $^{+.0005}_{-.0000}$ REAM

Fig. 20.40.   Yoke.

Fig. 20.41. Shifter Lever.

ROUNDS .06^R

Fig. 20.42. Bearing Bracket.

Fig. 20.43. Support Bracket.

Fig. 20.44. Control Pedal.

Fig. 20.45.   Inlet Flange.

Fig. 20.46.   Control Bracket.

30. (Fig. 20.47.)   Make a detail drawing of the cover.

Fig. 20.47.   Cover.

31. (Fig. 20.48.)   Make a complete two-view orthographic drawing of the guide bracket which is shown by a pictorial sketch.   The student is advised to give careful consideration to the choice of views remembering that it is the usual practice to show the circular form of each cylindrical feature on one of the selected views.   Dimension the views completely while keeping in mind the fact that dimensions are oftentimes not placed on a pictorial drawing as they should be placed on the orthographic drawing.   *Supplementary information:* 1) The centerline for the main $1''$ shaft is $2\frac{3}{8}''$ below the flat finished base surface.   The hole for this shaft is to be reamed.   2) The length of the cylindrical portion is $1\frac{3}{4}''$ between contact faces.   The O.D. is $1\frac{1}{2}''$.   3) The hole for the smaller shaft is to be reamed for a $\frac{5}{8}''$ shaft.   The O.D. of the cylinder is $1''$ and the distance between faces is $\frac{5}{8}''$.   The $\frac{3}{8}''$ ribs should be tangent to cylindrical surfaces.   4) The flat finished base surface is $1\frac{1}{8}'' \times 2\frac{3}{4}''$.   The holes which are to be drilled $\frac{1}{32}''$ over-size for $\frac{3}{8}$-UNC bolts are $1\frac{3}{4}''$ apart, and are centered in the direction parallel to the axes of the shafts.   5) Fillets and rounds $\frac{1}{8}$ R.

Fig. 20.48.   Guide Bracket.

32. (Fig. 20.49.)   Make a detail working drawing of the bracket or its mating part that clamps around the $1\frac{3}{4}''$ shaft.

The given pictorial drawing shows the adjustment bracket assembly of a positioning mechanism on a cartridge type core blower.   The bracket when attached to the vertical column supports a positioning clamp that may be tilted into different positions.   The clamp screw keeps the positioning clamp in a desired position when it is tightened down against the clamp plate.

Fig. 20.49.   Adjustment Bracket—Core Blower.

33. (Fig. 20.50.)   Make a detail working drawing of the bell crank.   The bell crank is a part of the control mechanism of a vertical single spindle boring machine. The rod which extends downward connects with a foot-operated control.   The link carries the movement to the drive unit.   *Supplementary design data:* 1) The distance from the pivot center of the crank to the center of the connecting pin for the rod is $3\frac{1}{2}''$, and the distance from the center of the crank to the pin connecting the link is $2\frac{1}{2}''$.   2) The limiting position for any counterclockwise movement of the bell crank is as shown; namely, that the line connecting the centers of the pivot and the rod-pin is horizontal.   The crank is to be drawn to allow the rod a $1\frac{1}{2}''$ downward movement.   The upper arm of the crank is to be located so that there will be exactly $\frac{1}{8}''$ clearance between the arm and the housing when the crank is in the extreme clockwise position.   The horizontal distance from the pivot center to the left face of the housing is $1\frac{5}{8}''$.   3) The end of the rod through which the pin passes is $1\frac{1}{2}''$ in diameter, and $\frac{3}{8}''$ thick.   Allow adequate clearance.   4) The crank pivots about a $1''$ diameter shoulder screw which is screwed into the bracket. Thread specification is $\frac{3}{4}$-16UNF.   5) The crank is of cast iron.   Fillets and rounds $\frac{1}{8}''$ R except as noted.

Fig. 20.50.   Bell Crank.

Fig. 20.51.   Automatic Safety Control—Counterweight Mechanism.

34. (Fig. 20.51.)   Make a detail working drawing of a counterweight.   Use an exact method for constructing the ellipse.   As a matter of interest in the operation of the automatic safety control, the device stops the machine it is designed to protect if and when the speed becomes too great.   As the main shaft, upon which the counterweights are attached, picks up speed, the counterweights are thrown farther and farther outward until a predetermined speed is reached.   Then one or both will strike a trip causing it to move upward against a trip pin that in turn cuts off the power.   *Supplementary information:* 1) The center-to-center distance between the studs is $4\frac{7}{16}''$.   2) The contact track is $\frac{3}{4}''$ wide.   3) The height of the hub is $\frac{3}{4}''$.   4) The major diameter of the ellipse is $4''$; the minor diameter is $2\frac{1}{2}''$.   5) The width of the slot for the spring is $\frac{1}{8}''$.   6) Thickness of rib $\frac{7}{16}''$. 7) Fillets and rounds $\frac{1}{8}''$ R except as shown.   8) Fillets and rounds have been purposely omitted from the pictorial drawing.   They are to be shown by the student where necessary and desirable.

35. (Fig. 20.52.)   Make a detail working drawing of the rocker arm.   Show a detail section taken through the ribs.   *Supplementary information:* 1) The distance from the center of the shaft to the center of the hole for the pin is $4.00''$. The distance from the shaft to the threaded hole is $4.50''$.   2) The nominal diameter of the hole for the shaft is $1.875''$.   The hole in the rocker arm is to be reamed for a definite fit.   Consult your instructor, but *do not* use a limit dimension for either the shaft or the pin.   The diameter of the pin is $.969''$.   3) The diameter of the threaded boss is $2.00''$.   4) The diameter of the roller is $2.25''$, and its length $1.46''$.   Total clearance between the roller and finished faces is to be $.03''$. 5) The inside faces of the arms are to be milled in towards the hub far enough to accommodate the roller.   6) The rib is $.62''$ thick.   7) The lock nut has $1\frac{1}{4}$-12 UNF thread.   8) Fillets and rounds $.12''$ R except where otherwise noted.

Fig. 20.52. Rocker Arm.

36. (Fig. 20.53.) Make a detail working drawing of the drum. The drum rotates when it is forced along the shaft into contact with the constantly rotating driving cone. The driving cone is fixed to the rotating shaft by a Pratt and Whitney key to insure rotary motion with the shaft, and by a taper pin to prevent longitudinal axial movement. As the drum rotates, it winds or unwinds a cable. The shaft is driven by a system of gears that is not shown. The partial orthographic views show the operating mechanism for sliding the drum along the shaft into contact with the driving cone. If after studying the drawings carefully you have further questions, please consult your instructor. *Supplementary information:* 1) The outside diameter of the drum is 30″. The diameter of the opening in the drum for the backing drum cone is $29\frac{1}{4}$″ and the taper is $2\frac{1}{2}$″ per ft. 2) The diameter of the cable section is 18″, and the width of opening for the cable is 10″. 3) The dimensions of the hub are: 8″ outside diameter (O.D.) and $12\frac{3}{8}$″ over-all length. 4) The O.D. of the bushing is $4\frac{1}{4}$″. 5) There are six $\frac{5}{8}$″ thick ribs which are equally spaced. 6) The hole in the hub for an oil fitting is tapped for a $\frac{1}{4}$″ pipe thread. The hole which is to provide access to the threaded hole is drilled $\frac{3}{4}$″ in diameter. The tapped hole is $6\frac{3}{4}$″ from the face of the hub. 7) The small hole for attaching the cable is $1\frac{3}{16}$″. It is located $\frac{3}{4}$″ from the face of the flange. 8) The thickness of all sections except for the ribs is $\frac{3}{4}$″. 9) There are 124 copper rivets required to fasten the brake lining to the drum. The holes in the drum are to be drilled $\frac{1}{4}$″ in diameter and are countersunk at 90°. 10) All small radii are $\frac{3}{4}$″ R.

37. (Fig. 20.53.) Make a detail working drawing of the driving cone. *Supplementary information:* 1) The surface of the driving cone which contacts the lining in the drum is tapered. The taper is $2\frac{1}{2}$″ per ft. 2) The diameter of the shaft on which the driving cone is fixed is $3\frac{3}{4}$″ dia. 3) It is suggested that a No. 34 Pratt and Whitney and No. 12 Std. taper be used for the driving cone. Taper pins have a taper of $\frac{1}{4}$″ per ft. 4) The 5″ dia. holes are to be cored in the casting.

Fig. 20.53.　Hoisting Machine—Drum, Cone, and Collar.

11	ZERK 35A FITTING		1
10	RETAINER	LEATHER	1
9	30307 MED. BEARING		2
8	NUT		6
7	BOLT		6
6	CASTELLATED NUT		1
5	SHAFT WASHER	M.S.	1
4	SHAFT	C.R.S.	1
3	HUB CAP	C.I.	1
2	WHEEL FLANGE	C.I.	1
1	WHEEL BODY	C.I.	1

Fig. 20.54.　Rail Wheel.

38. (Fig. 20.54.)　Make a detail drawing of an assigned part of the rail wheel. Determine the dimensions by transferring them from the drawing to the accompanying scale, by means of the dividers. Compose a suitable detail title giving the name of the part, the material, the number required, etc.

39. (Fig. 20.55.)　Make a detail drawing of an assigned part of the thermostatic radiator trap.

Courtesy Warren Webster & Co.

Fig. 20.55.　Thermostatic Radiator Trap.

40. (Fig. 20.56.)   Make a two-view freehand detail sketch of the fan spindle. Determine dimensions by transferring them from the drawing to the open-divided scale, by means of the dividers.   The material is SAE 1045, CRS.   The limits for the spindle may be found in Table XXXII, Appendix.   The last figure in the bearing number is the bearing bore number given in the tables.   Use an RC7 fit between spindle and felt retainer, spindle and felt-retaining washer, spindle and cone-clamp washer.

41. (Fig. 20.56.)   Make a complete two-view detail drawing of the fan pulley. It is suggested that a half-circular view and a full-sectional view be shown. Determine the dimensions as suggested in problem 40.   Housing limits for the given bearings will be found in Table XXXII, Appendix.

Fig. 20.56.   Fan Assembly.

42. (Figs. 20.57–20.58.)   Make a detail drawing of an assigned part of the air cleaner.   Determine the dimensions by transferring them from the drawing to the accompanying scale by means of the dividers.   Compose a suitable detail title, giving the name of the part, the material, etc.   Study Fig. 20.58.

Courtesy A. Schrader's Son Mfg. Co.

Fig. 20.58.   Air Cleaner.

Courtesy A. Schrader's Son Mfg. Co.

Fig. 20.57.   Air Cleaner.

43. (Fig. 20.59.)   Make a detail drawing of an assigned part of the motorcycle clutch.   Determine the dimensions by transferring them from the drawing to the accompanying scale, by means of the dividers.   Compose a suitable detail title, giving the information suggested in problem 38.

Courtesy Harley-Davidson Motor Co.

Fig. 20.59. Motorcycle Clutch Assembly.

44. (Fig. 20.60.)   Make a detail drawing of an assigned part of the pipe stand. Draw all necessary views and give all dimensions that will be required by the shop.   Compose a suitable title, giving the name of the part, the material, and the number required.

Fig. 20.60. Pipe Stand.

Courtesy Grinnell Co.

45. (Fig. 20.61.)   Make a detail working drawing of an assigned part of the flexible joint.   Compose a suitable title giving the name of the part, the material, etc.

Fig. 20.61. Flexible Joint.

46. (Fig. 20.62.)   Make a detail drawing of an assigned part of the tool holder.

PC	NAME	NO	MATL
1	BASE	1	C.I.
2	HOLDER	1	C.I.
3	SCREW	1	C.R.S.
4	BEARING PIN	1	DRILL ROD

$\frac{1}{2}$ REAM – CBORE
$\frac{5}{8}$ DIA × $\frac{11}{32}$ DEEP

FILLETS & ROUNDS $\frac{1}{8}$ R
EXCEPT AS SHOWN

HANDLE $\frac{3}{8}$ D. × $3\frac{1}{4}$ LONG
C.R.S. –CLASS FN1 FIT

$\frac{5}{16}$ DIA. × $3\frac{21}{32}$ LONG

NECK $\frac{1}{8}$ WIDE TO
THD. DEPTH

$\frac{5}{8}$ R SPHERICAL

$\frac{7}{16}$-16NS-2A

POLISH

CLASS FN1 FIT   CLASS LC1 FIT

Fig. 20.62. Tool Holder.

47. (Fig. 20.63.)   Make a detail working drawing of an assigned part of the self-aligning shaft support.   Compose a suitable title, giving the name of the part, the material, etc.

Courtesy Boston Gear Works, Inc.

Fig. 20.63.   Self-Aligning Shaft Support.

48. (Fig. 20.64.)   Make a detail drawing of an assigned part of the bearing bracket.   Compose a suitable detail title, giving the name of the part, the material, etc.

Fig. 20.64.   Bearing Bracket.

49. (Fig. 20.65.)   Make a detail drawing of an assigned part of the Simplex ball-bearing screw jack.

PC.NO.	NAME	QUAN.	MATERIAL	PC.NO.	NAME	QUAN.	MATERIAL
1	STANDARD	1	MALL. IRON	5	GROOVE PIN	3	$\frac{7}{32}$D.$\times\frac{5}{8}$ STEEL ROD
2	SCREW	1	S.A.E.1120 FORGING	6	LEVER BAR	1	REROLLED RAIL STK.
3	CAP	1	S.A.E.1045 FORGING	7	$\frac{7}{8}$ DIA. BALL BEARING	1	STD.
4	THRUST WASHER	1	S.A.E. 2315				

Courtesy Templeton, Kenly & Co.

Fig. 20.65.   Simplex Ball-Bearing Screw Jack.

PC NO	NAME	NO. REQ.
1	VALVE BODY	1
2	VALVE CAP	1
3	HINGE	1
4	VALVE	1
5	PIN SOCKET	1
6	PIN	1
7	RETAINING NUT	1
8	HINGE NUT	1
9	FIBER WASHER	1

Fig. 20.66. Check Valve.

50. (Figs. 20.66–20.67.) Make a detail drawing of an assigned part of the check valve.

Fig. 20.67. Check Valve.

51. (Fig. 20.68.) Make a detail drawing of an assigned part of the roller-bearing stud unit.

Fig. 20.68. Roller-Bearing Stud Unit.

Courtesy Ross Gear and Tool Co.

PART NO.	NAME
1	STUD
2	OUTER RACE
3	INNER RACE
4	HEX. NUT
5	WASHER

52. (Fig. 20.69.)   Make a detail drawing of an assigned part of the boring fixture.

PART NO	NAME	MATERIAL	NO. REQ'D
1	HOLDER	C.R.S	1
2	CLAMP STRAP	C.R.S	1
3	CLAMP	C.R.S.	1
4	CLAMP SCREW	C.R.S	1
5	PLUG	BRASS	1
6	THUMB SCREW	C.R.S	1
7	REST BUTTON	TOOL STEEL	2
8	BUSHING	TOOL STEEL	1
9	PIN	DRILL ROD	1

Fig. 20.69.   Boring Fixture.

53. (Fig. 20.70.) Make a detail drawing of an assigned part of the shaft support.

Fig. 20.70. Shaft Support.

54. (Fig. 20.71.) Make a detail drawing of an assigned part of the conveyor take-up unit.

Fig. 20.71. Conveyor Take-Up Unit.

PART NO	NAME OF PART	MATERIAL	NO. REQ.
1	FRAME	C.I.	1
2	FRAME CAP	C.I.	1
3	BEARING HOUSING	C.I.	1
4	SHAFT COLLAR	S.A.E. 1020	1
5	SCREW	S.A.E. 1030	1
6	SCREW COLLAR	S.A.E. 1040	1

55. (Fig. 20.72.) Make a detail drawing of an assigned part of the handle.

Fig. 20.72. Handle.

Courtesy R. C. Haskins Co.

56. (Fig. 20.73.)   Make a detail drawing of an assigned part of the air cylinder.

P.C NO	NAME	NO REQ	MAT
1	FRONT CYL HEAD	1	C.I.
2	REAR CYL HEAD	1	C.I
3	PACKING GLAND	1	BR
4	PISTON	1	C.I
5	PISTON COVER	1	C.I
6	PISTON ROD	1	STEEL
7	CYLINDER	1	STEEL TUBE
8	TIE ROD	6	STEEL
9	FOLLOWER	1	STEEL
10	LEATHER CUP	1	
11	PISTON LEATHER	2	

Fig. 20.73.   Air Cylinder.

57. (Fig. 20.74.)   Make a detail drawing of an assigned part of the gear pump.

GEAR DATA

NUMBER OF TEETH (N) —— 13
DIAMETRAL PITCH (DP)—— 10
OUTSIDE DIAMETER (OD) —1.50
PRESSURE ANGLE ——— 14½°

PC	NAME	NO.	MAT'L
1	HOUSING	1	C.BRO.
2	HOUSING COVER	1	C.BRO.
3	PULLEY	1	ALCOA 195-T6
4	GEAR	2	BRO.
5	GEAR STUD	1	BRASS
6	SHAFT	1	BRASS
7	NUT	2	BRO.
8	PACKING NUT	2	BRO.

Fig. 20.74.   Gear Pump.

58. (Fig. 20.75.) Make a detail drawing of an assigned part of the bench arbor press.

PART NO.	NAME	MATERIAL	NO. REQ.
1	BASE	C.I.	1
2	TABLE	C.I.	1
3	TURNTABLE	C.I.	1
4	RAM	S.A.E. 1045	1
5	RAM HEAD	S.A.E. 1040	1
6	SPINDLE	S.A.E. 1045	1
7	HANDLE	C.R.S.	1

Fig. 20.75. Bench Arbor Press.

59. (Fig. 20.76.) Make a detail drawing of an assigned part of the compensating collet chuck.

Fig. 20.76. Compensating Collet Chuck.

Courtesy Logansport Machine Co.

NO	NAME	REQ
1	COLLET BODY	1
2	COLLET	1
3	ADAPTER	1
4	DRAW SLEEVE	1
5	DRAW TUBE	1
6	TUBE COLLAR	1
7	DRIVE STUD	3
8	SPRING	3
9	SPRING	3
10	CHECK NUT	2
11	DRAW STUD	1

60. (Fig. 20.77.)   Make a detail working drawing of an assigned part of the bench grinder.

Fig. 20.77.   Bench Grinder.

NO	NAME	MAT	REQ
1	FRAME	CI	1
2	WHEEL GUARD	CI	2
3	TOOL REST BRACKET	CI	2
4	PULLEY	CI	1
5	WHEEL CLAMP WASHER	CI	4
6	SHAFT	CRS	1
7	BUSHING	BRO.	2
8	OIL PLUG	BR.	2

61. (Fig. 20.78.)   Make a complete set of working drawings of the flexible coupling.   The complete set should include detail drawings of the individual parts and an assembly drawing complete with bill of material.

Fig. 20.78.   Flexible Coupling.

62. (Fig. 20.79.) Make a complete set of working drawings of the link. The complete set should consist of detail drawings of the parts and an assembly drawing.

Fig. 20.79. Link.

Fig. 20.80.   Milling Jack.

63. (Fig. 20.80.)   Make a complete set of working drawings of the milling jack.   The complete set should be composed of detail drawings of the parts and an assembly drawing showing the parts in their relative positions.

64. (Figs. 20.81–20.82.)   Make detail drawings and an assembly drawing of the machine clamp.

Fig. 20.81.   Machine Clamp.

$\frac{1}{32} \times 45°$ CHAMFER-BOTH ENDS

$\frac{15}{16}$

.5 D
$\frac{5}{16}$

PIN
C.R.S. 1 REQ'D.

JAW SPRING
$1\frac{1}{8}$ I.D. $4\frac{1}{2}$ COILS
#12 STEEL WIRE 1 REQ'D.

$1\frac{7}{16}$

$\frac{1}{4}$ D

PIN
C.R.S. 1 REQ'D.

$\frac{1}{32} \times 45°$ CHAMFER
BOTH ENDS

$\frac{3}{32}$

WASHER
S.A.E. 1020 1 REQ'D.

CLAMP SPRING
$1\frac{1}{8}$ I.D. 6 COILS
#8 STEEL WIRE 1 REQ'D.

$\frac{1}{16} \times 45°$ CHAMFER

$5\frac{1}{4}$

$\frac{1}{16}$

$\frac{1}{4}$ REAM

$\frac{5}{16}$ REAM

$\frac{3}{4}$ D

$\frac{9}{16}$

$\frac{13}{16}$

$\frac{11}{32}$ R

SHAFT
C.R.S. 1 REQ'D.

SLOT $\frac{1}{4}$ WIDE

1-14NF-3 BOTH ENDS

$\frac{3}{16}$

1-14NF-3

COLLAR
S.A.E. 1020 1 REQ'D.

$\frac{5}{16}$

$1\frac{3}{8}$

$\frac{1}{16}$

$4\frac{1}{2}$

$\frac{3}{4}$ D

SLEEVE
1 O.D., $\frac{3}{4}$ I.D. STEEL TUBING
1 REQ'D.

$\frac{3}{4}$

1-14NF-3

$\frac{3}{16}$

$4\frac{1}{4}$

$\frac{15}{16}$

$\frac{5}{16}$

$\frac{5}{16}$ REAM

$1\frac{1}{4}$ D

$\frac{1}{8}$ R

1 REAM

CAM CLAMP
C.S. 1 REQ'D.

$\frac{9}{16}$

$\frac{1}{2}$ R

$3\frac{1}{8}$

$1\frac{7}{16}$

$\frac{1}{8}$ R

$\frac{3}{8}$ $\frac{3}{8}$

$\frac{17}{32}$ DRILL
4 HOLES
$\frac{3}{4}$ REAM

$\frac{5}{8}$

$\frac{3}{4}$

$1\frac{5}{8}$

$\frac{3}{4}$

$\frac{5}{32}$

$\frac{7}{16}$

$\frac{3}{4}$

$\frac{5}{32}$

$1\frac{1}{4}$ R

$\frac{7}{8}$ D

$\frac{3}{8}$ R

$\frac{1}{16}$

$\frac{5}{32}$

$3\frac{1}{8}$

$\frac{1}{4}$

$\frac{1}{2}$

$1\frac{7}{8}$

$4\frac{3}{8}$

$1\frac{1}{2}$

60°

JAW
C.R.S. 1 REQ'D.

FILLETS ROUNDS $\frac{1}{8}$ R

FRAME
C.I. 1 REQ'D.

Fig. 20.82. Machine Clamp.

65. (Fig. 20.83.) Make a complete set of working drawings of the tool holder. The complete set should consist of detail drawings of the parts and an assembly drawing.

Fig. 20.83. Tool Holder.

66. (Fig. 20.84.)   Make a complete set of working drawings of the vise. The complete set of drawings should be composed of detail drawings of the parts (except standard parts) and an assembly drawing.

Fig. 20.84. Vise.

67. (Fig. 20.85.)   Make detail drawings of the rest body and the rest block. Make an assembly drawing showing the parts of the stock rest assembled in their relative positions.

Fig. 20.85.   Stock Rest.

68. (Fig. 20.86.) Make a complete set of working drawings of the roller rest. The complete set should include detail drawings of the individual parts and an assembly drawing complete with a bill of material.

Fig. 20.86.   Roller Rest.

HOLES DIAMETRICALLY OPPOSITE

1.750 DIA.

.25 .12×30°

.312 DRILL .12 DEEP 2 HOLES

3/4-10UNC-2A

1.00

.38 .12 .94 1.25

.9740 DIA.

.06×45°

NECK FOR RELIEF BOTH SIDES

3.75

1.2509 1.2503

P&W KEYWAY .16 DEEP

KEYWAYS 90° APART

NECK .12 WIDE TO THD. DEPTH

DRILL SHAFT M.S. 1 REQ'D.

3/8-UNC HEX.HD.CAP SC. 2 REQ'D.

1.25

NECK FOR RELIEF

.98 .75

.62 DIA.

Slight R 59°

.500 PRESS FIT

.03×45°

LAP FOR #12(.189) DRILL

BUSHING M.S. 2 REQ'D.

.781 DIA.

.25

1.75 DIA.

WASHER C.R.S. 1 REQ'D.

3.50 .38 R

.50 R 1.00

1.75 .44

.50

5/8-11UNC-2B

CLAMP PLATE M.S. 1 REQ'D.

.250 DIA.

2.25

HANDLE C.R.S. 1 REQ'D.

.62 .13

.16

NO.6 P&W KEY 2 REQ'D.

.500 REAM - C'BORE .875 DIA.×.31 DEEP-2 HOLES

3.76 .76 1.98 3.50

1.88 1.88 .86

.12 4.50 1.14

2.25 1.2500 1.2506

KEYWAY .16 WIDE ×.08 DEEP 1.75

.32 .12×45°

.516 DIA.

1.38 DIA.

.06×45°

CLAMP BUTTON M.S. 1 REQ'D.

3/4-UNC STD. NUT 1 REQ'D.

C OF HOLE

.06×45°

90° 90°

1.50 1.56

1.75

.250 DRILL .32

.75 SPHER.R

1.38 .66

2.38

5/8-11UNC-2A

PEEN OVER IN ASSEMBLY WITH CLAMP BUTTON

.500 DIA.

CLAMP SCREW M.S. 1 REQ'D.

.41 .44 DIA. SPHERE

BALL C.R.S. 2 REQ'D.

.250 DIA. .22 DEEP

1.88

3.76

3/8-16UNC-2B .88 DEEP-2 HOLES

JIG BASE C.I. 1 REQ'D.

Courtesy Fairfield Mfg. Co.

Fig. 20.87. Tumble Jig.

69. (Fig. 20.87.) Make a complete set of working drawings of the tumble jig. The complete set should consist of detail drawings of the individual parts (except standard parts) and an assembly drawing complete with a bill of material.

Fig. 20.88. Tool Holder.

70. (Fig. 20.88.) Make detail drawings of the carrier and the holder. Make an assembly drawing showing all of the parts in their relative positions.

71. (Fig. 20.89.) Make a complete set of working drawings of the adjustable attachment. The complete set should consist of detail drawings of the individual parts and an assembly drawing complete with a bill of material.

Fig. 20.89. Adjustable Attachment.

72. (Figs. 20.90, 20.91, and 20.92.)   Make an assembly drawing of the pipe vise, using the given details.   Use the schematic symbol for screw threads.

Courtesy The Borden Co.

Fig. 20.90.   Pipe Vise (Patented).

BASE
M.I. 1 REQ'D.

Courtesy The Borden Co.

Fig. 20.91.   Pipe Vise Details (Patented).

Fig. 20.92.   Pipe Vise Details (Patented).

73. (Figs. 20.93 and 20.94.)   Make an assembly drawing of the idler pulley, using the given details.   Use the schematic symbol for screw threads.

Fig. 20.93.   Idler Pulley.

Fig. 20.94. Idler Pulley Details.

74. (Fig. 20.95.)   Make a two-view assembly drawing of the cup center using the given details.   Use the schematic symbol for screw threads.   Study the pictorial drawing carefully before starting the views.

Fig. 20.95.   Cup Center Details.

75. (Fig. 20.96.)   Make an assembly drawing of the radial engine unit, using the given details.   It is suggested that one piston be shown in full section so that the relative positions of the parts will be revealed.

Fig. **20.96.**   Radial Engine Details.

76. (Figs. 20.97, 20.98, and 20.99.)   Make detail drawings and an assembly drawing of the speed reducer.

Fig. 20.97.   Speed Reducer.

Fig. 20.98. Speed Reducer.

Fig. 20.99. Speed Reducer.

77. (Figs. 20.100, 20.101, and 20.102.) Make an assembly drawing of the hand clamp vise, using the given details. Use the schematic symbol for screw threads.

PART NO.	NAME OF PART	MATERIAL	NO. REQ.
11	NO.6 TAPER PIN		1
10	SPECIAL MACHINE SC.	M.S.	4
9	SPECIAL FLAT HD. SC.	M.S.	2
8	LINK	C.R.S.	1
7	COUPLING	C.R.S.	1
6	WEDGE	C.R.S.	1
5	JAW PLATE	C.R.S.	2
4	SHOE	C.R.S.	1
3	HAND SCREW	C.R.S.	1
2	JAW	C.I.	1
1	BASE	C.I.	1

Fig. 20.100.   Hand Clamp Vise.

FILLETS & ROUNDS $\frac{1}{8}R$

#12-24NC-2 -$\frac{1}{2}$DEEP
2 HOLES

PC #1 BASE
C.I. 1 REQ'D

Fig. 20.101.   Hand Clamp Vise Details.

Fig. 20.102. Hand Clamp Vise Details.

78. (Figs. 20.103 and 20.104.)   Make an assembly drawing of the drill jig.

Fig. 20.103.   Drill Jig.

Courtesy Ross Gear and Tool Co.

Fig. 20.104. Drill Jig Details.

79. (Figs. 20.105, 20.106, and 20.107.)   Make an assembly drawing of the blow gun.

Courtesy A. Schrader's Son Mfg. Co.

Fig. 20.105.   Blow Gun.

BODY
STAINLESS STEEL FORGING

Fig. 20.106.   Blow Gun Details.

WASHER
STEEL   I REQ'D.

PLUNGER WASHER
BLACK RUBBER I REQ'D.

WASHER
LEATHER I REQ'D.

CUP
LEATHER   I REQ'D.

NOSE
BRASS I REQ'D.

PLUNGER
STAINLESS STEEL I REQ'D.

BUSHING
BRASS I REQ'D.

NUT
STAINLESS STEEL I REQ'D.

DEFLATOR
BRASS I REQ'D.

PIN
DRILL ROD I REQ'D.

SPRING
PIANO WIRE I REQ'D.

Fig. 20.107. Blow Gun.

80. (Figs. 20.108, 20.109, and 20.110.)   Make an assembly drawing of the hand grinder.

Fig. 20.108.   Hand Grinder.

Fig. 20.109. Hand Grinder Details.

Fig. 20.110.   Hand Grinder Details.

81. (Figs. 20.111, 20.112, and 20.113.) Make an assembly drawing of the right-angle head using the given details.

Courtesy R. C. Haskins Co.

Fig. 20.111. Right-Angle Head Details.

Fig. 20.112.   Right-Angle Head Details.

SPIRAL GEAR & PINION
S.A.E 4620

	GEAR	PINION
PITCH	15.5	15.5
PITCH ANGLE	64° 8'	25° 52'
FACE	3/8	3/8
FACE ANGLE	66° 38'	30° 14'
NO. OF TEETH	33	16

GREASE PLUG
7/8 D. BRASS ROD

N.D. #3201 BRG.

SPECIAL NUT
5/8 HEX. C.R.S

CLAMP NUT
AL.

N.D. #3303 BRG.

SLEEVE NUT
C.R.S.

N.D. #3202 BRG.

N.D. #3300 BRG.

Fig. 20.113. Right-Angle Head Details.

21

Machine Elements*

21.1. Gears. The draftsman frequently is called upon to make representations of gears and gear teeth. It is therefore important for him to know the general proportions and nomenclature pertaining to gearing. In Fig. 21.1 the nomenclature for bevel gears is shown. It will be noted that, in general, the definitions pertaining to gear-tooth parts can be represented in a right section of the gear.

Fig. 21.1. Bevel-Gear Nomenclature.

The theory of gears is a part of the study of mechanism. In working drawings of gears and toothed wheels it is necessary to draw at least one tooth of each gear. Some of the terms used in defining gear teeth are shown in Fig. 21.2.

Two systems of generating tooth curves are in general use, the involute system and the cycloidal system. The curve most commonly used for gear-tooth profiles is the involute of a circle.

An involute is the curve generated by a point on a straightedge as the

---

* Material covering Gears and Cams prepared by Professor E. W. Azpell, Purdue University.

530

straightedge is rolled on a cylinder. It also may be defined as the curve generated by a point on a taut string as the string is unwrapped from a cylinder. The circle from which the involute is developed is called the *base circle*.

A method of constructing an involute curve is shown in Fig. 21.3. Starting with point 0, on the base circle, divide the base circle into a convenient number of equal arcs of length 0–1, 1–2, 2–3, and so forth.

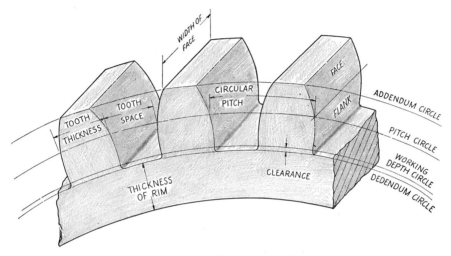

Fig. 21.2. Spur-Gear Nomenclature.

(Where the lengths of the divisions on the base circle are not too great, the chord can be taken as the length of the arc.) Draw a tangent to the base circle, at point 0, and divide this line to the left of 0 into equal parts of the same lengths as the arcs. Next, draw tangents to the circle from points 1, 2, 3, and so on. With the center of the base circle "0" as a pivot, draw concentric arcs from 1', 2', 3', and so forth, until they intersect the tangent lines drawn from 1, 2, 3, and so forth. The intersection of the arcs and the tangents are points on the required involute curve, such as 1'', 2'', 3'', and so forth. The illustration at the right in Fig. 21.3 shows the portion XY of the tooth outline as part of the involute curve.

Fig. 21.3.   Involute Tooth.

The cycloidal system, as the name implies, has tooth curves of cycloidal form. A cycloid is the curve generated by a point on the circumference of a circle as the circle rolls on a straight line. If the circle rolls on the outside of another circle, the curve generated is called an epicycloid; if it rolls on the inside of another circle, the curve generated is called a hypocycloid. In Fig. 21.4, let R be the radius of the fixed circle and r be the radius of the rolling circle. Draw through a a circle arc, AB, concentric with the fixed circle. Lay off on the rolling circle a convenient number of divisions, such as 0-1, 1-2, 2-3, and so forth; then divide the fixed-circle circumference into divisions of the same length, such as 0-1', 1'-2', 2'-3', and so on. Through these points on the fixed circle, draw radii and extend them to intersect the arc AB, thus producing points a_1, a_2, a_3, and so on. These points will be the centers of the successive positions of the rolling circle. Draw the positions of the rolling circle, using the centers a_1, a_2, a_3, and so forth. Next draw, on the rolling circle with the center "0" of the fixed circle as the pivot point, concentric arcs through

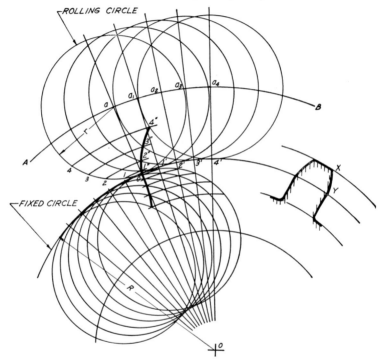

Fig. 21.4. Tooth Curves—Cycloidal Form.

points 1, 2, 3, and so forth. The intersection of these arcs with the rolling circles about a_1, a_2, a_3, and so forth, determine points, such as 1'', 2'', 3'', and so forth, on the epicyclic curve. The illustration at the right in Fig. 21.4 shows XY of the tooth outline as part of the epicyclic curve.

The hypocyclic curve construction is the same as that for the epicyclic curve. In the construction of the hypocyclic curve, if the rolling circle has a diameter equal to one-half of the diameter of the fixed circle, the hypocyclic curve thus generated will be a radial line of the fixed circle.

GEAR TERMS

1. The addendum circle is drawn with its center at the center of the gear and bounds the ends of the teeth. (See Fig. 21.2.)

2. The dedendum circle, or root circle, is drawn with its center at the center of the gear and bounds the bottoms of the teeth. (See Fig. 21.2.)

3. The pitch circle is a right section of the equivalent cylinder the toothed gear may be considered to replace.

4. Pitch diameter is the diameter of the pitch circle.

5. The addendum is the radial distance from the pitch circle to the outer end of the tooth.

6. The dedendum is the radial distance from the pitch circle to the bottom of the tooth.

7. The clearance is the difference between the dedendum of one gear and the addendum of the mating gear.

8. The face of a tooth is that portion of the tooth surface lying outside the pitch circle.

9. The flank of a tooth is that portion of the tooth surface lying inside the pitch circle.

10. The thickness of a tooth is measured on the arc of the pitch circle. It is the length of an arc and not the length of a straight line.

11. The tooth space is the space between the teeth measured on the pitch circle.

12. Backlash is the difference between the tooth thickness of one gear and the tooth space on the mating gear, measured on the pitch circles.

13. The circular pitch of a gear is the distance between a point on one tooth and the corresponding point on the adjacent tooth, measured along the arc of the pitch circle. The circular pitches of two gears in mesh are equal.

14. The diametral pitch is the number of teeth per inch of pitch diameter. It is obtained by dividing the number of teeth by the pitch diameter.

15. The face of a gear is the width of its rim measured parallel to the axis. It should not be confused with the face of a tooth, for the two are entirely different.

16. The pitch point is on the line joining the centers of the two gears where the pitch circles touch.

17. The common tangent is the line tangent to the pitch circles at the pitch point.

18. The pressure angle is the angle between the line of action and the common tangent.

19. The line of action is a line drawn through the pitch point at an angle (equal to the pressure angle) to the common tangent.

20. The base circle is used in involute gearing to generate the involutes that form the tooth outlines. It is drawn from the center of each pair of mating gears tangent to the line of action.

21. When two gears mesh with each other, the larger is called the *gear* and the smaller the *pinion*.

It should be noted that *circular pitch* is a linear dimension expressed in inches, whereas *diametral pitch* is a ratio. There must be a whole number of teeth on the circumference of a gear. Thus it is necessary that the circumference of the pitch circle, divided by the circular pitch, be a whole number.

For circular pitch, let P' = circular pitch in inches, D = pitch diameter, and T = number of teeth. Then

$$TP' = \pi D, \qquad T = \frac{\pi D}{P'}, \qquad P' = \frac{\pi D}{T}, \qquad \text{and} \qquad D = \frac{TP'}{\pi}.$$

For diametral pitch, let P = diametral pitch, D = pitch diameter, and T = number of teeth. Then

$$T = PD, \qquad D = \frac{T}{P}, \qquad \text{and} \qquad P = \frac{T}{D}.$$

The Brown and Sharpe $14\frac{1}{2}$-degree involute system has been adopted as one of the American standards and is commonly known as the $14\frac{1}{2}$-Degree Composite System. The tooth proportions of this system are given in terms of the diametral pitch P and circular pitch P'.

Pressure angle $= 14\frac{1}{2}°$.

Addendum (inches) $= \dfrac{1}{\text{diametral pitch}} = \dfrac{1}{P}.$

Dedendum (inches) $=$ addendum plus clearance $= \dfrac{1}{P} + 0.05P'.$

Clearance $= 0.05 \times$ circular pitch $= 0.05P'.$

Whole depth of tooth $= 2 \times$ addendum $+$ clearance $= 2 \times \dfrac{1}{P} + 0.05P'.$

Working depth of tooth $= 2 \times$ addendum $= 2 \times \dfrac{1}{P}.$

Thickness of tooth $= \dfrac{\text{circular pitch}}{2} = \dfrac{P'}{2}.$

Width of tooth space $= \dfrac{\text{circular pitch}}{2} = \dfrac{P'}{2}.$

Minimum radius of fillet $=$ clearance $= 0.05P'.$

In the above calculations the backlash is zero. Actually, however, it is common practice to provide backlash, and this is accomplished by using standard cutters and cutting the teeth slightly deeper than for standard teeth.

21.2. To lay out a pair of standard involute spur gears. The following facts are known regarding the laying out of a pair of standard spur gears: (1) number of teeth on each gear—large gear 24, small gear 16, (2) diametral pitch $= 2$, (3) pressure angle $= 14\frac{1}{2}°$.

To draw a pair of spur gears, determine the pitch diameters, thus:

$$D = \frac{T}{P} = \frac{24}{2} = 12'' \text{ for large gear.}$$

$$D = \frac{T}{P} = \frac{16}{2} = 8'' \text{ for small gear.}$$

In Fig. 21.5, with radii O_1P and O_2P equal to $6''$ and $4''$ respectively; draw the pitch circles and, through P, draw the common tangent. Draw the line of action XY at an angle of $14\frac{1}{2}°$ to the common tangent. Drop perpendiculars from the centers O_1 and O_2, cutting the line of action at A and B, respectively. O_1A and O_2B are the radii of the base circles that can now be drawn.

From Sec. 21.1, determine the addendum and dedendum of the teeth, and draw in the respective addendum and dedendum circles.

Divide the pitch circle of the smaller gear into 16 equal parts and the pitch circle of the larger gear into 24 equal parts, which will give the circular pitch. Assuming that no allowance is made for backlash, bisect the circular pitch on each of the gears, which will give 32 equal divisions on the small gear and 48 equal divisions on the large gear.

At any point on the base circle of each gear, develop an involute (see Fig. 21.3) and draw in the curves between the base and addendum circles through alternate points on the pitch circles.   This produces one side of

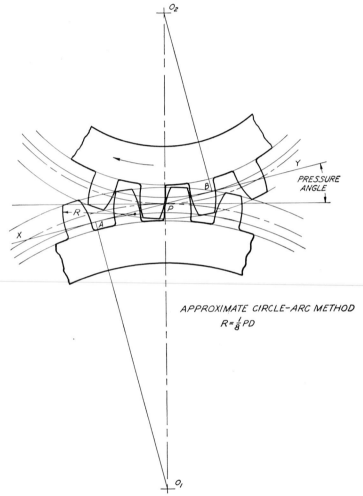

APPROXIMATE CIRCLE-ARC METHOD

$R = \frac{1}{8}PD$

Fig. 21.5.   To Draw a Pair of Spur Gears.

all the teeth in each gear.   The curve for the other side of the tooth is the reverse of the side just drawn.   The part of the tooth between the base and dedendum circles is part of a radial line drawn from the base circles to the centers of the gears.   The tooth is finished by putting in a small fillet between the working depth and dedendum circles.

21.3. Dimensioning gears.   On a detail drawing, a gear may be represented by a one-view section, except for the larger sizes, where it is

necessary to show spokes, and for the small sizes, when a full description
of some feature would not be given.   A second view was drawn in Fig. 21.6
to reveal the shape of the keyway.   In dimensioning, it is recommended
that the dimensions be given on the view or views as shown in Figs. 21.6
and 21.7 and that the cutting data be incorporated in an accompanying
table.

21.4. Working drawings of gears.   Figure 21.6 shows a working
drawing of a helical gear.   In practice it is customary to show one view in
section and just enough of the circular view to supply needed information
for the shop.   Individual teeth are never shown on the circular view unless

TEETH TO BE SHAVED

MAX. PITCH LINE RUNOUT .003
TOTAL INDICATOR READING

CUTTING DATA			
NO. OF TEETH	32	PITCH DIAM.	4.250
CHOR. ADD. — ADD.	.125	DIAM. PITCH	8.0 NORM.
DEDENDUM	.145	PRESS ANGLE	20°
FULL DEPTH	.270	HELIX ANGLE	19°45' RH.
CENTER DIST.	4.251	BACKLASH	.004 .008

MAT.- N.E 8645
HARDNESS ROCKWELL "C" 38-42

Courtesy Fairfield Mfg. Co.

Fig. 21.6.   Detail Drawing of a Helical Gear.

the drawing is to be used for display purposes.   In some drafting rooms
where practice requires a full circular view, the addendum circle is represented by a fine solid line, the pitch circle is given as a center line, and the
root circle is shown by a dashed line.

It should be noted that the dimensions for the gear blank are given on
the sectioned view while the necessary data for cutting the teeth are given
in a table.   This is in accordance with the practice recommended in Sec.
21.3.

A working drawing of a spiral bevel gear is shown in Fig. 21.7.   The
same practices apply as for spur gears.   Before starting to prepare a
working drawing of a bevel gear one should study Fig. 21.1, which illustrates bevel-gear nomenclature.

Figure 21.8 shows a working drawing of a worm.

Courtesy Fairfield Mfg. Co.

Fig. 21.7. Detail Drawing of a Spiral Bevel Gear.

Courtesy Warner & Swasey Co.

Fig. 21.8. Detail Drawing of a Worm.

21.5. Cams.   A cam is a plate, cylinder, or any solid having a curved outline or curved groove that, by its oscillating or rotating motion, gives a predetermined motion to another piece, called the follower, in contact with it.   The cam plays a very important part in the operation of many classes of machines.   Cam mechanisms are commonly used to operate valves in automobiles and stationary and marine internal combustion engines.   They also are used in automatic screw machines, clocks, locks, printing machinery, and in nearly all kinds of machinery that we generally regard as "automatic machines."   The applications of cams are practically unlimited, and their shapes or outlines are found in wide variety.

All cam mechanisms consist of at least three parts: (1) the cam, which has a contact surface either curved or straight; (2) the follower, whose motion is produced by contact with the cam surface; and (3) the frame, which supports the cam and guides the follower.

The most common type of cam is the disc or plate cam.   Here the cam takes the form of a revolving disc or plate, the circumference of the disc or plate forming the profile with which the follower makes contact.   In Figs. 21.9 and 21.10, two simple examples of a disc cam and follower are shown.   In Fig. 21.9, the cam is given a motion of rotation, thus causing the follower to rise and then return again to its initial position.   In cams of this type it is necessary to use some external force, such as the spring, to keep the follower in contact with the cam at all times.   Contact between the follower and the cam is made through a roller, which serves to reduce friction.   It is sometimes necessary to use a flat-faced follower, instead of the roller type, an example of which is shown in Fig. 21.10.   The follower face that comes in contact with the cam is usually provided with a hardened surface, to prevent excessive wear.

Fig. 21.9.   Disc Cam and Follower.

Another type of cam is one in which the follower is constrained to move in a definite path without the application of external forces.   (See Fig. 21.11.)   In this type, two contact surfaces of the follower bear on the cam at the same time, thus controlling the motion of the follower in two directions.

21.6. Design of a cam.   The design of a cam outline is governed by the requirements with respect to the motion of the follower.   In the layout of a cam, the initial position, displacement, and character of the motion of the follower are generally known.   It is convenient to make first a graphical representation of the follower movement, a procedure which is called *making a displacement diagram*.   This is a linear curve in which the length of the diagram represents the time for one revolution of the cam.   The height of the diagram represents the total displacement of the follower; the length is made to any convenient length and is divided into equal time intervals, the total representing one rotation of the cam.

In Fig. 21.12 is shown a displacement diagram in which the follower rises 2″ during 180° of rotation of the cam, then rests for 30° and returns to its initial position for the remainder of the cam revolution. Cam outlines should be designed to avoid sudden changes of motion at the beginning and end of the follower stroke. This can be accomplished by having

Fig. 21.10. Disc Cam and Follower.   Fig. 21.11. Cam and Follower.

a uniformly accelerated and decelerated motion at the beginning and end of the constant-velocity curve. The construction for uniformly accelerated motion is shown in Fig. 21.12. On a line, OX, making any convenient angle with OA, mark off any unit of length in this figure equal to Oa. The next point, b, is found by marking off, from O, 4 units of length. Point c is found by marking off 9 units of length. Next, project the intersection (point s) of time unit 3 and the constant-velocity line over to the line OA, thus locating point t. Connect points c and t with a straight line and draw parallel lines from a and b intersecting the line OA. From these intersections draw lines parallel to ts, intersecting the time-unit lines

1 and 2, respectively. These intersections are points on the displacement curve. With uniformly decelerated motion, the series of points are laid off in the reverse order, such as 9-4-1. It will be noted that the units are laid off according to the square of the time unit. Thus, if there were four time units, the acceleration curve would be laid off according to the ratio of 1, 4, 9, 16, and the deceleration, 16, 9, 4, 1.

The construction for the displacement diagram for simple harmonic motion is shown in the same figure. A semicircle is drawn as shown, the follower displacement being used as a diameter, and is then divided into a convenient number of parts equal to the number of cam displacement units. Horizontal projection lines are drawn from the semicircle, and the intersections of these lines with the cam displacement lines are points on the displacement curve. Thus, the projection of point 15 on the semi-circle to time unit line 15 locates one point on the displacement curve for simple harmonic motion.

Fig. 21.12. A Displacement Diagram.

The next step is that of finding the cam profile necessary to produce these movements. The construction is shown in Fig. 21.13. Select a base circle of convenient size, and on it lay off radial lines according to the number of time units of cam displacement. Draw line OB extended to W, and on it lay off the distances y_1, y_2, y_3, and so forth, obtained from the displacement diagram, from the center of the roller shown in the starting position, thus locating points B_1, B_2, B_3, and so forth. With O as a center, draw arcs B_1-B_1', B_2-B_2', B_3-B_3', and so forth, and at B_1', B_2', B_3', and so forth draw in the circles representing the diameter of the roller. To complete the cam outline, draw a smooth curve tangent to the positions of the roller.

21.7. Bearings. A draftsman ordinarily is never called upon to make a detail drawing of a ball or roller bearing, because bearings of these two types are precision-made units that are purchased from reliable manufacturers. All draftsmen working on machine drawings, however, should be familiar with the various types commonly used, and should be able to represent them correctly on an assembly drawing. An engineer will find it necessary to determine shaft-mounting fits and housing-mounting fits from a manufacturers' handbook, in order to place the correct limits on

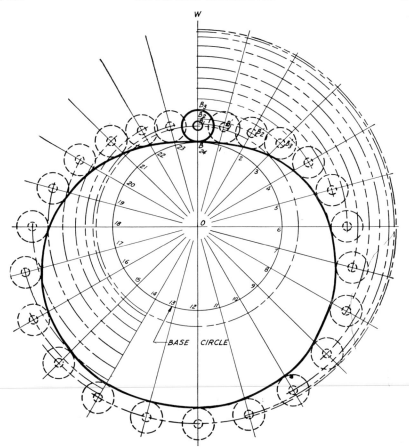

Fig. 21.13.   Construction for Cam Profile.

SINGLE   DOUBLE
ROW   ROW
(a)   (b)

Fig. 21.14.   Ball Bearings.

Fig. 21.15.   Roller Bearing.

shafts and housings.　Figure 21.14 shows two types of ball bearings.　A roller bearing is shown in Fig. 21.15.

Ball bearings may be designed for loads either perpendicular or parallel to the shaft.　In the former, they are known as radial bearings, in the latter, as thrust bearings.　Other types, designated by various names, are made to take both radial and thrust loads, either light or heavy.　In most designs, bearings are forced to take both radial and thrust loads.　Ball bearings are designated by a letter and code number, the last number of which represents the bearing bore.　They may be extra light, light, medium, or heavy, and still have the same bore number.　That is, bearings of different capacities and different outer diameters can fit shafts

Courtesy New Departure Bearing Co., Division of General Motors.

Fig. 21.16.　Ball Bearings.

having the same nominal size.　Tables **XXXI** and **XXXII**, in the Appendix, give all the necessary information concerning the bearings used in the problems of this text.　Figure 21.16 shows typical mountings in a single mechanism.

Roller bearings are designed for both radial and thrust loads.　The bearing consists of tapered rollers that roll between an inner and an outer race.　The rollers are enclosed in a retainer (cage) that keeps them properly spaced.

21.8. Problems.　Gears and cams.

Gear Problems

1–6. Following the method shown in Sec. 21.2, lay out a pair of standard involute spur gears as assigned from the given table.　The pinion is the driver.

	GEAR				PINION				
Prob. No.	Circular Pitch	Diametral Pitch	Pitch Dia.	No. of Teeth	Circular Pitch	Diametral Pitch	Pitch Dia.	No. of Teeth	Pressure Angle
1	1.31″			24	1.31″			16	$14\frac{1}{2}°$
2		2		20		2		14	$14\frac{1}{2}°$
3		2.5	10			2.5	8		$14\frac{1}{2}°$
4	1.0			30	1.0			20	$14\frac{1}{2}°$
5	2.0			18	2.0			12	$14\frac{1}{2}°$
6		3	8			3	6		$14\frac{1}{2}°$

CAM PROBLEMS

Cam Data:

Diameter of Cam Shaft........... $1\frac{1}{4}″$
Diameter of Cam Hub........... $2\frac{1}{4}″$
Diameter of Roller............... $1″$
Keyway......................... $\frac{1}{4}″ \times \frac{1}{8}″$
Diameter of Base Circle.......... $2\frac{3}{4}″$
Follower Displacement........... $2″$
Scale: Full size
Cam rotation: As noted

Determine points on the cam profiles at intervals of 15°.

7. Using the above data, design a plate cam to satisfy the following conditions: (*a*) a rise of 2″ in 180°, with constant velocity, except for uniform acceleration for the first 30° and uniform deceleration for the last 45°; (*b*) rest 30°; (*c*) return with simple harmonic motion. Use clockwise cam rotation.

8. Same as problem 7, except that the follower is of the flat-face type and is $2\frac{1}{2}″$ wide.

9. Using the data for problem 7, design a plate cam to satisfy the following conditions: (*a*) rise of 2″ during 180°, the first 45° of which is uniformly accelerated motion, the next 60° being constant velocity, and the last 75° of rise being uniformly decelerated motion; (*b*) rest 15°; (*c*) return to starting position with simple harmonic motion. Use counterclockwise cam rotation.

10. Same as problem 9, except that the follower is of the flat-face type and is $2\frac{1}{2}″$ wide.

11. Using the data for problem 7, design a plate cam to satisfy the following conditions: (*a*) rise to 2″ during 150°, by simple harmonic motion; (*b*) rest 30°; (*c*) return to starting position during remainder of the revolution, with uniformly accelerated and decelerated motion, the value of the deceleration being two times that of the acceleration. Use clockwise cam rotation.

12. Using the data for problem 7, except that the follower is to be of the flat-face type, $2\frac{1}{2}″$ wide, design a plate cam to satisfy the following conditions: (*a*) rise of 2″, with simple harmonic motion, in 120°; (*b*) rest 30°; (*c*) return in 150°, with constant velocity, except for uniform acceleration for the first 45° and uniform deceleration for the last 30° of fall; (*d*) rest the balance of the revolution. Use counterclockwise cam rotation.

Structural Drawing

22.1. Although structural drawings are prepared in accordance with the general principles of projection, they differ somewhat from machine drawings in certain practices. These differences, which have gradually developed due to the type of raw material used and methods of fabrication, have become established drawing room customs that are recognized universally throughout the industry and must be understood and adhered to by every prospective structural engineer.

Steel structures vary widely and include almost everything fabricated from rolled shapes and plates.

Fig. 22.1. Structural Shapes.

Fabrication consists in shearing, flame cutting, punching, bending, forging, and machining, then fitting and aligning the parts, and finally permanently fastening the assembly by bolting, riveting, or welding. Although small roof trusses and girder bridges may be assembled as complete units in the shop, the size of most structures makes necessary the fabrication of subassemblies and shipment in knock-down form.

Sections of the principal shapes (angles, I-beams, channels, wide flange sections, and plates) are shown in Fig. 22.1.

The dimensions of the various standard shapes and other available information required by a structural detailer are given in structural steel handbooks published by different manufacturers and by the American Institute of Steel Construction.

22.2. Equipment of a structural draftsman. The equipment needed by a structural draftsman is the same as for any other line of industrial drafting with a few additions. Smaley's tables of trigonometric functions and logarithms, and Smaley's tables of slopes and rises are a necessity. A copy of the structural handbook published by the American Institute of Steel Construction must be readily available for constant use.

Some companies furnish each draftsman with a book that gives drawing room standards. Included are typical drawings illustrating the arrangement of views, approved dimensioning practices, and notes for various types of structures. Some information also may be given about plant equipment.

22.3. Classes of structural drawings. Most of the large steel fabricators maintain a design office and a detailing office. The former prepares design drawings and estimates costs in the preparation of bids and frequently serves in a consulting capacity on designs furnished by a customer. The detailing office, which is usually located at the fabricating plant, orders material and prepares shop and erection plans from the design sheets.

Design drawings usually are line diagrams showing the shape of a structure, the principal dimensions, structural sections, and in some cases the stresses to be used in detailing the connections. Figure 22.2 is an example of a design drawing.

For the use of the layout man a set of design drawings may contain elaborate design details, showing the type of connections, thickness of gusset plates, and the number of rivets. Figure 22.3 is the design detail for joint L_0 of the truss shown in Fig. 22.2. Design drawings of this type, however, are furnished only for important or complicated structures. Quite often the design of connections becomes a detailer's task.

A set of specifications covering special conditions, unit stresses, materials to be used, and so forth, is considered as part of the design information.

Shop detail drawings show all of the information necessary for shop fabrication.

Erection plans, which are prepared primarily for use in the field, consist of line diagrams giving dimensions, shipping marks, and notes in sufficient detail to guide the erector in assembling the parts to complete the finished structure.

22.4. Layouts. The first step in the development of structural steel detail drawings is the drawing of the layout sheets. These are intermediate drawings that are used only in the drafting room of the fabricating shop. Layouts are used for ordering material, obtaining early approval of details, and co-ordinating the work of the several draftsmen who may be employed on the project. As a general rule, layouts are made only when the complexity of the work demands a carefully scaled picture. For example, layouts would be necessary for all types of skewed work, and for truss joints. Layouts may be drawn to any appropriate scale, but usually the detail drawing and layout scales are the same. They usually are made on bond paper that is thin enough to permit blueprinting. Layouts are not completely dimensioned, but the layout man may indicate any dimensions he wishes to be used.

Figure 22.4 is a layout of the cross frame of a deck-girder bridge. The detailer takes a layout of this kind, in addition to the design drawings for the project, and completely details the structure so that it may be used in the shop for fabricating.

22.5. Detail drawings. The making of the detail drawing is the final step in the process of creating structural steel working drawings.

Fig. 22.2. Stress Sheet

Fig. 22.3.   Design Sheet.

Fig. 22.4. Layout for Internal Cross Frame.

These drawings must be clear and concise, to enable men in the shop to do their portion of the work efficiently. To insure accuracy, a thorough check of all arrangements and dimensions is made in the drafting room by a checker.

Parts to be riveted together in the shop are detailed in their assembled positions in the structure, instead of being detailed individually, as is the practice for machine work. Figure 22.5 is a detail drawing of a cross

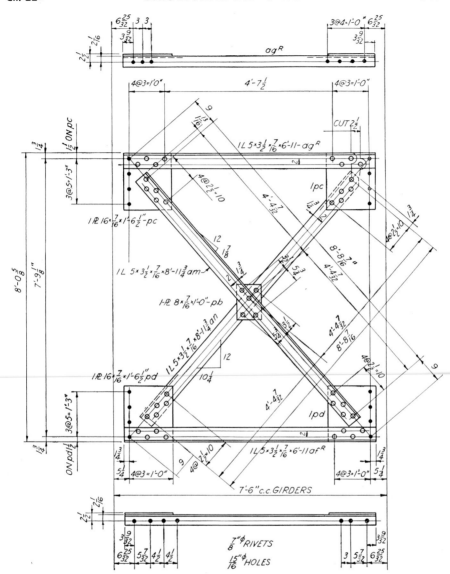

Fig. 22.5. Detail Drawing of a Cross Frame.

frame. It describes each plate and main member and shows the relations of the various elements of the structure to one another. When the structure is too large to be completely assembled in the shop and shipped in one piece, an assembly or erection diagram becomes necessary.

The scales in general use are not large enough to permit direct scaling of dimensions. One of the scales most commonly used in structural work is: $\frac{3}{4}'' = 1'$. Often structural members are too long to be drawn to scale and yet be contained on the sheet of drawing paper. In this event, the transverse dimensions and the details are drawn to one scale and the longitudinal dimensions are shortened or drawn to a smaller scale.

Structural steel drawings incorporate a few practices of projection which differ from other types of work. In all structural work the view of the structure which corresponds to the front view in a machine drawing is termed the *elevation* of the structure. The view that corresponds to the top view in a machine drawing is called the *plan view* of the structure. The view below the cross frame in Fig. 22.5 is a plan view of the lower-chord member and is not a bottom view. Likewise, the two views at the bottom of the sheet in Fig. 22.3 are not bottom views of the joint but are sectional views looking downward. The left view shows the location of the anchor bolts and the right view shows both the top and the bottom of the member L_0-L_1 where it frames into the joint. Shop men prefer the use of bottom sections because the elevation of a piece, while being fitted, corresponds to the elevation on the drawings. Any fitting or inspection of the bottom is more easily accomplished by looking down than by crawling under and looking upward.

Angular dimensions on structural drawings are shown as slopes that are expressed in inches per foot. A slope triangle is a right triangle constructed with its hypotenuse on the gage or working line whose slope is to be shown. The longer of the two legs is always given as 12″, and the length of the shorter leg determines the slope. These slope triangles are not drawn to scale but are constructed any convenient size (Fig. 22.5).

Structural drawings are currently made in pencil on translucent bond paper. Pencil work requires particular care on the part of the draftsman to make his lines black enough to blueprint clearly. The outlines of the structural members should be wider than the gage lines and dimension lines because the contrast makes the blueprints easier to read.

Pencil tracings on special cloth or ink tracings on cloth are required by certain customers.

22.6. Structural definitions and notations.

′ = foot or feet	∠ = angle
″ = inch or inches	I = I-beam
ϕ = diameter	⌴ = channel
# = pound or pounds	Wᶠ = wide flange section

Anchor bolt. A bolt used to fasten steel girders, columns, trusses, and so on, to masonry.

Beam. A horizontal structural member (usually an I-beam or Wᶠ beam).

Bearing plate. A plate used under the end of a truss, beam, or girder, to increase the bearing area.

Chip. To chip off projecting parts with a chisel (pneumatic chisel).

Clearance. A general term applying to an opening or space between two adjacent pieces, without which interference would result (Fig. 22.10).

Column. A general term for a vertical member supporting beams or trusses.

Countersink. The operation of chamfering the edges of a hole to receive the conical head of a bolt, rivet, or screw.

Detail.   To prepare a working structural drawing. (Working drawings are called details.) (Fig. 22.5.)

Driving clearance.   The distance from the center of a rivet to the nearest obstruction that would interfere with the driving of the rivet.

Edge distance.   The distance from the center of a rivet or hole to the edge of the member (Fig. 22.10).

Erection diagram.   An assembly diagram drawn to aid the erector in placing members of the structure in their proper position.

Fabrication.   The shop work of converting rolled shapes into complete structural members.

Field clearance.   Minimum distance between unfinished edges that abut when erected at the site.   Usually $\frac{1}{2}''$ to $\frac{3}{4}''$.

Field rivet.   A rivet driven in the structure at the site of construction.

Filler.   A plate or washer used to fill up space between two surfaces.

Flame cut.   To cut by hand or by a machine-guided oxyacetylene torch.

Flange.   A general term for the outstanding part of a member (Fig. 22.1).

Gage.   The distance from the back of an angle or channel to the center line of a row of rivets, or the distance between the center lines of two rows of rivets (Fig. 22.13).

Gage line.   The center line of a row of rivets (Fig. 22.13).

Girder.   A horizontal member built up of plates and angles.

Grip.   The combined thickness of members connected by a rivet.

Gusset plate.   A connection plate used to connect several members of a truss (Fig. 22.10).

Layout.   A preliminary scale drawing made in the detailing department prior to detailing, for the purpose of ordering material and co-ordinating the work of the several detailers (Fig. 22.4).

Leg.   The name for either of the two flanges of an angle (Fig. 22.1).

Line diagram.   A drawing in which each member is represented by a single line (Fig. 22.2).

Pitch.   The center-to-center longitudinal distance between adjacent rivets (Fig. 22.13).

Plate.   A flat piece of structural steel having a rectangular cross section (Fig. 22.1).

Punch.   To make a hole by forcing a nonrotating tool through the material.

Ream.   To enlarge and finish a punched hole, using a rotating fluted cutter.

Rivet.   A cylindrical rod of steel that is used to fasten together members of a steel structure.   It has one head formed when manufactured, the other is formed after the rivet is in position.

Shape.   The structural term for rolled steel having any cross section (except a steel plate). (See Fig. 22.1.)

Shop clearance.   Minimum distance between unfinished abutting edges of members assembled in the shop.   Usually $\frac{1}{4}''$.

Shop drawing.   A working drawing made for the shop.   Commonly called a *detail* drawing (Fig. 22.5).

Slope. The inclination of a line designated by a slope triangle expressed in inches of rise to a base of 12″ (Fig. 22.5).

Span. The center-to-center distance between the supports of a beam, girder, or truss.

Staggered rivets. Rivets spaced alternately in parallel rows (Fig. 22.13).

Stitch rivets. Rivets spaced at intervals along a built-up member to cause the component parts to act as a unit.

Stress sheet. A drawing having a line diagram on which are recorded the stresses in the main members of a structure (Fig. 22.2).

Truss. A rigid framed structure, in the form of a series of triangles, which acts as a beam (Fig. 22.14).

Web. The thin portion between the flanges of a member. (See Fig. 22.1.)

Weldment. Any welded assembly or subassembly.

Working point. The point of intersection of working lines (usually gage lines) (Fig. 22.14).

22.7. Sizes of standard members. The following structural specifications and abbreviations are those adopted by the American Institute of Steel Construction.

Plates. Width (in inches) × thickness × length. (Pl 15 × $\frac{3}{8}$ × 1′-10″.) If it is a connection plate on a truss, cross frame, and so on, which is fabricated in the shop, the specification will be followed by the letters *pa, pb, pc,* or *pd,* and so on, which indicate the location of the plate. (Pl 15 × $\frac{3}{8}$ × 1′-10″ *pa.*)

Angles—Equal legs. Size of leg × size of leg × thickness × length. ($\angle 3\frac{1}{2}$ × $3\frac{1}{2}$ × $\frac{3}{8}$ × 7′-6″.)

Angles—Unequal legs. Size of leg shown × size of outstanding leg × thickness × length. ($\angle 4$ × 3 × $\frac{5}{16}$ × 24′-7″.)

I-Beams. Depth of *I*-weight per ft. × length. (12″ *I* 31.8# × 15′-4″.)

Channels. Depth of ⌐-weight per ft. × length. (10″ ⌐ 15.3# × 15′-10″.)

Wide flange sections. Depth of W⁻-weight per ft. × length. (24″ W⁻ 74# × 12′-6″.)

22.8. Detailing information. The type of rivets and their treatment are indicated on structural drawings by the American Standard conventional symbols shown in Fig. 22.6.

The holes for field rivets are indicated in solid black on a drawing, while shop rivets are shown by open circles having the same diameter as the rivet head (Fig. 22.11). Rivets should be drawn with either a drop pen or a bow pencil. In practice, the circles representing rivets are often drawn freehand on pencil drawings.

22.9. Location of dimension lines. Since shopmen are never permitted to scale a drawing, all dimensions must be placed in such a manner that they will be easily understood. Principal dimensions are generally obtained from the design sheets; other dimensions necessary for detailing are found in tables or are determined by the detailer.

Dimensions for rivet spacing, minor location and size dimensions, and so on, are placed close to the view, while the longer dimensions such as over-all lengths are placed farther away so that extension lines will not cross dimension lines (Figs. 22.7, 22.8, and 22.9).

Dimension figures are generally placed above continuous (unbroken) dimension lines, which are made narrow and black. These lines usually should be placed off the view, but oftentimes added clearness may be obtained by putting a few dimensions in an open area on the view itself. Dimension lines ordinarily should not be placed less than $\frac{3}{8}''$ apart or closer to the view than $\frac{1}{2}''$. All of the above rules for the location of dimension lines may be modified to suit the available space (Fig. 22.8).

22.10. Dimensions and notes in structural detailing.

1. Figures may be compressed without reducing their height in order to place them in a limited space between arrowheads.

SHOP RIVETS						FIELD RIVETS	
BUTTON HEADS	COUNTERSUNK AND CHIPPED	COUNTERSUNK NOT CHIPPED	FLATTENED TO $\frac{1}{4}$ HIGH FOR $\frac{1}{2}''$ AND $\frac{5}{8}''$ RIVETS	FLATTENED TO $\frac{3}{8}$ HIGH FOR $\frac{3}{4}''$ TO $1''$ RIVETS	FULL HEADS	COUNTERSUNK AND CHIPPED	

Fig. 22.6.   Conventional Symbols for Rivets.

2. Figures can be placed to one side, with a leader to the dimension line, if the available space is very small.

3. Figures and notes must read from the bottom and the right side of the sheet because shopmen are accustomed to reading from these positions (Fig. 22.7).

4. For dimensions less than one foot, the inch marks ($''$) may be omitted (Fig. 22.9).

5. With the exception of widths of plates and depths of sections, all dimensions of one foot or more are expressed in feet and inches (Fig. 22.7).

Correct	Incorrect
$\frac{1}{4}$	$0\frac{1}{4}$
9	$0'$-$9''$
10	$10''$
$1'$-$0''$	$12''$
$2'$-$3\frac{1}{4}''$	$2'$-$03\frac{1}{4}''$
$4'$-$0\frac{1}{4}''$	$4'\frac{1}{4}''$

6. Usually, dimensions for rivet spacing are given in multiples of $\frac{1}{8}''$ or, preferably, $\frac{1}{4}''$. It is not desirable to use multiples of $\frac{1}{16}''$ or $\frac{1}{32}''$, except in rare cases.

Fig. 22.7.   Structural Dimensioning.

Courtesy American Bridge Co.

Fig. 22.8. Dimensioning a Column.

7. Decimals found in tables should be converted into fractions to the nearest $\frac{1}{16}''$ (except for machine shop drawings for gears, shafts, and so forth).

8. To avoid complications that arise when corrections are made, dimensions shown on one view should not be repeated on another.

9. Rivets and holes are located by dimensions from center to center (Fig. 22.7).

Courtesy American Bridge Co.

Fig. 22.9. Structural Dimensioning.

10. Edge distances are frequently omitted, unless they are necessary to insure clearances with connecting parts. (The shopmen understand that the distances on opposite edges are to be made equal.)

11. Dimensions *always* should be given to the center lines of I-beams and to the backs of angles and channels. (See Sec. 22.6, "gage.")

12. When three or more rivet spaces for a line of rivets are equal, they should be dimensioned as a group (4 @ 3″ = 1′-0″). Staggered rivets are dimensioned as if they were on one gage line (Fig. 22.7).

13. Since a workman must use a rule or tape to lay off angles, a slope triangle should be shown to give the inclination of a working line (Fig. 22.9).

14. A man in the shop never should be compelled to add or subtract to obtain a necessary dimension.

15. A general note is usually placed on a detail drawing giving painting instructions, size of rivets, size of open holes, reaming instructions, and so on.

16. Members that are shipped separately for field erection are given a shipping mark of a letter and number that appears on the detail drawing and on the erection plan (Fig. 22.7).

17. The size of a member is indicated by a specification (in the form of a note) parallel to it (Fig. 22.7).

18. The width of a plate is always given in inches (Fig. 22.7).

Fig. 22.10.   Steps for Making Layout of Gusset.

22.11. Procedure for making a layout of a gusset plate. The general procedure for making the layout of a gusset plate that connects two members of a roof truss to the bottom chord member is given in Fig. 22.10.   Each member is composed of two angles.

Step 1.   Calculate the slopes of the diagonal members and draw in the working lines [Fig. 22.10(1)].   Use a scale of $1\frac{1}{2}'' = 1'$ or $3'' = 1'$.   (Ordinarily the working lines will be gage lines.)

Step 2.   Determine the correct dimensions and gages (Fig. 22.13) and draw in the lines representing the outstanding and perpendicular legs of the angles on the proper sides of the working lines.   Draw in the clearance line at a preferred distance above the bottom chord angle and cut the diagonal angles perpendicular to their axes so that the corners fall on the clearance line.

Step 3.   Locate an initial rivet in each diagonal at the desired edge distance from the sheared edge of the member.   Since it is customary in structural drawing to give the distance from the working point to the first rivet, to the nearest $\frac{1}{4}''$, it usually will be found necessary to change either the edge distance or the clearance to meet this requirement. Locate the remaining rivets in each diagonal, using minimum spacing (3 × diameter of rivet), so that the plate will not be larger than is absolutely necessary.

BUTTON HEAD (a)   COUNTERSUNK HEAD (b)

Fig. 22.11.   Dimensions of Rivet Heads.

DIA. OF RIVET	EXTREME MINIMUM "e"	USUAL MINIMUM "e"	PREFERRED
$\frac{3}{8}$	$\frac{9}{16}$	$\frac{3}{4}$	$\frac{3}{4}$
$\frac{1}{2}$	$\frac{3}{4}$	1	1
$\frac{5}{8}$	$\frac{15}{16}$	$1\frac{1}{8}$	$1\frac{1}{4}$
$\frac{3}{4}$	$1\frac{1}{8}$	$1\frac{1}{4}$	$1\frac{1}{2}$
$\frac{7}{8}$	$1\frac{5}{16}$	$1\frac{1}{2}$	$1\frac{3}{4}$
1	$1\frac{1}{2}$	$1\frac{3}{4}$	2

EDGE DISTANCE "e"

Fig. 22.12.   Edge Distance "e."

Step 4.   Draw in the edges of the gusset plate, after giving some consideration to the factors involved in an economical treatment of the design.   The points to be observed are: (a) allow not less than minimum edge distance e from the center of each rivet to the nearest edge of the plate (Fig. 22.12); (b) allow no corners of the plate to project beyond the angle; (c) design the plate so that there will be a minimum number of cuts, for each cut increases the labor cost; (d) make at least two edges parallel at a distance apart equal to a standard plate width, so that unnecessary cuts and material waste may be avoided.

The shorter dimension usually is considered to be the width, and the longer dimension, the length.   If the longer dimension is across the plate between parallel sides, however, it should be given as the width, because the plate may be cut from a long plate of that width.   The length dimension usually is given to the nearest $\frac{1}{4}''$.   The dimensions of a plate are always those of a rectangle from which the plate may be cut.

22.12. Machine shop work.   The structural detailer will occasionally be called upon to prepare detail drawings for castings for bridge shoes and roadway expansion joints and at times drawings for complicated gearing and shafting for movable bridges.   Regular machine drawing practices apply, the principal difference being that bridge machinery in general is ponderous with single castings often weighing ten or fifteen tons.

MINIMUM X = 3 × DIA. OF RIVET

LEG	8	7	6	5	4	3½	3	2½	2	1¼	1½	1⅜	1¼	1	¾
GAGE G₁	4½	4	3½	3	2½	2	1¾	1⅜	1⅛	1	⅞	¾	⅝	½	
GAGE G₂	3	2½	2½	2	—	—	—	—	—	—	—	—	—	—	—
GAGE G₃	3	3	2¼	1¾	—	—	—	—	—	—	—	—	—	—	—
MAX. RIVET	1⅛	1	1	1	1	⅞	⅞	¾	⅝	½	⅜	⅜	⅜	¼	¼

Fig. 22.13.   Gage Distances.

22.13. Structural welding.   Since a large portion of structural work is either partially or completely welded, a working knowledge of the use of welding symbols (see Chapter 17) is a requirement for a structural draftsman.

Sizes and location of welds are usually given on the design drawing, but very often connections and minor details are left to the detailer.

22.14. Problems.   The following problems are intended to furnish experience in the preparation of layouts and to emphasize the principles of structural drawing.

1. Make a pencil layout, plan, and elevation, of joint A, Fig. 22.14.   Follow carefully the steps outlined in Sec. 22.11 for making a layout of a gusset plate. The following requirements must be observed.

Use $\frac{3}{4}''\ \phi$ rivets.

Make the minimum allowable clearance between members $= \frac{1}{4}''$.

Use minimum rivet spacing $= 3 \times$ diameter of rivets.

Use the preferred edge distance given in the table in Fig. 22.12.

Use standard gage distances as given in the table in Fig. 22.13.

Make the width of the plate equal to the width of a standard plate.   The variation of plate widths is by inches.

Fig. 22.14.   Roof Truss Layout.

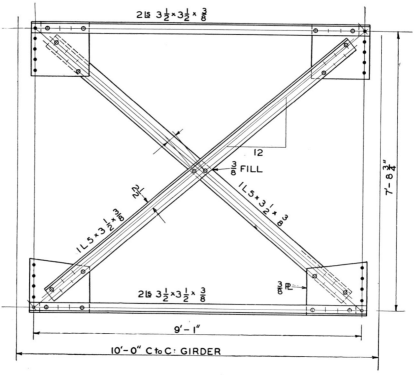

Fig. 22.15.   Layout of Interior Cross-Frame for 100 ft. Railroad Deck Girder Span.

The bearing plate is a $9'' \times \frac{3}{4}'' \times 1'\text{-}0''$ steel plate. The rivet pitch in the plan view should be equal to the pitch of the rivets in the vertical leg, and they must be so located that the distances $c, f,$ and k are equal to or exceed the minimum values for these distances for a $\frac{3}{4}''$ rivet as given in structural handbooks. The minimum value of f for a $\frac{3}{4}''$ rivet is $1\frac{1}{4}''$; the minimum value of k is $1\frac{3}{4}''$; and, the minimum value of c is $1\frac{1}{4}''$. These three values represent minimum driving clearance for a $\frac{3}{4}''$ rivet.

The holes for the anchor bolts are $\frac{13}{16}''$ in diameter. Letter the correct specifications for the gusset plate.

2. Make a pencil drawing of the cross frame shown in Fig. 22.15. The following requirements must be observed:

Use $\frac{7}{8}''$ rivets.

Use a minimum rivet pitch of $2\frac{1}{2}''$.

The elevation of the cross frame is the only view that is required.

Use standard gage and preferred edge distances as shown in Figs. 22.12 and 22.13.

Use Fig. 22.5 as a model for the placing of complete dimensions.

The open holes are spaced at $3\frac{1}{2}''$ pitch.

23

Architectural Drawing*

23.1. Introduction. The principles of architectural drafting are the same as those for other technical drawing work, except that the application of these principles requires special methods, symbols, and conventions. Architectural drawings of a building include floor plans, elevations, sections, and details sufficiently descriptive to permit the construction of the building according to the architect's ideas.

Although the architect and the architectural draftsman work hand-in-hand in the preparation of a set of plans for a structure, there is a wide gap between the experience and knowledge that each possesses. The architect may be his own draftsman, but the draftsman cannot be his own architect. The draftsman's function, therefore, is to assist in the execution of the architect's ideas. The architect must know not only how to prepare accurate working drawings, but also, he must understand the best uses of buildings from the economic and social points of view; he must know business administration so that he may understand the financial and legal transactions incident to modern building construction; he must develop a sense of proportion and a knowledge of pleasing form and color through the study of the history of architecture; he must be familiar with the mechanical trades such as plumbing, heating, electricity, and other engineering features that have such an important bearing on the safety and durability of a structure.

23.2. Preliminary studies. Before the architect or draftsman is required to draw the plans and elevations or the working drawings of the house, the owner and architect should have reached certain conclusions about the general design or style of the house, the kind of material to be used, the size, and the approximate cost of the proposed structure. While it is impossible to give an accurate schedule of costs at this point, the following is an indication of the relative percentage of the cost of materials, labor, and land involved in building the average home.

Cost of Materials.............	45.40%
Construction Labor...........	29.80%
Overhead and Profit..........	12.20%
Cost of Land................	12.60%
	100.00%

---

* Prepared by William J. Hornung, Director of Training, National Technical Institute.

562

Following is an outline that the architect may prepare for further development by himself or his draftsman after consulting with the owner.

DESIGN FOR TWO-LEVEL STONE MASONRY AND FRAME HOUSE

ROOMS—MAIN FLOOR
1. Living room with fireplace
2. Dining room
3. Kitchen
4. Storage and heater room

SECOND FLOOR
5. Two bedrooms with closets
6. Bathroom
7. Terrace or sun deck

TYPE OF CONSTRUCTION
8. Concrete footings; masonry wall construction for first floor; frame walls for second floor; red wood siding

9. Double-hung frame windows; 6 lights for each frame
10. Flat canvas deck roofs, insulated
11. Heating: one-pipe hot water; recessed convectors
12. Sewage disposal: septic tank and leaching pool
13. Provide for future breeze-way and one-car garage

23.3. Preliminary sketches. In many instances the architect will prepare for himself or submit to the draftsman a freehand sketch of the

Fig. 23.1. Preliminary Sketches.

plan showing the arrangement of rooms and indicating the approximate size of each room (Fig. 23.1). From this sketch the draftsman will prepare a preliminary drawing to a scale of $\frac{1}{8}'' = 1'\text{-}0''$. Of course, certain considerations and adjustments must be made as far as the arrangement and general dimensions of rooms are concerned, because the scale drawing will never quite work out in exact accordance with the preliminary rough sketch. When good circulation and a suitable arrangement of rooms are obtained, the draftsman will then layout the $\frac{1}{4}$-in. scale drawing of the main floor plan.

23.4. Presentation drawings. The primary purpose of presentation drawings is to give the owner a general, realistic picture of the proposed structure.   Presentation drawings may be made in several ways. One method is to prepare a perspective view of the exterior of the building, rendered in pencil, ink, or color.   Walks, shrubbery, or trees that may surround the building are included.   With the rendered perspective it is customary to show the main-floor plan giving the names and sizes of rooms in order that the client may study the room arrangement.   A rendered perspective drawing is shown in Fig. 23.2(a and b).

In place of the rendered perspective, actual scale models of the proposed buildings are finding favor with many architects.   Models are made in the drafting room, using drawing paper and cardboard, cut to size and glued together forming an exact replica of the proposed building.   The effect of shrubbery, trees, hedges, and grass can be attained by colored sponges, sawdust, and sand.   Such models are of great value to both architect and client because they can be viewed from all angles and their proportions can be studied more accurately.

23.5. Working drawings.   A set of working drawings consists of all of the drawings that are necessary for the contractor to erect the building. The set is composed of the plans, elevations, sections, details, and the lettered notes that assist in the interpretation of the drawings.   In addition to the working drawings, the contractor also receives written instructions called *the specifications.*   These specifications cover all the features that are not shown on the blueprints, such as the quality and quantity of the materials, and the methods to be used in the construction, or the manner in which the work is to be conducted.   Like the plans, the specifications are indispensable to the builder.   They are typed and accompany a set of working drawings.

23.6. The plans.   When a set of working drawings is prepared, the main-floor plan is generally drawn first, as in Fig. 23.3.   This plan is a horizontal cut taken through the building at a level half-way up the windows.   Its purpose is to show the builder the location of both outside and inside walls, their thicknesses, lengths, and the materials of which they are constructed.   The location of windows and doors, stairs and fireplace, and other data pertaining to electrical outlets, fixtures, floor finishes, and the direction and sizes of overhead floor joists are indicated.

From the main- or first-floor plan the outlines of other floor plans are traced, such as the basement or foundation plan, the second-floor plan (Fig. 23.4), or the roof plan.   Since many drawings are needed in the erection of a building, it is quite common to use a separate sheet for each plan.   Special details that apply to the particular drawing are included.

23.7. The elevations.   The primary purpose of the elevation drawings (Figs. 23.5 and 23.6) is to give the builder the height dimensions of doors, windows, floor-to-floor heights, ridge heights, chimney height, and the finished grade level in relation to the finished floor level.   On the elevations are also indicated the type of outside wall finishes, roof finishes, and the style of doors and windows.   In many cases two elevation drawings, front and side, are sufficient to give the necessary information, but it is advisable to draw the four elevations of the building when each elevation has a distinct feature that could not be clearly shown on other drawings.

Fig. 23.2(*a*). Presentation Drawing.

FIRST FLOOR PLAN

SCALE ¼" = 1'-0"

Fig. 23.2(*b*).

Fig. 23.3. First-Floor Plan.

Fig. 23.4. Second-Floor Plan.

TYPICAL DETAILS OF
DOUBLE-HUNG WINDOW
ON 2ND FLOOR
ORIGINAL SCALE 3"-1'-0"

KITCHEN ELEVATION
ORIGINAL SCALE 1/4"-1'-0"

TYPICAL DETAIL
MASONRY WALLS
ORIGINAL SCALE 1 1/2"-1'-0"

Fig. 23.5.   Elevation.

Fig. 23.6. Elevation.

23.8. The plot plan. One of the functions of a plot plan is to locate the house on the lot so that the builder knows where to begin. When a tract of land is intended for a home development site it is generally the practice to lay in public utilities, such as sewerage disposal systems, water, gas, and electricity. This necessitates a pattern of streets and avenues with sidewalks forming blocks. A block is generally understood to mean an area of land rectangular in form bounded by streets and avenues. Each block, in turn, is subdivided into lots of the same or varying sizes (Fig. 23.7). Local building regulations frequently call for certain restrictions on the "frontage" or the distance that must be maintained between the street and the location of the house on the lot. In such cases the plot plan must show the exact location of the house on the lot. In unrestricted areas a land owner may build his house without defining the location of the house on the land, as shown in Fig. 23.8. Plot plans also show where sewer lines, water, gas, and drainage lines are

Fig. 23.7.   Rectangular Block Bounded by Streets and Avenues Subdivided into Lots.

located. If driveways and walks are to be built, they must also be shown. Shrubbery, existing trees, and the points of the compass are included on a finished-plot plan.

23.9. Sections. In addition to the plans and elevations, "part sections" are often used to clarify the drawings further. These "part sections" (Fig. 23.9) are often shown on the same drawing with the elevations, but generally are of larger scale. The longitudinal or cross section is intended to show the interior construction and architectural treatment. It is a cut taken on a vertical plane through the center of the building. This cutting plane need not be continuous, but may be staggered to include as much information as possible. Longitudinal or cross sections, as shown in Fig. 23.10, are of definite value to the builder. They show him the construction of the building from the footings to the roof rafters. The type of outside-wall construction is represented by its symbols; floor and ceiling joists are clearly shown and their sizes given; partition walls, stairs, fireplace, and interior wall finishes can be indicated. Important height dimensions given from finished floor to finished ceiling are a definite aid in understanding the construction. On longitudinal sections cellar

PLOT PLAN
ORIGINAL SCALE ⅛"=1'-0"

Fig. 23.8. Plot Plan.

floor constructions can also be indicated with dimensions and specifications so that in many instances larger details are not required.

23.10. Wall sections. On smaller construction it is often desirable to draw a "wall section" in place of the longitudinal or cross section so that all the necessary height dimensions and the construction can be shown. Wall sections are drawn to scales of $\frac{1}{2}''$, $\frac{3}{4}''$, or $1'' = 1'\text{-}0''$. A wall section such as that shown in Fig. 23.11 gives the depth of the footing below grade and the dimensions of the footing and the foundation wall. The 4'' concrete floor on 6'' cinder fill, on earth, is understood to be typical throughout. The section includes a window located by dimension above the finished floor level, and the height and type is shown. The method of

SECTION OF SILL
IN BRICK VENEER
SCALE 1"=1'-0"

SECTION OF 8" BRICK WALL
SCALE 1"=1'-0"

Fig. 23.9. Part Sections.

spanning the window opening by a precast reinforced concrete lintel is indicated. The section further shows a built-up roof properly flashed to the wall. The exterior and interior wall finish can be represented by symbols and notes.

23.11. Details. A set of working drawings is never quite complete without the large-scale detail drawings. Large-scale details are made when other drawings cannot describe the construction clearly. They are drawn to a scale of full size, half size, $3'' = 1'\text{-}0''$, $1\frac{1}{2}'' = 1'\text{-}0''$, $1'' = 1'\text{-}0''$, $\frac{3}{4}'' = 1'\text{-}0''$, $\frac{1}{2}'' = 1'\text{-}0''$. Typical details, such as that shown for the small house (Fig. 23.12), include the elevation of the fireplace wall in the living room, special lighting fixtures, entrance door details, and other details that can be clearly described but could not be shown on other drawings at smaller scales. For larger buildings many additional detail drawings must be prepared, as illustrated in the window detail in Fig. 23.13. To be able to prepare good detail drawings the draftsman needs

Fig. 23.10. Longitudinal Section.

LIMESTONE COPING

¼" THREADED BRASS DOWELS 2 PER SECTION.

5"

ASPHALT COATED OR CEM. COATED

16 OZ COPPER CAP FLASHING

2'-3"

4-PLY BUILT-UP ROOFING CAP SHEET FINISH

1"X6" SHIPLAP ROOF BOARDS

2"X4" BUILT-UP ROOF 16" O C

2"X4" STRUTS EVERY 4TH JOIST

1" CEMENT FINISH

2"X10" D.F. JOISTS 16" O.C WITH 1¼"X3" X-BRDNG NOT OVER 8'-0" APART

BRICK

8"X8" REINF. CONC. LINTEL

⅝" Ø RODS

FIRE RETARDED WITH METAL LATH & ¾" CEM. PLASTER

6'-2⅝" MASONRY OPENING

9'-6" TOP OF ALL WINDOWS

10'-6"

LIMESTONE COPING

3'-3⅝"

8" CON. BL. WALL

GRADE

FIN. FL.

4" CON. FL.

6" CINDER FILL

CONC. F'D'N WALL

4'-0"

6"   12"   6"

CONC. FOOTING

12"

TYPICAL WALL SECTION

SCALE ¾"=1'-0"

Fig. 23.11.   Wall Section.

ELEVATION OF FIREPLACE WALL (LIVING ROOM)
ORIGINAL SCALE 3/8"=1'-0"

PLYWOOD
HOMASOTE FINISH
BOILER FLUE
1/2"x4"
WHITE PINE BATTENS
3 PLY 1/4" PLYWOOD
COMMON RED BRICK
DAMPER
FIELD STONE

DETAIL PLAN OF DIAGONAL WINDOW
ORIGINAL SCALE 3/8"=1'-0"

LIVING ROOM FIXTURE
ORIGINAL SCALE: 1"=1'-0"
CENTER OF 2"x8"
2"x8"
PLASTER
ROCK WOOL
BLOCKING
POLISHED COPPER

DINING ROOM FIXTURE
ORIGINAL SCALE: 1"=1'-0"
OUTLET BOX
CIRCULAR FROSTED GLASS
POLISHED COPPER

FLUSH DOOR
SCALE: 1/2"=1'-0"
ORIGINAL

MAIN ENTRANCE DOOR
DETAIL OF HEAD
SECTION C-C
SCALE: 1 1/2"=1'-0"
ORIGINAL
STOCK FLUSH DOOR
FIXED SASH

DETAIL OF PIPE RAIL
ORIGINAL SCALE: 3/4"=1'-0"
1" O.D. PIPE RAIL
SHOE
SET IN WHITE LEAD
SCREWS

Fig. 23.12. Typical Details.

SECTION

SCALE ¾"=1'-0"

Fig. 23.13. Window Detail.

much experience in the use of trade literature, catalogs, and books dealing with the principles of construction. It might be well to mention here that in order to draw complex details the draftsman is largely dependent upon manufacturers' information and previous similar drawings.

23.12. Special features. In present-day building construction, many parts that are used are manufactured by firms specializing in one particular item. As an example, wood sash details vary with different manufacturers. The architect gets scale details from the makers and draws his building to conform. Figure 23.14 shows a detail of a double-hung window and a table of cellar window and picture window sizes as supplied by the manufacturer. Other items such as stair parts, doors, railings, fans, radiators, heating equipment, and many other special features are always planned from drawings supplied by the manufacturers.

23.13. Symbols. The working drawings for a structure are composed largely of symbols and conventions representing manufactured items and materials. For example, in a plan a foundation wall made up of concrete block has a symbol of cross lines and dots. This symbol is universally understood to mean concrete blocks. The symbol for concrete is represented by small triangles, circles, and dots representing crushed stone or gravel, sand, and cement. All architects, draftsmen, and builders understand these symbols that form a language of lines and correlate thought in the trade. Many symbols for materials have been standardized by the American Standards Association to facilitate understanding. Some of the new materials that have been added to the building industry in recent years have not as yet been standardized. When such materials are used on drawings a key to the materials must be included with the work. Figure 23.15 shows materials and conventions that have been standardized.

23.14. Dimensioning. Dimensioning of the working plans and elevations is governed primarily by knowledge of building construction. Dimensions must be so placed that they are most convenient for the workman. On plans it is desirable to show dimensions around the outside of the plan whenever possible. Inside dimensions are generally those locating partitions, columns, beams, doors, or other openings. Dimensions on frame plans are given from the outside faces of studs on exterior walls to the center line of the window or door opening. Stud partitions may be located to the center of the partition or to the stud face. On masonry, outside walls dimensions are given from the outer face of the wall to the opening of the window or door, then across the opening. Masonry wall openings, such as doors and windows, may also be dimensioned to the center line of the opening. The elevations or cross sections must give the height or vertical dimensions of floors, windows, beams, roofs, and chimney. The plans in Figs. 23.3 and 23.4 and the elevations and cross section in Figs. 23.5, 23.6, and 23.10 should be carefully studied by the student before he attempts to place dimensions on a drawing.

23.15. Special notes. In addition to the written specifications furnished the contractor, special notes are lettered on the drawings to clarify the work. Builders are apt to overlook a point mentioned only in the

HEAD

SIDE

$1\frac{3}{8}$" SASH

SILL

HEIGHT

BASEMENT
WINDOW SIZES

2813
2817
2820

DOUBLE-HUNG
WINDOW
DETAILS

PICTURE WINDOW SIZES AND DETAILS

342 542 343 543 344
352 552 353 553 354

COURTESY   ANDERSEN   CORP.,   BAYPORT, MINN

Fig. 23.14. Drawings Supplied by the Manufacturer.

specifications, but because they are using the drawings constantly they will be sure to see a reference or note on the drawing of the part in question. It is also common practice to use "schedules"—notes laid out in tabular form.   The finish schedule shown in Fig. 23.16 gives finish treatments of rooms, floors, and ceilings.   Door schedules and window schedules are

Fig. 23.15. Symbols and Conventions.

also commonly used on drawings so that the work will be better understood by the tradesmen.

23.16. Lettering. The lettering on drawings is as important as the plans of the building, because without lettered explanatory notes, titles, and dimensions, the plans could hardly be understood. The single stroke architectural letter shown in Fig. 23.17 is typical of that used by the architect. The style is closely related to the old Roman form. It is becoming increasingly evident that single stroke upper-case architectural letters are gaining favor over the lower-case form and the trend is towards letters that resemble more closely the mechanical style of letter used in previous chapters of this text. In large architectural firms where many draftsmen are employed, mechanical guides are used for lettering in order to minimize individuality of style of the draftsman and to make the drawings more consistent in character. Another type of lettering the architect is called upon to execute is the *incised* or the old Roman style

FINISH SCHEDULE						
ROOM	FLOOR	BASE	WAINSCOT	WALLS	CEILING	TRIM
SALES	CONCRETE	WOOD PAINTED	PLASTER PAINTED		PLASTER PAINTED	WOOD PAINTED
TOILETS	CERAMIC TILE	CERAMIC TILE	CERAMIC TILE	PLASTER PAINTED	PLASTER PAINTED	WOOD PAINTED
STORAGE	CONCRETE	NONE	MASONRY CLEANED UNPAINTED		CEMENT PLASTER UNPAINTED	WOOD PAINTED
SERVICE ROOMS	CONCRETE	NONE	MASONRY PAINTED		CEMENT PLASTER PAINTED	WOOD PAINTED
NOTE:	FOR COLOR OF PAINT AND NUMBER OF COATS SEE SPECIFICATIONS					

Fig. 23.16. Finish Schedule.

ABCDEFGHIJKLMN
OPQRSTUVWXYZ&

1234567890

COMPRESSED FORM *for* LIMITED SPACE

INCISED

Fig. 23.17. Architectural Lettering.

that is used when letters are cut into stone, bronze, or other material used in connection with design (Fig. 23.17).

23.17. Problems. The following problems permit the student to prepare the necessary working drawings for building construction and introduce him to the study of Architectural Design. The problems may be modified or amplified by the teacher to the particular student needs.

1. Draw the first-floor plan of a small house similar to the one represented in Fig. 23.3. The student may modify the plan or create one of his own design.

It is advisable first to prepare rough, freehand thumbnail sketches of the plan to study room arrangements, window locations, and space for furniture. Have instructor check preliminary sketches and then proceed to draw a $\frac{1}{8}''$ scale plan. After studying the plan again, proceed with the final $\frac{1}{4}'' = 1'\text{-}0''$ scale plan and dimension it completely. Check Fig. 23.3 for conventional representations of windows, doors, fireplace, stairs, fixtures, and material symbols.

2. Draw the foundation plan of the house to a scale of $\frac{1}{4}'' = 1'\text{-}0''$. Indicate concrete footings, foundation walls, footing for chimney, lally columns, if any, and windows. Completely letter and dimension the plan.

3. Draw the remaining two elevations of the house shown in Figs. 23.5 and 23.6. Refer to the plans in Figs. 23.3 and 23.4. Use scale of $\frac{1}{4}'' = 1'\text{-}0''$. Particular attention should be given to the conventional representations of windows on the elevation, and the important height dimensions.

4. Draw the detail of a window used in the plan of your own design showing the head section, jamb, and sill, to a scale of either $1\frac{1}{2}'' = 1'\text{-}0''$, or $3'' = 1'\text{-}0''$. Refer to window detail Fig. 23.13 or 23.14. Indicate the rough openings and sash openings. These dimensions can be secured from manufacturers' catalogs.

5. Draw the front elevation to the plan drawn in problem 1, to a scale of $\frac{1}{4}'' = 1'\text{-}0''$. Make preliminary sketches of the elevation and have them checked by the instructor before proceeding with the scale drawing. Check Figs. 23.5 and 23.6 for correct window conventions in elevation and symbols for exterior treatment. Place the necessary height dimensions on your drawing.

6. Draw a side elevation for the plan drawn in problem 1, to a scale of $\frac{1}{4}'' = 1'\text{-}0''$. Heights, such as floor, grade, ceiling, and roof may be projected from the front elevation. Make use of the plans for location of windows and doors.

7. Make the framing plans of the house of your design. Trace the outline of the foundation plan in problem 2, and select joist sizes from standard tables on "Joist Spans and Sizes." Double the floor joists where partitions run parallel to the joists. Study the framing around stairwell and chimney openings.

8. Draw a longitudinal cross section through the house of your design. Use scale of $\frac{1}{4}'' = 1'\text{-}0''$. Refer to plans and elevations for lengths and heights. Take section through stair and fireplace if possible. Use Fig. 23.10 for reference. Indicate all material by proper symbol and dimension section completely.

9. To a scale of $1\frac{1}{2}'' = 1'\text{-}0''$, draw a wall section showing the footing, foundation wall, sill construction, window-in-wall section, and cornice construction. Show all necessary dimensions. Refer to Fig. 23.11 for methods of dimensioning.

10. Draw any details necessary to clarify fully the working drawings completed. For suggestions as to the type of details, refer to Fig. 23.12.

24

Topographic and Engineering Map Drawing

24.1. Map drawing. A map is a drawing that represents a portion of the earth's surface area. Since it usually represents a relatively small part, and the third dimension (the height) is not shown except in some cases by contour lines, a map may be thought of as a one-view orthographic projection (Fig. 24.1). Various forms of maps have been devised to satisfy different requirements. Land maps, plats, and so on, which fulfill their purpose

Fig. 24.1. A Section from an Engineering Map.

by revealing only the natural and man-made features along with imaginary division lines and geometrical measurements, show only two dimensions. Others, such as topographical maps, show three dimensions, by representing height by means of contours.

24.2. Classification of maps. Maps of interest to the engineer may be grouped for study into four general classes, in accordance with their purpose and method of preparation. The recognized classes are: (1) topographical, (2) cadastral, (3) engineering, and (4) aerial photographic.

24.3. Topographic maps. Topographic maps, although they are drawn to a relatively small scale, contain much detail. All natural features, such as lakes, streams, forests, fields, mines, and so on, and important permanent man-made creations, such as buildings, bridges, and houses, may be represented if necessary to fulfill the purpose of a map. Topographic maps, prepared by the United States Geological Survey to a scale of approximately one inch to a mile $\left(\dfrac{1}{62,500}\right)$, naturally do not contain very much detail. The form of the surface of the ground is represented by contour lines. Any one contour line passes through points of the same elevation and closes either on the map or beyond its limits. Closed contour lines represent either a hill or a depression. Figure 24.5 shows a topographic map.

24.4. Cadastral maps. The major portion of this group consists of city plats, city development maps, town maps, county maps, and maps prepared to show ownership (particularly for the purpose of governmental control and for taxation). These maps, although they show practically no detail, must be accurate and for this reason are drawn to a large scale. Property lines, political boundaries, and a few important features, such as streams, roads, and towns, may be given on township and county maps, to enable a reader to identify particular locations.

24.5. Engineering maps. Working maps prepared for engineering projects are known as engineering maps. They may be drawn for either reconnaissance or construction purposes. They usually are made to a large scale, and accurately show the location of all property lines and important features. On maps of a topographic nature, practically all natural and man-made features along a right-of-way or on a site are shown, and the form of the surface of the ground is indicated by means of contours.

24.6. Plats of land surveys. A plat of a tract of land should contain a complete description of the land surveyed. It should show the lengths and bearings of the bounding sides and division lines, the included acreages, the locations of the monuments, and the names of the owners of the adjoining properties. Figure 24.2 shows a plat of a typical land survey. Note that a clear, concise title is lettered in the large open area. A certification of the survey is generally required by law. In most states, a plat must bear the seal of a licensed surveyor.

24.7. Subdivision plats. A plat of a real-estate development should show the measurements and angles of the survey of the whole tract of land, the size of the included lots, the widths of the streets and drives, and the location of all monuments. Plats of subdivisions must be complete and accurate, since they are filed as a public record in the county recorder's office. Sufficient information must be given to enable a surveyor to locate the corners of any lot with precision when making a re-survey at a later date. Figure 24.3 is a plat of a city subdivision.

24.8. Plats and partial city maps. Plats made from subdivision plats or city maps are prepared by the engineering departments of cities and public utilities. The purpose of these partial maps is to record special information concerning such things as proposed improvement projects, the location of lines of transportation, and the location of existing and proposed water mains, sewers, and so on. It is not necessary for such a map to contain all the information given on the subdivision plat from

Fig. 24.2.   A Plat of a Land Survey.

Fig. 24.4.   A Plat or Partial City Map Showing the Proposed Location of Water Mains and Fire Hydrants.

which it is made. The location of monuments and angles generally is not shown. The widths of streets and the sizes of lots may or may not be shown, depending upon the usefulness of such information. A few important buildings may be indicated for the sake of aiding the reader in orienting himself. Figure 24.4 shows the proposed location of water mains and fire hydrants in a portion of a city.

24.9. Topographic drawing. As previously stated, a topographic map is a reproduction, to scale, of a small area. On a complete topographic map, the natural and artificial features are represented by recognized conventional symbols and the form of the ground is shown by contours. Excessive detail should be avoided, and only necessary surface features should be shown. All names and required notes should be lettered in a position where they can be easily read; a complete title should be lettered in the lower right-hand corner. Ordinarily, single-stroke Reinhardt lettering is preferable on topographic maps prepared solely for construction projects, while vertical modern Roman is more desirable on finished maps where effect and pleasing appearance are important. Figure 24.5 shows a topographic map.

The scale to be used for a topographic map depends upon the size of the area and the amount of the detail that must be shown. Scales range from 1 inch = 100 feet to 1 inch = 4 miles. Maps prepared by the United States Geological Survey are usually drawn to 1:62,500, which is almost one inch to a mile.

24.10. Standard topographic symbols (U.S.G.S.). Recognized signs and symbols are used to represent the natural and artificial features on a topographic map. Many of these symbols have been designed to bear some pictorial resemblance to the feature or object represented and, for convenience, may be grouped as follows: (1) physical features (buildings, highways, railroads, and so on); (2) ground formations (elevations and depressions); (3) water-surface features (rivers, lakes, and streams); and (4) vegetation growths (grass, trees, and cultivated crops).

Conventional symbols used by the United States Geological Survey for representing the works and structures of man are shown in Fig. 24.6. Symbols for natural land formations, water features, and vegetation growths, both natural and cultivated, are shown in Figs. 24.7 to 24.9.

24.11. The drawing of symbols. Topographic symbols are drawn either freehand or mechanically, depending upon the character of the features to be represented. For example, the symbols representing natural features are drawn freehand, while those representing artificial works are drawn mechanically. (See Figs. 24.6 to 24.9.) On topographic maps prepared for engineering projects, the symbols are drawn in India ink. When colors are used, as in finished maps, the artificial features (buildings, bridges, railroads, and so on) are drawn in black, the contours in brown, the water features in blue, and vegetation growths in green.

Although the size of symbols may vary somewhat with the size of the map, they are never to scale but are always exaggerations. The usual mistake of the beginner is to draw symbols too large or too close together. Either fault produces a disagreeable appearance and tends to attract the reader's attention away from more important features. The symbols representing prominent features are made to stand out from those of lesser importance by being drawn slightly larger and with heavier lines.

The beginner should study carefully the symbols as given in the various illustrations, so as not to miss some of the essential points in their construction. For instance, he should note that the symbol for a tree (Fig. 24.9) is composed of separate lines, irregularly located, and not of

Fig. 24.5. A Topographic Map.*

one closed line drawn without lifting the pen. The symbols for grass, corn, and other vegetation should be placed with the bases of the tufts and stocks parallel to the lower border line.

24.12. The drawing of water lines. Water lining, used to indicate water surfaces, is done entirely freehand with an ordinary lettering pen. The starting line (shore line) should be fairly heavy, and each successive

_____

* A portion of a topographic map taken from a manual prepared by the U.S. Department of the Interior.

House

Building
any Kind

Unimproved Highway

Single Track

City or Town

Church

School

Improved Highway

Double Track

Trail

Electric Railroad

Ferry

Highway
Bridge

Railroad
Bridge

Ford

Dam

Telephone-Telegraph
Line

Power Line

State Line

County Line

Township Line

City Corporate Limits

State
Capitol

County
Seat

Town

Fence (Any Kind)

Rail Fence

Barbed Wire Fence

Smooth Wire Fence

Stone Fence

Hedge Fence

Cemetery

Mine
Quarry

Shaft

Mine Tunnel
Opening

Direction of
Mine Tunnel

Oil or Gas
Wells

Tanks

Cut

Embankment

Levee

Army, Navy, or Marine Corps Field

Dept. of Commerce Intermediate Field

Commercial or Municipal Field

Revolving Beacon

Flashing Beacon

Marked Auxiliary Field

From Standard Symbols, *published by the U.S. Geological Survey*

Fig. 24.6. Standard Symbols for Works and Structures.

Fig. 24.7.   Relief (Natural Land Formations).

Contours   Depression   Hill   Hachures *
                Contours   Contours

Bluffs   Sand   Sand   Glaciers
                                  Dunes

Stream   River   Lake   Rapids

Tidal Swamp   Cypress Swamp   Fresh-Water   Salt-Water
                                  Swamp   Swamp

Fig. 24.8.   Hydrographic Symbols.

Trees   Trees   Willows   Orchard
Deciduous   Coniferous

Meadow   Cultivated   Corn   Cotton

Fig. 24.9.   Vegetation Symbols.

line should decrease in width until the center of the body of water is reached. (See Fig. 24.8.) The line next to the shore line should be drawn parallel to it throughout its entire length, and the space between should be equal to the width of the shore line. The spacing between suc-

* From topographic map shown in Fig. 24.5.

ceeding lines should increase gradually to the center, but the change
should be so slight that no marked increase will be noticeable.   Each
added line should show fewer of the small irregularities of the shore line,
the last few following only the prominent ones.

If several bodies of water are to be indicated on the same map, a good
way to obtain uniformity is to draw all the shore lines first, then all the
lines next to the shore lines, and so on, working back and forth from one

Fig. 24.10.   A Contour Map of a Small Area.

body of water to another until the representations are completed.   Excessive waviness gives these lines an unnatural appearance and should be
avoided.

24.13.   Contour lines.   A contour line is a line through points of the
same elevation on the surface of the ground.   Theoretically, the contour
lines on a map may be thought of as the lines of intersection of a series of
horizontal planes and the ground surface.   In practice, the imaginary
planes are equally spaced vertically so that the contour intervals will be
equal and the horizontal distances between contours on a map will indicate the steepness of the rise or descent of the surface.   The closer they
are together, the greater the slope, and conversely, the farther they are
apart, the less the slope.   An arrangement of contour lines that close
indicates either a hill or a depression.   The case, whatever it is, usually

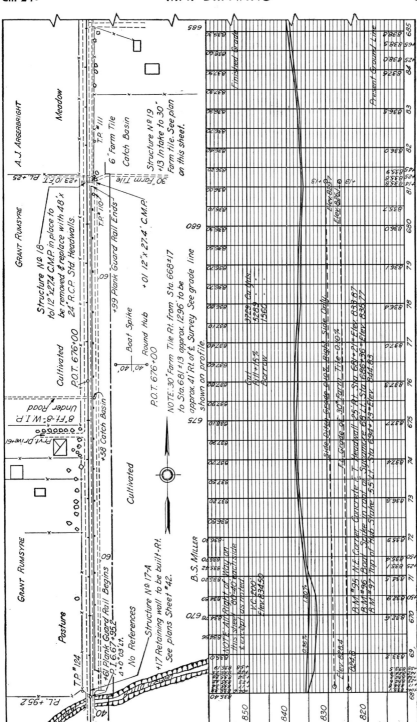

Fig. 24.11. A Sheet Showing a Plan and Profile of a Proposed Highway Project.

can be determined by reading the values of the elevations of the contours. Usually, each fifth contour is drawn heavier than the others and has a break in it where its elevation above a datum plane is recorded.   If a U.S.G.S. bench mark is used, the datum plane will be at mean sea level.

The selection of the contour interval (vertical distance between contour planes) for a topographic survey is determined by the nature of the ground forms and the purpose for which the map will be prepared.   For instance, if the area is relatively level, a one- or two-foot interval probably would be desirable while, if the area is rugged, an interval of fifty feet or even one hundred feet might be used.

Contour lines are plotted from survey notes made in the field.   In the case of small areas, the usual method for locating contours is to divide the area into squares and take level readings at every intersection and at intermediate points where a pronounced change in slope takes place (Fig. 24.10).   On the assumption that the slope of the ground is uniform between two points, the contours are sketched in by interpolating between the readings to establish the points at which the contours cross the survey lines.   The interpolation may be done by eye or by calculation.

Frequently, contours are determined from level readings taken along known lines or from stadia survey notes.   When extreme accuracy is necessary and the land is fairly level, contours are established by finding and locating points directly on each contour.

24.14. Profiles.   The profile of a line is prepared to show the relative elevation of every point on the line.   Theoretically, it may be thought of as a view showing the line of intersection of a vertical plane through the line and the ground surface.   Figure 24.11 shows a plan view and a profile of a section of a proposed highway project.   Profiles are plotted to an exaggerated vertical scale, in order to magnify the relative differences in elevations of points along the line.   When the plan and profile are on the same sheet, as in the illustration, the horizontal scale for the profile should be the same as the scale for the plan view ($1'' = 100$) and the vertical scale should be 10 or 20 feet to the inch, depending upon the amount of vertical exaggeration needed to emphasize surface irregularities. In deciding upon the vertical scale to be used, a draftsman should determine the range of elevations and then should make his selection so that the heavy horizontal lines represent full feet at regular intervals such as 820, 830, 840, and so on.   In cases where it is impossible to plot a profile within the range of the grid, it is permissible to break the profile at a heavy vertical line and start again at a lower level.   When the line is broken in this way, however, it is necessary to indicate the changed range of elevations by lettering in the new values for the heavy horizontal lines to the right of the "break line."

Profiles are drawn by plotting elevations computed from level readings taken at regular intervals on the ground and at points where the ground changes in slope.   Since the slope between adjacent points is assumed to be uniform, a profile consists of a series of straight lines joining successive points.

25 | Engineering Graphs and Charts

25.1. A properly designed graphical representation will convey correlated data and facts to an average individual more rapidly and effectively than a verbal, written, or tabulated description, because a visual impression is easily comprehended and requires less mental effort than would be necessary to ascertain the facts from complex tables and reports (Fig. 25.1). It is

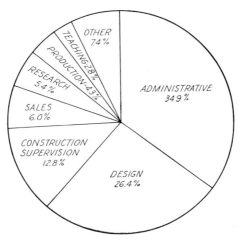

PROFESSIONAL ENGINEERS
THE KIND OF WORK THEY DO

Fig. 25.1. A Pie Chart.

because of this that diverse kinds of graphs and charts have been developed to present scientific, statistical, and technical information. Note how quickly the relationship presented by the line graph in Fig. 25.2 can be interpreted.

Engineers, even though they are concerned mainly with technical graphs, should be familiar also with the popular forms, for every industrial concern frequently must prepare popular types of graphs in order to strengthen their relationship with the public.

It is impossible to treat exhaustively the subject of graphical representation in a single chapter. Only a few of the most common forms used to analyze economic, scientific, and technical data can be discussed in detail.   Many of the principles followed in the construction of engineering graphs, however, apply to the other types.

As much drafting skill is required in the execution of a graph as in making any other type of technical drawing.   Good appearance is important and can be achieved only with the help of good lettering and smooth, uniform, and properly contrasted lines.

Courtesy Blast Furnace and Steel Plant Magazine

Fig. 25.2.   An Engineering Graph Prepared for Publication.

25.2.   Classification of charts, graphs, and diagrams.   Graphs, charts, and diagrams may be divided into two classes in accordance with their use, and then further subdivided according to type.   When classified according to use, the two divisions are, first, those used for strictly scientific and technical purposes and, second, those used for the purpose of popular appeal.   The classification according to type is as follows:

    1. Rectilinear charts
    2. Semilogarithmic charts
    3. Logarithmic charts
    4. Barographs, area, and volume charts
    5. Percentage charts
    6. Polar charts
    7. Trilinear charts
    8. Alignment charts (nomographs)
    9. Pictorial charts

25.3.   Quantitative and qualitative charts and graphs.   In general, charts and diagrams are used for one of two purposes, either to read values or to present a comparative picture relationship between variables.

If a chart or graph is prepared for reading values, it is called a *quantitative* graph; if prepared for presenting a comparative relationship, it is called *qualitative*. Obviously, some charts serve both purposes and cannot be classified strictly as either type. One of these purposes, however, must be predominant. Since a number of features in the preparation depend upon the predominant purpose, such purpose must be determined before attempting to construct a graph.

25.4. Ordinary rectangular co-ordinate graphs. Most engineering graphs, prepared for laboratory and office use, are drawn on ruled rectangular graph paper and are plotted in the first quadrant (upper right-hand), with the intersection of the X (horizontal) axis and Y (vertical) axis at the lower left used as the zero point or origin of co-ordinates. The paper is ruled with equispaced horizontal and vertical lines, forming small rectangles. The type most commonly used for chart work in experimental engineering is $8\frac{1}{2}'' \times 11''$ and is ruled to form one-twentieth-inch

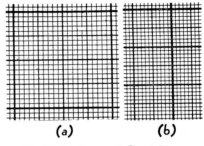

(a)   (b)

Fig. 25.3.   Types of Graph Paper.

squares (Fig. 25.3a), every fifth line being heavy. Another type of paper frequently used, which is suitable for most laboratory reports in technical schools, has rulings that form one-millimeter and one-centimeter squares

Fig. 25.4.   Rectangular Graph.

(Fig. 25.3b). Other rulings run $\frac{1}{16}''$, $\frac{1}{8}''$, or $\frac{1}{4}''$ apart. Ordinarily the ruled lines are spaced well apart on charts prepared for reproduction in popular and technical literature (Fig. 25.2). The principal advantage of having greater spacing between the lines is that large squares or rectangles tend to make the graph easier to read. Ready printed graph papers are available with various rulings in several colors.

Fig. 25.5. Independent and Dependent Variables.

Ordinary co-ordinate line graphs are used extensively because they are easily constructed and easily read. The known relationship between the variables is expressed by one or more continuous lines, which may be straight, broken, or curved.

The graph in Fig. 25.4 shows the approximate barometric pressure at different heights above sea level.

A graphical representation may be drawn easily and correctly if, after the required data have been assembled, careful consideration is given to the principles of curve drawing discussed in the following articles.

Fig. 25.6. Stress-Strain Diagram.

25.5. The determination of the variables for ordinate and abscissa. The independent variable, the quantity arbitrarily varied during the experiment, usually is chosen for the abscissa (Fig. 25.5). Certain kinds of experimental data, however, such as a stress-strain diagram (Fig. 25.6), are plotted with the independent variable along the ordinate.

25.6. The selection of suitable scales. * The American Society of Mechanical Engineers in a standard for engineering and scientific graphs recommends:

(*a*) Very careful consideration should be given to the choice of scales since this has a controlling influence on the slope of the curve. The slope of the curve, as a whole and also at intermediate points, provides a visual impression of the degree of change in the dependent variable for a given increment in the independent variable. Creating the right impression of the relationship to be shown by a line graph is, therefore, probably controlled more critically by the relative stretching of the vertical and horizontal scales than by any other feature involved in the design of the graph.

(*b*) The range of scales should be chosen to insure effective and efficient use of the co-ordinate area in attaining the objective of the chart.

(*c*) The zero line should be included, if visual comparison of plotted magnitudes is desired.

(If the chart is quantitative, the intersection of the axes need not be at the origin of co-ordinates. If it is qualitative, however, both the ordinate and abscissa generally should have zero value at the intersection of the axes, as in Fig. 25.2.)

(*d*) For arithmetic scales, the scale numbers shown on the graph and space between co-ordinate rulings should preferably correspond to 1, 2, or 5 units of measurement, multiplied or divided by 1, 10, 100, etc.

(Other units could be used except for the fact that they create situations where it becomes difficult to interpolate values. For example, one square should equal one of the following.)

0.01	0.1	1	10	100	etc.
0.02	0.2	2	20	200	etc.
0.04	0.4	4	40	400	etc.
0.05	0.5	5	50	500	etc.
etc.	etc.	etc.	etc.	etc.	etc.

(*e*) The horizontal (independent variable) scale values should usually increase from left to right and the vertical (dependent variable) from bottom to top.

25.7. Locating the axes and marking the values of the variables. On graphs prepared for laboratory reports and not for publication, the axes should be located 1″ or more inside the border of the co-ordinate ruling. (See Fig. 25.7.) When selecting the scale units and locating the axes, it should be remembered that the abscissa may be taken either the long way or short way of the co-ordinate paper, depending upon the range of the scales.

Concerning the numbers, the ASME standard recommends:

The use of many digits in scale numbers should be avoided. This can usually be accomplished by a suitable designation in the scale caption.

---

* These statements were abstracted from the American Standard for Engineering and Scientific Graphs for Publication (ASA Z15.3–1943).

EXAMPLE: PRESSURE, MM. OF HG. $\times 10^{-5}$; RESISTANCE, THOUSANDS OF OHMS.

The numbers should read from the bottom when possible (Fig. 25.7). For the sake of good appearance, they never should be crowded.   Always

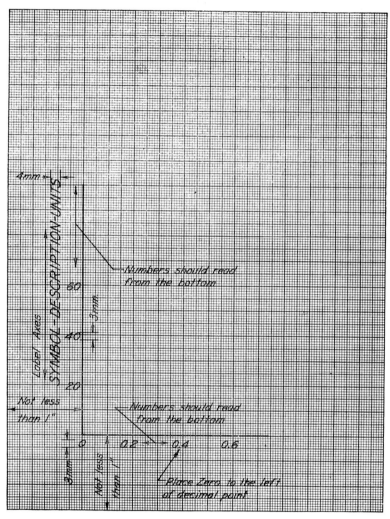

Fig. 25.7.   Graph Construction.

place a cipher to the left of the decimal point when the quantity is less than one.

Usually, only the heavy co-ordinate lines are marked to indicate their values or distance from the origin, and, even then, the values may be shown only at a regular selected interval.   (See Fig. 25.7.)   These numbers should be placed to the left of the Y-axis and just below the X-axis.

When several curves representing different variables are to appear on the same graph, a separate axis generally is required for each variable. (See Fig. 25.8.) In this case, a corresponding description should be given along each axis. The axes should be grouped at the left or at the bottom of the graph, unless it is desirable to place some at the right or along the top.

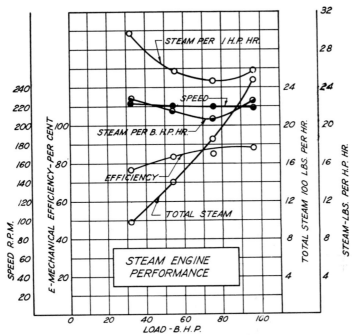

Fig. 25.8. Representation of Several Curves on a Graph.

25.8. Indicating plotted points representing the data. If the data represent a set of experimental observations, the plotted points of a single-curve graph should be marked by small circles approximately 0.1″ in diameter (see Fig. 25.9). The following practice is recommended: open circles, filled-in circles, and partially filled-in circles (○ ● ◐) rather than crosses, squares, and triangles should be used to differentiate observed points of several curves on a graph. Filled-in symbols may be made smaller than those not filled in.

Mathematical curves are frequently drawn without distinguishing marks at computed positions.

Fig. 25.9. Identification Symbols.

25.9. Drawing a curve. Since most physical phenomena are continuous, curves on engineering graphs usually represent an average of plotted points. (See Fig. 25.10.) Discontinuous data should be plotted with a broken line, as shown in Fig. 25.11.

It is preferable to represent curves by solid lines. If more than one curve appears on a graph, differentiation may be secured by varied types of lines; but the most important curve should be represented by a solid one.   A very fine line should be used for a quantitative curve if values are to be read accurately.   A heavy line ($\frac{1}{40}''$ width) is recommended for a qualitative curve.   It should be observed in Figs. 25.10 and 25.11 that the curve line does not pass through open circles.

For ordinary qualitative graphs, the ASME standard proposes:

(*a*) When more than one curve is presented on a graph, relative emphasis or differentiation of the curves may be secured by using different types of line, i.e., solid, dashed, dotted, etc.   A solid line is recommended for the most important curve.

(*b*) When more than one curve is presented on a graph, each should bear a suitable designation.

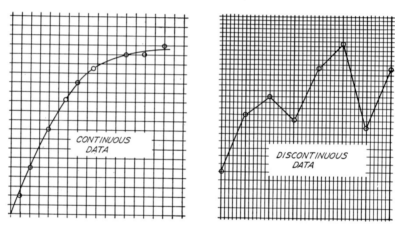

Fig. 25.10.   Continuous Curve.   Fig. 25.11.   Discontinuous Data.

(*c*) Curves should, if practicable, be designated by brief labels placed close to the curves (horizontally or along the curves) rather than by letters, numbers or other devices requiring a key.   [See Fig. 25.8.]

25.10. The labeling of the scales.   Each scale caption should give a description of the variable represented and the unit of measurement. The captions on engineering graphs frequently contain an added identifying symbol such as "N-EFFICIENCY-PER CENT" or "P-OUTPUT-H.P."

All lettering should be readable from the bottom and right side of the graph (not the left side).   When space is limited, standard abbreviations should be used, particularly for designating the unit of measurement. To avoid confusing the reader, the draftsman should use only recognized word contractions.

25.11. Titles, legends, notes, and so on.   The title of a graph should be clear, concise, complete, and symmetrical.   It should give the name of the curve, the source of the data, the date, and other important information (Fig. 25.12).   It should be so placed that it gives a balanced effect to the completed drawing.   (See Fig. 25.2.)   In addition to the title, a wiring diagram, pictorial diagram, formula, or explanatory note is often necessary to give a clear picture of the nature of the experiment.

For example, if there is any great irregularity in the plotted points or a condition that may have affected the values as shown by the data, a note of explanation should be given. A legend or key is sometimes included to explain a set of curves in greater detail.

STRESS - STRAIN DIAGRAM
FOR
COMPRESSION
IN
CAST IRON

Fig. 25.12.   A Title.

In commercial practice, alcohol is often used to clear a rectangular area of co-ordinate lines in order that the title may be printed in an open space.

25.12. Procedure for making a graphical representation in ink.

1. Select the type of co-ordinate paper.

2. Determine the variables for ordinate and abscissa.

3. Determine the scale units.

4. Locate the axes and mark the scale values in pencil.

5. Plot the points representing the data.   [Many draftsmen ink the symbol (○ ◑) indicating the points at this stage.]

6. Draw the curve.   If the curve is to strike an average among the plotted points, a trial curve should be drawn in pencil.   If the curve consists of a broken line, as is the case with discontinuous data, the curve need not be drawn until the graph is traced in ink.

7. Label the axes directly in ink.

8. Letter the title, notes, and so on.   The title should be lettered on a trial sheet that can be used as a guide for lettering directly in ink on the graph.

9. Check the work and complete the diagram by tracing the curve in ink.

25.13. Logarithmic graphs.   Logarithmic co-ordinate graphs are constructed on prepared paper on which the parallel horizontal and parallel vertical rulings are spaced proportional to the logarithms of numbers (Fig. 25.13).   This type of graph has two principal advantages over the ordinary co-ordinate type.   First, the error in plotting or reading values is a constant percentage, and, second, an algebraic equation of the form $y = ax^b$ appears as a straight line if x has a value other than 0. The exponent b may be either plus or minus.

The equation for a falling body, $D = \frac{1}{2}gt^2$, is represented in Figs. 25.13 and 25.14.   A practical application of interest to engineers is in the design of drop hammers.   In this equation, based on uniform accelerated motion, t represents time in seconds and D the distance traveled in t seconds by a freely falling body with no initial velocity.   Observe that the plotted points form a parabolic curve on ordinary co-ordinate graph paper, and a straight line on logarithmic paper.   To draw the line on the graph in Fig. 25.13, it is necessary to calculate and locate only two points, while in Fig. 25.14 several points must be plotted to establish the location of the corresponding curved-line representation.   The line on Fig. 25.13 has a slope of 2 to 1, because the exponent of t is 2.   Therefore, the line could

Fig. 25.13.   Logarithmic Graph.

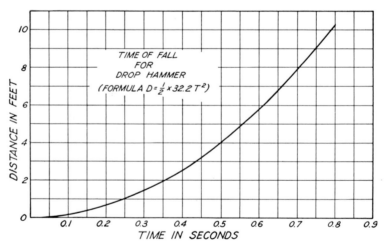

Fig. 25.14.   Co-ordinate Graph.

be drawn by utilizing one point and the slope, instead of plotting two points and joining them with a straight line.

Log paper is available with rulings in one or more cycles for any range of values to be plotted.   Part-cycle and split-cycle papers may also be purchased.

25.14. Semilogarithmic graphs. Semilogarithmic paper has ruled lines that are spaced to a uniform scale in one direction and to a logarithmic scale in the other direction (Fig. 25.15). Charts drawn on this form of paper are used extensively in scientific studies, because functions having values in the form of geometric progressions are represented by straight lines. In any case, the main reason for the use of semilogarithmic paper is that the slope of the resulting curve indicates rate of change rather than amount of change, the opposite being true in the case of

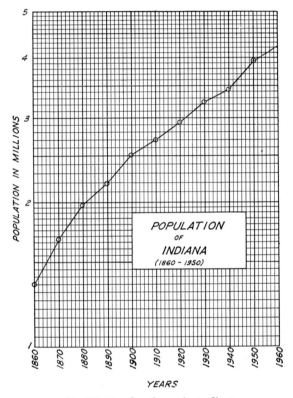

Fig. 25.15.   Semilogarithmic Chart.

curves on ordinary co-ordinate graph paper. If those who are interested desire, they may determine the rate of increase or decrease at any point by measuring the slope. A straight line indicates a constant rate of change. In commercial work this form of paper is generally called "ratio paper," and the charts are known as "rate-of-change charts."

As previously stated, the choice of a type of graph paper depends upon the information to be revealed. Curves drawn on uniform co-ordinate graph paper to illustrate the percentage of expansion or contraction of sales, and so on, present a misleading picture. The same data plotted on semilogarithmic paper would reveal the true rate of change to the business management. For this reason, semilogarithmic paper should be used whenever percentage of change rather than quantity change is to be shown. In scientific work, when the value of one variable increases in a geometric progression and the other in an arithmetic progression, this form is valuable.

25.15. Bar charts. Bar charts or barographs are used principally in popular literature covering economic and industrial surveys. They are a simple diagrammatic form giving a pictorial summary of statistical data and can be easily understood by the average person. Logarithmic and uniform co-ordinate graphs are less suited for this purpose, because few people know the procedure for reading curves or understand their picture qualities.

Whenever values or quantities are illustrated, as in Fig. 25.16, by consecutive heavy bars whose lengths are proportional to the amounts they represent, the resulting representation is called a *bar chart*.

The bars on this type of diagram may be drawn either horizontally or vertically, but all should start at the same zero line. Their lengths should be to some fixed scale, the division values of which may be given in the margin along the bottom or left side of the graph. When it is necessary to give the exact values represented, the figures should be placed along each bar in a direction parallel to it. To place the values at the end gives the illusion of increasing the length of the bars. Usually, the names of the items are lettered to the left of the vertical starting line on a horizontal chart and below the starting line on a vertical chart.

Fig. 25.16.   A Bar Chart.

25.16. Area (percentage) charts. An area diagram can be used profitably when it is desirable to present pictorially a comparison of related quantities in percentage. This form of representation illustrates the relative magnitudes of the component divisions of a total of the distribution of income, the composition of the population, and so on. Two common types of the various forms of area diagrams used in informative literature are illustrated in Figs. 25.17 and 25.18. Percentages, when represented by sectors of a circle or subdivisions of a bar, are easy to interpolate.

The pie chart (Fig. 25.17) is the most popular form of area diagram, as well as the easiest to construct. The area of the circle represents 100 per cent and the sectors represent percentages of the total. In order to make the chart effective, a description of each quantity and its corresponding percentage should be lettered in its individual sector. All lettering should be completed before the areas are crosshatched or colored. The percentage bar chart shown in Fig. 25.18 fulfills the same purpose as the pie chart. The all-over area of the bar represents 100 per cent. Note that each percentage division is crosshatched in a different direction.

The descriptions may be placed on either side of the bar; the percentages should be on the bar or at the side.

25.17. Polar charts. Certain types of technical data can be more easily plotted and better represented on polar co-ordinate paper. Polar

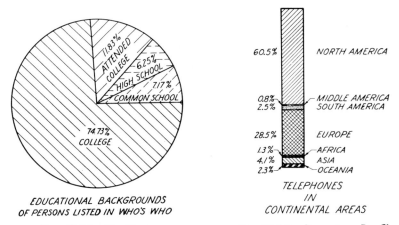

EDUCATIONAL BACKGROUNDS
OF PERSONS LISTED IN WHO'S WHO

Fig. 25.17. Pie Chart.

Fig. 25.18. Percentage Bar Chart.

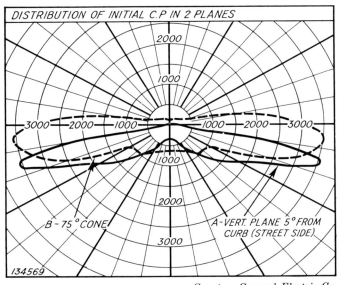

Courtesy General Electric Co.

Fig. 25.19. Polar Chart.

charts drawn by self-recording instruments, polar diagrams, and plotted polar curves representing various kinds of scientific data are very common. Polar curves are used to represent the intensity of diffused light, intensity of heat, and so on. The polar chart in Fig. 25.19 gives, in terms of candle power, the intensity of light in two planes.

25.18. Trilinear charts.   Trilinear charts are used principally in the study of the properties of chemical compounds, mixtures, solutions, and alloys (Fig. 25.20).   Basically this is a 100 per cent chart the use of which, owing to its geometrical form, is limited to the investigation of that which is composed of three constituents or variables.   Its use depends upon the geometrical principle that the sum of the three perpendiculars from any point is equal to the altitude.   If the altitude represents 100 per cent, the perpendiculars will represent the percentages of the three variables composing the whole.

The ruling can be accomplished conveniently by dividing any two sides of the triangle into the number of equal percentage divisions desired and drawing through these points lines parallel to the sides of the triangle.

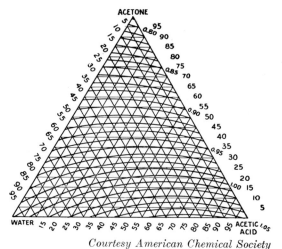

Courtesy American Chemical Society

Fig. 25.20.   Trilinear Chart.

25.19. Chemical engineering charts.   Figure 25.21 shows a type of flow chart that must be prepared frequently by chemical engineers in industrial practice.

25.20. Alignment charts (nomographs).   The purpose of alignment charts is to eliminate many of the laborious calculations necessary to solve formulae containing three or more variables.   Such a chart is often complicated and difficult to construct, but if it can be used repeatedly the labor involved in making it will be justified.   In the commercial field, these charts appear in varied forms, which may be very simple or very complicated.   Figure 25.22 illustrates an alignment chart consisting of three graduated parallel lines.

Briefly stated, the simplest form of alignment chart consists of a set of three or more inclined or vertical scales so spaced and graduated as to represent graphically the variables in a formula.   The scales may be divided into logarithmic units or some other types of functions, depending upon the form of equation.   As illustrated in Fig. 25.22, the unknown value may be found by aligning the working edge of a triangle to the points representing known values on two of the scales.   With the triangle

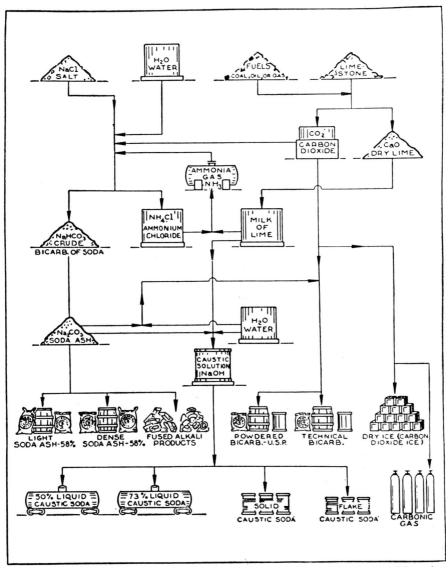

Courtesy Chemical Industries Magazine

Fig. 25.21.   Flow Chart of Ammonia-Soda Operations.

so placed, the numerical value representing the solution of the equation can be read on the third scale at the point of intersection.

Although alignment charts are being used more and more by engineers, it is impossible in this brief treatment of charts and graphs to explain fully the mathematics involved in their construction.   The purpose here is merely to arouse the student's interest in this form of graphical representation.   To satisfy the growing demand for training in nomographic

Fig. 25.22.   Alignment Chart.

Courtesy Indiana State Planning Board

Fig. 25.23.   Population Chart.

drawing, many technical schools have added special courses dealing with alignment charts, special slide rules, and so on.

Additional information on the construction of simple alignment charts may be found in the author's text, *Graphics for Engineers*. Several reliable books on more complex alignment charts are available (see "Bibliography of Engineering Drawing and Allied Subjects" in the Appendix).

25.21. Pictorial charts. Pictorial charts are quite generally used to present data in reports prepared for nontechnical readers. Usually, such charts present comparisons of populations (Fig. 25.23), expenditures, costs, and so forth. Stacks of silver dollars may represent expenditures; size of animals can represent livestock production; and human figures can present employment data.

25.22. Problems. The following problems have been designed to emphasize the fundamental principles underlying the preparation and use of technical graphs and charts.

1. Determine the values for the following equations, as assigned, and plot the curve in each case for quantitative purposes.

$$\text{Parabola} \quad Y = 4x^2, x \text{ from 0 to 5}$$

$$\text{Ellipse} \quad Y^2 = 100 - 2x^2$$

$$\text{Sines} \quad Y = \sin x, x \text{ from } 0° \text{ to } 360°$$

$$\text{Cosines} \quad Y = \cos x, x \text{ from } 0° \text{ to } 360°$$

$$\text{Logarithms} \quad Y = \log x, x \text{ from 1 to 10}$$

$$\text{Reciprocals} \quad Y = \frac{1}{x}, x \text{ from 1 to 10}$$

2. The freezing temperature for two common antifreeze solutions for various compositions are given below.

PRESTONE		DENATURED ALCOHOL	
% by Vol.	*Temp. °F.*	*% by Vol.*	*Temp. °F.*
10	25	10	25
20	16.5	20	17.5
25	11	25	14
30	5	30	5
35	−3	35	−1
40	−12	40	−11
45	−25	45	−18
50	−38	50	−25
55	−47	55	−32
		65	−45

Prepare a chart for these data, mainly quantitative in character, from which the required per cent volume can be read for any desired freezing temperature. Use India ink and the type of paper shown in Fig. 25.3(*b*).

3. Approximate barometric pressures at different heights above sea level are given below. Prepare a qualitative chart for the given data, using India ink on rectangular co-ordinate paper.

Note that the curve would be straight on semilogarithmic paper.

\multicolumn{11}{c}{*H—Altitude in miles*}
0	1	2	3	4	5	6	7	8	9	10
29.92	24.5	20.0	16.2	13.45	11.0	8.9	7.28	5.95	4.87	4.0
\multicolumn{11}{c}{*B—Barometric pressure, in. of Hg.*}

4. Data on rate of growth are frequently plotted on semilogarithmic paper, because the slope of the curve then represents the rate of growth. On semilogarithmic paper, plot the data for the enrollment in a university.

Year	Enrollment	Year	Enrollment	Year	Enrollment	Year	Enrollment
1920	3199	1930	5745	1940	8,231	1950	12,122
1921	3331	1931	5273	1941	8,457	1951	9,018
1922	3360	1932	4564	1942	6,013	1952	8,976
1923	3414	1933	4278	1943	4,376	1953	9,451
1924	3660	1934	4534	1944	4,122	1954	10,313
1925	4010	1935	5364	1945	4,451	1955	11,287
1926	4239	1936	6332	1946	10,698	1956	12,111
1927	4573	1937	7125	1947	14,291	1957	12,850
1928	4960	1938	7613	1948	14,012	1958	13,431
1929	5364	1939	7923	1949	13,287		

Place the vertical axis 1 unit in from the left edge and the horizontal axis at the extreme bottom of the page ruling. Letter in an appropriate title.

Draw also the curve of the general trend and enter on the chart, just below the title, what the enrollment would be in 1961 if the same rate of growth is maintained.

5. In a hydraulics laboratory, the construction of a quantitative curve that would give the weight of water contained in tubes of various diameters and lengths was desired. This was accomplished by filling tubes of known diameters with water to a depth of one foot and observing the weight of water thus added. The water was kept at a temperature for maximum density and the following data were obtained:

D = Diam. of Tube in Inches	W = Weight of 1 Ft. Col. of Water	D = Diam. of Tube in Inches	W = Weight of 1 Ft. Col. of Water
2	1.362	5	8.512
$2\frac{1}{2}$	2.128	$5\frac{1}{2}$	10.299
3	3.064	6	12.257
$3\frac{1}{2}$	4.171	$6\frac{1}{2}$	14.385
4	5.448	7	16.683
$4\frac{1}{2}$	6.895	$7\frac{1}{2}$	19.152
		8	21.790

On a sheet of graph paper (Fig. 25.3*b*), plot the above data. Place the axes 3 centimeters in from the edges. Letter the title in any convenient open space.

6. Owing to uncontrollable factors, such as lack of absolute uniformity of material or test procedure, repeated tests of samples of material do not give identical results. Also, it has been observed in many practical situations that:

1. Large departures from the average seldom occur.
2. Small variations from average occur quite often.
3. The variations are equally likely to be above average and below average.

The foregoing statements are borne out by the accompanying data showing the results of 4,000 measurements of tensile strength of malleable iron.

On a sheet of co-ordinate graph paper (Fig. 25.3*a* or *b*) prepare a graph showing frequency of occurrence of various strength values as ordinates, and tensile strength as abscissa. Draw a smooth symmetrical curve approximating the given data.

Range of Tensile Strength Values in Lb. per Sq. In.	No. of Observations
Under 45,000	0
45,000–45,999	1
46,000–46,999	2
47,000–47,999	3
48,000–48,999	6
49,000–49,999	20
50,000–50,999	232
51,000–51,999	376
52,000–52,999	590
53,000–53,999	740
54,000–54,999	771
55,000–55,999	604
56,000–56,999	383
57,000–57,999	184
58,000–58,999	60
59,000–59,999	20
Over 60,000	8
	4,000

7. On a sheet of paper, of the type shown in Fig. 25.3(*b*), using India ink, plot a curve to represent the data given below. *Note: For stress-strain diagrams*, although the load is the independent variable, it is plotted as ordinate, contrary to the general rule as given in Sec. 25.5. Figure 25.6 shows a similar chart. In performing tests of this nature, some load is imposed before any readings of elongation are taken.

It is suggested that the label along the abscissa be marked "Strain, 0.00001 in. per in.," then fewer figures will be required along the axis.

Stress, Lb. per Sq. In.	Strain, In. per In.	Stress, Lb. per Sq. In.	Strain, In. per In.
3,000	0.0001	25,000	0.00090
5,000	0.0002	30,000	0.00106
10,000	0.00035	32,000	0.00112
15,000	0.00054	33,000	0.00130
20,000	0.00070	34,000	0.00140

8. Make a vertical multiple bar chart showing the enrollment at_____ University from 1945–1958. Obtain data from problem 4.

9. Make a semilogarithmic graph showing the enrollment of your school for the last twenty years.

26

Shade Lining
and Surface Shading

26.1. Shade lines. In the preparation of certain types of drawings, such as Patent Office drawings, display drawings for advertising literature, and so forth, draftsmen convey the impression of solidity by using the effect of illumination. This is done conventionally by making the object lines that separate dark surfaces from light surfaces considerably heavier than the other lines (Fig. 26.1). The scheme is known as *shade lining*, and the heavy lines are called *shade lines*.

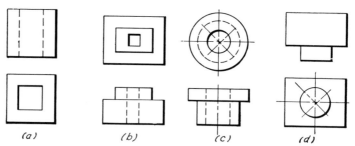

Fig. 26.1. The Effect of Shade Lines.

Shade lines are seldom used on ordinary working drawings. Any small advantage that might be gained in the form of increased legibility is not worth the extra labor involved. On Patent Office drawings, however, they are required. On drawings prepared for advertising literature or technical publications, they may or may not be used, depending upon the importance of the idea of shape.

26.2. The conventional method for drawing shade lines. In accordance with the accepted system of shade lining, an object is considered to be illuminated from a source an infinite distance away. Theoretically, the light rays are assumed to be parallel and to come downward from the left, at an angle of 45°, in the direction of a body diagonal of a cube. In the cube shown in Fig. 26.2(*a*), the illuminated faces would be the left, front, and top. The shaded edges would be the back and right-hand edges in the top view and the lower and right-hand edges in the front view. In practice, however, it is customary to ignore theory and arbitrarily to shade the lower and right-hand edges of all views, as illustrated in Fig. 26.2(*b*). In other words, the conventional practice is to treat all views as front views. Shade lines should be about three times as wide as

612

the other visible object lines.   The extra thickness should be added on the outside surface of solids and on the inside surface of openings.   Hidden object lines are never shaded.

Circles and circular arcs are shaded in accordance with the same scheme.   In shading a circle representing a cylinder (Fig. 26.3a), the center is shifted downward to the right, along a 45° line, by an amount equal to the width of the shade line; then a semicircle is drawn.   The semicircle starts and stops at the 45° tangent points.   It has the same radius as the full circle.   When the cylinder has a circular hole (Fig. 26.3b), the same center is used for shading both circles.

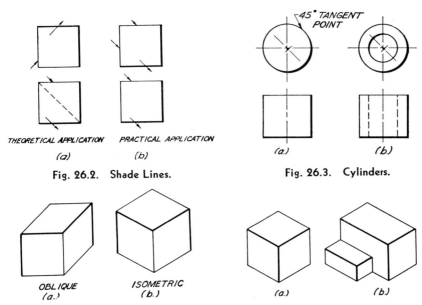

THEORETICAL APPLICATION   PRACTICAL APPLICATION

(a)   (b)

Fig. 26.2.   Shade Lines.

45° TANGENT POINT

(a.)   (b.)

Fig. 26.3.   Cylinders.

OBLIQUE   ISOMETRIC
(a.)   (b.)

Fig. 26.4.   Shaded Pictorial Drawings.

(a.)   (b.)

Fig. 26.5.   Conventional Shading.

In general, although shade lines may make a pictorial view more attractive, they have little value from a practical standpoint.   They neither improve the pictorial effect nor make the drawing easier to read. When a pictorial drawing of a cube is treated conventionally, the shade lines appear as shown in Fig. 26.4.   Some draftsmen, however, shade the edges intersecting at the nearest corners instead.   (See Fig. 26.5.)

In dimensioning shaded views, each extension line limiting a dimension to a shaded edge should form an extension of the original line representing the edge before it was shaded (Fig. 26.6).

26.3.   Surface shading by means of lines.   Line shading is a conventional method of representing, by ruled lines, the varying degrees of illumination on the surfaces of an object.   It is a means of giving clearer definition to the shapes of objects and a finished appearance to certain types of drawings.   In practice, line shading is used on Patent Office drawings, display drawings, and on some illustrations prepared for publications.   It is never used on ordinary drawings, and for this reason few draftsmen ever gain the experience necessary to enable them to employ it effectively.

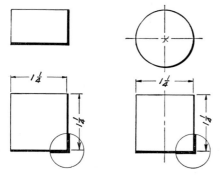

Fig. 26.6.   **Dimensions on Shaded Views.**

In shading surfaces, the bright areas are left white and the dark areas are represented by parallel shade lines (Fig. 26.7). Varying degrees of shade may be represented in one of the following ways (Fig. 26.8):

1. By varying the weight of the lines while keeping the spacing uniform, as in (*a*).

2. By using uniform straight lines and varying the spacing, as in (*b*).

3. By varying both the weight of the lines and the spacing, as in (*c*).

As in the case of shade lines, the rays of light are assumed to be parallel and coming from the left, over the shoulder of the draftsman (Fig. 26.9). In accordance with this, two of the visible faces of the hexagonal prism, shown in Fig. 26.9, would be illuminated, while the remaining visible

(a)   (b)   (c)

Fig. 26.7.   **The Effect of Surface Shading.**

inclined face would be dark.   It should be noted that the general principle of shading is modified in the case of flat inclined surfaces, which, theoretically, would be uniformly lighted.   Such surfaces are shaded in accordance with a conventional scheme, the governing rule of which may be stated as follows: *The portion of an illuminated inclined surface nearest the eye is the lightest, while the portion of a shaded inclined surface nearest the eye is the darkest.*   In the application of this rule, the shading on an inclined illuminated face will increase in density as the face recedes, while on an unilluminated inclined surface it will decrease in density as the face recedes, as shown in Fig. 26.9.

A cylinder would be shaded as shown in Fig. 26.10.   The lightest area on the surface is at the *brilliant line,* where light strikes it and is reflected directly to the eye; the darkest is along the *shade line*, where the light rays are tangent to the surface. The brilliant line passes through the point at which the bisector for the angle formed by a light ray to the center and the visual ray from the center line to the eye would pierce the external surface. In shading a cylinder, the density of the shading is increased in both directions, from the bright area along the brilliant line to the contour element on the left and the shade line on the right. The density of the shading is slightly decreased on the shaded portion beyond the shade line. Since one would expect this area to be even darker, some

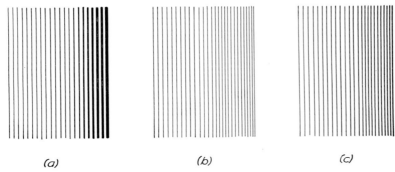

(a)   (b)   (c)

Fig. 26.8.   Conventional Methods of Surface Shading.

Fig. 26.9.
Surface Shading
on a Prism.

Fig. 26.10.
Surface Shading
on a Cylinder.

Fig. 26.11.
Pyramid.

Fig. 26.12.
Cone.

draftsmen extend the dark portion to the contour element. On very small cylinders, the bright side (left side) usually is not shaded.

A sphere is shaded by drawing concentric circles having either the geometric center of the view or the "brilliant point" as a center (Fig. 26.13). The darkest portion of the surface is along the shade line, where the parallel rays of light are tangent to the sphere and the lightest portion is around the *brilliant point*. The *brilliant point* is where the bisector of the angle between a light ray to the center and the visual ray from the center to the eye pierces the external surface. The construction necessary to determine the dark line and the brilliant point is shown in Fig. 26.13(b).

Although good line shading requires much practice and some artistic sense, a skillful draftsman should not avoid shading the surfaces of an object simply because he never before has attempted to do so. After careful study, he should be able to produce fairly satisfactory results. Often the shading of a view makes it possible to eliminate another view that otherwise would be necessary.

Figures 26.14 and 26.15 show applications of line shading on technical illustrations.

26.4. Illustrators' papers. Craftint papers are used extensively by illustrators in making industrial and catalogue drawings. Figure 26.16 shows how various objects might be shaded using one of the two available

Fig. 26.13.   Surface Shading on a Sphere.

From Doyle, Tool Engineering, *Prentice-Hall, Inc.*   *Courtesy Socony-Vacuum Oil Co.*

Fig. 26.14.   A Line-Shaded Drawing.   Fig. 26.15.   A Line-Shaded Pictorial Drawing.

types of Craftint papers. An illustrator has a choice between a single-tone and a double-tone paper.

In using these papers, the drawing is "inked-in" on the Craftint paper in black waterproof ink. Then, the shading is added by brushing on special developers over the areas to be shaded. A single-tone paper requires the use of only one developer and gives a single pattern. On a double-tone paper, it is necessary to use two types of developing fluids and two patterns are obtained. Both developers may be used over the same area to obtain a dark shading. Various patterns are available for both types of papers.

Another form of paper that is popular with illustrators is known to the trade as Ross-board. This special board, one type of which was used

Fig. 26.16.   Shading on Craftint Paper.*

for the shaded illustrations in this text, is available with several surface textures formed on a plaster base with a heavy paper back.   Ross-board is suitable for both ink and pencil, but the shading must be done with a very soft jet-black pencil.   It will be found difficult to draw fine ink lines on Ross-board because the ruling pen becomes clogged with plaster from the surface and the indentations of the pattern discourages the beginner who attempts some lettering.

* Reproduction of drawings made on Craftint Doubletone by Link Aviation Devices, Inc., Binghamton, N.Y.

27 Patent Office Drawings

27.1. A person who has invented a new machine or device, or an improvement for an existing machine, and who applies for a patent, is required by law to submit a drawing showing every important feature of his invention. When the invention is an improvement, the drawing must contain one or more views of the invention, alone, and a separate view showing it attached to the portion of the machine for which it is intended.

Patent drawings must be carefully prepared in accordance with the strict rules of the Patent Office. These rules are published in a pamphlet entitled "Rules of Practice in the United States Patent Office," which may be obtained, without charge, by writing to the Commissioner of Patents, Washington, D.C.

In the case of a machine or mechanical device, the complete application for a patent will consist of a petition, a "specification" (written description), and a drawing. An applicant should employ a patent attorney, preferably one who is connected with or regularly employs competent draftsmen capable of producing well-executed drawings that conform with all of the rules. Ordinary draftsmen lack the skill and experience necessary to produce such drawings. Two sheets of drawings for a patent for a ship's ladder are shown in Figs. 27.1 and 27.2.

27.2. Rules. The following rules (49–55) are quoted verbatim from the pamphlet, "Rules of Practice in the United States Patent Office":

49. The applicant for a patent is required by law to furnish a drawing of his invention whenever the nature of the case admits of it.

50. The drawing may be signed by the inventor or one of the persons indicated in rule 25, or the name of the applicant may be signed on the drawing by his attorney in fact. The drawing must show every feature of the invention covered by the claims, and the figures should be consecutively numbered, if possible. When the invention consists of an improvement on an old machine, the drawing must exhibit, in one or more views, the invention itself, disconnected from the old structure, and also in another view, so much only of the old structure as will suffice to show the connection of the invention therewith.

51. Two editions of patent drawings are printed and published—one for office use, certified copies, etc., of the size and character of those attached to patents, the work being about 6 by $9\frac{1}{2}$ inches; and one reduction of a selected portion of each drawing for the Official Gazette.

52. This work is done by the photolithographic process, and therefore the character of each original drawing must be brought as nearly as possible to a uniform standard of excellence, suited to the requirements of the process, to give the best results, in the interests of inventors, of the office, and of the public. The

following rules will therefore be rigidly enforced, and any departure from them will be certain to cause delay in the examination of an application for letters patent:

(a) Drawings must be made upon pure white paper of a thickness corresponding to two-sheet or three-sheet Bristol board. The surface of the paper must be calendered and smooth. India ink alone must be used, to secure perfectly black and solid lines.

(b) The size of a sheet on which a drawing is made must be exactly 10 by 15 inches. One inch from its edges a single marginal line is to be drawn, leaving the "sight" precisely 8 by 13 inches. Within this margin all work and signatures must be included. One of the shorter sides of the sheet is regarded as its top, and measuring downwardly from the marginal line, a space of not less than $1\frac{1}{4}$ inches is to be left blank for the heading of title, name, number, and date.

(c) All drawings must be made with the pen only. Every line and letter (signatures included) must be absolutely black. This direction applies to all lines, however fine, to shading, and to lines representing cut surfaces in sectional views. All lines must be clean, sharp, and solid, and they must not be too fine or crowded. Surface shading, when used, should be open. Sectional shading should be made by oblique parallel lines, which may be about one-twentieth of an inch apart. Solid black should not be used for sectional or surface shading. Free-hand work should be avoided wherever it is possible to do so.

(d) Drawings should be made with the fewest lines possible consistent with clearness. By the observance of this rule the effectiveness of the work after reduction will be much increased. Shading (except on sectional views) should be used only on convex and concave surfaces, where it should be used sparingly, and may even there be dispensed with if the drawing be otherwise well executed. The plane upon which a sectional view is taken should be indicated on the general view by a broken or dotted line, which should be designated by numerals corresponding to the number of the sectional view. Heavy lines on the shade sides of objects should be used, except where they tend to thicken the work and obscure letters of reference. The light is always supposed to come from the upper left-hand corner at an angle of 45°.

(e) The scale to which a drawing is made ought to be large enough to show the mechanism without crowding, and two or more sheets should be used if one does not give sufficient room to accomplish this end; but the number of sheets must never be more than is absolutely necessary.

(f) The different views should be consecutively numbered. Letters and figures of reference must be carefully formed. They should, if possible, measure at least one-eighth of an inch in height, so that they may bear reduction to one twenty-fourth of an inch; and they may be much larger when there is sufficient room. They must be so placed in the close and complex parts of drawings as not to interfere with a thorough comprehension of the same, and therefore should rarely cross or mingle with the lines. When necessarily grouped around a certain part they should be placed at a little distance, where there is available space, and connected by lines with the parts to which they refer. They should not be placed upon shaded surfaces, but when it is difficult to avoid this, a blank space must be left in the shading where the letter occurs, so that it shall appear perfectly distinct and separate from the work. If the same part of an invention appears in more than one view of the drawing, it must always be represented by the same character, and the same character must never be used to designate different parts.

(g) The signature of the applicant should be placed at the lower right-hand corner of each sheet, and the signatures of the witnesses, if any, at the lower left-hand corner, all within the marginal line, but in no instance should they trespass upon the drawings. The title should be written with pencil on the back

Aug. 31, 1948.   J. J. WALLACE   2,448,335

ACCOMMODATION LADDER FOR SHIPS

Filed June 27, 1945   6 Sheets-Sheet 2

FIG. 3.

FIG. 5

FIG. 4.

FIG.6.

INVENTOR.
John J. Wallace
BY John L. Ruckman
Attorney

Fig. 27.1. A Patent Drawing.

Aug. 31, 1948.   J. J. WALLACE   2,448,335

ACCOMMODATION LADDER FOR SHIPS

Filed June 27, 1945   6 Sheets-Sheet 6

FIG. 27.

INVENTOR.
John J. Wallace
BY   John H. Ruckman
Attorney.

Fig. 27.2.   A Patent Drawing.

of the sheet. The permanent names and title constituting the heading will be applied subsequently by the office in uniform style.

(*h*) All views on the same sheet must stand in the same direction and must, if possible, stand so that they can be read with the sheet held in an upright position. If views longer than the width of the sheet are necessary for the proper illustration of the invention, the sheet may be turned on its side. The space for heading must then be reserved at the right and the signatures placed at the left, occupying the same space and position as in the upright views and being horizontal when the sheet is held in an upright position. One figure must not be placed upon another or within the outline of another.

(*i*) As a rule, one view only of each invention can be shown in the Gazette illustrations. The selection of that portion of a drawing best calculated to explain the nature of the specific improvement would be facilitated and the final result improved by the judicious execution of a figure with express reference to the Gazette, but which must at the same time serve as one of the figures referred to in the specification. For this purpose the figure may be a plan, elevation, section, or perspective view, according to the judgment of the draftsman. All its parts should be especially open and distinct, with very little or no shading, and it must illustrate the invention claimed only, to the exclusion of all other details. (See specimen drawing.) When well executed it will be used without curtailment or change, but any excessive fineness or crowding or unnecessary elaborateness of detail will necessitate its exclusion from the Gazette.

(*j*) Drawings transmitted to the office should be sent flat, protected by a sheet of heavy binder's board; or should be rolled for transmission in a suitable mailing tube, but should never be folded.

(*k*) An agent's or attorney's stamp, or advertisement, or written address will not be permitted upon the face of a drawing, within or without the marginal line.

53. In reissue applications the drawings upon which the original patent was issued may be used upon the filing of suitable permanent photographic copies thereof, if no changes are to be made in the drawings.

54. The foregoing rules relating to drawings will be rigidly enforced. A drawing not executed in conformity thereto may be admitted for purposes of examination if it sufficiently illustrates the invention, but in such case the drawing must be corrected or a new one furnished before the application will be allowed. The necessary corrections will be made by the office, upon applicant's request and at his expense.

55. Applicants are advised to employ competent draftsmen to make their drawings.

The office will furnish the drawings at cost, as promptly as its draftsmen can make them, for applicants who cannot otherwise conveniently procure them.

28

Reproduction and Duplication of Engineering Drawings

28.1. Usually it is necessary to duplicate a set of drawings of a machine or structure, one or more copies being made for the office and extra copies for interested persons connected with the home organization or an outside co-operating firm. Sometimes many sets are required. Under modern production methods, the various parts of a machine or structure may be produced in numerous departments and plants that are located miles apart. Each of these departments must have exact copies of the original drawings. To satisfy this demand, several economical processes have been devised.

The various processes may be grouped in accordance with the general similarity in methods. The mechanical processes form a group that includes mimeographing, hectographing, and printing; the photochemical processes, using reflected light, include photography and photocopying; the photochemical processes, requiring transmitted light, include blueprinting, Ozalid printing, Van Dyke printing, and so on. A few processes, such as photolithography, are combinations of methods.

28.2. Blueprints. At present the blueprint process is more widely used than any other method of reproduction, despite the fact that some of the others offer more advantages. The method for making blueprints was first introduced in the United States about 1876.

A blueprint may be considered a photographic copy of an original drawing in that the process is similar to that of photography. A piece of sensitized paper is exposed to light transmitted through a negative (tracing) and then is developed in water to bring out the image. The negative is a transparent sheet of paper or transparentized cloth upon which the image of the original drawing has been traced with opaque lines. The printing paper is a white paper that has been coated with a solution of ammonia citrate of iron and ferrocyanide of potassium. When the paper is exposed through the tracing, a chemical action takes place wherever the light is able to reach the sensitized surface. In the first bath of clear water, the coating is washed away from the parts of the surface protected by these lines, exposing the original surface of the paper against a developed blue background. The contrast between the blue background and white lines may be intensified by dipping the print in an oxidizing solution of potassium bichromate in water, after which the print must be rinsed thoroughly in clean water to avoid stain marks.

The best results are always obtained with new blueprint paper which, when new, has a pale yellowish-green printing surface. The age of the

623

paper is an important factor, for it greatly affects the printing time. When not being used, it should be kept well wrapped and should be stored in a metal can or a cool dark room.

Notations and changes can be made on a blueprint by lettering and drawing with an alkaline solution strong enough to bleach out the blue compound. Although a solution of sodium hydroxide (caustic soda) is best for this purpose, ordinary sodium bicarbonate (baking soda) in water, may be used.

Blueprints may be made in a sun frame, if only a few prints are desired. The length of time for the exposure varies with the intensity of the light and the speed of the paper. In direct sunlight, the correct exposure may vary from thirty seconds (for fast paper) to as much as several minutes (for slow paper).

Courtesy C. F. Pease Co.

Fig. 28.1.   Continuous Electric Printing Machine.

Since a good print with clear white lines against a uniform brilliant blue background can be obtained only by proper timing of the exposure, it is well to make one or two trial (part) prints on small scraps of blueprint paper before making the final print. If the background is a pale blue, the trial print was underexposed and the time of exposure should be increased; if the trial print has a scorched appearance with indistinct lines against a very dark blue background, the print was overexposed and the time of exposure should be decreased.

28.3. Typed material. In preparing a typewritten original for printing, a "soft record" ribbon should be used and the sheet should be "backed" with a piece of carbon paper so that the typed characters will be on two sides. Troublesome smearing can be somewhat reduced by spraying the sheet (both sides) with "fixative."

28.4. Blueprint machines. All large industrial firms and commercial blueprint concerns use printing machines having some form of an electric exposing lamp. (See Figs. 28.1 and 28.2.)

For a large quantity of prints some form of continuous machine is desirable. On such a machine the paper unwinds continuously from a roll, as the tracings are "fed in" with the inked sides up. The exposure is made as the tracing passes upward in contact with a glass cylinder containing a bank of arc lights. Some machines are equipped with a washer and drier, thus allowing the prints to be made in one operation (Fig. 28.2), but these are so expensive that only firms making a great number of prints daily find them a worth-while investment. Small firms have found it much cheaper to have their prints made by commercial printing concerns, of which there are at least one or two in every fairly large industrial city.

Courtesy C. F. Pease Co.

Fig. 28.2. Continuous Printing Machine with Washer and Drier.

28.5. Brown prints. A negative brown print is made on so-called Van Dyke paper, a thin printing paper with a yellowish-green sensitized surface that turns to a light bronze on exposure and a deep brown when washed in water. In order to intensify a developed brown print and make it permanent, it is "fixed" in a solution of sodium hyposulphite and again washed in water. If the print is to be used for making positive prints, it should be made by exposing with the tracing reversed so that the inked lines are toward the Van Dyke paper. A reversed negative will print faster and will produce sharper lines if it has been transparentized by rubbing the back with a specially prepared oil (white Vaseline in benzine).

A positive brown print, having brown lines on white background, is made on brown print paper by using a brown print negative as a substitute for the original tracing. Prints showing a change may be made without altering the original tracing if the part to be changed is "blocked out" on the negative print and drawn in on the positive print.

28.6. Blue-line prints. A positive blue-line print, having blue lines on a white background, may be made on regular blueprint paper by exposing with a brown print negative in the place of the original tracing. Such prints also may be made from an original tracing, if a paper coated with a solution of gum arabic, ammonia citrate of iron, and chloride of iron is used. When the print is developed in solution of ferrocyanide of potassium, the coated surface turns blue where it has been protected from light and remains white where it has been exposed. The print must be washed thoroughly in water when it is taken from the developer.

An advantage offered by blue-line prints is that alterations may be more easily indicated and read on a white background. Furthermore, if the prints are made on blueprint paper using a negative print, the original tracing is protected against wear.

28.7. Ozalid prints. Ozalid prints, depending upon the type of Ozalid paper used, show black, blue, or maroon lines on a white background. The prints are exposed in the same manner as for other contact processes. They are developed in controlled dry ammonia vapor and, since no liquid solution is used with this process, a finished print will be an undistorted exact-scale reproduction of the original tracing.

Until recently the Ozalid process was not used to any great extent by industrial concerns, because there were no satisfactory developing machines available. Simple tube developers could be purchased, but they were unsuitable for the rapid production of a number of prints. With the introduction of modern combined printing and developing machines, the Ozalid process has received wide acceptance. Ozalid printer-developer units, such as the one shown in Fig. 28.3, produce finished prints in two simple steps without any auxiliary apparatus. No washing, fixing, rinsing, or drying is required.

An Ozalid duplicate tracing, which is known as an intermediate, may be made on either Ozalid sepia-line papers (single and double coated), Ozalid sepia-line cloth, or Ozalid foil. Since each of these types of intermediate materials is translucent, an intermediate on any one type may be used in place of the original tracing to produce drawing room and shop prints. The use of intermediates makes it possible to file away the original drawing where it will not be damaged or smudged and will be safe from fire. The intermediate can be used for all reference work and may be altered when design changes become necessary. Changes may be made and obsolete detail removed with a corrector fluid and the new lines, dimensions, and notes may then be added. A second intermediate may then be made from the first one. The use of changed intermediates makes retracing unnecessary when rather extensive alterations in design become desirable. Also, the valuable original can remain untouched in the file for record purposes. As a matter of interest an intermediate will often make a much better print than an original tracing.

28.8. Black and white prints (*BW*). Positive black-line prints may be made direct from an original tracing by using a specially prepared black-print paper. When developed, the sensitized surface turns black where it has been protected and remains white where exposed.   Only two steps are required to obtain a fully developed print: exposure and development.   This method of printing is similar to that used for making blueprints, except that the print is developed by a solution in a special developing unit on top of the printer (Fig. 28.4).   Black and white prints are more desirable than blueprints, because of their greater legibility and the fact that they can be made in only two steps where blueprints require five.

Courtesy General Analine and Film Corp.

Fig. 28.3.   Ozalid Printing Machine.

This is one of the few methods that eventually should replace the blueprint method.

28.9. Duplicate tracings.   A duplicate tracing may be produced on a special waterproof reproduction cloth.   A negative brown print is used, and the cloth is exposed in a regular blueprint machine.   The sensitized surface of this waterproof cloth turns black where exposed to light and remains transparent where protected.   A few industrial firms produce "dupe" tracings, of original pencil drawings.   This is done by photographing a drawing and using the negative in exposing the cloth.   To obtain a satisfactory negative, careful consideration must be given to the weight of the pencil lines.   Full directions for making duplicate tracings may be secured from almost any large commercial distributor of drawing supplies. In view of the fact that "dupe" tracings from original pencil drawings eliminate all possible errors that might result from ink tracing, and cost only a fraction of the price of the latter to produce, this method eventually should become widely adopted.

28.10. Photocopies. Photocopies (photostat prints) are direct photographic reproductions made from original drawings or printed matter with an automatic machine equipped with a large camera that focuses

Courtesy Charles Bruning Company, Inc.

Fig. 28.4. BW Continuous Printing and Developing Machine.

an image directly upon a sensitized paper. After being properly exposed, the print is washed and dried within the machine. Copies may be made to any scale of reduction or enlargement.

Although photocopies made from original drawings are brown prints with white lines on a dark background, positive prints having dark lines on a white background may be made by rephotographing brown-print photocopies. Since photocopy paper is orthochromatic, black and white copies can be made from colored originals by copying through a color filter.

This method is used extensively for preparing drawings for engineering reports and, occasionally, for changing the scales of related drawings so that they may be combined.

A photostat machine is shown in Fig. 28.5.

28.11. Translucent masters—photographic method. Translucent masters, or so-called intermediates, may be made on photographic paper or cloth using photographic processes (Eastman Company). Intermediates may be made, either to safeguard valuable originals, or for the purpose of replacing worn or soiled drawings. Oftentimes, masters will produce better prints than original tracings, because line intensity is increased. This, in turn, permits faster printing speeds which lead to a saving of time and money.

Courtesy Photostat Corp.

Fig. 28.5. A Photostat Machine.

Frequently, an original may require a change, or it may contain material which should not appear on the finished print. An altered print may be produced by first making an intermediate print upon which unwanted lines, figures, and notes can be removed and the new material added in ink or pencil. Prints made directly from the altered intermediate bear all of the added changes without showing the unwanted material. Drafting time has been saved for use on the other tasks, and the original tracing remains untouched for record purposes. This method of alteration may be used to delete portions of an original that might be so confidential that it should not be reproduced.

28.12. Reproduction of worn or mutilated tracings. Worn or mutilated tracings, which have reached a stage where it is difficult to make readable prints, may be reproduced photographically rather than by hand tracing at a great saving in time and money.   If desired, the scale may be changed.   By taking advantage of the special types of film now available for this purpose, the intensity of the pencil lines can be increased to give a reproduction with clear and sharp lines.   Stains and discolorations may be eliminated by using a proper filter on the camera or by opaquing.

28.13. Use of glass cloth.   Glass cloth, which has been a rather recent development, is a translucent drawing material that is dimensionally stable.   It is similar to vellum and can be rolled for ease in handling, shipping, or storing.   It has an excellent drawing surface for either pencil or ink.

Because drawings made on glass cloth will remain unvaryingly accurate, its use has opened the door to short-cut methods which save both layout time and floor space.   In the aircraft industry, it has made possible a more accurate production of templates, dies, and form blocks at a distinct saving in time and money, because its use eliminates shop layouts by hand, camera photography, and other expensive and complicated reproduction methods which have been used in the past.   The use of glass cloth for the reproduction of layouts eliminates the necessity for a detailed checking that a hand-scribed layout requires.

In practice, the original full-scale drawing on glass cloth and the photosensitized template or tool stock are exposed together in a large contact printer.   Development is simple, in that only a moist sponging is required with a developer.   All work may be done under daylight, but not in sunlit areas.

The only drawing that need be prepared by the drafting room for use through final production is the original drawing on glass cloth.

28.14. Reproductions from layouts on metal sheets.   A reproduction may be made of a layout prepared on metal plate or other opaque material by the reflex contact method.   The original, if prepared on metal, is drawn directly in pencil or ink on a working surface that has been prepared by spraying it with a white matte, loft board surfacer.   The special Vinyl base film that is used for the intermediate is unique, in that the light that passes through it from the back during exposure strikes the prepared surface of the metal plate and is then reflected to the emulsion.   For this reason one must be certain that the emulsion side of the film has been placed in contact with the front side of the plate when preparing for the exposure.   After exposure, the film is removed and immersed in a developer for a few minutes and then fixed in hypo and washed.

The resulting negative may be used for making positive prints on cloth or paper or for making positive prints on metal as desired.   Prints on metal may be needed as copies for sub-contractors or for use as templates if the original layouts have been prepared full size.

28.15. Combining a line drawing with a photograph of a part or mechanism.   The use of photography in the preparation of assembly drawings of simple unit mechanisms has become increasingly popular because a photograph is readily understood by a relatively inexperienced person.   By referring back and forth between the line drawing showing the assembly and the picture, it is possible for one to gain a full understanding of the mechanism in much less time than would be possible without the photograph.

The first step in the preparation of a photographic assembly drawing is the making of a halftone enlargement of the piece of equipment using an orthotype film. Then, a positive intermediate is made from the original line drawing, and a window is cut into it at an open spot to accept the halftone positive. From this layout, consisting of a line drawing, a bill of material, a title block, and a halftone, a positive film intermediate is made that can be used to make needed prints on a direct process machine.

At times, it has been found desirable to present a photographic representation on a line drawing showing a single part.

28.16. Microfilming drawings. The practice of microfilming drawings is increasing rapidly, as many companies are giving more attention to their reproduction methods and are being forced to save filing space. Some companies have found that a microfilming program will reduce their storage space requirements by as much as seventy-five per cent.

Reduction in filing space is made possible, largely because obsolete drawings may be removed from the files and destroyed after they have been microfilmed.

Of equal importance is the protection offered when microfilm prints can be filed away in fire-proof vaults. Since lost original tracings may be quickly replaced by first making enlarged printing intermediates, it can be said that microfilming offers a form of insurance against both careless loss through handling and from fire.

The three sizes of film in general use today are the 16mm, 35mm, and 70mm. Although the most common size is the 35mm, the 16mm is often used for small drawings. One large corporation uses 70mm for tracings as large as 37 inches by 50 inches. Tracings, which may be as large as 54 inches by 20 feet, are microfilmed in sections, and related negatives are filed together so that prints can be made at a later time should the need arise.

Microfilm negatives are usually cut and filed individually in envelopes marked with the same number given the tracing. Negatives are made for subsequent revisions, thus permitting the destruction of unnecessary and outdated tracings.

An engineer may obtain any needed information concerning the progressive development of a part or mechanism by viewing the negative on a microfilm reader or by using a portable projector. When a full-size print, a reduced scale print, or an intermediate is needed, either can be quickly made by enlargement on paper or cloth by using the negative in a microfilm enlarger designed for printing from microfilm.

28.17. Lithoprinting. The planograph or photo-offset process (a form of photolithography) is used to produce a considerable number of copies of a drawing at a very low cost.

In this process a positive image is produced upon a flexible zinc or aluminum plate by the use of a photographic negative and a sensitizing emulsion. For satisfactory results, the plate must have a grained surface that will absorb water. In the press, the plate passes under a moistened felt roller that wets the background, so that when it next passes an ink roller only image will be inked (the ink will not stick to the wet surface). The plate finally passes a rubber roller where the inked image imparts a negative imprint that is transferred by this roller to the printing paper as a positive image.

28.18. The mechanical copying methods. Small line drawings and sketches may be reproduced by either the mimeograph process or the hectograph process.

In the former, a direct image is made on sheets of mimeograph copying paper by the use of a stencil and an inked pad. The stencil is a thin sheet having a prepared surface upon which the material to be copied is drawn, lettered, or typed. When the stencil has been cut and is ready to produce copies, it is stretched over a perforated metal cylinder that has a fixed inked pad. As the paper is fed through the mimeograph machine by

Fig. 28.6. BW Copyflex Machine.

rotating the cylinder, the ink from the pad passes through the stencil where the lines and letters have been cut and forms an image on the paper. By a photochemical method, the A. B. Dick Company is able to produce stencils of drawings to a reduced scale and to copy material that would be too complicated to be drawn satisfactorily by hand. For this purpose, the company uses a special stencil upon which it is impossible to type or draw.

In the hectograph process, copies are made by direct contact with a gelatin pad that has received an imprint from an original typed or drawn in aniline materials. Although, to obtain a transferred image having sharp rich-colored lines, a special type of paper should be used, copies frequently are made on various weights of paper, from the very thin to heavy card stock. In size, the copies range from small tags to large $22'' \times 34''$ sheets. "Master" copies must be made with a special reproducing ink, pencil, carbon paper, or typewriter ribbon. Copies made with ink may have as many as eight colors.

Various machines on the market employ the hectograph principle. A few run off copies at the rate of eighty per minute and produce as many as five or six hundred from an original "master." Some machines do not employ a gelatin pad but depend instead upon a special liquid that moistens the master copy so that the print may be taken directly from the master.

28.19. Copyflex positive prints. The BW Copyflex machine, shown in Fig. 28.6, copies any size of original matter up to $11\frac{1}{2}$ inches wide by any length. The Copyflex makes exact contact prints of letters, records, reports, or line drawings within itself. No stencil or negative is required. The BW Diazo process is employed and the machine needs no inks and does not give off any annoying fumes. The paper is coated with an aniline dye that during processing is bleached by actinic light rays except where the line drawing or record has markings.

If the original is on opaque stock the machine quickly copies it onto reflex film and the film is then used to make the desired copies.

28.20. Industrial practice in automobile body design. In automobile body design, full-sized drawings of each year's models are made on the painted surface of a large sheet of aluminum. The drawings are carefully laid out with instruments directly on the painted surface; then the lines are scratched in. A detail drawing, such as one showing the details of a doorpost on a particular model, is made by tracing directly from the aluminum sheet. Aluminum is used because a body-design drawing for a model must be prepared two or three years in advance of the production date and the medium on which it is prepared must be strong enough to withstand constant wear and rough treatment. Furthermore, a drawing on an aluminum sheet is not affected by weather changes.

Appendix

CONTENTS

635

Graphical Symbols for Electrical Diagrams

AMPLIFIER General	**DEVICE, VISUAL SIGNALING** Annunciator	**MICROPHONE**
ANTENNA General	**ELEMENT, THERMAL** Thermal Cutout, Flasher	**PATH, TRANSMISSION** General
Loop	Thermal Relay	Crossing, Not Connected
		Junction
ARRESTER General Multigap	or	Junction, Connected Paths
		Pair
BATTERY Multicell		Assembled Conductors; Cable Coaxial
BREAKER, CIRCUIT General	**FUSE** General	2-Conductor Cable
	Fusible Element	Grouping Leads
CAPACITOR General	**GROUND**	or
COIL Blowout (Broken line not part of symbol) Operating	**HANDSET** General	**RECEIVER** General Headset
CONNECTOR Female Contact Male Contact	**INDUCTOR WINDING** General or	**RECTIFIER** General
	LAMP Ballast Lamp	**REPEATER** 1-Way
CONTACT, ELECTRIC Fixed ∘ or Locking Nonlocking Rotating Closed or Open or	Incandescent	**RESISTOR** General
	MACHINE, ROTATING Basic Generator Motor Wound Rotor Armature	**SWITCH** General Single Throw Double Throw Knife
CORE Magnetic (General) Magnet or Relay	Winding Symbols 1-Phase 2-Phase	**THERMOCOUPLE** Temperature-Measuring
COUPLER, DIRECTIONAL General	3-Phase Wye 3-Phase Delta	**TRANSFORMER** Magnetic Core Shielded

ASA Y32.2–1954.

Graphical Electrical Symbols for Architectural Plans

Ceiling Wall   GENERAL OUTLETS

○   ⊸○   Outlet

Ⓑ   ⊸Ⓑ   Blanked Outlet

Ⓓ   Drop Cord

Ⓔ   ⊸Ⓔ   Electric Outlet; for use only when circle used alone might be confused with columns, plumbing symbols, etc

Ⓕ   ⊸Ⓕ   Fan Outlet

Ⓙ   ⊸Ⓙ   Junction Box

Ⓛ   ⊸Ⓛ   Lamp Holder

Ⓛps   ⊸Ⓛps   Lamp Holder with Pull Switch

Ⓢ   ⊸Ⓢ   Pull Switch

Ⓥ   ⊸Ⓥ   Outlet for Vapor Discharge Lamp

Ⓧ   ⊸Ⓧ   Exit Light Outlet

Ⓒ   ⊸Ⓒ   Clock Outlet (Specify Voltage)

                     CONVENIENCE OUTLETS

⊨⊖   Duplex Convenience Outlet

⊨⊖₁,₃   Convenience Outlet other than Duplex 1=Single, 3 =Triplex, etc

⊨⊖wp   Weatherproof Convenience Outlet

⊨⊖ᴿ   Range Outlet

⊨⊖s   Switch and Convenience Outlet

⊨⊖Ⓡ   Radio and Convenience Outlet

Ⓐ   Special Purpose Outlet (Des. in Spec.)

⊙   Floor Outlet

                      SWITCH OUTLETS

S   Single Pole Switch

S₂   Double Pole Switch

S₃   Three Way Switch

S₄   Four Way Switch

Sᴅ   Automatic Door Switch

Sᴇ   Electrolier Switch

Sᴋ   Key Operated Switch

Sᴘ   Switch and Pilot Lamp

Scв   Circuit Breaker

Swcв   Weatherproof Circuit Breaker

Sмc   Momentary Contact Switch

Sᴿc   Remote Control Switch

Swᴘ   Weatherproof Switch

Sꜰ   Fused Switch

Swꜰ   Weatherproof Fused Switch

                      SPECIAL OUTLETS

○a,b,c,etc   Any standard symbol as given above with the addition of a lower case subscript letter may be used to designate some special variation of standard equipment of particular interest in a specific set of architectural plans.

⊨⊖a,b,c,etc

Sa,b,c,etc
           When used they must be listed in the Key of Symbols on each drawing and if necessary further described in the specifications.

PANELS, CIRCUITS, AND MISCELLANEOUS

▨   Lighting Panel

▨   Power Panel

——   Branch Circuit; Concealed in Ceiling or Wall

– – –   Branch Circuit; Concealed in Floor

- - - - Branch Circuit; Exposed

↠   Home Run to Panel Board. Indicate number of circuits by number of arrows.
         Note: Any circuit without further designation indicates a two-wire circuit. For a greater number of wires indicate as follows: –⫫– (3 wires) –⫫⫫– (4 wires), etc.

———   Feeders. Note: Use heavy lines and designate by number corresponding to listing in Feeder Schedule.

⊒⊑   Underfloor Duct and Junction Box. Triple System. Note: For double or single systems eliminate one or two lines. This symbol is equally adaptable to auxiliary system layouts.

Ⓖ   Generator

Ⓜ   Motor

Ⓘ   Instrument

Ⓣ   Power Transformer (Or draw to scale.)

⊠   Controller

⊏ᴵ   Isolating Switch

                AUXILIARY SYSTEMS

▪   Pushbutton

◻/   Buzzer

◻ᴅ   Bell

◇   Annunciator

◀   Outside Telephone

◁   Interconnecting Telephone

◁◀   Telephone Switchboard

⊕   Bell-Ringing Transformer

Ⓓ   Electric Door Opener

Ⓕᴅ   Fire Alarm Bell

Ⓕ   Fire Alarm Station

⊠   City Fire Alarm Station

FA   Fire Alarm Central Station

FS   Automatic Fire Alarm Device

W   Watchman's Station

[W]   Watchman's Central Station

H   Horn

N   Nurse's Signal Plug

M   Maid's Signal Plug

R   Radio Outlet

[SC]   Signal Central Station

◻   Interconnection Box

▥   Battery

—·—·—   Auxiliary System Circuits
         Note: Any line without further designation indicates a 2-wire system. For a greater number of wires designate with numerals in manner similar to —·—· 12-No. 18W-3/4"C., or designate by number corresponding to listing in Schedule.

◻a,b,c   Special Auxiliary Outlets.
         Subscript letters refer to notes on plans or detailed description in specifications.

ASA Y32.9–1943.

Graphical Symbols for Heat-Power Apparatus

COMPRESSOR (Rotary)	FLUE GAS REHEATER (Intermediate Superheater)
CONDENSER (Surface)	LIVE ·STEAM SUPERHEATER
COOLER OR HEAT EXCHANGER	ORIFICE
COOLING TOWER	PRECIPITATOR (E-Electrostatic M-Mechanical W-Wet)
DEAERATOR	STEAM TRAP
DRAINER OR LIQUID LEVEL CONTROLLER	STRAINER (Single)
ENGINE (Steam)	STRAINER (Double)
EVAPORATOR	TANK (Closed)
EXTRACTOR	TANK (Open)
FAN-BLOWER (M-Motor; T-Turbine)	TANK (Flash or Pressure)
FILTER	TURBINE (Condensing)
FLOW NOZZLE	
FLUID DRIVE	STEAM TURBINE
HEATER (Air)	VENTURI TUBE

ASA Z32.2.6–1950.

Graphical Symbols for Plumbing Fixtures

BATH TUB	SHOWER	LAVATORY	SINK
1. ANGLE	11. HEAD (PLAN / ELEV.)	21. CORNER (L)	31. COMBINATION SINK AND DISHWASHER
2. CORNER	12. MULTI-STALL	22. DENTAL (DL)	32. COMBINATION SINK AND LAUNDRY TRAY (S& T)
3. RECESSED	13. STALL	23. MANICURE OR MEDICAL (ML)	33. KITCHEN (S)
4. ROLL RIM	14. OVERHEAD GANG (PLAN / ELEV.)	24. PEDESTAL (PL)	34. KITCHEN WITH DRAINBORADS
5. FOOT (FB)	WATER CLOSET — 15. HIGH TANK (H T)	25. WALL (WL)	35. WASH-WALL TYPE
6. SITZ (SB)	16. LOW TANK (L T)	URINAL — 26. CORNER TYPE	36. DISHWASHER (DW)
DRAIN — 7. DRAIN (D)	17. NO DRAIN	27. PEDESTAL TYPE	37. METER (M)
8. FLOOR WITH BACKWATER VALVE	DRINKING FOUNTAIN — 18. DRINKING FOUNTAIN (DF)	28. STALL TYPE	38. GREASE SEPARATOR (G)
9. HOT WATER TANK (HWT)	19. PEDESTAL TYPE (DF)	29. TROUGH TYPE	39. CLEANOUT (C/O)
10. WATER HEATER (WH)	20. TROUGH TYPE (DF)	30. WALL TYPE	40. GAS OUTLET (G)

ASA Z32.2–1949.

TABLE I

Standard Conversion Table

4ths	8ths	16ths	32nds	64ths	To 4 Places	To 3 Places	To 2 Places
				$\frac{1}{64}$	.0156	.016	.02
			$\frac{1}{32}$		.0312	.031	.03
				$\frac{3}{64}$	.0469	.047	.05
		$\frac{1}{16}$			.0625	.062	.06
				$\frac{5}{64}$	.0781	.078	.08
			$\frac{3}{32}$		.0938	.094	.09
				$\frac{7}{64}$	.1094	.109	.11
	$\frac{1}{8}$				.1250	.125	.12
				$\frac{9}{64}$	.1406	.141	.14
			$\frac{5}{32}$		.1562	.156	.16
				$\frac{11}{64}$	.1719	.172	.17
		$\frac{3}{16}$			.1875	.188	.19
				$\frac{13}{64}$	.2031	.203	.20
			$\frac{7}{32}$		.2188	.219	.22
				$\frac{15}{64}$	.2344	.234	.23
$\frac{1}{4}$					.2500	.250	.25
				$\frac{17}{64}$	.2656	.266	.27
			$\frac{9}{32}$		.2812	.281	.28
				$\frac{19}{64}$	.2969	.297	.30
		$\frac{5}{16}$			.3125	.312	.31
				$\frac{21}{64}$	.3281	.328	.33
			$\frac{11}{32}$		.3438	.344	.34
				$\frac{23}{64}$	.3594	.359	.36
	$\frac{3}{8}$				.3750	.375	.38
				$\frac{25}{64}$	.3906	.391	.39
			$\frac{13}{32}$		.4062	.406	.41
				$\frac{27}{64}$	.4219	.422	.42
		$\frac{7}{16}$			.4375	.438	.44
				$\frac{29}{64}$	.4531	.453	.45
			$\frac{15}{32}$		.4688	.469	.47
				$\frac{31}{64}$	.4844	.484	.48
					.5000	.500	.50
				$\frac{33}{64}$	.5156	.516	.52
			$\frac{17}{32}$		.5312	.531	.53
				$\frac{35}{64}$	.5469	.547	.55
		$\frac{9}{16}$			.5625	.562	.56
				$\frac{37}{64}$	.5781	.578	.58
			$\frac{19}{32}$		.5938	.594	.59
				$\frac{39}{64}$	.6094	.609	.61
	$\frac{5}{8}$				.6250	.625	.62
				$\frac{41}{64}$	.6406	.641	.64
			$\frac{21}{32}$		.6562	.656	.66
				$\frac{43}{64}$	.6719	.672	.67
		$\frac{11}{16}$			.6875	.688	.69
				$\frac{45}{64}$	.7031	.703	.70
			$\frac{23}{32}$		.7188	.719	.72
				$\frac{47}{64}$	.7344	.734	.73
$\frac{3}{4}$					.7500	.750	.75
				$\frac{49}{64}$	.7656	.766	.77
			$\frac{25}{32}$		.7812	.781	.78
				$\frac{51}{64}$	.7969	.797	.80
		$\frac{13}{16}$			.8125	.812	.81
				$\frac{53}{64}$	.8281	.828	.83
			$\frac{27}{32}$		.8438	.844	.84
				$\frac{55}{64}$	.8594	.859	.86
	$\frac{7}{8}$				.8750	.875	.88
				$\frac{57}{64}$	.8906	.891	.89
			$\frac{29}{32}$		.9062	.906	.91
				$\frac{59}{64}$	.9219	.922	.92
		$\frac{15}{16}$			.9375	.938	.94
				$\frac{61}{64}$	.9531	.953	.95
			$\frac{31}{32}$		.9688	.969	.97
				$\frac{63}{64}$	.9844	.984	.98
					1.0000	1.000	1.00

TABLE II
Unified and American Thread Series*

NOMINAL DIAMETER	Coarse (NC) (UNC)		Fine (NF) (UNF)		Extra Fine (NEF) (UNEF)	
	Threads per Inch	Tap Drill†	Threads per Inch	Tap Drill†	Threads per Inch	Tap Drill†
0	—	—	80	$\frac{3}{64}$	—	—
1	64	No. 53	72	No. 53	—	—
2	56	No. 50	64	No. 50	—	—
3	48	No. 47	56	No. 45	—	—
4	40	No. 43	48	No. 42	—	—
5	40	No. 38	44	No. 37	—	—
6	32	No. 36	40	No. 33	—	—
8	32	No. 29	36	No. 29	—	—
10	24	No. 25	32	No. 21	—	—
12	24	No. 16	28	No. 14	32	—
1/4	20	No. 7	28	No. 3	32	No. 2
5/16	18	F	24	I	32	K
3/8	16	$\frac{5}{16}$	24	Q	32	S
7/16	14	U	20	$\frac{25}{64}$	28	Y
1/2	13	$\frac{27}{64}$	20	$\frac{29}{64}$	28	$\frac{15}{32}$
9/16	12	$\frac{31}{64}$	18	$\frac{33}{64}$	24	$\frac{17}{32}$
5/8	11	$\frac{17}{32}$	18	$\frac{37}{64}$	24	$\frac{19}{32}$
3/4	10	$\frac{21}{32}$	16	$\frac{11}{16}$	20	$\frac{45}{64}$
7/8	9	$\frac{49}{64}$	14	$\frac{13}{16}$	20	$\frac{53}{64}$
1	8	$\frac{7}{8}$	12	$\frac{59}{64}$	20	$\frac{61}{64}$
1 1/8	7	$\frac{63}{64}$	12	$1\frac{3}{64}$	18	$1\frac{5}{64}$
1 1/4	7	$1\frac{7}{64}$	12	$1\frac{11}{64}$	18	$1\frac{13}{64}$
1 3/8	6	$1\frac{13}{64}$	12	$1\frac{19}{64}$	18	—
1 1/2	6	$1\frac{21}{64}$	12	$1\frac{27}{64}$	18	$1\frac{29}{64}$
1 3/4	5	$1\frac{35}{64}$	—	—	16	$1\frac{11}{16}$
2	4 1/2	$1\frac{25}{32}$	—	—	16	$1\frac{15}{16}$
2 1/4	4 1/2	$2\frac{1}{32}$	—	—	—	—
2 1/2	4	$2\frac{1}{4}$	—	—	—	—
2 3/4	4	$2\frac{1}{2}$	—	—	—	—
3	4	$2\frac{3}{4}$	—	—	—	—
3 1/4	4	3	—	—	—	—
3 1/2	4	$3\frac{1}{4}$	—	—	—	—
3 3/4	4	$3\frac{1}{2}$	—	—	—	—
4	4	$3\frac{3}{4}$	—	—	—	—

* ASA B1.1–1949 (third printing).

Bold type indicates Unified threads. To be designated UNC or UNF for sizes above $\frac{1}{4}''$.

Unified Standard—Classes 1A, 2A, 3A, 1B, 2B, 3B.

For recommended hole size limits before threading see Table 41, ASA B1.1–1949.

† Tap drill for a 75 per cent thread (not Unified—American Standard).

Bold type sizes smaller than $\frac{1}{4}''$ accepted for limited applications by the British, but the symbols NC or NF, as applicable, are retained.

TABLE III

Unified-American Special Threads*
(8 Pitch, 12 Pitch, and 16 Pitch Series)

Dia.	Threads per Inch			Dia.	Threads per Inch		
1/2	—	**12**	—	2 3/16	—	—	**16**
9/16	—	**12**	—	2 1/4	8	**12**	**16**
5/8	—	12	—	2 5/16	—	—	**16**
11/16	—	12	—	2 3/8	—	**12**	**16**
3/4	—	12	**16**	2 7/16	—	—	**16**
13/16	—	12	**16**	2 1/2	8	**12**	**16**
7/8	—	12	**16**	2 5/8	—	**12**	**16**
15/16	—	12	**16**	2 3/4	8	**12**	**16**
1	8	12	**16**	2 7/8	—	**12**	**16**
1 1/16	—	**12**	**16**	3	8	**12**	**16**
1 1/8	8	**12**	**16**	3 1/8	—	**12**	**16**
1 3/16	—	**12**	**16**	3 1/4	8	**12**	**16**
1 1/4	8	**12**	**16**	3 3/8	—	**12**	**16**
1 5/16	—	**12**	**16**	3 1/2	8	**12**	**16**
1 3/8	8	**12**	**16**	3 5/8	—	**12**	**16**
1 7/16	—	**12**	**16**	3 3/4	8	**12**	**16**
1 1/2	8	**12**	**16**	3 7/8	—	**12**	**16**
1 9/16	—	—	**16**	4	8	**12**	**16**
1 5/8	8	**12**	**16**	4 1/4	8	**12**	**16**
1 11/16	—	—	**16**	4 1/2	8	**12**	**16**
1 3/4	8	**12**	**16**	4 3/4	8	**12**	**16**
1 13/16	—	—	**16**	5	8	**12**	**16**
1 7/8	8	**12**	**16**	5 1/4	8	**12**	**16**
1 15/16	—	—	**16**	5 1/2	8	**12**	**16**
2	8	**12**	**16**	5 3/4	8	**12**	**16**
2 1/16	—	—	**16**	6	8	**12**	**16**
2 1/8	8	**12**	**16**				

* ASA B1.1–1949.
For recommended hole size limits before threading see Table 41, ASA B1.1–1949.
Bold type indicates Unified threads (UN).

TABLE IV
American Standard Acme and Stub Acme Threads

Nom. Dia.	Thds. per In.	Nom. Dia.	Thds. per In.
$\frac{1}{4}$	16	$1\frac{1}{2}$	4
$\frac{5}{16}$	14	$1\frac{3}{4}$	4
$\frac{3}{8}$	12	2	4
$\frac{7}{16}$	12	$2\frac{1}{4}$	3
$\frac{1}{2}$	10	$2\frac{1}{2}$	3
$\frac{5}{8}$	8	$2\frac{3}{4}$	3
$\frac{3}{4}$	6	3	2
$\frac{7}{8}$	6	$3\frac{1}{2}$	2
1	5	4	2
$1\frac{1}{8}$	5	$4\frac{1}{2}$	2
$1\frac{1}{4}$	5	5	2
$1\frac{3}{8}$	4		

ASA B1.5 and B1.8–1952.

TABLE V
Standard Bolts
Recommended Minimum Thread Lengths for Bolts†

Nominal Diameter of Bolt — Minimum Thread Length

Bolt* Length	No. 10, 1/4	5/16, 3/8	7/16, 1/2	9/16, 5/8	3/4	7/8	1	1 1/8, 1 1/4	1 3/8, 1 1/2	1 5/8, 1 3/4	1 7/8, 2	2 1/4	2 1/2	2 3/4	3
3/4	1/2														
1	5/8, 3/4	3/4													
1 1/4	5/8, 3/4	7/8, 1	1												
1 1/2	5/8, 3/4	7/8, 1	1 1/8, 1 1/4	1 1/4											
1 3/4	5/8, 3/4	7/8, 1	1 1/8, 1 1/4	1 3/8, 1 1/2	1 1/2										
2	5/8, 3/4	7/8, 1	1 1/8, 1 1/4	1 3/8, 1 1/2	1 3/4	1 3/4									
2 1/2	5/8, 3/4	7/8, 1	1 1/8, 1 1/4	1 3/8, 1 1/2	1 3/4	2	2 1/4	2 1/4							
3	5/8, 3/4	7/8, 1	1 1/8, 1 1/4	1 3/8, 1 1/2	1 3/4	2	2 1/4	2 1/2, 2 3/4	2 3/4						
4	5/8, 3/4	7/8, 1	1 1/8, 1 1/4	1 3/8, 1 1/2	1 3/4	2	2 1/4	2 1/2, 2 3/4	3, 3 1/4	3 1/2, 3 3/4	3 3/4				
5	5/8, 3/4	7/8, 1	1 1/8, 1 1/4	1 3/8, 1 1/2	1 3/4	2	2 1/4	2 1/2, 2 3/4	3, 3 1/4	3 1/2, 3 3/4	4, 4 1/4	4 3/4			
6	5/8, 3/4	7/8, 1	1 1/8, 1 1/4	1 3/8, 1 1/2	1 3/4	2	2 1/4	2 1/2, 2 3/4	3, 3 1/4	3 1/2, 3 3/4	4, 4 1/4	4 3/4	5 1/4	5 3/4	
8	7/8, 1	1 1/8, 1 1/4	1 3/8, 1 1/2	1 5/8, 1 3/4	2	2 1/4	2 1/2	2 3/4, 3	3 1/4, 3 1/2	3 3/4, 4	4 1/4, 4 1/2	5	5 1/2	6	6 1/2
10	7/8, 1	1 1/8, 1 1/4	1 3/8, 1 1/2	1 5/8, 1 3/4	2	2 1/4	2 1/2	2 3/4, 3	3 1/4, 3 1/2	3 3/4, 4	4 1/4, 4 1/2	5	5 1/2	6	6 1/2
12	7/8, 1	1 1/8, 1 1/4	1 3/8, 1 1/2	1 5/8, 1 3/4	2	2 1/4	2 1/2	2 3/4, 3	3 1/4, 3 1/2	3 3/4, 4	4 1/4, 4 1/2	5	5 1/2	6	6 1/2
16	7/8, 1	1 1/8, 1 1/4	1 3/8, 1 1/2	1 5/8, 1 3/4	2	2 1/4	2 1/2	2 3/4, 3	3 1/4, 3 1/2	3 3/4, 4	4 1/4, 4 1/2	5	5 1/2	6	6 1/2
20	7/8, 1	1 1/8, 1 1/4	1 3/8, 1 1/2	1 5/8, 1 3/4	2	2 1/4	2 1/2	2 3/4, 3	3 1/4, 3 1/2	3 3/4, 4	4 1/4, 4 1/2	5	5 1/2	6	6 1/2
30	7/8, 1	1 1/8, 1 1/4	1 3/8, 1 1/2	1 5/8, 1 3/4	2	2 1/4	2 1/2	2 3/4, 3	3 1/4, 3 1/2	3 3/4, 4	4 1/4, 4 1/2	5	5 1/2	6	6 1/2

† Recommended by the ASA but does not comprise a part of the standard ASA B18.2–1941 Appendix.

* For intermediate bolt lengths, the minimum thread length shall be the same as that specified in the table for the next shorter length of bolt of the same diameter.

All dimensions given in inches.

Minimum thread length is measured from the end of the bolt to the last complete thread.

TABLE VI

American Standard Wrench-Head Bolts and Nuts—Regular Series*

Bolt Dia. Nominal Size	Bolt Heads				Nuts				
	Width Across Flats	Height of Head			Width Across Flats	Thickness			
						Regular		Jam	
	Unfinished and Semifinished Square and Hex.¹	Unfinished Square	Unfinished Hexagon	Semifinished Hexagon	Unfinished Hex. Semifinished Hex. and Hex. Jam	Unfinished Square and Hex.	Semifinished Hex. and Hex. Slotted	Unfinished Hexagonal	Semifinished Hexagonal
$\frac{1}{4}$	$\left\{\begin{array}{l}\frac{3}{8}\text{ sq.}\\\frac{7}{16}\text{ Hex.}\end{array}\right.$	$\frac{11}{64}$	$\frac{11}{64}$	$\frac{5}{32}$	$\frac{7}{16}$	$\frac{7}{32}$	$\frac{13}{64}$	$\frac{5}{32}$	$\frac{9}{64}$
$\frac{5}{16}$	$\frac{1}{2}$	$\frac{13}{64}$	$\frac{7}{32}$	$\frac{13}{64}$	$\frac{9}{16}$	$\frac{17}{64}$	$\frac{1}{4}$	$\frac{3}{16}$	$\frac{11}{64}$
$\frac{3}{8}$	$\frac{9}{16}$	$\frac{1}{4}$	$\frac{1}{4}$	$\frac{15}{64}$	$\frac{5}{8}$	$\frac{21}{64}$	$\frac{5}{16}$	$\frac{7}{32}$	$\frac{13}{64}$
$\frac{7}{16}$	$\frac{5}{8}$	$\frac{19}{64}$	$\frac{19}{64}$	$\frac{9}{32}$	$\frac{3}{4}$	$\frac{3}{8}$	$\frac{23}{64}$	$\frac{1}{4}$	$\frac{15}{64}$
$\frac{1}{2}$	$\frac{3}{4}$	$\frac{21}{64}$	$\frac{11}{32}$	$\frac{5}{16}$	$\frac{13}{16}$	$\frac{7}{16}$	$\frac{27}{64}$	$\frac{5}{16}$	$\frac{19}{64}$
$\frac{9}{16}$	—	—	—	—	$\frac{7}{8}$	$\frac{1}{2}$	$\frac{31}{64}$	$\frac{11}{32}$	$\frac{21}{64}$
$\frac{5}{8}$	$\frac{15}{16}$	$\frac{27}{64}$	$\frac{27}{64}$	$\frac{25}{64}$	1	$\frac{35}{64}$	$\frac{17}{32}$	$\frac{3}{8}$	$\frac{23}{64}$
$\frac{3}{4}$	$1\frac{1}{8}$	$\frac{1}{2}$	$\frac{1}{2}$	$\frac{15}{32}$	$1\frac{1}{8}$	$\frac{21}{32}$	$\frac{41}{64}$	$\frac{7}{16}$	$\frac{27}{64}$
$\frac{7}{8}$	$1\frac{5}{16}$	$\frac{19}{32}$	$\frac{37}{64}$	$\frac{35}{64}$	$1\frac{5}{16}$	$\frac{49}{64}$	$\frac{3}{4}$	$\frac{1}{2}$	$\frac{31}{64}$
1	$1\frac{1}{2}$	$\frac{21}{32}$	$\frac{43}{64}$	$\frac{39}{64}$	$1\frac{1}{2}$	$\frac{7}{8}$	$\frac{55}{64}$	$\frac{9}{16}$	$\frac{35}{64}$
$1\frac{1}{8}$	$1\frac{11}{16}$	$\frac{3}{4}$	$\frac{3}{4}$	$\frac{11}{16}$	$1\frac{11}{16}$	1	$\frac{31}{32}$	$\frac{5}{8}$	$\frac{39}{64}$
$1\frac{1}{4}$	$1\frac{7}{8}$	$\frac{27}{32}$	$\frac{27}{32}$	$\frac{25}{32}$	$1\frac{7}{8}$	$1\frac{3}{32}$	$1\frac{1}{16}$	$\frac{3}{4}$	$\frac{23}{32}$
$1\frac{3}{8}$	$2\frac{1}{16}$	$\frac{29}{32}$	$\frac{29}{32}$	$\frac{27}{32}$	$2\frac{1}{16}$	$1\frac{13}{64}$	$1\frac{11}{64}$	$\frac{13}{16}$	$\frac{25}{32}$
$1\frac{1}{2}$	$2\frac{1}{4}$	1	1	$\frac{15}{16}$	$2\frac{1}{4}$	$1\frac{5}{16}$	$1\frac{9}{32}$	$\frac{7}{8}$	$\frac{27}{32}$
$1\frac{5}{8}$	$2\frac{7}{16}$	$1\frac{3}{32}$	—	—	$2\frac{7}{16}$	—	$1\frac{25}{64}$	—	$\frac{29}{32}$
$1\frac{3}{4}$	$2\frac{5}{8}$	—	$1\frac{5}{32}$	$1\frac{3}{32}$	$2\frac{5}{8}$	—	$1\frac{1}{2}$	—	$\frac{31}{32}$
$1\frac{7}{8}$	—	—	—	—	$2\frac{13}{16}$	—	$1\frac{39}{64}$	—	$1\frac{1}{32}$
2	3	—	$1\frac{11}{32}$	$1\frac{7}{32}$	3	—	$1\frac{23}{32}$	—	$1\frac{3}{32}$
$2\frac{1}{4}$	$3\frac{3}{8}$	—	$1\frac{1}{2}$	$1\frac{3}{8}$	$3\frac{3}{8}$	—	$1\frac{59}{64}$	—	$1\frac{13}{64}$
$2\frac{1}{2}$	$3\frac{3}{4}$	—	$1\frac{21}{32}$	$1\frac{17}{32}$	$3\frac{3}{4}$	—	$2\frac{9}{64}$	—	$1\frac{29}{64}$
$2\frac{3}{4}$	$4\frac{1}{8}$	—	$1\frac{13}{16}$	$1\frac{11}{16}$	$4\frac{1}{8}$	—	$2\frac{23}{64}$	—	$1\frac{37}{64}$
3	$4\frac{1}{2}$	—	2	$1\frac{7}{8}$	$4\frac{1}{2}$	—	$2\frac{37}{64}$	—	$1\frac{45}{64}$

* ASA B18.2–1955.   All dimensions in inches.

Threads-bolts: course-thread series, class 2A.

Threads-nuts: unfinished; coarse series, class 2B: semifinished; coarse, fine, or 8-pitch series.

TABLE VII
Elastic Stop Nuts

Nominal Size	Threads per Inch		Across Flats F	Std. Height H	Thin Height T
	NC	NF			
No. 2	56	64	$\frac{1}{4}$	$\frac{5}{32}$	
No. 3	48	56	$\frac{1}{4}$	$\frac{5}{32}$	
No. 4	40	48	$\frac{1}{4}$	$\frac{5}{32}$	$\frac{1}{8}$
No. 5	40	44	$\frac{1}{4}$	$\frac{5}{32}$	
No. 6	32	40	$\frac{5}{16}$	$\frac{3}{16}$	$\frac{9}{64}$
No. 8	32	36	$\frac{11}{32}$	$\frac{1}{4}$	$\frac{3}{16}$
No. 10	24	32	$\frac{3}{8}$	$\frac{1}{4}$	$\frac{3}{16}$
No. 12	24	28	$\frac{7}{16}$	$\frac{21}{64}$	$\frac{7}{32}$
HEAVY WEIGHT					
$\frac{1}{4}$	20		$\frac{1}{2}$	$\frac{3}{8}$	$\frac{3}{32}$
$\frac{5}{16}$	18		$\frac{9}{16}$	$\frac{7}{16}$	$\frac{5}{16}$
$\frac{3}{8}$	16		$\frac{11}{16}$	$\frac{35}{64}$	$\frac{13}{32}$
$\frac{7}{16}$	14		$\frac{3}{4}$	$\frac{19}{32}$	$\frac{7}{16}$
$\frac{1}{2}$	13		$\frac{7}{8}$	$\frac{45}{64}$	$\frac{17}{32}$
$\frac{9}{16}$	12		$\frac{15}{16}$	$\frac{13}{16}$	$\frac{9}{16}$
$\frac{5}{8}$	11		$1\frac{1}{16}$	$\frac{55}{64}$	$\frac{39}{64}$
$\frac{3}{4}$	10		$1\frac{1}{4}$	1	$\frac{45}{64}$
$\frac{7}{8}$	9		$1\frac{7}{16}$	$1\frac{1}{8}$	$\frac{25}{32}$
1	8		$1\frac{5}{8}$	$1\frac{3}{32}$	$\frac{57}{64}$
$1\frac{1}{8}$	7		$1\frac{13}{16}$	$1\frac{7}{16}$	$\frac{31}{32}$
$1\frac{1}{4}$	7		2	$1\frac{11}{64}$	$1\frac{7}{64}$
$1\frac{3}{8}$	6		$2\frac{3}{16}$	$1\frac{51}{64}$	$1\frac{3}{16}$
$1\frac{1}{2}$	6		$2\frac{3}{8}$	$1\frac{59}{64}$	$1\frac{5}{16}$
$1\frac{3}{4}$	5		$2\frac{3}{4}$	$2\frac{5}{16}$	$1\frac{11}{32}$
2	$4\frac{1}{2}$		$3\frac{1}{8}$	$2\frac{13}{32}$	$1\frac{11}{16}$
$2\frac{1}{4}$	$4\frac{1}{2}$		$3\frac{1}{2}$	$2\frac{13}{16}$	$1\frac{13}{16}$
LIGHT WEIGHT					
$\frac{1}{4}$		28	$\frac{7}{16}$	$\frac{21}{64}$	$\frac{7}{32}$
$\frac{5}{16}$		24	$\frac{1}{2}$	$\frac{23}{64}$	$\frac{17}{64}$
$\frac{3}{8}$		24	$\frac{9}{16}$	$\frac{15}{32}$	$\frac{9}{32}$
$\frac{7}{16}$		20	$\frac{5}{8}$	$\frac{15}{32}$	$\frac{21}{64}$
$\frac{1}{2}$		20	$\frac{3}{4}$	$\frac{39}{64}$	$\frac{21}{64}$
$\frac{9}{16}$		18	$\frac{7}{8}$	$\frac{45}{64}$	$\frac{3}{8}$
$\frac{5}{8}$		18	$\frac{15}{16}$	$\frac{49}{64}$	$\frac{13}{32}$
$\frac{3}{4}$		16	$1\frac{1}{16}$	$\frac{57}{64}$	$\frac{27}{64}$
$\frac{7}{8}$		14	$1\frac{1}{4}$	$1\frac{1}{64}$	$\frac{31}{64}$
1		14	$1\frac{7}{16}$	$1\frac{9}{64}$	$\frac{37}{64}$
$1\frac{1}{8}$		12	$1\frac{5}{8}$	$1\frac{17}{64}$	$\frac{43}{64}$
$1\frac{1}{4}$		12	$1\frac{13}{16}$	$1\frac{29}{64}$	$\frac{47}{64}$
$1\frac{3}{8}$		12	2	$1\frac{19}{32}$	$\frac{25}{32}$
$1\frac{1}{2}$		12	$2\frac{3}{16}$	$1\frac{3}{4}$	$\frac{13}{16}$

Note: All dimensions in inches. Compiled from catalogue of Elastic Stop Nut Corp. of America.

TABLE VIII

American Standard Finished Hexagon Castle Nuts*

Nominal Size	Threads per Inch		Thickness	Width across Flats	Slot		Dia. of Cylindrical Part Min.
	UNC	UNF			Depth	Width	
D			A	B	C	E	
$\frac{1}{4}$	20	28	$\frac{9}{32}$	$\frac{7}{16}$	0.094	0.078	0.371
$\frac{5}{16}$	18	24	$\frac{21}{64}$	$\frac{1}{2}$	0.094	0.094	0.425
$\frac{3}{8}$	16	24	$\frac{13}{32}$	$\frac{9}{16}$	0.125	0.125	0.478
$\frac{7}{16}$	14	20	$\frac{29}{64}$	$\frac{11}{16}$	0.156	0.125	0.582
$\frac{1}{2}$	13	20	$\frac{9}{16}$	$\frac{3}{4}$	0.156	0.156	0.637
$\frac{9}{16}$	12	18	$\frac{39}{64}$	$\frac{7}{8}$	0.188	0.156	0.744
$\frac{5}{8}$	11	18	$\frac{23}{32}$	$\frac{15}{16}$	0.219	0.188	0.797
$\frac{3}{4}$	10	16	$\frac{13}{16}$	$1\frac{1}{8}$	0.250	0.188	0.941
$\frac{7}{8}$	9	14	$\frac{29}{32}$	$1\frac{5}{16}$	0.250	0.188	1.097
1	8	12	1	$1\frac{1}{2}$	0.281	0.250	1.254
$1\frac{1}{8}$	7	12	$1\frac{5}{32}$	$1\frac{11}{16}$	0.344	0.250	1.411

* ASA B18.2–1955.

Thread may be coarse- or fine-thread series, class 2B tolerance; unless otherwise specified fine-thread series shall be furnished.

TABLE IX
American Standard Set Screws

| FLAT POINT | CUP POINT | CONE POINT | OVAL POINT | DOG POINT | HALF DOG POINT |

Nominal Size D	Slotted Headless			Hex. Socket (Min.)		Square Head (F-Max.)			Points								
									Cup and Flat (K-Max.)			Cone	Oval	Full and Half Dog (N-Max.)			
	A	B	R_1	C	D*	F	H	R_2	K	W	X	Y	R_3	L	M	N	Z
5	.023	.031	.125	$\frac{1}{16}$	.050	—	—	—	.067				.094	.060	.030	.083	
6	.025	.035	.138	$\frac{1}{16}$	.050	—	—	—	.074			$Y = 118° \pm 2°$	.109	.070	.035	.092	
8	.029	.041	.164	$\frac{5}{64}$	.062	—	—	—	.087				.125	.080	.040	.109	
10	.032	.048	.190	$\frac{3}{32}$	.075	.1875	$\frac{9}{64}$	$\frac{15}{32}$	.102				.141	.090	.045	.127	
12	.036	.054	.216	$\frac{3}{32}$	.075	.216	$\frac{5}{32}$	$\frac{35}{64}$	.115				.156	.110	.055	.144	
$\frac{1}{4}$	.045	.063	.250	$\frac{1}{8}$	.100	.250	$\frac{3}{16}$	$\frac{5}{8}$	.132			When L equals nominal diameter or less, $Y = 118° \pm 2°$; $Y = 90°$ (Draw as 90°)	.188	.125	.063	.156	
$\frac{5}{16}$	.051	.078	.313	$\frac{5}{32}$	.125	.3125	$\frac{15}{64}$	$\frac{25}{32}$	.172				.234	.156	.078	.203	$Z = 100°$ to $110°$
$\frac{3}{8}$	.064	.094	.375	$\frac{3}{16}$	.150	.375	$\frac{9}{32}$	$\frac{15}{16}$	.212				.281	.188	.094	.250	
$\frac{7}{16}$	.072	.109	.438	$\frac{7}{32}$	.175	.4375	$\frac{21}{64}$	$1\frac{3}{32}$	.252				.328	.219	.109	.297	
$\frac{1}{2}$	.081	.125	.500	$\frac{1}{4}$	.200	.500	$\frac{3}{8}$	$1\frac{1}{4}$	.291	$W = 80°$ to $90°$	$X = 118° \pm 5°$	When L exceeds nominal diameter, $Y = 90°$	.375	.250	.125	.344	
$\frac{9}{16}$	.091	.141	.563	$\frac{1}{4}$	.200	.5625	$\frac{27}{64}$	$1\frac{13}{32}$	.332				.422	.281	.140	.391	
$\frac{5}{8}$	.102	.156	.625	$\frac{5}{16}$	.250	.625	$\frac{15}{32}$	$1\frac{9}{16}$	.371				.469	.313	.156	.469	
$\frac{3}{4}$	.129	.188	.750	$\frac{3}{8}$	.300	.750	$\frac{9}{16}$	$1\frac{7}{8}$	.450				.563	.375	.188	.563	
$\frac{7}{8}$	—	—	—	$\frac{1}{2}$	.400	.875	$\frac{21}{32}$	$2\frac{3}{16}$	—				—	—	—	—	
1	—	—	—	$\frac{9}{16}$	.450	1.000	$\frac{3}{4}$	$2\frac{1}{2}$	—				—	—	—	—	
$1\frac{1}{8}$	—	—	—	$\frac{9}{16}$	.450	1.125	$\frac{27}{32}$	$2\frac{13}{16}$	—				—	—	—	—	
$1\frac{1}{4}$	—	—	—	$\frac{5}{8}$	.500	1.250	$\frac{15}{16}$	$3\frac{1}{8}$	—				—	—	—	—	
$1\frac{3}{8}$	—	—	—	$\frac{5}{8}$	.500	1.375	$1\frac{1}{32}$	$3\frac{7}{16}$	—				—	—	—	—	
$1\frac{1}{2}$	—	—	—	$\frac{3}{4}$	.600	1.500	$1\frac{1}{8}$	$3\frac{3}{4}$	—				—	—	—	—	

ASA B18.6.2–1956.
ASA B18.3–1954.

* Dimensions apply to cup and flat point screws one diameter in length or longer. For screws shorter than one diameter in length, and for other types of points, socket to be as deep as practicable.

TABLE X
American Standard Machine Screws

FLAT HEAD   ROUND HEAD   OVAL HEAD   FILLISTER HEAD

Size (Number) and Threads per Inch				American Standard Dimensions (Max.)												
Nominal Size	Diameter D	Thread		Head Diameter			Height Dimensions					Slot Width	Slot Depth			
		Coarse	Fine	A	B	C	E	F	G	H	K	J	L	M	N	O
0	.060	—	80	.119	.113	.096	.035	.053	.056	.045	.059	.023	.015	.039	.030	.025
1	.073	64	72	.146	.138	.118	.043	.061	.068	.053	.071	.026	.019	.044	.038	.031
2	.086	56	64	.172	.162	.140	.051	.069	.080	.062	.083	.031	.023	.048	.045	.037
3	.099	48	56	.199	.187	.161	.059	.078	.092	.070	.095	.035	.027	.053	.052	.043
4	.112	40	48	.225	.211	.183	.067	.086	.104	.079	.107	.039	.030	.058	.059	.048
5	.125	40	44	.252	.236	.205	.075	.095	.116	.088	.120	.043	.034	.063	.067	.054
6	.138	32	40	.279	.260	.226	.083	.103	.128	.096	.132	.048	.038	.068	.074	.060
8	.164	32	36	.332	.309	.270	.100	.120	.152	.113	.156	.054	.045	.077	.088	.071
10	.190	24	32	.385	.359	.313	.116	.137	.176	.130	.180	.060	.053	.087	.103	.083
12	.216	24	28	.438	.408	.357	.132	.153	.200	.148	.205	.067	.060	.096	.117	.094
$\frac{1}{4}$	.250	20	28	.507	.472	.414	.153	.175	.232	.170	.237	.075	.070	.109	.136	.109
$\frac{5}{16}$	.3125	18	24	.635	.590	.518	.191	.216	.290	.211	.295	.084	.088	.132	.171	.137
$\frac{3}{8}$	.375	16	24	.762	.708	.622	.230	.256	.347	.253	.355	.094	.106	.155	.206	.164
$\frac{7}{16}$	.4375	14	20	.812	.750	.625	.223	.328	.345	.265	.368	.094	.103	.196	.210	.170
$\frac{1}{2}$	.500	13	20	.875	.813	.750	.223	.355	.354	.297	.412	.106	.103	.211	.216	.190
$\frac{9}{16}$	.5625	12	18	1.000	.938	.812	.260	.410	.410	.336	.466	.118	.120	.242	.250	.214
$\frac{5}{8}$	.625	11	18	1.125	1.000	.875	.298	.438	.467	.375	.521	.133	.137	.258	.285	.240
$\frac{3}{4}$	.750	10	16	1.375	1.250	1.000	.372	.547	.578	.441	.612	.149	.171	.320	.353	.281

ASA B18.6-1947.

Thread length—screws 2 inches in length or less are threaded as close to the head as practicable. Screws longer than 2 inches should have a minimum thread length of $1\frac{3}{4}$ inches.

TABLE XI
American Standard Cap Screws

Nominal Size (Dia.)	Head Diameter					Height Dimensions					Slot Width	Slot Depth			Socket Dimensions	
	A	B	C	E	W	F Ave.	G	H Nom.	K	M	J	O	P	Q	N Min.	T Min.
1/4	.500	.437	.375	3/8	7/16	.140	.191	5/32	.172	.216	.075	.068	.117	.097	3/16	.120
5/16	.625	.562	.437	7/16	1/2	.177	.245	13/64	.203	.253	.084	.086	.151	.115	3/32	.151
3/8	.750	.625	.562	9/16	9/16	.210	.273	15/64	.250	.314	.094	.103	.168	.142	3/16	.182
7/16	.8125	.750	.625	5/8	5/8	.210	.328	9/32	.297	.368	.094	.103	.202	.168	5/16	.213
1/2	.875	.812	.750	3/4	3/4	.210	.354	5/16	.328	.413	.106	.103	.218	.193	3/8	.245
9/16	1.000	.937	.812	13/16	13/16	.244	.409	23/64	.375	.467	.118	.120	.252	.213	3/8	.276
5/8	1.125	1.000	.875	7/8	15/16	.281	.437	25/64	.422	.521	.133	.137	.270	.239	1/2	.307
3/4	1.375	1.250	1.000	1	1 1/8	.352	.546	15/32	.500	.612	.149	.171	.338	.283	9/16	.370
7/8	1.625	—	1.125	1 1/8	1 5/16	.423	—	35/64	.594	.720	.167	.206	—	.334	9/16	.432
1	1.875	—	1.312	1 5/16	1 1/2	.494	—	39/64	.656	.803	.188	.240	—	.371	5/8	.495
1 1/8	2.062	—	—	1 1/2	1 11/16	.529	—	11/16	—	—	.196	.257	—	—	3/4	.557
1 1/4	2.312	—	—	1 3/4	1 7/8	.600	—	25/32	—	—	.211	.291	—	—	3/4	.620
1 3/8	2.562	—	—	1 7/8	2 1/16	.665	—	27/32	—	—	.226	.326	—	—	3/4	.682
1 1/2	2.812	—	—	2	2 1/4	.742	—	15/16	—	—	.258	.360	—	—	1	.745

ASA B18.3–1954.
ASA B18.6.2–1956.
Bold type indicates products unified dimensionally with British and Canadian standards.
Minimum thread length shall be twice the diameter plus $\frac{1}{4}$ in. for lengths up to and including 6 inches.
Threads shall be coarse, fine, or 8-thread series, class 2A for plain (unplated) cap screws.

TABLE XII
Hexagonal-Head Self-Tapping Screws

Nom. Size	Across Flats F	Head Height H	Lengths											
			$\frac{3}{16}$	$\frac{1}{4}$	$\frac{3}{8}$	$\frac{1}{2}$	$\frac{5}{8}$	$\frac{3}{4}$	$\frac{7}{8}$	1	$1\frac{1}{4}$	$1\frac{1}{2}$	$1\frac{3}{4}$	2
No. 4	.187	.060	X	X										
No. 6	.250	.080	X	X	X									
No. 8	.250	.110		X	X	X	X	X	X	X				
No. 10	.312	.120			X	X	X	X	X	X				
No. 12	.312	.155				X	X	X	X	X	X	X		
$\frac{1}{4}$	.375	.190			X	X	X	X	X	X	X	X	X	X
$\frac{5}{16}$	.500	.230					X	X	X	X	X	X	X	
$\frac{3}{8}$	.562	.295						X	X	X	X	X	X	X
$\frac{7}{16}$	.625	.312							X	X	X	X	X	X
$\frac{1}{2}$	.750	.375							X	X	X	X	X	X

Note: All dimensions are in inches. Self-tapping screws are also available in the same head styles as machine screws. Dimensions of these head styles are the same as for machine screws.

Diameters of drilled holes for these screws vary with the thickness and type of material to be fastened. Consult manufacturers' catalogues for this data.

TABLE XIII

American Standard Wood Screws

FLAT HEAD

OVAL HEAD

ROUND HEAD

Screw No.	Dia. (D)	A Max.	B Max.	C Max.	E Max.	F Max.	G Max.	J Max.	K Max.	M Max.	Threads per Inch
0	.060	.119	.035	.023	.015	.021	.030	.113	.039	.053	32
1	.073	.146	.043	.026	.019	.025	.038	.138	.044	.061	28
2	.086	.172	.051	.031	.023	.029	.045	.162	.048	.069	26
3	.099	.199	.059	.035	.027	.033	.052	.187	.053	.078	24
4	.112	.225	.067	.039	.030	.037	.059	.211	.058	.086	22
5	.125	.252	.075	.043	.034	.041	.067	.236	.063	.095	20
6	.138	.279	.083	.048	.038	.045	.074	.260	.068	.103	18
7	.151	.305	.091	.048	.041	.049	.081	.285	.072	.111	16
8	.164	.332	.100	.054	.045	.052	.088	.309	.077	.120	15
9	.177	.358	.108	.054	.049	.056	.095	.334	.082	.128	14
10	.190	.385	.116	.060	.053	.060	.103	.359	.087	.137	13
12	.216	.438	.132	.067	.060	.068	.117	.408	.096	.153	11
14	.242	.491	.148	.075	.068	.076	.132	.457	.106	.170	10
16	.268	.544	.164	.075	.075	.084	.146	.506	.115	.187	9
18	.294	.597	.180	.084	.083	.092	.160	.555	.125	.204	8
20	.320	.650	.196	.084	.090	.100	.175	.604	.134	.220	8
24	.372	.756	.228	.094	.105	.116	.204	.702	.154	.254	7

Compiled from ASA B18.6.1–1956.
Dimensions in inches.

TABLE XIV
American Standard Washers

Nominal Size	PLAIN WASHERS[1]					
	LIGHT			MEDIUM		
	A ID	B OD	H Thickness	A ID	B OD	H Thickness
$\frac{1}{4}$	$\frac{9}{32}$	$\frac{5}{8}$	0.065	$\frac{5}{16}$	$\frac{3}{4}$	0.065
$\frac{5}{16}$	$\frac{11}{32}$	$\frac{11}{16}$	0.065	$\frac{3}{8}$	$\frac{3}{4}$	0.065
$\frac{3}{8}$	$\frac{13}{32}$	$\frac{13}{16}$	0.065	$\frac{7}{16}$	$\frac{7}{8}$	0.083
$\frac{7}{16}$	$\frac{15}{32}$	$\frac{59}{64}$	0.065	$\frac{1}{2}$	$1\frac{1}{8}$	0.083
$\frac{1}{2}$	$\frac{17}{32}$	$1\frac{1}{16}$	0.095	$\frac{9}{16}$	$1\frac{1}{4}$	0.109
$\frac{9}{16}$	$\frac{19}{32}$	$1\frac{3}{16}$	0.095	$\frac{5}{8}$	$1\frac{3}{8}$	0.109
$\frac{5}{8}$	$\frac{21}{32}$	$1\frac{5}{16}$	0.095	$\frac{11}{16}$	$1\frac{1}{2}$	0.134
$\frac{3}{4}$	$\frac{13}{16}$	$1\frac{1}{2}$	0.134	$\frac{13}{16}$	$1\frac{3}{4}$	0.148
$\frac{7}{8}$	$\frac{15}{16}$	$1\frac{3}{4}$	0.134	$\frac{15}{16}$	2	0.165
1	$1\frac{1}{16}$	2	0.134	$1\frac{1}{16}$	$2\frac{1}{4}$	0.165
$1\frac{1}{8}$	—	—	—	$1\frac{3}{16}$	$2\frac{1}{2}$	0.165
$1\frac{1}{4}$	—	—	—	$1\frac{5}{16}$	$2\frac{3}{4}$	0.165
$1\frac{3}{8}$	—	—	—	$1\frac{7}{16}$	3	0.180
$1\frac{1}{2}$	—	—	—	$1\frac{9}{16}$	$3\frac{1}{4}$	0.180

Nominal Size	LOCK WASHERS[2]					
	LIGHT			MEDIUM		
	C ID	D OD (Max.)	T Thickness (Min.)	C ID	D OD (Max.)	T Thickness (Min.)
$\frac{1}{4}$	0.255	0.489	0.047		0.493	0.062
$\frac{5}{16}$	0.319	0.575	0.056		0.591	0.078
$\frac{3}{8}$	0.382	0.678	0.070		0.688	0.094
$\frac{7}{16}$	0.446	0.780	0.085		0.784	0.109
$\frac{1}{2}$	0.509	0.877	0.099		0.879	0.125
$\frac{9}{16}$	0.573	0.975	0.113	Same as for Light Lock Washers	0.979	0.141
$\frac{5}{8}$	0.636	1.082	0.126		1.086	0.156
$\frac{11}{16}$	0.700	1.178	0.138		1.184	0.172
$\frac{3}{4}$	0.763	1.277	0.153		1.279	0.188
$\frac{7}{8}$	0.890	1.470	0.179		1.474	0.219
1	1.017	1.656	0.202		1.672	0.250
$1\frac{1}{8}$	1.144	1.837	0.224		1.865	0.281
$1\frac{1}{4}$	1.271	2.012	0.244		2.058	0.312
$1\frac{3}{8}$	1.398	2.183	0.264		2.253	0.344
$1\frac{1}{2}$	1.525	2.352	0.282		2.446	0.375

[1] ASA B27.2–1953.   All dimensions in inches.
[2] ASA B27.1–1950.   All dimensions in inches.
Dimensions for heavy and extra heavy washers may be found in the standards listed above.

TABLE XV

Lock Washers

EXTERNAL   INTERNAL

Screw Size	External Tooth		Internal Tooth	
	O.D.	Thickness	O.D.	Thickness
No. 2			$\frac{3}{16}$	.012
No. 3			$\frac{7}{32}$	.016
No. 4	$\frac{9}{32}$	.016	$\frac{17}{64}$	.016
No. 5	$\frac{1}{4}$	.018	$\frac{1}{4}$	.018
No. 6	$\frac{5}{16}$	.018	$\frac{9}{32}$	.018
No. 8	$\frac{3}{8}$	.020	$\frac{21}{64}$	.020
No. 10	$\frac{13}{32}$	.022	$\frac{3}{8}$	.022
No. 12	$\frac{15}{32}$	.022	$\frac{13}{32}$	.022
$\frac{1}{4}$	$\frac{1}{2}$	.025	$\frac{15}{32}$	.025
$\frac{5}{16}$	$\frac{19}{32}$	.030	$\frac{19}{32}$	.030
$\frac{3}{8}$	$\frac{11}{16}$	.035	$\frac{11}{16}$	.035
$\frac{7}{16}$	$\frac{3}{4}$	.035	$\frac{25}{32}$	.035
$\frac{1}{2}$	$\frac{57}{64}$	.040	$\frac{7}{8}$	.040
$\frac{9}{16}$	$\frac{31}{32}$	.040	$\frac{31}{32}$	.040
$\frac{5}{8}$	$1\frac{1}{16}$	.045	$1\frac{1}{16}$	.045
$\frac{11}{16}$			$1\frac{5}{32}$	.045
$\frac{3}{4}$	$1\frac{1}{4}$	.050	$1\frac{1}{4}$	.050
$\frac{13}{16}$		.	$1\frac{3}{8}$	.050
$\frac{7}{8}$	$1\frac{13}{32}$	.055	$1\frac{3}{8}$	.055
1	$1\frac{5}{8}$	.062	$1\frac{5}{8}$	.062
$1\frac{1}{8}$			$1\frac{13}{16}$	.062
$1\frac{5}{16}$			$1\frac{15}{16}$	.062
$1\frac{1}{2}$			$2\frac{1}{4}$	.078
$1\frac{3}{4}$			$2\frac{5}{8}$	.078
$1\frac{7}{8}$			$2\frac{1}{2}$	.078

Note: All dimensions are in inches.

TABLE XVI
Cotter Pins

Bolt and Rod Dia. (NC)	Cotter Pins					
	Cotter Dia.	A	B	Drill No.	Length	
					Short	Long
$\frac{1}{4}$	$\frac{1}{16}$	$\frac{3}{32}$	$\frac{5}{32}$	48	$\frac{1}{2}$	$\frac{5}{8}$
$\frac{5}{16}$	$\frac{1}{16}$	$\frac{3}{32}$	$\frac{5}{32}$	48	$\frac{5}{8}$	$\frac{3}{4}$
$\frac{3}{8}$	$\frac{3}{32}$	$\frac{1}{8}$	$\frac{7}{32}$	36	$\frac{3}{4}$	$\frac{7}{8}$
$\frac{7}{16}$	$\frac{3}{32}$	$\frac{1}{8}$	$\frac{7}{32}$	36	$\frac{3}{4}$	1
$\frac{1}{2}$	$\frac{3}{32}$	$\frac{1}{8}$	$\frac{7}{32}$	36	$\frac{7}{8}$	$1\frac{1}{8}$
$\frac{9}{16}$	$\frac{1}{8}$	$\frac{5}{32}$	$\frac{9}{32}$	28	1	$1\frac{1}{4}$
$\frac{5}{8}$	$\frac{1}{8}$	$\frac{5}{32}$	$\frac{9}{32}$	28	$1\frac{1}{8}$	$1\frac{3}{8}$
$\frac{3}{4}$	$\frac{1}{8}$	$\frac{5}{32}$	$\frac{9}{32}$	28	$1\frac{1}{4}$	$1\frac{1}{2}$
$\frac{7}{8}$	$\frac{1}{8}$	$\frac{5}{32}$	$\frac{9}{32}$	28	$1\frac{3}{8}$	$1\frac{3}{4}$
1	$\frac{1}{8}$	$\frac{5}{32}$	$\frac{9}{32}$	28	$1\frac{5}{8}$	2

TABLE XVII
American Standard Machine Screw and Stove Bolt Nuts

Diameter		Number Size										$\frac{1}{4}$	$\frac{5}{16}$	$\frac{3}{8}$
		0	1	2	3	4	5	6	8	10	12			
Across Flats (Nom.)		$\frac{5}{32}$	$\frac{5}{32}$	$\frac{3}{16}$	$\frac{3}{16}$	$\frac{1}{4}$	$\frac{5}{16}$	$\frac{5}{16}$	$\frac{11}{32}$	$\frac{3}{8}$	$\frac{7}{16}$	$\frac{7}{16}$	$\frac{9}{16}$	$\frac{5}{8}$
Across Corners (Min.)	Hex.	.171	.171	.205	.205	.275	.344	.344	.378	.413	.482	.482	.621	.692
	Square	.206	.206	.247	.247	.331	.415	.415	.456	.497	.581	.581	.748	.833
Thickness (Nom.)		$\frac{3}{64}$	$\frac{3}{64}$	$\frac{1}{16}$	$\frac{1}{16}$	$\frac{3}{32}$	$\frac{7}{64}$	$\frac{7}{64}$	$\frac{1}{8}$	$\frac{1}{8}$	$\frac{3}{32}$	$\frac{7}{16}$	$\frac{7}{32}$	$\frac{1}{4}$

ASA B18.2–1955.
Dimensions in inches.

TABLE XVIII
American Standard Small Rivets

FLAT HEAD · COUNTERSUNK HEAD · BUTTON HEAD · PAN HEAD · TRUSS HEAD

RIVET DIAMETER D	FLAT Dia. A Max.	FLAT Height B Max.	CSK. Dia. C Max.	CSK. Height E	BUTTON Dia. F Max.	BUTTON Height G Max.	BUTTON Rad. H	PAN Dia. J Max.	PAN Height K Max.	PAN Rad. L	PAN Rad. M	PAN Rad. N	TRUSS Dia. O Max.	TRUSS Height P Max.	TRUSS Rad. Q
1/16	.140	.027	.118	.027	.122	.052	.055	.118	.040	.217	.052	.019	—	—	—
3/32	.200	.038	.176	.040	.182	.077	.084	.173	.060	.326	.080	.030	.226	.038	.239
1/8	.260	.048	.235	.053	.235	.100	.111	.225	.078	.429	.106	.039	.297	.048	.314
5/32	.323	.059	.293	.066	.290	.124	.138	.279	.096	.535	.133	.049	.368	.059	.392
3/16	.387	.069	.351	.079	.348	.147	.166	.334	.114	.641	.159	.059	.442	.069	.470
7/32	.453	.080	.413	.094	.405	.172	.195	.391	.133	.754	.186	.069	.515	.080	.555
1/4	.515	.091	.469	.106	.460	.196	.221	.444	.151	.858	.213	.079	.590	.091	.628
9/32	.579	.103	.528	.119	.518	.220	.249	.499	.170	.963	.239	.088	.661	.103	.706
5/16	.641	.113	.588	.133	.572	.243	.276	.552	.187	1.070	.266	.098	.732	.113	.784
11/32	.705	.124	.646	.146	.630	.267	.304	.608	.206	1.176	.292	.108	.806	.124	.862
3/8	.769	.135	.704	.159	.684	.291	.332	.663	.225	1.286	.319	.118	.878	.135	.942
13/32	.834	.146	.763	.172	.743	.316	.358	.719	.243	1.392	.345	.127	.949	.145	1.028
7/16	.896	.157	.823	.186	.798	.339	.387	.772	.261	1.500	.372	.137	1.020	.157	1.098

ASA B18.1–1955.

The length of a rivet is measured from the under side (bearing surface) of the head to the end of the shank except in the case of a rivet with a countersunk head. The length of a countersunk head rivet is measured from the top of the head to the end of the shank.

TABLE XIX

American Standard Square and Flat Keys*

SQUARE KEY

FLAT KEY

Shaft Diameter	Square Stock Key W	Flat Stock Key $W \times H$	Shaft Diameter	Square Stock Key W	Flat Stock Key $W \times H$
$\frac{1}{2}-\frac{9}{16}$	$\frac{1}{8}$	$\frac{1}{8} \times \frac{3}{32}$	$2\frac{5}{16}-2\frac{3}{4}$	$\frac{5}{8}$	$\frac{5}{8} \times \frac{7}{16}$
$\frac{5}{8}-\frac{7}{8}$	$\frac{3}{16}$	$\frac{3}{16} \times \frac{1}{8}$	$2\frac{7}{8}-3\frac{1}{4}$	$\frac{3}{4}$	$\frac{3}{4} \times \frac{1}{2}$
$\frac{15}{16}-1\frac{1}{4}$	$\frac{1}{4}$	$\frac{1}{4} \times \frac{3}{16}$	$3\frac{3}{8}-3\frac{3}{4}$	$\frac{7}{8}$	$\frac{7}{8} \times \frac{5}{8}$
$1\frac{5}{16}-1\frac{3}{8}$	$\frac{5}{16}$	$\frac{5}{16} \times \frac{1}{4}$	$3\frac{7}{8}-4\frac{1}{2}$	1	$1 \times \frac{3}{4}$
$1\frac{7}{16}-1\frac{3}{4}$	$\frac{3}{8}$	$\frac{3}{8} \times \frac{1}{4}$	$4\frac{3}{4}-5\frac{1}{2}$	$1\frac{1}{4}$	$1\frac{1}{4} \times \frac{7}{8}$
$1\frac{13}{16}-2\frac{1}{4}$	$\frac{1}{2}$	$\frac{1}{2} \times \frac{3}{8}$	$5\frac{3}{4}-6$	$1\frac{1}{2}$	$1\frac{1}{2} \times 1$

* ASA B17.1-1943.
All dimensions in inches.

TABLE XX
American Standard Plain Taper and Gib Head Keys

Plain Taper and Gib Head Keys (Square and Flat)			Gib Head					
			Square			Flat		
Diameter of Shaft	Square Type	Flat Type	Height of Head	Length	Height to Chamfer	Height of Head	Length	Height to Chamfer
D	$W = H$	$W \times H$	C	D	E	C	D	E
$\frac{1}{2} - \frac{9}{16}$	$\frac{1}{8}$	$\frac{1}{8} \times \frac{3}{32}$	$\frac{1}{4}$	$\frac{7}{32}$	$\frac{5}{32}$	$\frac{3}{16}$	$\frac{1}{8}$	$\frac{1}{8}$
$\frac{5}{8} - \frac{7}{8}$	$\frac{3}{16}$	$\frac{3}{16} \times \frac{1}{8}$	$\frac{5}{16}$	$\frac{9}{32}$	$\frac{7}{32}$	$\frac{1}{4}$	$\frac{3}{16}$	$\frac{5}{32}$
$\frac{15}{16} - 1\frac{1}{4}$	$\frac{1}{4}$	$\frac{1}{4} \times \frac{3}{16}$	$\frac{7}{16}$	$\frac{11}{32}$	$\frac{11}{32}$	$\frac{5}{16}$	$\frac{1}{4}$	$\frac{3}{16}$
$1\frac{5}{16} - 1\frac{3}{8}$	$\frac{5}{16}$	$\frac{5}{16} \times \frac{1}{4}$	$\frac{9}{16}$	$\frac{13}{32}$	$\frac{13}{32}$	$\frac{3}{8}$	$\frac{5}{16}$	$\frac{1}{4}$
$1\frac{7}{16} - 1\frac{3}{4}$	$\frac{3}{8}$	$\frac{3}{8} \times \frac{1}{4}$	$\frac{11}{16}$	$\frac{15}{32}$	$\frac{15}{32}$	$\frac{7}{16}$	$\frac{3}{8}$	$\frac{5}{16}$
$1\frac{13}{16} - 2\frac{1}{4}$	$\frac{1}{2}$	$\frac{1}{2} \times \frac{3}{8}$	$\frac{7}{8}$	$\frac{19}{32}$	$\frac{5}{8}$	$\frac{5}{8}$	$\frac{1}{2}$	$\frac{7}{16}$
$2\frac{5}{16} - 2\frac{3}{4}$	$\frac{5}{8}$	$\frac{5}{8} \times \frac{7}{16}$	$1\frac{1}{16}$	$\frac{23}{32}$	$\frac{3}{4}$	$\frac{3}{4}$	$\frac{5}{8}$	$\frac{1}{2}$
$2\frac{7}{8} - 3\frac{1}{4}$	$\frac{3}{4}$	$\frac{3}{4} \times \frac{1}{2}$	$1\frac{1}{4}$	$\frac{7}{8}$	$\frac{7}{8}$	$\frac{7}{8}$	$\frac{3}{4}$	$\frac{5}{8}$
$3\frac{3}{8} - 3\frac{3}{4}$	$\frac{7}{8}$	$\frac{7}{8} \times \frac{5}{8}$	$1\frac{1}{2}$	1	1	$1\frac{1}{16}$	$\frac{7}{8}$	$\frac{3}{4}$
$3\frac{7}{8} - 4\frac{1}{2}$	1	$1 \times \frac{3}{4}$	$1\frac{3}{4}$	$1\frac{3}{16}$	$1\frac{3}{16}$	$1\frac{1}{4}$	1	$\frac{13}{16}$
$4\frac{3}{4} - 5\frac{1}{2}$	$1\frac{1}{4}$	$1\frac{1}{4} \times \frac{7}{8}$	2	$1\frac{7}{16}$	$1\frac{7}{16}$	$1\frac{1}{2}$	$1\frac{1}{4}$	1
$5\frac{3}{4} - 6$	$1\frac{1}{2}$	$1\frac{1}{2} \times 1$	$2\frac{1}{2}$	$1\frac{3}{4}$	$1\frac{3}{4}$	$1\frac{3}{4}$	$1\frac{1}{2}$	$1\frac{1}{4}$

ASA B17.1–1943.
All dimensions in inches.   Minimum length $= 4W$.   Maximum length $= 16W$.

TABLE XXI
American Standard Woodruff Keys

Key[1] Number	Nominal Size $A \times B$	Height of Key $C_{\max.}$	Height of Key $D_{\max.}$	Distance above Center E	Depth of Key Slot in Shaft
204	$\frac{1}{16} \times \frac{1}{2}$	0.203	.194	$\frac{3}{64}$	.1718
304	$\frac{3}{32} \times \frac{1}{2}$	.203	.194	$\frac{3}{64}$	.1561
305	$\frac{3}{32} \times \frac{5}{8}$	.250	.240	$\frac{1}{16}$	.2031
404	$\frac{1}{8} \times \frac{1}{2}$	.203	.194	$\frac{3}{64}$	.1405
405	$\frac{1}{8} \times \frac{5}{8}$	.250	.240	$\frac{1}{16}$	.1875
406	$\frac{1}{8} \times \frac{3}{4}$	.313	.303	$\frac{1}{16}$	.2505
505	$\frac{5}{32} \times \frac{5}{8}$	.250	.240	$\frac{1}{16}$	.1719
506	$\frac{5}{32} \times \frac{3}{4}$	.313	.303	$\frac{1}{16}$	.2349
507	$\frac{5}{32} \times \frac{7}{8}$	.375	.365	$\frac{1}{16}$	.2969
606	$\frac{3}{16} \times \frac{3}{4}$	.313	.303	$\frac{1}{16}$	.2193
607	$\frac{3}{16} \times \frac{7}{8}$	.375	.365	$\frac{1}{16}$	.2813
608	$\frac{3}{16} \times 1$	.438	.428	$\frac{1}{16}$	.3443
609	$\frac{3}{16} \times 1\frac{1}{8}$	.484	.475	$\frac{5}{64}$	.3903
807	$\frac{1}{4} \times \frac{7}{8}$	.375	.365	$\frac{1}{16}$	.2500
808	$\frac{1}{4} \times 1$	.438	.428	$\frac{1}{16}$	.3130
809	$\frac{1}{4} \times 1\frac{1}{8}$	.484	.475	$\frac{5}{64}$	.3590
810	$\frac{1}{4} \times 1\frac{1}{4}$	.547	.537	$\frac{5}{64}$	.4220
811	$\frac{1}{4} \times 1\frac{3}{8}$	.594	.584	$\frac{3}{32}$	.4690
812	$\frac{1}{4} \times 1\frac{1}{2}$	.641	.631	$\frac{7}{64}$	.5160
1008	$\frac{5}{16} \times 1$	.438	.428	$\frac{1}{16}$	.2818
1009	$\frac{5}{16} \times 1\frac{1}{8}$	.484	.475	$\frac{5}{64}$	.3278
1010	$\frac{5}{16} \times 1\frac{1}{4}$	.547	.537	$\frac{5}{64}$	.3908
1011	$\frac{5}{16} \times 1\frac{3}{8}$	.594	.584	$\frac{3}{32}$	.4378
1012	$\frac{5}{16} \times 1\frac{1}{2}$	.641	.631	$\frac{7}{64}$	.4848
1210	$\frac{3}{8} \times 1\frac{1}{4}$	.547	.537	$\frac{5}{64}$	.3595
1211	$\frac{3}{8} \times 1\frac{3}{8}$	.594	.584	$\frac{3}{32}$	.4065
1212	$\frac{3}{8} \times 1\frac{1}{2}$	.641	.631	$\frac{7}{64}$	.4535

ASA B17f–1930 (R1955).

[1] All dimensions in inches. Key numbers indicate the nominal key dimensions. The last two digits give the nominal diameter in eighths of an inch and the digits preceding the last two give the nominal width in thirty-seconds of an inch.

TABLE XXII

Pratt and Whitney Keys

SHAFT & KEY

Key No.	L	W	H	D	Key No.	L	W	H	D
1	$\frac{1}{2}$	$\frac{1}{16}$	$\frac{3}{32}$	$\frac{1}{16}$	22	$1\frac{3}{8}$	$\frac{1}{4}$	$\frac{3}{8}$	$\frac{1}{4}$
2	$\frac{1}{2}$	$\frac{3}{32}$	$\frac{9}{64}$	$\frac{3}{32}$	23	$1\frac{3}{8}$	$\frac{5}{16}$	$\frac{15}{32}$	$\frac{5}{16}$
3	$\frac{1}{2}$	$\frac{1}{8}$	$\frac{3}{16}$	$\frac{1}{8}$	F	$1\frac{3}{8}$	$\frac{3}{8}$	$\frac{9}{16}$	$\frac{3}{8}$
4	$\frac{5}{8}$	$\frac{3}{32}$	$\frac{9}{64}$	$\frac{3}{32}$	24	$1\frac{1}{2}$	$\frac{1}{4}$	$\frac{3}{8}$	$\frac{1}{4}$
5	$\frac{5}{8}$	$\frac{1}{8}$	$\frac{3}{16}$	$\frac{1}{8}$	25	$1\frac{1}{2}$	$\frac{5}{16}$	$\frac{15}{32}$	$\frac{5}{16}$
6	$\frac{5}{8}$	$\frac{5}{32}$	$\frac{15}{64}$	$\frac{5}{32}$	G	$1\frac{1}{2}$	$\frac{3}{8}$	$\frac{9}{16}$	$\frac{3}{8}$
7	$\frac{3}{4}$	$\frac{1}{8}$	$\frac{3}{16}$	$\frac{1}{8}$	51	$1\frac{3}{4}$	$\frac{1}{4}$	$\frac{3}{8}$	$\frac{1}{4}$
8	$\frac{3}{4}$	$\frac{5}{32}$	$\frac{15}{64}$	$\frac{5}{32}$	52	$1\frac{3}{4}$	$\frac{5}{16}$	$\frac{15}{32}$	$\frac{5}{16}$
9	$\frac{3}{4}$	$\frac{3}{16}$	$\frac{9}{32}$	$\frac{3}{16}$	53	$1\frac{3}{4}$	$\frac{3}{8}$	$\frac{9}{16}$	$\frac{3}{8}$
10	$\frac{7}{8}$	$\frac{5}{32}$	$\frac{15}{64}$	$\frac{5}{32}$	26	2	$\frac{3}{16}$	$\frac{9}{32}$	$\frac{3}{16}$
11	$\frac{7}{8}$	$\frac{3}{16}$	$\frac{9}{32}$	$\frac{3}{16}$	27	2	$\frac{1}{4}$	$\frac{3}{8}$	$\frac{1}{4}$
12	$\frac{7}{8}$	$\frac{7}{32}$	$\frac{21}{64}$	$\frac{7}{32}$	28	2	$\frac{5}{16}$	$\frac{15}{32}$	$\frac{5}{16}$
A	$\frac{7}{8}$	$\frac{1}{4}$	$\frac{3}{8}$	$\frac{1}{4}$	29	2	$\frac{3}{8}$	$\frac{9}{16}$	$\frac{3}{8}$
13	1	$\frac{3}{16}$	$\frac{9}{32}$	$\frac{3}{16}$	54	$2\frac{1}{4}$	$\frac{1}{4}$	$\frac{3}{8}$	$\frac{1}{4}$
14	1	$\frac{7}{32}$	$\frac{21}{64}$	$\frac{7}{32}$	55	$2\frac{1}{4}$	$\frac{5}{16}$	$\frac{15}{32}$	$\frac{5}{16}$
15	1	$\frac{1}{4}$	$\frac{3}{8}$	$\frac{1}{4}$	56	$2\frac{1}{4}$	$\frac{3}{8}$	$\frac{9}{16}$	$\frac{3}{8}$
B	1	$\frac{5}{16}$	$\frac{15}{32}$	$\frac{5}{16}$	57	$2\frac{1}{4}$	$\frac{7}{16}$	$\frac{21}{32}$	$\frac{7}{16}$
16	$1\frac{1}{8}$	$\frac{3}{16}$	$\frac{9}{32}$	$\frac{3}{16}$	58	$2\frac{1}{2}$	$\frac{5}{16}$	$\frac{15}{32}$	$\frac{5}{16}$
17	$1\frac{1}{8}$	$\frac{7}{32}$	$\frac{21}{64}$	$\frac{7}{32}$	59	$2\frac{1}{2}$	$\frac{3}{8}$	$\frac{9}{16}$	$\frac{3}{8}$
18	$1\frac{1}{4}$	$\frac{1}{4}$	$\frac{3}{8}$	$\frac{1}{4}$	60	$2\frac{1}{2}$	$\frac{7}{16}$	$\frac{21}{32}$	$\frac{7}{16}$
C	$1\frac{1}{4}$	$\frac{5}{16}$	$\frac{15}{32}$	$\frac{5}{16}$	61	$2\frac{1}{2}$	$\frac{1}{2}$	$\frac{3}{4}$	$\frac{1}{2}$
19	$1\frac{1}{4}$	$\frac{3}{16}$	$\frac{9}{32}$	$\frac{3}{16}$	30	3	$\frac{3}{8}$	$\frac{9}{16}$	$\frac{3}{8}$
20	$1\frac{1}{4}$	$\frac{7}{32}$	$\frac{21}{64}$	$\frac{7}{32}$	31	3	$\frac{7}{16}$	$\frac{21}{32}$	$\frac{7}{16}$
21	$1\frac{1}{4}$	$\frac{1}{4}$	$\frac{3}{8}$	$\frac{1}{4}$	32	3	$\frac{1}{2}$	$\frac{3}{4}$	$\frac{1}{2}$
D	$1\frac{1}{4}$	$\frac{5}{16}$	$\frac{15}{32}$	$\frac{5}{16}$	33	3	$\frac{9}{16}$	$\frac{27}{32}$	$\frac{9}{16}$
E	$1\frac{1}{4}$	$\frac{3}{8}$	$\frac{9}{16}$	$\frac{3}{8}$	34	3	$\frac{5}{8}$	$\frac{15}{16}$	$\frac{5}{8}$

The length L may vary but should always be at least $2W$.

TABLE XXIII

Standard Taper Pins

No. of Pin	Diameter at Large End		Max. Length
	D	D	L
00000	.094	$\frac{3}{32}$	$\frac{3}{4}$
0000	.109	$\frac{7}{64}$	$\frac{7}{8}$
000	.125	$\frac{1}{8}$	1
00	.141	$\frac{9}{64}$	$1\frac{1}{8}$
0	.156	$\frac{5}{32}$	$1\frac{1}{4}$
1	.172	$\frac{11}{64}$	$1\frac{1}{4}$
2	.193	$\frac{3}{16}$	$1\frac{1}{2}$
3	.219	$\frac{7}{32}$	$1\frac{3}{4}$
4	.250	$\frac{1}{4}$	2
5	.289	$\frac{19}{64}$	$2\frac{1}{4}$
6	.341	$\frac{11}{32}$	3
7	.409	$\frac{13}{32}$	$3\frac{3}{4}$
8	.492	$\frac{1}{2}$	$4\frac{1}{2}$
9	.591	$\frac{19}{32}$	$5\frac{1}{4}$
10	.706	$\frac{23}{32}$	6
11	.860	$\frac{55}{64}$	$7\frac{1}{4}$
12	1.032	$1\frac{1}{32}$	9
13	1.241	$1\frac{15}{64}$	11
14	1.523	$1\frac{33}{64}$	13

Standard Taper Pins—Diameters at Small End

Length	Number of Pin										
	0	1	2	3	4	5	6	7	8	9	10
$\frac{3}{4}$	.140	.156	.177	.203	.235	.273	.325				
1	.135	.151	.172	.198	.230	.268	.320	.388			
$1\frac{1}{4}$		.146	.167	.193	.224	.263	.315	.383	.466		
$1\frac{1}{2}$			.162	.188	.219	.258	.310	.378	.461	.560	.675
$1\frac{3}{4}$				.182	.214	.252	.304	.372	.455	.554	.669
2					.209	.247	.299	.367	.450	.549	.664
$2\frac{1}{4}$						.242	.294	.362	.445	.544	.659
$2\frac{1}{2}$							.289	.357	.440	.539	.654
$2\frac{3}{4}$							.284	.352	.435	.534	.649
3							.279	.346	.429	.528	.643

APPENDIX

TABLE XXIV
Dowel Pins

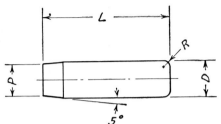

Nominal Dia.	Max Dia. D	Min Dia. D	Point Dia. P	Radius R	Lengths L
$\frac{1}{8}$	.1253	.1251	.119	$\frac{3}{64}$	Every $\frac{1}{8}$ from $\frac{3}{8}$ to 1
$\frac{1}{8}$	.1261	.1259	.119	$\frac{3}{64}$	Every $\frac{1}{4}$ from 1 to 2
$\frac{3}{16}$	.1878	.1876	.176	$\frac{3}{64}$	Every $\frac{1}{8}$ from $\frac{1}{2}$ to 1
$\frac{3}{16}$	.1886	.1884	.176	$\frac{3}{64}$	Every $\frac{1}{4}$ from 1 to 2
$\frac{1}{4}$	.2503	.2501	.239	$\frac{1}{16}$	Every $\frac{1}{8}$ from $\frac{1}{2}$ to 1
$\frac{1}{4}$	.2511	.2509	.239	$\frac{1}{16}$	Every $\frac{1}{4}$ from $\frac{1}{2}$ to $2\frac{1}{2}$
$\frac{5}{16}$	.3128	.3126	.301	$\frac{1}{16}$	Every $\frac{1}{8}$ from $\frac{1}{2}$ to 1
$\frac{5}{16}$	.3136	.3134	.301	$\frac{1}{16}$	Every $\frac{1}{4}$ from 1 to $3\frac{1}{2}$
$\frac{3}{8}$	.3753	.3751	.364	$\frac{5}{64}$	Every $\frac{1}{8}$ from $\frac{1}{2}$ to 1
$\frac{3}{8}$	.3761	.3759	.364	$\frac{5}{64}$	Every $\frac{1}{4}$ from 1 to $3\frac{3}{4}$
$\frac{7}{16}$	.4378	.4376	.4205	$\frac{3}{32}$	Every $\frac{1}{8}$ from $\frac{1}{2}$ to 1
$\frac{7}{16}$	.4386	.4384	.4205	$\frac{3}{32}$	Every $\frac{1}{4}$ from 1 to 4
$\frac{1}{2}$	.5003	.5001	.483	$\frac{7}{64}$	Every $\frac{1}{8}$ from $\frac{5}{8}$ to 1
$\frac{1}{2}$	.5011	.5009	.483	$\frac{7}{64}$	Every $\frac{1}{4}$ from 1 to 4
$\frac{5}{8}$	.6253	.6251	.608	$\frac{1}{8}$	Every $\frac{1}{4}$ from 1 to 5
$\frac{5}{8}$	.6261	.6259	.608	$\frac{1}{8}$	
$\frac{3}{4}$	.7503	.7501	.728	$\frac{1}{8}$	Every $\frac{1}{4}$ from 2 to 6
$\frac{3}{4}$	.7511	.7509	.728	$\frac{1}{8}$	
$\frac{7}{8}$	.8753	.8751	.853	$\frac{1}{8}$	Every $\frac{1}{4}$ from 2 to 6
$\frac{7}{8}$	.8761	.8759	.853	$\frac{1}{8}$	
1	1.0003	1.0001	.978	$\frac{1}{8}$	Every $\frac{1}{4}$ from 2 to 6
1	1.011	1.0009	.978	$\frac{1}{8}$	

Notes: All dimensions are in inches. Two sizes of pin are available in each nominal diameter.

Compiled from catalogue of The Allen Mfg. Co., Hartford, Conn.

TABLE XXV
American Standard Wrought-Iron and Steel Pipe

| | | | | | STANDARD WEIGHT | | | HEAVY | | | |
| Nominal Size | Outside Diameter (All Weights) | Threads per Inch | Tap Drill Sizes[1] | Distance Pipe Enters Fitting | Nominal Wall Thickness | | Extra Heavy | | Double Extra Heavy | | |
					Wrought Iron	Steel	Wrought Iron	Steel	Wrought Iron	Steel
$\frac{1}{8}$	.405	72	$\frac{11}{32}$	$\frac{5}{16}$	.069	.068	.099	.095	—	—
$\frac{1}{4}$	.540	18	$\frac{7}{16}$	$\frac{7}{16}$	.090	.088	.122	.119	—	—
$\frac{3}{8}$	.675	18	$\frac{19}{32}$	$\frac{7}{16}$	.093	.091	.129	.126	—	—
$\frac{1}{2}$	.840	14	$\frac{23}{32}$	$\frac{9}{16}$	.111	.109	.151	.147	.307	.294
$\frac{3}{4}$	1.050	14	$\frac{15}{16}$	$\frac{9}{16}$	.115	.113	.157	.154	.318	.308
1	1.315	$11\frac{1}{2}$	$1\frac{5}{32}$	$\frac{11}{16}$	.136	.133	.183	.179	.369	.358
$1\frac{1}{4}$	1.660	$11\frac{1}{2}$	$1\frac{1}{2}$	$\frac{11}{16}$	.143	.140	.195	.191	.393	.382
$1\frac{1}{2}$	1.900	$11\frac{1}{2}$	$1\frac{23}{32}$	$\frac{11}{16}$	.148	.145	.204	.200	.411	.400
2	2.375	$11\frac{1}{2}$	$2\frac{3}{16}$	$\frac{3}{4}$	.158	.154	.223	.218	.447	.436
$2\frac{1}{2}$	2.875	8	$2\frac{5}{8}$	$1\frac{1}{16}$	.208	.203	.282	.276	.567	.552
3	3.500	8	$3\frac{1}{4}$	$1\frac{1}{8}$	.221	.216	.306	.300	.615	.600
$3\frac{1}{2}$	4.000	8	$3\frac{3}{4}$	$1\frac{3}{16}$	.231	.226	.325	.318	—	—
4	4.500	8	$4\frac{1}{4}$	$1\frac{3}{16}$	.242	.237	.344	.337	.690	.674
5	5.563	8	$5\frac{5}{16}$	$1\frac{5}{16}$	.263	.258	.383	.375	.768	.750
6	6.625	8	$6\frac{3}{8}$	$1\frac{3}{8}$	.286	.280	.441	.432	.884	.864
8	8.625	8	—	—	.329	.322	.510	.500	.895	.875

ASA B36.10–1950.
ASA B2.1–1945.
All dimensions in inches.
[1] Not American Standard.
See ASA B36.10–1950 for sizes larger than 8″.

TABLE XXVI

American Standard Malleable-Iron Screwed Fittings

For use under maximum working steam pressures of 150 lbs. per sq. in.

Nominal Pipe Size	A, Center to End, Elbows, Tees and Crosses	B Min., Length of Thread	C, Center to End 45-Deg. Elbows	E Min., Width of Band	F Min., Inside Diameter of Fitting	F Max.	G, Metal Thickness	H, Outside Diameter of Band	J, Center to Male End Elbows, Tees	K, Center to Male End 45° Elbows	L Min., Length of External Thread	M, Length of Reducing Couplings	N Max., Port Diameter Male End	T, Center to End Inlet	U, Center to End Outlet	V, End to End	W, Length of Straight Couplings	Thickness of Ribs of Couplings
1/8	0.69	0.25	—	0.200	0.405	0.435	0.090	0.693	1.00	—	0.2638	—	0.20	—	—	—	—	0.090
1/4	0.81	0.32	0.73	0.215	0.540	0.584	0.095	0.844	1.19	0.94	0.4018	1.00	0.26	—	—	—	0.96	0.095
3/8	0.95	0.36	0.80	0.230	0.675	0.719	0.100	1.015	1.44	1.03	0.4078	1.13	0.37	0.50	1.43	1.93	1.06	0.100
1/2	1.12	0.43	0.88	0.249	0.840	0.897	0.105	1.197	1.63	1.15	0.5337	1.25	0.51	0.61	1.71	2.32	1.16	0.105
3/4	1.31	0.50	0.98	0.273	1.050	1.107	0.120	1.458	1.89	1.29	0.5457	1.44	0.69	0.72	2.05	2.77	1.34	0.120
1	1.50	0.58	1.12	0.302	1.315	1.385	0.134	1.771	2.14	1.47	0.6828	1.69	0.91	0.85	2.43	3.28	1.52	0.134
1 1/4	1.75	0.67	1.29	0.341	1.660	1.730	0.145	2.153	2.45	1.71	0.7068	2.06	1.19	1.02	2.92	3.94	1.67	0.145
1 1/2	1.94	0.70	1.43	0.368	1.900	1.970	0.155	2.427	2.69	1.88	0.7235	2.31	1.39	1.10	3.28	4.38	1.93	0.155
2	2.25	0.75	1.68	0.422	2.375	2.445	0.173	2.963	3.26	2.22	0.7565	2.81	1.79	1.24	3.93	5.17	2.15	0.173
2 1/2	2.70	0.92	1.95	0.478	2.875	2.975	0.210	3.589	3.86	2.57	1.1375	3.25	2.20	1.52	4.73	6.25	2.53	0.210
3	3.08	0.98	2.17	0.548	3.500	3.600	0.231	4.285	4.51	3.00	1.2000	3.69	2.78	1.71	5.55	7.26	2.88	0.231
3 1/2	3.42	1.03	2.39	0.604	4.000	4.100	0.248	4.843	—	—	—	—	—	—	—	—	3.18	—
4	3.79	1.08	2.61	0.661	4.500	4.600	0.265	5.401	5.69	3.70	1.3000	4.38	3.70	2.01	6.97	8.98	—	0.265
5	4.50	1.18	3.05	0.780	5.563	5.663	0.300	6.583	6.86	—	1.4063	—	4.69	—	—	—	3.69	—
6	5.13	1.28	3.46	0.900	6.625	6.725	0.336	7.767	8.03	—	1.5125	—	5.67	—	—	—	—	—

ELBOW   TEE   CROSS   45° ELBOW   45° Y-BRANCH   STREET ELBOW   45° STREET ELBOW   STREET TEE   STRAIGHT REDUCING COUPLINGS

ASA B16.3-1951.

TABLE XXVII

125 lb. American Standard Cast-Iron Screwed Fittings

Nominal Pipe Size	Center to End, Elbows, Tees, and Crosses	Length of Thread	Center to End, 45-deg. Elbows	Width of Band	Inside Diameter of Fitting		Metal Thickness	Outside Diameter of Band
	A	B Min.	C	E Min.	F Min.	F Max.	G Min.	H Min.
$\frac{1}{4}$	0.81	0.32	0.73	0.38	0.540	0.584	0.110	0.93
$\frac{3}{8}$	0.95	0.36	0.80	0.44	0.675	0.719	0.120	1.12
$\frac{1}{2}$	1.12	0.43	0.88	0.50	0.840	0.897	0.130	1.34
$\frac{3}{4}$	1.31	0.50	0.98	0.56	1.050	1.107	0.155	1.63
1	1.50	0.58	1.12	0.62	1.315	1.385	0.170	1.95
$1\frac{1}{4}$	1.75	0.67	1.29	0.69	1.660	1.730	0.185	2.39
$1\frac{1}{2}$	1.94	0.70	1.43	0.75	1.900	1.970	0.200	2.68
2	2.25	0.75	1.68	0.84	2.375	2.445	0.220	3.28
$2\frac{1}{2}$	2.70	0.92	1.95	0.94	2.875	2.975	0.240	3.86
3	3.08	0.98	2.17	1.00	3.500	3.600	0.260	4.62
$3\frac{1}{2}$	3.42	1.03	2.39	1.06	4.000	4.100	0.280	5.20
4	3.79	1.08	2.61	1.12	4.500	4.600	0.310	5.79
5	4.50	1.18	3.05	1.18	5.563	5.663	0.380	7.05
6	5.13	1.28	3.46	1.28	6.625	6.725	0.430	8.28
8	6.56	1.47	4.28	1.47	8.625	8.725	0.550	10.63
10	8.08	1.68	5.16	1.68	10.750	10.850	0.690	13.12
12	9.50	1.88	5.97	1.88	12.750	12.850	0.800	15.47

ASA B16.4–1949 (R1953).
All dimensions in inches.

TABLE XXVIII

American Standard Pipe Plugs and Caps

PLUG

CAP

Nominal Pipe Size	PLUG			CAP*						
	Length of Thread	Height of Square	Width Across Flats	Length of Thread	Width of Band	Inside Diameter of Fitting	Metal Thickness	Outside Diameter of Band	Height	Thickness of Ribs
	A Min.	B Min.	C Nom.	D Min.	E Min.	F Max.	G	H Min.	P Min.	
$\frac{1}{8}$	.37	.24	$\frac{9}{32}$	.25	.200	.435	.090	.693	.53	—
$\frac{1}{4}$	.44	.28	$\frac{3}{8}$	.32	.215	.584	.095	.844	.63	—
$\frac{3}{8}$	.48	.31	$\frac{7}{16}$	.36	.230	.719	.100	1.015	.74	—
$\frac{1}{2}$	.56	.38	$\frac{9}{16}$	.43	.249	.897	.105	1.197	.87	.105
$\frac{3}{4}$	.63	.44	$\frac{5}{8}$	.50	.273	1.107	.120	1.458	.97	.120
1	.75	.50	$\frac{13}{16}$	.58	.302	1.385	.134	1.771	1.16	.134
$1\frac{1}{4}$	.80	.56	$\frac{15}{16}$	.67	.341	1.730	.145	2.153	1.28	.145
$1\frac{1}{2}$	.83	.62	$1\frac{1}{8}$	.70	.368	1.970	.155	2.427	1.33	.155
2	.88	.68	$1\frac{5}{16}$	.75	.422	2.445	.173	2.963	1.45	.173
$2\frac{1}{2}$	1.07	.74	$1\frac{1}{2}$	.92	.478	2.975	.210	3.589	1.70	.210
3	1.13	.80	$1\frac{11}{16}$	.98	.548	3.600	.231	4.285	1.80	.231
$3\frac{1}{2}$	1.18	.86	$1\frac{7}{8}$	1.03	.604	4.100	.248	4.843	1.90	.248
4	—	—	—	1.08	.661	4.600	.265	5.401	2.08	.265
5	—	—	—	1.18	.780	5.663	.300	6.583	2.32	.300
6	—	—	—	1.28	.900	6.725	.336	7.767	2.55	.336

* ASA B16.3–1951.

The outside radius of top of cap is equal to $3 \times F$.

TABLE XXIX

American Standard Cast-Iron Pipe Flanges and Flanged Fittings

For use under maximum working pressures of 125 lbs. per sq. in.

Nominal Pipe Size	Center to Face, Elbow Tees, Etc. (A)	Center to Face, Long Radius Elbow (B)	Center to Face, 45-deg. Elbow (C)	Face to Face, Lateral (D)	Center to Face, Lateral (E)	Center to Face, "Y" and Lateral (F)	Face to Face Reducer (G)	Diameter of Flange (H)	Thickness of Flange (T)	Diameter of Hub (X)	Length of Hub (Y)	Diameter of Holes in Flanges	Number of Bolts for Flanges	Diameter of Bolts for Flanges	Length of Bolts for Flanges	Diameter of Bolt Circle
1	3½	5	1¾	7½	5¾	1¾	…	4¼	7/16	1 15/16	11/16	5/8	4	½	1¾	3⅛
1¼	3¾	5½	2	8	6¼	1¾	…	4⅝	½	2 5/16	13/16	5/8	4	½	2	3½
1½	4	6	2¼	9	7	2	…	5	9/16	2 9/16	7/8	5/8	4	½	2	3⅞
2	4½	6½	2½	10½	8	2½	5	6	5/8	3 1/16	1	¾	4	⅝	2¼	4¾
2½	5	7	3	12	9¼	2½	5½	7	11/16	3 9/16	1⅛	¾	4	⅝	2¼	5½
3	5½	7¾	3½	13	10	3	6	7½	¾	4 1/16	1 3/16	¾	4	⅝	2½	6
3½	6	8½	3½	14½	11½	3	6½	8½	13/16	4 13/16	1⅜	¾	8	⅝	2½	7
4	6½	9	4	15	12	3	7	9	15/16	5 6/16	1 7/16	¾	8	⅝	3	7½
5	7½	10¼	4½	17	13½	3½	8	10	15/16	6 5/16	1⅝	⅞	8	¾	3	8½
6	8	11½	5	18	14½	3½	9	11	1	7 9/16	1 9/16	⅞	8	¾	3¼	9½
8	9	14	5½	22	17½	4½	11	13½	1⅛	9 11/16	1⅝	⅞	8	¾	3¼	11¾
10	11	16½	6½	25½	20½	5	12	16	1 3/16	11 15/16	1 15/16	1	12	⅞	3¾	14¼
12	12	19	7½	30	24½	5½	14	19	1¼	14 1/16	2 3/16	1	12	⅞	3¾	17

FLANGE — FLANGE — ECCENTRIC REDUCER — REDUCER — LATERAL — CROSS — SIDE OUTLET — TEE — REDUCING SIDE ELBOW OUTLET — 45° ELBOW — 90° ELBOW LONG RAD ELBOW

ASA B16.1–1948 (R1953).

TABLE XXX-A

Running and Sliding Fits[1]

Limits are in thousandths of an inch. Limits for hole and shaft are applied algebraically to the basic size to obtain the limits of size for the parts. Symbols H5, g5, etc., are Hole and Shaft designations used in ABC System.[2]

Nominal Size Range Inches (Over – To)	Class RC 1 Limits of Clearance	Class RC 1 Standard Limits Hole H5	Class RC 1 Standard Limits Shaft g4	Class RC 2 Limits of Clearance	Class RC 2 Standard Limits Hole H6	Class RC 2 Standard Limits Shaft g5	Class RC 3 Limits of Clearance	Class RC 3 Standard Limits Hole H6	Class RC 3 Standard Limits Shaft f6	Class RC 4 Limits of Clearance	Class RC 4 Standard Limits Hole H7	Class RC 4 Standard Limits Shaft f7
0.04–0.12	0.1 / 0.45	+0.2 / 0	−0.1 / −0.25	0.1 / 0.55	+0.25 / 0	−0.1 / −0.3	0.3 / 0.8	+0.25 / 0	−0.3 / −0.55	0.3 / 1.1	+0.4 / 0	−0.3 / −0.7
0.12–0.24	0.15 / 0.5	+0.2 / 0	−0.15 / −0.3	0.15 / 0.65	+0.3 / 0	−0.15 / −0.35	0.4 / 1.0	+0.3 / 0	−0.4 / −0.7	0.4 / 1.4	+0.5 / 0	−0.4 / −0.9
0.24–0.40	0.2 / 0.6	+0.25 / 0	−0.2 / −0.35	0.2 / 0.85	+0.4 / 0	−0.2 / −0.45	0.5 / 1.3	+0.4 / 0	−0.5 / −0.9	0.5 / 1.7	+0.6 / 0	−0.5 / −1.1
0.40–0.71	0.25 / 0.75	+0.3 / 0	−0.25 / −0.45	0.25 / 0.95	+0.4 / 0	−0.25 / −0.55	0.6 / 1.4	+0.4 / 0	−0.6 / −1.0	0.6 / 2.0	+0.7 / 0	−0.6 / −1.3
0.71–1.19	0.3 / 0.95	+0.4 / 0	−0.3 / −0.55	0.3 / 1.2	+0.5 / 0	−0.3 / −0.7	0.8 / 1.8	+0.5 / 0	−0.8 / −1.3	0.8 / 2.4	+0.8 / 0	−0.8 / −1.6
1.19–1.97	0.4 / 1.1	+0.4 / 0	−0.4 / −0.7	0.4 / 1.4	+0.6 / 0	−0.4 / −0.8	1.0 / 2.2	+0.6 / 0	−1.0 / −1.6	1.0 / 3.0	+1.0 / 0	−1.0 / −2.0
1.97–3.15	0.4 / 1.2	+0.5 / 0	−0.4 / −0.7	0.4 / 1.6	+0.7 / 0	−0.4 / −0.9	1.2 / 2.6	+0.7 / 0	−1.2 / −1.9	1.2 / 3.6	+1.2 / 0	−1.2 / −2.4
3.15–4.73	0.5 / 1.5	+0.6 / 0	−0.5 / −0.9	0.5 / 2.0	+0.9 / 0	−0.5 / −1.1	1.4 / 3.2	+0.9 / 0	−1.4 / −2.3	1.4 / 4.2	+1.4 / 0	−1.4 / −2.8
4.73–7.09	0.6 / 1.8	+0.7 / 0	−0.6 / −1.1	0.6 / 2.3	+1.0 / 0	−0.6 / −1.3	1.6 / 3.6	+1.0 / 0	−1.6 / −2.6	1.6 / 4.8	+1.6 / 0	−1.6 / −3.2
7.09–9.85	0.6 / 2.0	+0.8 / 0	−0.6 / −1.2	0.6 / 2.6	+1.2 / 0	−0.6 / −1.4	2.0 / 4.4	+1.2 / 0	−2.0 / −3.2	2.0 / 5.6	+1.8 / 0	−2.0 / −3.8

[1] Extracted from ASA B4.1–1955 (Table 1).
[2] Data are in accordance with ABC agreements.
For diameters greater than 9.85 inches see standard.

TABLE XXX-A (cont.)
Running and Sliding Fits

Limits are in thousandths of an inch. Limits for hole and shaft are applied algebraically to the basic size to obtain the limits of size for the parts. Symbols H7, e7, etc., are Hole and Shaft designations used in ABC System.

Nominal Size Range Inches (Over–To)	Class RC 5 Limits of Clearance	Class RC 5 Standard Limits Hole H7	Class RC 5 Standard Limits Shaft e7	Class RC 6 Limits of Clearance	Class RC 6 Standard Limits Hole H8	Class RC 6 Standard Limits Shaft e8	Class RC 7 Limits of Clearance	Class RC 7 Standard Limits Hole H9	Class RC 7 Standard Limits Shaft d8	Class RC 8 Limits of Clearance	Class RC 8 Standard Limits Hole H10	Class RC 8 Standard Limits Shaft c9	Class RC 9 Limits of Clearance	Class RC 9 Standard Limits Hole H11	Class RC 9 Standard Limits Shaft
0.04–0.12	0.6 / 1.4	+0.4 / 0	−0.6 / −1.0	0.6 / 1.8	+0.6 / 0	−0.6 / −1.2	1.0 / 2.6	+1.0 / 0	−1.0 / −1.6	2.5 / 5.1	+1.6 / 0	−2.5 / −3.5	4.0 / 8.1	+2.5 / 0	−4.0 / −5.6
0.12–0.24	0.8 / 1.8	+0.5 / 0	−0.8 / −1.3	0.8 / 2.2	+0.7 / 0	−0.8 / −1.5	1.2 / 3.1	+1.2 / 0	−1.2 / −1.9	2.8 / 5.8	+1.8 / 0	−2.8 / −4.0	4.5 / 9.3	+3.0 / 0	−4.5 / −6.0
0.24–0.40	1.0 / 2.2	+0.6 / 0	−1.0 / −1.6	1.0 / 2.8	+0.9 / 0	−1.0 / −1.9	1.6 / 3.9	+1.4 / 0	−1.6 / −2.5	3.0 / 6.6	+2.2 / 0	−3.0 / −4.4	5.0 / 10.7	+3.5 / 0	−5.0 / −7.2
0.40–0.71	1.2 / 2.6	+0.7 / 0	−1.2 / −1.9	1.2 / 3.2	+1.0 / 0	−1.2 / −2.2	2.0 / 4.6	+1.6 / 0	−2.0 / −3.0	3.5 / 7.9	+2.8 / 0	−3.5 / −5.1	6.0 / 12.8	+4.0 / 0	−6.0 / −8.8
0.71–1.19	1.6 / 3.2	+0.8 / 0	−1.6 / −2.4	1.6 / 4.0	+1.2 / 0	−1.6 / −2.8	2.5 / 5.7	+2.0 / 0	−2.5 / −3.7	4.5 / 10.0	+3.5 / 0	−4.5 / −6.5	7.0 / 15.5	+5.0 / 0	−7.0 / −10.5
1.19–1.97	2.0 / 4.0	+1.0 / 0	−2.0 / −3.0	2.0 / 5.2	+1.6 / 0	−2.0 / −3.6	3.0 / 7.1	+2.5 / 0	−3.0 / −4.6	5.0 / 11.5	+4.0 / 0	−5.0 / −7.5	8.0 / 18.0	+6.0 / 0	−8.0 / −12.0
1.97–3.15	2.5 / 4.9	+1.2 / 0	−2.5 / −3.7	2.5 / 6.1	+1.8 / 0	−2.5 / −4.3	4.0 / 8.8	+3.0 / 0	−4.0 / −5.8	6.0 / 13.5	+4.5 / 0	−6.0 / −9.0	9.0 / 20.5	+7.0 / 0	−9.0 / −13.5
3.15–4.73	3.0 / 5.8	+1.4 / 0	−3.0 / −4.4	3.0 / 7.4	+2.2 / 0	−3.0 / −5.2	5.0 / 10.7	+3.5 / 0	−5.0 / −7.2	7.0 / 15.5	+5.0 / 0	−7.0 / −10.5	10.0 / 24.0	+9.0 / 0	−10.0 / −15.0
4.73–7.09	3.5 / 6.7	+1.6 / 0	−3.5 / −5.1	3.5 / 8.5	+2.5 / 0	−3.5 / −6.0	6.0 / 12.5	+4.0 / 0	−6.0 / −8.5	8.0 / 18.0	+6.0 / 0	−8.0 / −12.0	12.0 / 28.0	+10.0 / 0	−12.0 / −18.0
7.09–9.85	4.0 / 7.6	+1.8 / 0	−4.0 / −5.8	4.0 / 9.6	+2.8 / 0	−4.0 / −6.8	7.0 / 14.3	+4.5 / 0	−7.0 / −9.8	10.0 / 21.5	+7.0 / 0	−10.0 / −14.5	15.0 / 34.0	+12.0 / 0	−15.0 / −22.0

TABLE XXX-B

Clearance Locational Fits[1]

Limits are in thousandths of an inch. Limits for hole and shaft are applied algebraically to the basic size to obtain the limits of size for the parts. Symbols H6, h5, etc., are Hole and Shaft designations used in ABC System.[2]

Nominal Size Range Inches Over To	Class LC 1 Limits of Clearance	Class LC 1 Standard Limits Hole H6	Class LC 1 Standard Limits Shaft h5	Class LC 2 Limits of Clearance	Class LC 2 Standard Limits Hole H7	Class LC 2 Standard Limits Shaft h6	Class LC 3 Limits of Clearance	Class LC 3 Standard Limits Hole H8	Class LC 3 Standard Limits Shaft h7	Class LC 4 Limits of Clearance	Class LC 4 Standard Limits Hole H9	Class LC 4 Standard Limits Shaft h9	Class LC 5 Limits of Clearance	Class LC 5 Standard Limits Hole H7	Class LC 5 Standard Limits Shaft g6
0.04–0.12	0 / 0.45	+0.25 / −0	+0 / −0.2	0 / 0.65	+0.4 / −0	+0 / −0.25	0 / 1	+0.6 / −0	+0 / −0.4	0 / 2.0	+1.0 / −0	+0 / −1.0	0.1 / 0.75	+0.4 / −0	−0.1 / −0.35
0.12–0.24	0 / 0.5	+0.3 / −0	+0 / −0.2	0 / 0.8	+0.5 / −0	+0 / −0.3	0 / 1.2	+0.7 / −0	+0 / −0.5	0 / 2.4	+1.2 / −0	+0 / −1.2	0.15 / 0.95	+0.5 / −0	−0.15 / −0.45
0.24–0.40	0 / 0.65	+0.4 / −0	+0 / −0.25	0 / 1.0	+0.6 / −0	+0 / −0.4	0 / 1.5	+0.9 / −0	+0 / −0.6	0 / 2.8	+1.4 / −0	+0 / −1.4	0.2 / 1.2	+0.6 / −0	−0.2 / −0.6
0.40–0.71	0 / 0.7	+0.4 / −0	+0 / −0.3	0 / 1.1	+0.7 / −0	+0 / −0.4	0 / 1.7	+1.0 / −0	+0 / −0.7	0 / 3.2	+1.6 / −0	+0 / −1.6	0.25 / 1.35	+0.7 / −0	−0.25 / −0.65
0.71–1.19	0 / 0.9	+0.5 / −0	+0 / −0.4	0 / 1.3	+0.8 / −0	+0 / −0.5	0 / 2	+1.2 / −0	+0 / −0.8	0 / 4	+2.0 / −0	+0 / −2.0	0.3 / 1.6	+0.8 / −0	−0.3 / −0.8
1.19–1.97	0 / 1.0	+0.6 / −0	+0 / −0.4	0 / 1.6	+1.0 / −0	+0 / −0.6	0 / 2.6	+1.6 / −0	+0 / −1	0 / 5	+2.5 / −0	+0 / −2.5	0.4 / 2.0	+1.0 / −0	−0.4 / −1.0
1.97–3.15	0 / 1.2	+0.7 / −0	+0 / −0.5	0 / 1.9	+1.2 / −0	+0 / −0.7	0 / 3	+1.8 / −0	+0 / −1.2	0 / 6	+3 / −0	+0 / −3	0.4 / 2.3	+1.2 / −0	−0.4 / −1.1
3.15–4.73	0 / 1.5	+0.9 / −0	+0 / −0.6	0 / 2.3	+1.4 / −0	+0 / −0.9	0 / 3.6	+2.2 / −0	+0 / −1.4	0 / 7	+3.5 / −0	+0 / −3.5	0.5 / 2.8	+1.4 / −0	−0.5 / −1.4
4.73–7.09	0 / 1.7	+1.0 / −0	+0 / −0.7	0 / 2.6	+1.6 / −0	+0 / −1.0	0 / 4.1	+2.5 / −0	+0 / −1.6	0 / 8	+4 / −0	+0 / −4	0.6 / 3.2	+1.6 / −0	−0.6 / −1.6
7.09–9.85	0 / 2.0	+1.2 / −0	+0 / −0.8	0 / 3.0	+1.8 / −0	+0 / −1.2	0 / 4.6	+2.8 / −0	+0 / −1.8	0 / 9	+4.5 / −0	+0 / −4.5	0.6 / 3.6	+1.8 / −0	−0.6 / −1.8

[1] Extracted from ASA B4.1–1955 (Table 2).

[2] Data are in accordance with ABC agreements. For diameters greater than 9.85 inches see standard.

TABLE XXX-B (cont.)
Clearance Locational Fits

Limits are in thousandths of an inch. Limits for hole and shaft are applied algebraically to the basic size to obtain the limits of size for the parts. Symbols H8, f8, etc., are Hole and Shaft designations used in ABC System.

Nominal Size Range Inches Over / To	Class LC 6 Limits of Clearance	Class LC 6 Hole H8	Class LC 6 Shaft f8	Class LC 7 Limits of Clearance	Class LC 7 Hole H9	Class LC 7 Shaft e9	Class LC 8 Limits of Clearance	Class LC 8 Hole H10	Class LC 8 Shaft d9	Class LC 9 Limits of Clearance	Class LC 9 Hole H11	Class LC 9 Shaft c11	Class LC 10 Limits of Clearance	Class LC 10 Hole H12	Class LC 10 Shaft	Class LC 11 Limits of Clearance	Class LC 11 Hole H13	Class LC 11 Shaft
0.04–0.12	0.3 / 1.5	+0.6 / −0	−0.3 / −0.9	0.6 / 2.6	+1.0 / −0	−0.6 / −1.6	1.0 / 2.0	+1.6 / −0	−1.0 / −2.0	2.5 / 7.5	+2.5 / −0	−2.5 / −5.0	4 / 12	+4 / −0	−4 / −8	5 / 17	+6 / −0	−5 / −11
0.12–0.24	0.4 / 1.8	+0.7 / −0	−0.4 / −1.1	0.8 / 3.2	+1.2 / −0	−0.8 / −2.0	1.2 / 4.2	+1.8 / −0	−1.2 / −2.4	2.8 / 8.8	+3.0 / −0	−2.8 / −5.8	4.5 / 14.5	+5 / −0	−4.5 / −9.5	6 / 20	+7 / −0	−6 / −13
0.24–0.40	0.5 / 2.3	+0.9 / −0	−0.5 / −1.4	1.0 / 3.8	+1.4 / −0	−1.0 / −2.4	1.6 / 5.2	+2.2 / −0	−1.6 / −3.0	3.0 / 10.0	+3.5 / −0	−3.0 / −6.5	5 / 17	+6 / −0	−5 / −11	7 / 25	+9 / −0	−7 / −16
0.40–0.71	0.6 / 2.6	+1.0 / −0	−0.6 / −1.6	1.2 / 4.4	+1.6 / −0	−1.2 / −2.8	2.0 / 6.4	+2.8 / −0	−2.0 / −3.6	3.5 / 11.5	+4.0 / −0	−3.5 / −7.5	6 / 20	+7 / −0	−6 / −13	8 / 28	+10 / −0	−8 / −18
0.71–1.19	0.8 / 3.2	+1.2 / −0	−0.8 / −2.0	1.6 / 5.6	+2.0 / −0	−1.6 / −3.6	2.5 / 8.0	+3.5 / −0	−2.5 / −4.5	4.5 / 14.5	+5.0 / −0	−4.5 / −9.5	7 / 23	+8 / −0	−7 / −15	10 / 34	+12 / −0	−10 / −22
1.19–1.97	1.0 / 4.2	+1.6 / −0	−1.0 / −2.6	2.0 / 7.0	+2.5 / −0	−2.0 / −4.5	3.6 / 9.5	+4.0 / −0	−3.6 / −5.5	5 / 17	+6 / −0	−5 / −11	8 / 28	+10 / −0	−8 / −18	12 / 44	+16 / −0	−12 / −28
1.97–3.15	1.2 / 4.8	+1.8 / −0	−1.0 / −3.0	2.5 / 8.5	+3.0 / −0	−2.5 / −5.5	4.0 / 11.5	+4.5 / −0	−4.0 / −7.0	6 / 20	+7 / −0	−6 / −13	10 / 34	+12 / −0	−10 / −22	14 / 50	+18 / −0	−14 / −32
3.15–4.73	1.4 / 5.8	+2.2 / −0	−1.4 / −3.6	3.0 / 10.0	+3.5 / −0	−3.0 / −6.5	5.0 / 13.5	+5.0 / −0	−5.0 / −8.5	7 / 25	+9 / −0	−7 / −16	11 / 39	+14 / −0	−11 / −25	16 / 60	+22 / −0	−16 / −38
4.73–7.09	1.6 / 6.6	+2.5 / −0	−1.6 / −4.1	3.5 / 11.5	+4.0 / −0	−3.5 / −7.5	6 / 16	+6 / −0	−6 / −10	8 / 28	+10 / −0	−8 / −18	12 / 44	+16 / −0	−12 / −28	18 / 68	+25 / −0	−18 / −43
7.09–9.85	2.0 / 7.6	+2.8 / −0	−2.0 / −4.8	4.0 / 13.0	+4.5 / −0	−4.0 / −8.5	7 / 18.5	+7 / −0	−7 / −11.5	10 / 34	+12 / −0	−10 / −22	16 / 52	+18 / −0	−16 / −34	22 / 78	+28 / −0	−22 / −50

TABLE XXX-C

Transition Locational Fits [1]

Limits are in thousandths of an inch. Limits for hole and shaft are applied algebraically to the basic size to obtain the limits of size for the mating parts. "Fit" represents the maximum interference (minus values) and the maximum clearance (plus values). Symbols H8, j6, etc., are Hole and Shaft designations used in ABC System.

Nominal Size Range Inches Over / To	Class LT 1 Fit	Class LT 1 Hole H7	Class LT 1 Shaft j6	Class LT 2 Fit	Class LT 2 Hole H8	Class LT 2 Shaft j7	Class LT 3 Fit	Class LT 3 Hole H7	Class LT 3 Shaft k6	Class LT 4 Fit	Class LT 4 Hole H8	Class LT 4 Shaft k7	Class LT 6 Fit	Class LT 6 Hole H8	Class LT 6 Shaft m7	Class LT 7 Fit	Class LT 7 Hole H7	Class LT 7 Shaft h6
0.04–0.12	−0.15 / +0.5	+0.4 / −0	+0.15 / −0.1	−0.3 / +0.7	+0.6 / −0	+0.3 / −0.1							−0.55 / +0.45	+0.6 / −0	+0.55 / +0.15	−0.5 / +0.15	+0.4 / −0	+0.5 / +0.25
0.12–0.24	−0.2 / +0.6	+0.5 / −0	+0.2 / −0.1	−0.4 / +0.8	+0.7 / −0	+0.4 / −0.1							−0.7 / +0.5	+0.7 / −0	+0.7 / +0.2	−0.6 / +0.2	+0.5 / −0	+0.6 / +0.3
0.24–0.40	−0.3 / +0.7	+0.6 / −0	+0.3 / −0.1	−0.4 / +1.1	+0.9 / −0	+0.4 / −0.2	−0.5 / +0.5	+0.6 / −0	+0.5 / +0.1	−0.7 / +0.8	+0.9 / −0	+0.7 / +0.1	−0.8 / +0.7	+0.9 / −0	+0.8 / +0.2	−0.8 / +0.2	+0.6 / −0	+0.8 / +0.4
0.40–0.71	−0.3 / +0.8	+0.7 / −0	+0.3 / −0.1	−0.5 / +1.2	+1.0 / −0	+0.5 / −0.2	−0.5 / +0.6	+0.7 / −0	+0.5 / +0.1	−0.8 / +0.9	+1.0 / −0	+0.8 / +0.1	−1.0 / +0.7	+1.0 / −0	+1.0 / +0.3	−0.9 / +0.2	+0.7 / −0	+0.9 / +0.5
0.71–1.19	−0.3 / +1.0	+0.8 / −0	+0.3 / −0.2	−0.5 / +1.5	+1.2 / −0	+0.5 / −0.3	−0.6 / +0.7	+0.8 / −0	+0.6 / +0.1	−0.9 / +1.1	+1.2 / −0	+0.9 / +0.1	−1.1 / +0.9	+1.2 / −0	+1.1 / +0.3	−1.1 / +0.2	+0.8 / −0	+1.1 / +0.6
1.19–1.97	−0.4 / +1.2	+1.0 / −0	+0.4 / −0.2	−0.6 / +2.0	+1.6 / −0	+0.6 / −0.4	−0.7 / +0.9	+1.0 / −0	+0.7 / +0.1	−1.1 / +1.2	+1.6 / −0	+1.1 / +0.1	−1.4 / +1.2	+1.6 / −0	+1.4 / +0.4	−1.3 / +0.3	+1.0 / −0	+1.3 / +0.7
1.97–3.15	−0.4 / +1.5	+1.2 / −0	+0.4 / −0.3	−0.7 / +2.3	+1.8 / −0	+0.7 / −0.5	−0.8 / +1.1	+1.2 / −0	+0.8 / +0.1	−1.3 / +1.7	+1.8 / −0	+1.3 / +0.1	−1.7 / +1.3	+1.8 / −0	+1.7 / +0.5	−1.5 / +0.4	+1.2 / −0	+1.5 / +0.8
3.15–4.73	−0.5 / +1.8	+1.4 / −0	+0.5 / −0.4	−0.8 / +2.8	+2.2 / −0	+0.8 / −0.6	−1.0 / +1.3	+1.4 / −0	+1.0 / +0.1	−1.5 / +2.1	+2.2 / −0	+1.5 / +0.1	−1.9 / +1.7	+2.2 / −0	+1.9 / +0.5	−1.9 / +0.4	+1.4 / −0	+1.9 / +1.0
4.73–7.09	−0.6 / +2.0	+1.6 / −0	+0.6 / −0.4	−0.9 / +3.2	+2.5 / −0	+0.9 / −0.7	−1.1 / +1.5	+1.6 / −0	+1.1 / +0.1	−1.7 / +2.4	+2.5 / −0	+1.7 / +0.1	−2.2 / +1.9	+2.5 / −0	+2.2 / +0.6	−2.2 / +0.4	+1.6 / −0	+2.2 / +1.2
7.09–9.85	−0.7 / +2.3	+1.8 / −0	+0.7 / −0.5	−1.0 / +3.6	+2.8 / −0	+1.0 / −0.8	−1.4 / +1.6	+1.8 / −0	+1.4 / +0.2	−2.0 / +2.6	+2.8 / −0	+2.0 / +0.2	−2.4 / +2.2	+2.8 / −0	+2.4 / +0.6	−2.6 / +0.4	+1.8 / −0	+2.6 / +1.4

[1] Extracted from ASA B4.1–1955 (Table 3).
[2] Data are in accordance with ABC agreements.
For diameters greater than 9.85 inches see standard.

APPENDIX

ABLE XXX-D

Interference Locational Fits[1]

Limits are in thousandths of an inch. Limits for hole and shaft are applied algebraically to the basic size to obtain the limits of size for the parts. Symbols H7, p6, etc., are Hole and Shaft designations used in ABC System.[2]

Nominal Size Range Inches	Class LN 2			Class LN 3		
	Limits of Interference	Standard Limits		Limits of Interference	Standard Limits	
Over To		Hole H7	Shaft p6		Hole H7	Shaft r6
0.04–0.12	0 0.65	+0.4 − 0	+0.65 +0.4	0.1 0.75	+0.4 − 0	+0.75 +0.5
0.12–0.24	0 0.8	+0.5 − 0	+0.8 +0.5	0.1 0.9	+0.5 − 0	+0.9 +0.6
0.24–0.40	0 1.0	+0.6 − 0	+1.0 +0.6	0.2 1.2	+0.6 − 0	+1.2 +0.8
0.40–0.71	0 1.1	+0.7 − 0	+1.1 +0.7	0.3 1.4	+0.7 − 0	+1.4 +1.0
0.71–1.19	0 1.3	+0.8 − 0	+1.3 +0.8	0.4 1.7	+0.8 − 0	+1.7 +1.2
1.19–1.97	0 1.6	+1.0 − 0	+1.6 +1.0	0.4 2.0	+1.0 − 0	+2.0 +1.4
1.97–3.15	0.2 2.1	+1.2 − 0	+2.1 +1.4	0.4 2.3	+1.2 − 0	+2.3 +1.6
3.15–4.73	0.2 2.5	+1.4 − 0	+2.5 +1.6	0.6 2.9	+1.4 − 0	+2.9 +2.0
4.73–7.09	0.2 2.8	+1.6 − 0	+2.8 +1.8	0.9 3.5	+1.6 − 0	+3.5 +2.5
7.09–9.85	0.2 3.2	+1.8 − 0	+3.2 +2.0	1.2 4.2	+1.8 − 0	+4.2 +3.0

[1] Extracted from ASA B4.1–1955 (Table 4).
[2] Data are in accordance with ABC agreements.
  For diameters greater than 9.85 inches see standard.

TABLE XXX-E

Force and Shrink Fits[1]

Limits are in thousandths of an inch. Limits for hole and shaft are applied algebraically to the basic size to obtain the limits of size for the parts. Symbols H7, s6, etc., are Hole and Shaft designations used in ABC System.[2]

Nominal Size Range Inches Over	To	Class FN 1 Limits of Interference	Class FN 1 Standard Limits Hole H6	Class FN 1 Standard Limits Shaft	Class FN 2 Limits of Interference	Class FN 2 Standard Limits Hole H7	Class FN 2 Standard Limits Shaft s6	Class FN 3 Limits of Interference	Class FN 3 Standard Limits Hole H7	Class FN 3 Standard Limits Shaft t6	Class FN 4 Limits of Interference	Class FN 4 Standard Limits Hole H7	Class FN 4 Standard Limits Shaft u6	Class FN 5 Limits of Interference	Class FN 5 Standard Limits Hole H7	Class FN 5 Standard Limits Shaft x7
0.04	0.12	0.05 / 0.5	+0.25 / −0	+0.5 / +0.3	0.2 / 0.85	+0.4 / −0	+0.85 / +0.6				0.3 / 0.95	+0.4 / −0	+0.95 / +0.7	0.5 / 1.3	+0.4 / −0	+1.3 / +0.9
0.12	0.24	0.1 / 0.6	+0.3 / −0	+0.6 / +0.4	0.2 / 1.0	+0.5 / −0	+1.0 / +0.7				0.4 / 1.2	+0.5 / −0	+1.2 / +0.9	0.7 / 1.7	+0.5 / −0	+1.7 / +1.2
0.24	0.40	0.1 / 0.75	+0.4 / −0	+0.75 / +0.5	0.4 / 1.4	+0.6 / −0	+1.4 / +1.0				0.6 / 1.6	+0.6 / −0	+1.6 / +1.2	0.8 / 2.0	+0.6 / −0	+2.0 / +1.4
0.40	0.56	0.1 / 0.8	+0.4 / −0	+0.8 / +0.5	0.5 / 1.6	+0.7 / −0	+1.6 / +1.2				0.7 / 1.8	+0.7 / −0	+1.8 / +1.4	0.9 / 2.3	+0.7 / −0	+2.3 / +1.6
0.56	0.71	0.2 / 0.9	+0.4 / −0	+0.9 / +0.6	0.5 / 1.6	+0.7 / −0	+1.6 / +1.2				0.7 / 1.8	+0.7 / −0	+1.8 / +1.4	1.1 / 2.5	+0.7 / −0	+2.5 / +1.8
0.71	0.95	0.2 / 1.1	+0.5 / −0	+1.1 / +0.7	0.6 / 1.9	+0.8 / −0	+1.9 / +1.4	0.8 / 2.1	+0.8 / −0	+2.1 / +1.6	0.8 / 2.1	+0.8 / −0	+2.1 / +1.6	1.4 / 3.0	+0.8 / −0	+3.0 / +2.2
0.95	1.19	0.3 / 1.2	+0.5 / −0	+1.2 / +0.8	0.6 / 1.9	+0.8 / −0	+1.9 / +1.4	0.8 / 2.4	+1.0 / −0	+2.4 / +1.8	1.0 / 2.3	+0.8 / −0	+2.3 / +1.8	1.7 / 3.3	+0.8 / −0	+3.3 / +2.5
1.19	1.58	0.3 / 1.3	+0.6 / −0	+1.3 / +0.9	0.8 / 2.4	+1.0 / −0	+2.4 / +1.8	1.0 / 2.6	+1.0 / −0	+2.6 / +2.0	1.5 / 3.1	+1.0 / −0	+3.1 / +2.5	2.0 / 4.0	+1.0 / −0	+4.0 / +3.0
1.58	1.97	0.4 / 1.4	+0.6 / −0	+1.4 / +1.0	0.8 / 2.4	+1.0 / −0	+2.4 / +1.8	1.2 / 2.8	+1.0 / −0	+2.8 / +2.2	1.8 / 3.4	+1.0 / −0	+3.4 / +2.8	3.0 / 5.0	+1.0 / −0	+5.0 / +4.0
1.97	2.56	0.6 / 1.8	+0.7 / −0	+1.8 / +1.3	0.8 / 2.7	+1.2 / −0	+2.7 / +2.0	1.3 / 3.2	+1.2 / −0	+3.2 / +2.5	2.3 / 4.2	+1.2 / −0	+4.2 / +3.5	3.8 / 6.2	+1.2 / −0	+6.2 / +5.0
2.56	3.15	0.7 / 1.9	+0.7 / −0	+1.9 / +1.4	1.0 / 2.9	+1.2 / −0	+2.9 / +2.2	1.8 / 3.7	+1.2 / −0	+3.7 / +3.0	2.8 / 4.7	+1.2 / −0	+4.7 / +4.0	4.8 / 7.2	+1.2 / −0	+7.2 / +6.0

[1] Extracted from ASA B4.1–1955 (Table 5).
[2] Data are in accordance with ABC agreements. For diameters greater than 3.15 inches see standard.

TABLE XXXI

Single Row Radial Bearings—Type 3000

Principal Dimensions

For radial or combined loads from either direction where thrust is to be resisted by a single bearing and is not great enough to require use of angular contact type. For capacities under thrust or combined loads, use factors "*F*" given under "Bearing Selection."

Brg. No.	Bore B		Diameter D		Width W		Balls		Radius r*
	Mm	*Inch*	*Mm*	*Inch*	*Mm*	*Inch*	Diam.	No.	
3200	10	.3937	30	1.1811	9	.3543	$\frac{7}{32}$	7	.025
3300	10	.3937	35	1.3780	11	.4331	$\frac{1}{4}$	7	.025
3201	12	.4724	32	1.2598	10	.3937	.210	8	.025
3301	12	.4724	37	1.4567	12	.4724	$\frac{9}{32}$	7	.04
3202	15	.5906	35	1.3780	11	.4331	.210	9	.025
3302	15	.5906	42	1.6535	13	.5118	$\frac{5}{16}$	7	.04
3203	17	.6693	40	1.5748	12	.4724	$\frac{9}{32}$	8	.04
3303	17	.6693	47	1.8504	14	.5512	$\frac{11}{32}$	7	.04
3204	20	.7874	47	1.8504	14	.5512	$\frac{5}{16}$	8	.04
3304	20	.7874	52	2.0472	15	.5906	$\frac{13}{32}$	7	.04
3205	25	.9843	52	2.0472	15	.5906	$\frac{5}{16}$	9	.04
3305	25	.9843	62	2.4409	17	.6693	$\frac{13}{32}$	8	.04
3206	30	1.1811	62	2.4409	16	.6299	$\frac{11}{32}$	9	.04
3306	30	1.1811	72	2.8346	19	.7480	$\frac{15}{32}$	8	.04
3207	35	1.3780	72	2.8346	17	.6693	$\frac{7}{16}$	9	.04
3307	35	1.3780	80	3.1496	21	.8268	$\frac{17}{32}$	8	.06
3208	40	1.5748	80	3.1496	18	.7087	$\frac{15}{32}$	9	.04
3308	40	1.5748	90	3.5433	23	.9055	$\frac{19}{32}$	8	.06
3209	45	1.7717	85	3.3465	19	.7480	$\frac{15}{32}$	10	.04
3309	45	1.7717	100	3.9370	25	.9843	$\frac{21}{32}$	8	.06
3210	50	1.9685	90	3.5433	20	.7874	$\frac{15}{32}$	11	.04
3310	50	1.9685	110	4.3307	27	1.0630	$\frac{23}{32}$	8	.08
3211	55	2.1654	100	3.9370	21	.8268	$\frac{1}{2}$	11	.06
3311	55	2.1654	120	4.7244	29	1.1417	$\frac{25}{32}$	8	.08

* Radius *r* indicates maximum fillet radius in housing or on shaft which bearing radius will clear.

Pages 140–143 from Vol. I, *New Departure Hand Book.*

TABLE XXXI (cont.)
Radax Bearings—Type 30,000

Principal Dimensions

Single row angular contact; provide maximum capacity for one-direction thrust loads. Mounted two bearings opposed for combined loads or thrust from either direction. For capacities under these loads, use factors "*F*" given under "Bearing Selection."

Brg. No.	Bore B		Diameter D		Width W		Balls		Radius r*
	Mm	Inch	Mm	Inch	Mm	Inch	Diam.	No.	
30204			47	1.8504	14	.5512	$\frac{11}{32}$	10	
30304	20	.7874	52	2.0472	15	.5906	$\frac{3}{8}$	10	.04
30404			72	2.8346	19	.7480	$\frac{9}{16}$	8	
30205			52	2.0472	15	.5906	$\frac{11}{32}$	11	.04
30305	25	.9843	62	2.4409	17	.6693	$\frac{7}{16}$	10	.04
30405			80	3.1496	21	.8268	$\frac{5}{8}$	9	.06
30206			62	2.4409	16	.6299	$\frac{3}{8}$	12	.04
30306	30	1.1811	72	2.8346	19	.7480	$\frac{1}{2}$	10	.04
30406			90	3.5433	23	.9055	$\frac{11}{16}$	9	.06
30207			72	2.8346	17	.6693	$\frac{7}{16}$	12	.04
30307	35	1.3780	80	3.1496	21	.8268	$\frac{9}{16}$	11	.06
30407			100	3.9370	25	.9843	$\frac{3}{4}$	9	.06
30208			80	3.1496	18	.7087	$\frac{1}{2}$	12	.04
30308	40	1.5748	90	3.5433	23	.9055	$\frac{5}{8}$	11	.06
30408			110	4.3307	27	1.0630	$\frac{13}{16}$	10	.08
30209			85	3.3465	19	.7480	$\frac{1}{2}$	13	.04
30309	45	1.7717	100	3.9370	25	.9843	$\frac{11}{16}$	11	.06
30409			120	4.7244	29	1.1417	$\frac{7}{8}$	10	.08
30210			90	3.5433	20	.7874	$\frac{1}{2}$	14	.04
30310	50	1.9685	110	4.3307	27	1.0630	$\frac{3}{4}$	11	.08
30410			130	5.1181	31	1.2205	$\frac{15}{16}$	10	.08
30211			100	3.9370	21	.8268	$\frac{9}{16}$	14	.06
30311	55	2.1654	120	4.7244	29	1.1417	$\frac{13}{16}$	12	.08
30411			140	5.5118	33	1.2992	1	10	.08
30212			110	4.3307	22	.8661	$\frac{5}{8}$	14	.06
30312	60	2.3622	130	5.1181	31	1.2205	$\frac{7}{8}$	12	.08
30412			150	5.9055	35	1.3780	$1\frac{1}{16}$	10	.08

* Radius *r* indicates maximum fillet radius in housing or on shaft which bearing radius will clear.

Page 143 from Vol. I, *New Departure Hand Book.*

TABLE XXXII*

Shaft Mounting Fits for SAE or A.B.E.C.-1 Standard Bearings

The *"theoretical fits"* given in this table are those which could result if the shaft diameters and bearing bores were to vary the full limits of their respective tolerances. Actually, bearing bores are ground uniformly close to the minimum limit, and investigation by the Annular Bearing Engineers Committee has proved that well over 95% of actual installations result in the *"expected fits"* given below.

Bearing and Bore Numbers	Bearing Bore Diameters		Shaft Revolving						Shaft Stationary					
			Diameters		Expected Fit		Theoret. Fit		Diameters		Expected Fit		Theoret. Fit	
	Max.	Min.	Max.	Min.	Loose or Tight	Tight	Loose	Tight	Max.	Min.	Max. Loose	Min. Loose	Loose	Tight
34	.1575	.1572	.1576	.1573					.1573	.1570				
35	.1969	.1966	.1970	.1967	.0001L	.0003	.0002	.0004	.1967	.1964	.0004	.0000	.0005	.0001
36	.2362	.2359	.2363	.2360					.2360	.2357				
37	.2756	.2753	.2757	.2754					.2754	.2751				
38	.3150	.3147	.3151	.3148	.0001L	.0003	.0002	.0004	.3148	.3145	.0004	.0000	.0005	.0001
39	.3543	.3540	.3544	.3541					.3541	.3538				
8006	.2362	.2359	.2363	.2360					.2360	.2357				
8007, 8102	.2756	.2753	.2757	.2754	.0001L	.0003	.0002	.0004	.2754	.2751	.0004	.0000	.0005	.0001
8008, 8103	.3150	.3147	.3151	.3148					.3148	.3145				
8009	.3543	.3540	.3544	.3541	.0001L	.0003	.0002	.0004	.3541	.3538				
8011	.4331	.4328	.4333	.4330	.0000L	.0004	.0001	.0005	.4329	.4326	.0004	.0000	.0005	.0001
8013	.5118	.5115	.5120	.5117	.0000L	.0004	.0001	.0005	.5116	.5113				
8014	.5512	.5509	.5514	.5511	.0000L	.0004	.0001	.0005	.5510	.5507	.0004	.0000	.0005	.0001
8016	.6299	.6296	.6301	.6298	.0000L	.0004	.0001	.0005	.6297	.6294	.0004	.0000	.0005	.0001
8026	1.0236	1.0232	1.0239	1.0235	.0000L	.0006	.0001	.0007	1.0233	1.0229	.0006	.0000	.0007	.0001
N.D. 8-6	.2362	.2359	.2363	.2360					.2360	.2357				
N.D. 8-7	.2756	.2753	.2757	.2754	.0001L	.0003	.0002	.0004	.2754	.2751	.0004	.0000	.0005	.0001
N.D. 8	.3150	.3147	.3151	.3148					.3148	.3145				
N.D. 10-9	.3543	.3540	.3544	.3541	.0001L	.0003	.0002	.0004	.3541	.3538				
N.D. 10	.3937	.3934	.3939	.3936	.0000L	.0004	.0001	.0005	.3935	.3932	.0004	.0000	.0005	.0001
N.D. 12-11	.4331	.4328	.4333	.4330	.0000L	.0004	.0001	.0005	.4329	.4326				
N.D. 12	.4724	.4721	.4726	.4723	.0000L	.0004	.0001	.0005	.4722	.4719				
N.D. 13	.5118	.5115	.5120	.5117					.5116	.5113				
N.D. 15	.5906	.5903	.5908	.5905	.0000L	.0004	.0001	.0005	.5904	.5901	.0004	.0000	.0005	.0001
N.D. 16	.6299	.6296	.6301	.6298					.6297	.6294				
N.D. 17	.6693	.6690	.6695	.6692	.0000L	.0004	.0001	.0005	.6691	.6688	.0004	.0000	.0005	.0001
N.D. 20	.7874	.7870	.7877	.7873	.0000L	.0006	.0001	.0007	.7871	.7867	.0006	.0000	.0007	.0001
N.D. 25	.9843	.9839	.9846	.9842	.0000L	.0006	.0001	.0007	.9840	.9836	.0006	.0000	.0007	.0001
0	.3937	.3934	.3939	.3936					.3935	.3932				
1	.4724	.4721	.4726	.4723	.0000L	.0004	.0001	.0005	.4722	.4719	.0004	.0000	.0005	.0001
2	.5906	.5903	.5908	.5905					.5904	.5901				
3	.6693	.6690	.6605	.6692	.0000L	.0004	.0001	.0005	.6691	.6688	.0004	.0000	.0005	.0001
4	.7874	.7870	.7877	.7873	.0000L	.0006	.0001	.0007	.7871	.7867	.0006	.0000	.0007	.0001
5	.9843	.9839	.9846	.9842	.0000L	.0006	.0001	.0007	.9840	.9836	.0006	.0000	.0007	.0001
6	1.1811	1.1807	1.1814	1.1810	.0000L	.0006	.0001	.0007	1.1808	1.1804	.0006	.0000	.0007	.0001
7	1.3780	1.3775	1.3784	1.3779	.0001T	.0007	.0001	.0009	1.3776	1.3771	.0007	.0001	.0009	.0001
8	1.5748	1.5743	1.5752	1.5747	.0001T	.0007	.0001	.0009	1.5744	1.5739	.0007	.0001	.0009	.0001
9	1.7717	1.7712	1.7721	1.7716	.0001T	.0007	.0001	.0009	1.7713	1.7708	.0007	.0001	.0009	.0001
10	1.9685	1.9680	1.9689	1.9684	.0001T	.0007	.0001	.0009	1.9681	1.9676	.0007	.0001	.0009	.0001
11	2.1654	2.1648	2.1659	2.1653	.0001T	.0009	.0001	.0011	2.1649	2.1643	.0009	.0001	.0011	.0001
12	2.3622	2.3616	2.3627	2.3621					2.3617	2.3611				
13	2.5591	2.5585	2.5596	2.5590	.0001T	.0009	.0001	.0011	2.5586	2.5580	.0009	.0001	.0011	.0001
14	2.7559	2.7553	2.7564	2.7558					2.7554	2.7548				
15	2.9528	2.9522	2.9533	2.9527	.0001T	.0009	.0001	.0011	2.9523	2.9517	.0009	.0001	.0011	.0001
16	3.1496	3.1490	3.1501	3.1495	.0001T	.0009	.0001	.0011	3.1491	3.1485	.0009	.0001	.0011	.0001
17	3.3465	3.3457	3.3471	3.3464	.0002T	.0012	.0001	.0014	3.3458	3.3451	.0012	.0002	.0014	.0001
18	3.5433	3.5425	3.5439	3.5432					3.5426	3.5419				
19	3.7402	3.7394	3.7408	3.7401	.0002T	.0012	.0001	.0014	3.7395	3.7388	.0012	.0002	.0014	.0001
20	3.9370	3.9362	3.9376	3.9369					3.9363	3.9356				
21	4.1339	4.1331	4.1345	4.1338	.0002T	.0012	.0001	.0014	4.1332	4.1325	.0012	.0002	.0014	.0001
22	4.3307	4.3299	4.3313	4.3306					4.3300	4.3293				

* Reproduced with permission from Vol. I, *New Departure Hand Book.*

TABLE XXXII (cont.)

Housing Mounting Fits for A.B.E.C.-1 and A.B.E.C.-2 Bearings

The housing fits given in this table are those which would result if the bearing diameters and housing bores were to vary the full allowable limits. Actually, bearing diameters are ground uniformly close to the maximum and with housings properly bored, fits well within the limits given will be obtained in practice.

Bearing and Bore Numbers (Series)			Bearing Outer Diam.		Housing Stationary — Diameters		Expect. Fit (Min. Loose)	Expect. Fit (Max. Loose)	Theoret. Fit (Tight)	Theoret. Fit (Loose)	Housing Revolving — Diameters		Expect. Fit (Tight)	Expect. Fit (Loose)	Theoret. Fit (Tight)	Theoret. Fit (Loose)
Lgt.	Med.	Hvy.	Max.	Min.	Max.	Min.					Max.	Min.				
34			.6299	.6295	.6303	.6298					.6298	.6293				
35, 36			.7480	.7476	.7484	.7479	.0000	.0005	.0001	.0008	.7479	.7474				
37, 38			.8661	.8657	.8665	.8660					.8660	.8655	.0002	.0002	.0006	.0003
39			1.0236	1.0232	1.0240	1.0235					1.0235	1.0230				
8102, 8103			.8661	.8657	.8665	.8660					.8660	.8655				
8006, 7 & 8			.9449	.9445	.9453	.9448	.0000	.0005	.0001	.0008	.9448	.9443	.0002	.0002	.0006	.0003
8009			1.1811	1.1807	1.1815	1.1810					1.1810	1.1805				
8011, 8013			1.2598	1.2593	1.2603	1.2597	.0000	.0007	.0001	.0010	1.2597	1.2591	.0003	.0003	.0007	.0004
8014, 8016			1.3780	1.3775	1.3785	1.3779	.0000	.0007	.0001	.0010	1.3779	1.3773	.0003	.0003	.0007	.0004
8026			2.0472	2.0466	2.0479	2.0479	.0000	.0010	.0001	.0013	2.0472	2.0464	.0004	.0004	.0008	.0006
N.D. 8-6, 8-7, 8			.9453	.9449	.9457	.9452	.0000	.0005	.0001	.0008	.9452	.9447	.0002	.0002	.0006	.0003
N.D. 10-9, 10			1.1028	1.1024	1.1032	1.1027	.0000	.0005	.0001	.0008	1.1027	1.1022	.0002	.0002	.0006	.0003
N.D. 12-11, 12			1.2603	1.2598	1.2608	1.2602	.0000	.0007	.0001	.0010	1.2602	1.2596	.0003	.0003	.0007	.0004
N.D. 13			1.1816	1.1811	1.1821	1.1815					1.1815	1.1809				
N.D. 15			1.3785	1.3780	1.3790	1.3784	.0000	.0007	.0001	.0010	1.3784	1.3778	.0003	.0003	.0007	.0004
N.D. 16			1.4966	1.4961	1.4971	1.4965					1.4965	1.4959				
N.D. 17			1.7328	1.7323	1.7333	1.7327					1.7327	1.7321				
N.D. 20			1.8509	1.8504	1.8514	1.8508	.0000	.0007	.0001	.0010	1.8508	1.8502	.0003	.0003	.0007	.0004
N.D. 25			2.0477	2.0472	2.0482	2.0476					2.0476	2.0470				
0			1.1811	1.1807	1.1815	1.1810	.0000	.0005	.0001	.0008	1.1810	1.1805	.0002	.0002	.0006	.0003
1			1.2598	1.2593	1.2603	1.2597	.0000	.0007	.0001	.0010	1.2597	1.2591	.0003	.0003	.0007	.0004
2	0		1.3780	1.3775	1.3785	1.3779	.0000	.0007	.0001	.0010	1.3779	1.3773	.0003	.0003	.0007	.0004
	1		1.4567	1.4562	1.4572	1.4566					1.4566	1.4560				
3	2		1.5748	1.5743	1.5753	1.5747	.0000	.0007	.0001	.0010	1.5747	1.5741	.0003	.0003	.0007	.0004
			1.6535	1.6530	1.6540	1.6534					1.6534	1.6528				
4	3		1.8504	1.8499	1.8509	1.8503	.0000	.0007	.0001	.0010	1.8503	1.8497	.0003	.0003	.0007	.0004
5	4		2.0472	2.0466	2.0479	2.0471	.0000	.0010	.0001	.0013	2.0472	2.0464	.0004	.0004	.0008	.0006
6	5		2.4409	2.4403	2.4416	2.4408	.0000	.0010	.0001	.0013	2.4409	2.4401	.0004	.0004	.0008	.0006
7	6	4	2.8346	2.8340	2.8353	2.8345	.0000	.0010	.0001	.0013	2.8346	2.8338	.0004	.0004	.0008	.0006
8	7	5	3.1496	3.1490	3.1503	3.1495	.0000	.0010	.0001	.0013	3.1496	3.1488	.0004	.0004	.0008	.0006
9			3.3465	3.3457	3.3473	3.3463	.0000	.0012	.0002	.0016	3.3466	3.3456	.0005	.0004	.0009	.0009
10	8	6	3.5433	3.5425	3.5441	3.5431					3.5434	3.5424				
11	9	7	3.9370	3.9362	3.9378	3.9368	.0000	.0012	.0002	.0016	3.9371	3.9361	.0005	.0004	.0009	.0009
12	10	8	4.3307	4.3299	4.3315	4.3305					4.3308	4.3298				
13	11	9	4.7244	4.7236	4.7252	4.7242	.0000	.0012	.0002	.0016	4.7245	4.7235	.0005	.0004	.0009	.0009
14			4.9213	4.9203	4.9223	4.9211	.0001	.0015	.0002	.0020	4.9214	4.9202	.0006	.0005	.0011	.0011
15	12	10	5.1181	5.1171	5.1191	5.1179	.0001	.0015	.0002	.0020	5.1182	5.1170	.0006	.0005	.0011	.0011
16	13	11	5.5118	5.5108	5.5128	5.5116					5.5119	5.5107				
17	14	12	5.9055	5.9045	5.9065	5.9053	.0001	.0015	.0002	.0020	5.9056	5.9044	.0006	.0005	.0011	.0011
18	15	13	6.2992	6.2982	6.3002	6.2990					6.2993	6.2981				
19	16		6.6929	6.6919	6.6939	6.6927	.0001	.0015	.0002	.0020	6.6930	6.6918	.0006	.0005	.0011	.0011
20	17	14	7.0866	7.0856	7.0876	7.0864	.0001	.0015	.0002	.0020	7.0867	7.0855	.0006	.0005	.0011	.0011
21	18	15	7.4803	7.4791	7.4815	7.4801	.0001	.0018	.0002	.0024	7.4804	7.4790	.0007	.0007	.0013	.0013
22	19	16	7.8740	7.8728	7.8752	7.8738					7.8741	7.8727				
		17	8.2677	8.2665	8.2689	8.2675	.0001	.0018	.0002	.0024	8.2678	8.2664	.0007	.0007	.0013	.0013
	20		8.4646	8.4634	8.4658	8.4644					8.4647	8.4633				
21	18		8.8583	8.8571	8.8595	8.8581	.0001	.0018	.0002	.0024	8.8584	8.8570	.0007	.0007	.0013	.0013
22			9.4488	9.4476	9.4500	9.4486					9.4489	9.4475				

APPENDIX

TABLE XXXIII
Twist Drill Sizes*

	Number Sizes			Letter Sizes	
No. Size	Decimal Equivalents	No. Size	Decimal Equivalents	Size Letter	Decimal Equivalents
1	.2280	41	.0960	A	.234
2	.2210	42	.0935	B	.238
3	.2130	43	.0890	C	.242
4	.2090	44	.0860	D	.246
5	.2055	45	.0820	E	.250
6	.2040	46	.0810	F	.257
7	.2010	47	.0785	G	.261
8	.1990	48	.0760	H	.266
9	.1960	49	.0730	I	.272
10	.1935	50	.0700	J	.277
11	.1910	51	.0670	K	.281
12	.1890	52	.0635	L	.290
13	.1850	53	.0595	M	.295
14	.1820	54	.0550	N	.302
15	.1800	55	.0520	O	.316
16	.1770	56	.0465	P	.323
17	.1730	57	.0430	Q	.332
18	.1695	58	.0420	R	.339
19	.1660	59	.0410	S	.348
20	.1610	60	.0400	T	.358
21	.1590	61	.0390	U	.368
22	.1570	62	.0380	V	.377
23	.1540	63	.0370	W	.386
24	.1520	64	.0360	X	.397
25	.1495	65	.0350	Y	.404
26	.1470	66	.0330	Z	.413
27	.1440	67	.0320		
28	.1405	68	.0310		
29	.1360	69	.0292		
30	.1285	70	.0280		
31	.1200	71	.0260		
32	.1160	72	.0250		
33	.1130	73	.0240		
34	.1110	74	.0225		
35	.1100	75	.0210		
36	.1065	76	.0200		
37	.1040	77	.0180		
38	.1015	78	.0160		
39	.0995	79	.0145		
40	.0980	80	.0135		

* Fraction size drills range in size from $\frac{1}{16}$–4″ and over in diameter—by 64ths.

TABLE XXXIV

Standard Wire and Sheet-Metal Gages

(Dimensions in decimal parts of an inch)

Gage Number	(A) Brown & Sharpe or American	(B) American Steel & Wire Co.	(C) Piano Wire	(E) U.S. St'd.	Gage Number
0000000	.6513	.4900	. . . .	.5000	0000000
000000	.5800	.4615	.004	.4688	000000
00000	.5165	.4305	.005	.4375	00000
0000	.4600	.3938	.006	.4063	0000
000	.4096	.3625	.007	.3750	000
00	.3648	.3310	.008	.3438	00
0	.3249	.3065	.009	.3125	0
1	.2893	.2830	.010	.2813	1
2	.2576	.2625	.011	.2656	2
3	.2294	.2437	.012	.2500	3
4	.2043	.2253	.013	.2344	4
5	.1819	.2070	.014	.2188	5
6	.1620	.1920	.016	.2031	6
7	.1443	.1770	.018	.1875	7
8	.1285	.1620	.020	.1719	8
9	.1144	.1483	.022	.1563	9
10	.1019	.1350	.024	.1406	10
11	.0907	.1205	.026	.1250	11
12	.0808	.1055	.029	.1094	12
13	.0720	.0915	.031	.0938	13
14	.0641	.0800	.033	.0781	14
15	.0571	.0720	.035	.0703	15
16	.0508	.0625	.037	.0625	16
17	.0453	.0540	.039	.0563	17
18	.0403	.0475	.041	.0500	18
19	.0359	.0410	.043	.0438	19
20	.0320	.0348	.045	.0375	20
21	.0285	.0317	.047	.0344	21
22	.0253	.0286	.049	.0313	22
23	.0226	.0258	.051	.0281	23
24	.0201	.0230	.055	.0250	24
25	.0179	.0204	.059	.0219	25
26	.0159	.0181	.063	.0188	26
27	.0142	.0173	.067	.0172	27
28	.0126	.0162	.071	.0156	28
29	.0113	.0150	.075	.0141	29
30	.0100	.0140	.080	.0125	30
31	.0089	.0132	.085	.0109	31
32	.0080	.0128	.090	.0102	32
33	.0071	.0118	.095	.0094	33
34	.0063	.0104	.100	.0086	34
35	.0056	.0095	.106	.0078	35
36	.0050	.0090	.112	.0070	36
37	.0045	.0085	.118	.0066	37
38	.0040	.0080	.124	.0063	38
39	.0035	.0075	.130	. . . . .	39
40	.0031	.0070	.138	. . . . .	40

(A) Standard in U.S. for sheet metal and wire (except steel & iron).
(B) Standard for iron and steel wire (U.S. Steel Wire Gage).
(C) American Steel and Wire Company's music (or piano) wire gage sizes. Recognized by U.S. Bureau of Standards.
(E) U.S. Standard for iron and steel plate. However, plate is now generally specified by its thickness in decimals of an inch.

APPENDIX

TABLE XXXV

Trigonometric Functions

Angle	Sine	Cosine	Tan	Co-Tan	Angle
0°	0.0000	1.0000	0.0000	*Infin.*	90°
1°	0.0175	0.9998	0.0175	57.290	89°
2°	.0349	.9994	.0349	28.636	88°
3°	.0523	.9986	.0524	19.081	87°
4°	.0698	.9976	.0699	14.301	86°
5°	.0872	.9962	.0875	11.430	85°
6°	.1045	.9945	.1051	9.5144	84°
7°	.1219	.9925	.1228	8.1443	83°
8°	.1392	.9903	.1405	7.1154	82°
9°	.1564	.9877	.1584	6.3138	81°
10°	.1736	.9848	.1763	5.6713	80°
11°	.1908	.9816	.1944	5.1446	79°
12°	.2079	.9781	.2126	4.7046	78°
13°	.2250	.9744	.2309	4.3315	77°
14°	.2419	.9703	.2493	4.0108	76°
15°	.2588	.9659	.2679	3.7321	75°
16°	.2756	.9613	.2867	3.4874	74°
17°	.2924	.9563	.3057	3.2709	73°
18°	.3090	.9511	.3249	3.0777	72°
19°	.3256	.9455	.3443	2.9042	71°
20°	.3420	.9397	.3640	2.7475	70°
21°	.3584	.9336	.3839	2.6051	69°
22°	.3746	.9272	.4040	2.4751	68°
23°	.3907	.9205	.4245	2.3559	67°
24°	.4067	.9135	.4452	2.2460	66
25°	.4226	.9063	.4663	2.1445	65°
26°	.4384	.8988	.4877	2.0503	64°
27°	.4540	.8910	.5095	1.9626	63°
28°	.4695	.8829	.5317	1.8807	62°
29°	.4848	.8746	.5543	1.8040	61°
30°	.5000	.8660	.5774	1.7321	60°
31°	.5150	.8572	.6009	1.6643	59°
32°	.5299	.8480	.6249	1.6003	58°
33°	.5446	.8387	.6494	1.5399	57°
34°	.5592	.8290	.6745	1.4826	56°
35°	.5736	.8192	.7002	1.4281	55°
36°	.5878	.8090	.7265	1.3764	54°
37°	.6018	.7986	.7536	1.3270	53°
38°	.6157	.7880	.7813	1.2799	52°
39°	.6293	.7771	.8098	1.2349	51°
40°	.6428	.7660	.8391	1.1918	50°
41°	.6561	.7547	.8693	1.1504	49°
42°	.6691	.7431	.9004	1.1106	48°
43°	.6820	.7314	.9325	1.0724	47°
44°	.6947	.7193	.9657	1.0355	46°
45°	.7071	.7071	1.0000	1.0000	45°
Angle	Cosine	Sine	Co-Tan	Tan	Angle

TABLE XXXVI

Table of Chords

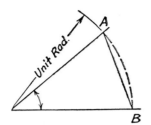

Chord AB is tabulated

TABLE OF CHORDS

TABULATED VALUES ARE CHORD LENGTHS OF ARCS OF UNIT RADIUS
SUBTENDING THE SPECIFIED ANGLES. USE MULTIPLES FOR ACCURACY.

DEGREES	0′	10′	20′	30′	40′	50′
0	.0000	.0029	.0058	.0087	.0116	.0145
1	.0174	.0204	.0233	.0202	.0291	.0320
2	.0349	.0378	.0407	.0436	.0465	.0494
3	.0523	.0553	.0582	.0611	.0640	.0669
4	.0698	.0727	.0756	.0785	.0814	.0843
5	.0872	.0901	.0930	.0959	.0988	.1017
6	.1047	.1076	.1105	.1134	.1163	.1192
7	.1221	.1250	.1279	.1308	.1337	.1366
8	.1395	.1424	.1453	.1482	.1511	.1540
9	.1569	.1598	.1627	.1656	.1685	.1714
10	.1743	.1772	.1801	.1830	.1859	.1888
11	.1917	.1946	.1975	.2004	.2033	.2062
12	.2090	.2119	.2148	.2177	.2206	.2235
13	.2264	.2293	.2322	.2351	.2380	.2409
14	.2437	.2466	.2495	.2524	.2553	.2582
15	.2610	.2639	.2668	.2697	.2726	.2755
16	.2783	.2812	.2841	.2870	.2899	.2927
17	.2956	.2985	.3014	.3042	.3071	.3100
18	.3129	.3157	.3186	.3215	.3243	.3272
19	.3301	.3330	.3358	.3387	.3416	.3444
20	.3473	.3502	.3530	.3559	.3587	.3616
21	.3645	.3673	.3702	.3730	.3759	.3788
22	.3816	.3845	.3873	.3902	.3930	.3959
23	.3987	.4016	.4044	.4073	.4101	.4130
24	.4158	.4187	.4215	.4243	.4272	.4300
25	.4329	.4357	.4385	.4414	.4442	.4471
26	.4499	.4527	.4556	.4584	.4612	.4641
27	.4669	.4697	.4725	.4754	.4782	.4810
28	.4838	.4867	.4895	.4923	.4951	.4979
29	.5008	.5036	.5064	.5092	.5120	.5148
30	.5176	.5204	.5232	.5261	.5289	.5317
31	.5345	.5373	.5401	.5429	.5457	.5485
32	.5513	.5541	.5569	.5596	.5624	.5652
33	.5680	.5708	.5736	.5764	.5792	.5820
34	.5847	.5875	.5903	.5931	.5959	.5986
35	.6014	.6042	.6069	.6097	.6125	.6153
36	.6180	.6208	.6236	.6263	.6291	.6318
37	.6346	.6374	.6401	.6429	.6456	.6484
38	.6511	.6539	.6566	.6594	.6621	.6649
39	6676	.6703	.6731	.6758	.6786	.6813
40	.6840	.6868	.6895	.6922	.6950	.6977
41	.7004	.7031	.7059	.7086	.7113	.7140
42	.7167	.7194	.7222	.7249	.7276	.7303
43	.7330	.7357	.7384	.7411	.7438	.7465
44	.7492	.7519	.7546	.7573	.7600	.7627
45	.7654	.7680	.7680	.7734	.7761	.7788

TABLE XXXVII

Abbreviations and Symbols

Alternating current	a-c	Lateral	lat.
Aluminum	Al.	Long	lg.
American Standard	Am. Std.	Longitudinal	long.
Approved	App.	Linear foot	lin. ft.
Average	avg.	Machine	mach.
Ball bearing	bb	Malleable iron	Mal. I.
Brown & Sharpe	B & S	Material	mat.
Babbitt	Bab.	Maximum	max.
Brass	Br.	Meter	m.
Bronze	Bro.	Mile	mile
Brinell hardness number	Bhn.	Millimeter	mm.
Cast iron	C.I.	Miles per hour	mph
Center line	CL or ℄	Minimum	min.
Center to center	c to c.	Minute (angular measure)	'
Centimeter	cm.	Minute (time)	min.
Chemical	chem.	Outside diameter	O.D.
Circular	cir.	Pattern	patt.
Circular pitch	CP	Phosphor bronze	Phos. Bro.
Copper	Cop.	Piece	pc.
Cold rolled steel	C.R.S.	Pitch	P
Counterbore	c'bore	Pitch diameter	P.D.
Countersink	c's'k	Plate	pl.
Cubic	cu.	Pound	# or lb.
Cubic inch	cu.in.	Pounds per square foot	lb.per.sq.ft.
Cubic foot	cu.ft.	Pounds per square inch	lb.per.sq.in.
Cubic yard	cu.yd.	Pratt & Whitney	P & W.
Cylinder	cyl.	Quantity	quan.
Degree	deg. or °	Radius	R or Rad.
Diameter	D., Dia., or Diam.	Required	req. or req'd.
Direct current	d-c	Revolution per minute	rpm
Diagonal	diag.	Right hand	R.H.
Diametral pitch	DP	Round	rd.
Drawing	Dwg.	Round bar	ϕ
Drawn	Dr.	Screw	sc.
Detail drawing	Dtl.dwg.	Second (time)	sec.
Efficiency	eff.	Second (angular measure)	''
Electric	elec.	Section	sec.
Engineer	engr.	Society of Automotive Engineers	SAE
External	ext.	Square	sq.
Fabricate	fab.	Square inch	sq.in.
Fillister	fil.	Square foot	sq.ft.
Finish	fin.	Standard	std.
Foot	ft. or '	Steel	Stl.
Gallon	gal.	Steel casting	Stl.C.
Galvanized iron	G.I.	Thousand	M
Grind	G or gr.	Ton	ton
Harden	hdn.	Thread	thd.
Hexagonal	hex.	Traced	Tr.
Horsepower	hp.	Volt	v
Hour	hr.	Watt	w
Impregnate	impreg.	Weight	wt.
Inch	in. or ''	Woodruff key	Wdrf. key
Inside Diameter	I. D.	Wrought iron	W. I.
Internal	int.	Yard	yd.
Left hand	L.H.	Year	yr.

TABLE XXXVIII
Code for Indicating Criticisms

A code consisting of letters and numerals that can be used in combination to indicate errors on a drawing is given below. A student should note each error and then if he feels that he does not understand the true nature of a mistake he should consult his instructor.

Item Letter	Item	Defect Number	Defects
E	Entire Drawing	1	Not Neat
V	View	2	Balance or Spacing Poor
L	Line	3	Off Scale
D	Dimension	4	Out of Projection
S	Scale	5	Wrong
F	Figure, Fraction or Letter	6	Omitted
T	Thread	7	Unnecessary
N	Notation	8	Poorly Made
		9	Location Poor

Examples: Dimension off scale......... D-3   Thread omitted......... T-6

ASA STANDARDS

A few of the more than 500 standards approved by the American Standards Association are listed below. Copies may be obtained from the Association's Sales Department at 70 East 45th Street, New York 17, N.Y.

A13.1-1956	Identification of Piping Systems, Scheme for
B1.1-1949	Unified and American Screw Threads for Screws, Bolts, Nuts, and Other Threaded Parts
B1.2–1951	Screw Thread Gages and Gaging
B1.5–1952	Acme Screw Threads
B2.1–1945	Pipe Threads
B4.1–1955	Preferred Limits and Fits for Cylindrical Parts
B5.6–1941	Jig Bushings
B5.10–1953	Machine Tapers, Self-holding and Steep Taper Series
B5.15–1950	Involute Splines, Side Bearing
B5.20–1954	Machine Pins
B6.1–1932	Spur Gear Tooth Form
B16.1–1948	Cast-Iron Pipe Flanges and Flanged Fittings, Class 125
B16b–1944 (R1953)	Cast-Iron Pipe Flanges and Flanged Fittings for Maximum WSP of 250 lb
B16b2–1931	Cast-Iron Pipe Flanges and Flanged Fittings for Maximum WSP of 25 lb
B16.3–1951	Malleable-Iron Screwed Fittings, 150 lb
B16.4–1949	Cast-Iron Screwed Fittings for Maximum WSP of 125 and 250 lb
B16.5–1953	Steel Pipe Flanges and Flanged Fittings
B16.9–1951	Steel Butt-Welding Fittings
B16.10–1957	Face-to-Face and End-to-End Dimensions of Ferrous Valves
B17f–1930	Woodruff Keys, Keyslots, and Cutters

B17.1–1943	Shafting and Stock Keys
B18.1–1955	Small Solid Rivets
B18.2–1955	Square and Hexagon Bolts and Nuts
B18.3–1954	Socket Set Screws and Socket Head Cap Screws
B18.4–1950	Large Rivets
B18.5–1952	Round Head Bolts
B18.6.2–1956	Hexagon Head Cap Screws, Slotted Head Cap Screws, Square Head Set Screws, and Slotted Headless Set Screws
B36.1–1956	Welded and Seamless Steel Pipe (ASTM A53-44)
B36.2–1956	Welded Wrought-Iron Pipe
B36.10–1950	Wrought-Iron and Wrought-Steel Pipe
B45.1–1932	Foundry Patterns of Wood (CS 19-32)
B48.1–1933	Inch-Millimeter Conversion for Industrial Use
Y14.1–1957	Size and Format
Y14.2–1957	Line Conventions, Sectioning and Lettering
Y14.3–1957	Projections
Y14.4–1957	Pictorial Drawing
Y14.5–1957	Dimensioning and Notes
Y14.6–1957	Screw Threads
Y32.2–1954	Graphical Symbols for Electrical Diagrams
Z10.1–1941	Abbreviations for Scientific Engineering Terms*
Z10.5–1949	Electrical Quantities, Letter Symbols for*
Z15.1–1932	Engineering and Scientific Charts for Lantern Slides*
Z15.2–1938	Time-Series Charts, Manual of Design and Construction*
Z15.3–1943	Engineering and Scientific Graphs for Publications*
Z32.2.1–1949 (R1953)	Welding Symbols and Instructions for Their Use*
Z32.3–1946	Graphical Symbols for Power Control and Measurement*
Z32.5–1944	Symbols for Telephone, Telegraph, and Radio Use*

* Y is the new letter assigned to standards for abbreviations, charts and graphs, drawings, graphical symbols, and letter symbols. The Z will be changed to Y as the standards are revised and reaffirmed.

GLOSSARY OF COMMON SHOP TERMS

(For structural terms see Chapter 22)

Anneal (*v*).   To heat a piece of metal to a particular temperature and then allow it to cool slowly for the purpose of removing internal stresses.

Bore (*v*).   To enlarge a hole using a boring bar in order to make it smooth, round, and co-axial.   Boring is usually done on a lathe or boring mill.

Boss (*n*).   A circular projection which is raised above a principal surface of a casting or forging.

Braze (*v*).   To join two pieces of metal by the use of hard solder.   The solder is usually a copper-zinc alloy.

Broach (*v*).   To machine a hole to a desired shape, usually other than round. The cutting tool, known as a broach, is pushed or pulled through the rough finished hole.   It has transverse cutting edges.

Burnish (*v*).   To smooth or apply a brilliant finish.

Bushing (*n*).   A removable cylindrical sleeve which is used to provide a bearing surface.

Carburize (*v*).   To harden the surface of a piece of low grade steel by heating in a carbonizing material to increase the carbon content and then quenching.

Case-harden (*v*).   To harden a surface as described above or through the use of potassium cyanide.

Chamfer (*v*).   To bevel an external edge or corner.

Chase (*v*).   To cut screw threads on a lathe using a chaser, a tool shaped to the profile of a thread.

Chill (*v*).   To cool the surface of a casting suddenly so that the surface will be white and hard.

Chip (*v*).   To cut away or remove surface defects with a chisel.

Color-harden (*v*).   See case-harden.   A piece is color-hardened mainly for the sake of appearance.

Core (*v*).   To form a hole or hollow cavity in a casting through the use of a core.

Counterbore (*v*).   To enlarge the end of a cylindrical hole to a certain depth, as is often done to accommodate the head of a fillister head screw.   (*n*) The name of the tool used to produce the enlargement.

Countersink (*v*).   To form a conical enlargement at the end of a cylindrical hole to accommodate the head of a screw or rivet.   (*n*) The name of the tool used to form a conical shaped enlargement.

Crown (*n*).   The angular or curved contour of the outer surface of a part such as on a pulley.

Die (*n*).   A metal block used for forming or stamping operations.   A thread-cutting tool for producing external threads.

Die Casting (*n*).   A casting which has been produced by forcing a molten alloy having an aluminum, copper, zinc, tin, or lead base into a metal mold composed of two halves.

Die Stamping (*n*).   A piece which has been cut or formed from sheet metal through the use of a die.

Draw (*v*).   To form metal, which may be either cold or hot, by a distorting or stretching process.   To temper steel by gradual or intermittent quenching.

Drill (*v*).   To form a cylindrical hole in metal.   (*n*) A revolving cutting tool designed for cutting at the point.

Drop Forging (*n*). A piece formed while hot between two dies under a drop hammer.

Face (*v*). To machine on a lathe a flat face which is perpendicular to the axis of rotation of the piece.

Feather (*n*). A rectangular sliding key which permits a pulley to move along the shaft parallel to its axis.

File (*v*). To shape, finish, or trim with a fine-toothed metal cutting tool which is used with the hands.

Fillet (*n*). A rounded filling which increases the strength at the junction of two surfaces which form an internal angle.

Fit (*n*). The tightness of adjustment between the contacting surfaces of mating parts.

Flange (*n*). The top and bottom member of a beam. A projecting rim added on the end of a pipe or fitting for making a connection.

Forge (*v*). To shape hot metals by hammering, using a hand-hammer or machine.

Galvanize (*v*). To coat steel or iron by immersion in a bath of zinc.

Graduate (*v*). To mark off or divide a scale into intervals.

Grind (*v*). To finish a surface through the action of a revolving abrasive wheel.

Key (*n*). A piece used between a shaft and a hub to prevent the movement of one relative to the other.

Keyway or **Keyseat** (*n*). A longitudinal groove cut in a shaft or a hub to receive a key. A key rests in a keyseat and slides in a keyway.

Knurl (*v*). To roughen a cylindrical surface to produce a better grip for the fingers.

Lap (*v*). To finish or polish with a piece of soft metal, wood, or leather impregnated with an abrasive.

Lug (*n*). A projection or ear which has been cast or forged as a portion of a piece to provide a support or to allow the attachment of another part.

Malleable Casting (*n*). A casting which has been annealed to toughen it.

Mill (*v*). To machine a piece on a milling machine by means of a rotating toothed cutter.

Neck (*v*). To cut a circumferential groove around a shaft.

Pack-harden (*v*). To case-carburize and harden.

Peen (*v*). To stretch or bend over metal using the peen end (ball end) of a hammer.

Pickle (*v*). To remove scale and rust from a casting or forging by immersing it in an acid bath.

Plane (*v*). To machine a flat surface on a planer, a machine having a fixed tool and a reciprocating bed.

Polish (*v*). To make a surface smooth and lustrous through the use of a fine abrasive.

Punch (*v*). To perforate a thin piece of metal by shearing out a circular wad with a non-rotating tool under pressure.

Ream (*v*). To finish a hole to an exact size using a rotating fluted cutting tool known as a reamer.

Rivet (*n*). A headed shank which more or less permanently unites two pieces. (*v*) To fasten steel plates with rivets.

Round (*n*). A rounded external corner on a casting.

Sandblast (*v*). To clean the surface of castings or forgings by means of sand forced from a nozzle at a high velocity.

Shear (*v*). To cut off sheet or bar metal through the shearing action of two blades.

Shim (*n*). A thin metal plate which is inserted between two surfaces for the purpose of adjustment.

Spline (*n*). A keyway, usually for a feather key. See feather.

Spotface (*v*). To finish a round spot on the rough surface of a casting at a drilled hole for the purpose of providing a smooth seat for a bolt or screw head.

Spot Weld (*v*). To weld two overlapping metal sheets in spots by means of the heat of resistance to an electric current between a pair of electrodes.

Steel Casting (*n*). A casting made of cast iron to which scrap steel has been added.

Swage (*v*). To form metal with a "swage block," a tool so constructed that through hammering or pressure the work may be made to take a desired shape.

Sweat (*v*). To solder together by clamping the pieces in contact with soft solder between and then heating.

Tack Weld (*n*). A weld of short intermittent sections.

Tap (*v*). To cut an internal thread, by hand or with power, by screwing into the hole a fluted tapered tool having thread-cutting edges.

Temper (*v*). To reduce the hardness of a piece of hardened steel through reheating and sudden quenching.

Template (*n*). A pattern cut to a desired shape which is used in layout work to establish shearing lines, to locate holes, etc.

Tumble (*v*). To clean and smooth castings and forgings through contact in a revolving barrel. To further the results, small pieces of scrap are added.

Turn (*v*). To turn-down or machine a cylindrical surface on a lathe.

Upset (*v*). To increase the diameter or form a shoulder on a piece during forging.

Weld (*v*). To join two pieces of metal by pressure or hammering after heating to the fusion point.

BIBLIOGRAPHY OF ENGINEERING DRAWING
AND ALLIED SUBJECTS

Aeronautical Drafting and Engineering

Anderson, N. H., *Aircraft Layout and Detail Design.* McGraw-Hill.
Apalategui, J. J., *Aircraft Analytic Geometry with Applications to Aircraft.* Macmillan.
Faulconer, T. P., *Introduction to Aircraft Design.* McGraw-Hill.
Katz, H. H., *Aircraft Drafting.* Macmillan.
Leavell, S., and S. Bungay, *Aircraft Production Standards.* McGraw-Hill.
LeMaster, C. A., *Aircraft Sheet Metal Work.* American Technical Society.
Meadowcroft, N., *Aircraft Detail Drafting.* McGraw-Hill.
Nelson, W., *Airplane Lofting.* McGraw-Hill.
Svensen, C. L., *A Manual of Aircraft Drafting.* Van Nostrand.
Tharratt, G., *Aircraft Production Illustration.* McGraw-Hill.

Architectural Drawing

Field, W. B., *An Introduction to Architectural Drawing.* McGraw-Hill.
Morgan, S. W., *Architectural Drawing.* McGraw-Hill.
Turner, W. W., *Fundamentals of Architectural Design.* McGraw-Hill.

Blueprint Reading

Bush, G. F., *Reading Engineering Drawings.* Wiley.
DeVette, W. A., and D. E. Kellogg, *Blueprint Reading for the Metal Trades.* Bruce.
Dick, A. A., *Blueprint Reading.* Ronald.
Dwight, C., *Blueprint Reading in the Machine Industries.* McGraw-Hill.
Heine, G. M., and C. H. Dunlap, *How to Read Electrical Blueprints.* American Technical Society.
Hobart, D. E., *Notes and Problems in Blueprint Reading of Machine Drawings.* Harper.
Lincoln Electric Co., *Simple Blueprint Reading.* Cleveland.
Norcross, C., *Aircraft Blueprints and How to Read Them.* McGraw-Hill.
Owens, A. A., and B. F. Slingluff, *How to Read Blueprints.* Winston.
Spencer, H. C., and H. E. Grant, *Blueprint Language of the Machine Industries.* Macmillan.
Thayer, H. R., *Blueprint Reading and Sketching.* McGraw-Hill.
Weir, J. J., *Blueprint Reading.* McGraw-Hill.

Castings

Campbell, H. I., *Metal Castings.* Wiley.

Catalogs
(Instruments)

Alteneder, Theo., and Sons, Philadelphia, Pa.
Boston Gear Works, Inc., Chicago, Ill. (Gears, etc.)

Crane Co., Chicago, Ill. (Pipe Fittings.)
Elliott, B. K., Co., Pittsburgh, Pa.
Eugene Dietzgen Co., Chicago, Ill.
Frederic Post Co., Chicago, Ill.
Keuffel & Esser Co., Hoboken, N. J.
New Departure, Bristol, Conn. (Ball-Bearing Handbook.)
Timken Roller Bearing Co., Canton, Ohio. (Roller Bearings.)
U.S. Blue Co., Chicago, Ill.

Descriptive Geometry

Bradley, H. C., and E. H. Uhler, *Descriptive Geometry for Engineers*. International.
Grant, H. E., *Practical Descriptive Geometry*. McGraw-Hill.
Hood, G. J., *Geometry of Engineering Drawing*. McGraw-Hill.
Johnson, L. O., and I. Wladaver, *Elements of Descriptive Geometry*. Prentice-Hall.
Larkins, J. T., Jr., *Descriptive Geometry*. Prentice-Hall.
Levens, A. S., and H. Eggers, *Descriptive Geometry*. Harper.
Street, W. E., *Technical Descriptive Geometry*. Van Nostrand.
Warner, F. M., *Applied Descriptive Geometry*. McGraw-Hill.
Watts, E. F., and J. T. Rule, *Descriptive Geometry*. Prentice-Hall.
Wellman, B. L., *Technical Descriptive Geometry*. McGraw-Hill.

Descriptive Geometry Problems

Paré, E. G., and others, *Descriptive Geometry Worksheets*. Macmillan.
Turner, W. W., *Basic Problems in Descriptive Geometry*. Ronald.
Uhler, E. H., *Problems in Descriptive Geometry*. International.
Watts, E. F., and A. L. Goodrich, *Problems in Descriptive Geometry*. Prentice-Hall.

Die Casting

Chase, H., *Die Castings*. Wiley.

Engineering Drawing

Arnold, J. N., *Introductory Graphics*. McGraw-Hill.
French, T. E., and C. J. Vierck, *Engineering Drawing*. McGraw-Hill.
Giesecke, F. E., and others, *Technical Drawing*. Macmillan.
Hesse, H. C., *A Manual in Engineering Drawing*. Macmillan.
Hobart, D. E., *Engineering Drawing*. Heath.
Hoelscher, R. P., and others, *Industrial Production Illustration*. McGraw-Hill.
Hoelscher, R. P., and C. H. Springer, *Engineering Drawing and Geometry*. Wiley.
Levens, A. S., *Graphics in Engineering and Science*. Wiley.
Luzadder, W. J., *Graphics for Engineers*. Prentice-Hall.
————, *Technical Drafting Essentials*, 2nd ed. Prentice-Hall.
Orth, H. D., R. R. Worsencroft, and H. B. Doke, *Basic Engineering Drawing*. Ronald.
Radzinsky, H., *Making Patent Drawings*. Macmillan.
Sahag, L. M., *Engineering Drawing*. Ronald.
Schumann, C. H., *Technical Drafting*. Harper.
Svensen, C. L., *Drafting for Engineers*. Van Nostrand.

————, *Essentials of Drafting*, 3rd ed. Van Nostrand.
Thayer, H. R., *Industrial Drawing*. McGraw-Hill.
Turner, W. W., and others, *Basic Engineering Drawing*. Ronald.
Zozzoro, F., *Engineering Drawing*. McGraw-Hill.

Engineering Drawing Problems

Cooper, C. D., and others, *Engineering Drawing Problems*. McGraw-Hill.
French, T. E., and H. M. McCully, *Engineering Drawing Sheets*. McGraw-Hill.
Giesecke, F. E., and others, *Technical Drawing Problems*. Macmillan.
Higbee, F. G., and J. M. Russ, *Engineering Drawing Problems*. Wiley.
Levens, A. S., and A. E. Edstrom, *Problems in Engineering Drawing*. McGraw-Hill.
Luzadder, W. J., J. N. Arnold, and F. H. Thompson, *Problems in Engineering Drawing*. Prentice-Hall.
————, *Problems in Engineering Drawing*, Abridged. Prentice-Hall.
————, R. H. Hammond, C. J. Rogers, and C. T. Seeley, *Problems in Engineering Graphics*. Prentice-Hall.
————, and R. E. Bolles, *Problems in Drafting Fundamentals*. Prentice-Hall.
Orth, H. D., R. R. Worsencroft, and H. B. Doke, *Problems in Basic Engineering Drawing*. Irwin-Farnham.
Russ, J. M., *Quiz Questions*. McGraw-Hill.
Spencer, H. C., and H. E. Grant, *Technical Drawing Problems*. Macmillan.
Turner, W. W., *Basic Problems in Engineering Drawing*. Ronald.

Graphical Representation and Computation

Adams, D. P., *Index of Nomograms*. Wiley.
Davis, D. S., *Empirical Equations and Nomography*. McGraw-Hill.
Douglass, R. D., and D. P. Adams, *Elements of Nomography*. McGraw-Hill.
Hoelscher, R. P., J. N. Arnold, and S. H. Pierce, *Graphic Aids in Engineering Computations*. McGraw-Hill.
Karsten, K. G., *Charts and Graphs*. Prentice-Hall.
Levens, A. S., *Nomography*. Wiley.
————, *Graphics in Engineering and Science*. Wiley.
Lipka, J., *Graphical and Mechanical Computation*. Wiley.
Mackey, C. O., *Graphic Solutions*. Wiley.
Mavis, F. T., *The Construction of Nomographic Charts*. International.

Handbooks

Colvin, F. H., *Aircraft Handbook*. McGraw-Hill.
————, and F. A. Stanley, *American Machinists Handbook and Dictionary of Shop Terms*. McGraw-Hill.
Kent, W., *Mechanical Engineers Handbook*. Wiley.
Lawle, F. F., *Standard Handbook for Electrical Engineers*. McGraw-Hill.
Machinery Handbook. Industrial Press.
Marks, L. S., *Mechanical Engineers Handbook*. McGraw-Hill.
Merriman, T., *American Civil Engineers Handbook*. Wiley.
O'Rourke, C. E., *General Engineering Handbook*. McGraw-Hill.
Perry, J. H., *Chemical Engineers Handbook*. McGraw-Hill.
Steel Construction. American Institute of Steel Construction.
Tool Engineers Handbook. Am. Soc. of Tool Engineers.
Walker, J. H., S. Crocker, and J. R. Allen, *Piping Handbook*. McGraw-Hill.

Jig and Fixture Design

Bryant, L. A., and T. A., Dickinson, *Jigs and Fixtures*. Pitman.
Colvin, F. H., and L. L. Haas, *Jigs and Fixtures*. McGraw-Hill.
Hinman, C. W., *Die Engineering Layouts and Formulas*. McGraw-Hill.
Jones, F. D., *Jig and Fixture Design*. Industrial Press.

Lettering

De Garmo, E. P., and F. Jonassen, *Technical Lettering*. Macmillan.
French, T. E., and W. D. Turnbill, *Lessons in Lettering*, Vols. 1 and 2. McGraw-Hill.

Machine Design

Faires, V. M., *Design of Machine Elements*. Macmillan.
Maleev, V. L., *Machine Design*. International.
Norman, C. A., E. S. Ault, and I. F. Zarobsky, *Fundamentals of Machine Design*. Macmillan.
Sahag, L. M., *Kinematics of Machines*. Ronald.
Spotts, M. F., *Design of Machine Elements*. Prentice-Hall.

Machine Drawing

Lent, D., *Design of Machine Elements*. Prentice-Hall.
Svensen, C. L., *Machine Drawing*. Van Nostrand.

Map and Topographic Drawing

Deetz, C. H., *Cartography*. U.S. Printing Office.
Greitzer, S. L., *Elementary Topography and Map Reading*. McGraw-Hill.
Hinks, A. R., *Maps and Surveys*. Cambridge (Macmillan).
Sloane, R. C., and I. M. Montz, *Elements of Topographic Drawing*. McGraw-Hill.

Pattern Design

Hall, B. R., and H. E. Kiley, *Pattern Design*. International.

Perspective

Brahdy, J., *Perspective Drawing*. Macmillan.
Everett, H. E., and W. H. Lawrence, *Freehand and Perspective Drawing*. American Technical Society.
Lawson, P. J., *Practical Perspective Drawing*. McGraw-Hill.
Lubschez, B. J., *Perspective*. Van Nostrand.
Turner, W. W., *Simplified Perspective*. Ronald.

Pipe

Crocker, S., *Piping Hand Book*. McGraw-Hill.
Day, L. J., *Standard Plumbing Details*. Wiley.
Svensen, C. L., *A Handbook on Piping*. Van Nostrand.

Sheet-Metal Work

Atkins, E. A., *Practical Sheet and Plate Metal Work.*   Pitman.
Frazer, R. H., and O. Berthiaume, *Practical Aircraft Sheet-metal Work.*   McGraw-Hill.
Norcross, C., and J. D. Quinn, *How to Do Aircraft Sheetmetal Work.*   McGraw-Hill.
O'Rourke, F. J., *Sheet-metal Pattern Drafting.*   McGraw-Hill.

Shop Practice

Begeman, M. L., *Manufacturing Processes.*   Wiley.
Boston, O. W., *Engineering Shop Practice*, Vol. 1.   Wiley.
——, *Metal Processing.*   Wiley.
Campbell, H. L., *The Working, Heating, Treating, and Welding of Steel.*   Wiley.
Marek, C. T., *The Production and Design of Castings.*   Wiley.
Wendt, R. E., *Foundry Work.*   McGraw-Hill.
Young, J. F., *Materials and Processes.*   Wiley.

Sketching

Katz, H., *Technical Sketching.*   Macmillan.
Turner, W. W., *Freehand Sketching for Engineers.*   Ronald.
Zipprich, A. E., *Freehand Drafting.*   Van Nostrand.

Structural Drafting

Bishop, C. T., *Structural Drafting.*   Wiley.

Technical Dictionary

Tweney, C. F., and L. E. C. Hughes, *Chambers Technical Dictionary.*   Macmillan.

Tool Design

Cole, C. B., *Tool Design.*   American Technical Society.
Donaldson, C., and G. H. LeCain, *Tool Design.*   Harper.
Doyle, L. E., *Tool Engineering.*   Prentice-Hall.

Welding

Churchill, H. D., and J. B. Austin, *Weld Design.*   Prentice-Hall.
Elzea, L. S., *Aircraft Welding.*   McGraw-Hill.
Lincoln Electric Co., *Simple Blueprint Reading.*   Cleveland.
——, *Procedure Handbook of Arc Welding Design and Practice.*   Cleveland.

Text Films

"Engineering Drawing."   7 films, 6 strips.   McGraw-Hill.
"Engineering Drawing."   16 films.   Purdue University.

PURDUE UNIVERSITY
ENGINEERING DRAWING FILMS

Key to Symbols

S—Secondary School   Si—Silent Motion Picture
C—College   Sd—Sound Motion Picture
A—Adult   B&W—Black and White

Applied Geometry   16 min.   Si   B&W   C-A
This demonstration film is divided into nine parts, each showing how to draw a geometric figure. At the end of each part the student solves a similar problem on a previously-prepared work sheet.

Auxiliary Views   17 min.   Si   B&W   C-A
Demonstration film on principles of auxiliary views by means of models. Method for constructing auxiliary views for straight line and curved line figures. Film divided into three parts; at the end of each the student works a suitable problem. Lantern slides for chalk board projection permit the instructor to show his students the correct solutions.

Capital Letters   21 min.   Sd   B&W   S-C-A
A work demonstration film on the construction of single stroke inclined commercial gothic letters, ampersand, and numerals. On work sheets students reproduce the characters. Blank film of proper length allows time between each demonstration for class activity while room lights are controlled by the teacher.

Development of Surfaces   22 min.   Si   B&W   C-A
Explains the construction of the patterns of surfaces by means of models and drawings. Describes the methods for right prism and oblique prism, for right cylinders, right pyramids, right cone and oblique cone. The demonstration is divided into four parts; at the end of each the student works a suitable problem. Lantern slides for chalk board projection permit the instructor to show the students the correct solution.

Freehand Drafting   12 min.   Si   B&W   C-A
Demonstrates proper strokes for sketching various lines; short and long horizontal, vertical, and inclined lines, large and small circles and ellipses. Demonstration is divided into several parts so the student can complete a suitable exercise at the end of each.

Intersections of Surfaces   9 min.   Si   B&W   C-A
This film explains by means of models and drawings the principles for finding the lines of intersection between intersecting surfaces. It discusses the problem of finding the intersection of two prisms, of two cylinders, of cylinder and cone. The demonstration is divided into four parts at the end of each of which the student works a suitable problem. Lantern slides for chalk board projection permit the instructor to show the student the correct solution.

Lower Case Letters   17 min.   Sd   B&W   S-C-A
Explains and demonstrates the construction of the 26 lower case letters. After each letter, room lights are turned on to permit the student to make the letter. Blank film between scenes premits projector to be run continuously and insures a lesson completed in the time allowed.

Multiview Drawing   **24 min.**   **Si**   **B&W**   **S-C-A**
Demonstrates with models the proper way to represent an object by means of three orthographic views. Shows use of the scale for making measurements and use of T-square and triangle for constructing views; method of transferring a measurement from one view to another, of constructing the third view by projecting from the other. The lesson is divided into four parts. At the end of each the student works a suitable problem on a work sheet. Lantern slides for chalk board projection permit the instructor to show the student the correct solution of the problem.

Pictorial Drawing   **21 min.**   **Si**   **B&W**   **C-A**
Demonstrates principles of isometric drawing by means of models; shows construction of objects with isometric and nonisometric lines and circles. Lesson divided into three parts; at the end of each the student works a suitable exercise. Lantern slides for chalk board projection permit instructor to show correct solutions.

Screw Threads   **22 min.**   **Si**   **B&W**   **C-A**
Defines, by means of models and drawings, the important terms associated with screw threads. Complete step-by-step constructions of national threads and square threads, with the meaning of each line explained by reference to a model. The lesson is divided into parts. At the end of each the student completes a suitable exercise on a work sheet. Lantern slides for chalk board projection permits instructor to show student the correct solution of each problem.

Sectional Views   **15 min.**   **Si**   **B&W**   **C-A**
Illustrates principles of sectioning by means of models and celluloid cutting planes. Full section, half section, and offset sections. Demonstration is divided into four parts. At the end of each the student works a suitable problem. Lantern slides for chalk board projection permit instructor to show the students the correct solutions to the problems.

Shape Description   **31 min.**   **Sd**   **B&W**   **C-A**
Demonstrates for each of five objects the making of one pictorial and three principal views, with stopping places at appropriate intervals for the students to sketch these views. The first object is a simple rectangular block; the last requires circles in its representation. Slides are provided for projecting photographs of the objects on the screen, and negative slides are included for blackboard projection so that the instructor may demonstrate and discuss the completion of each exercise. This film demonstrates the relation between the object itself, its pictorial representation and its representation by three orthographic views.

Structural Drawing   **20 min.**   **Si**   **B&W**   **C-A**
The preparation and use of the chisel-pointed pencil for making pencil drawings on tracing paper for blueprinting. The following steps in making a structural drawing are completed as follows:

1. Location of gage lines
2. Location of members determined by size of members and minimum clearance
3. Size of plates determined by number of rivets in a group, edge distance and spacing of rivets

Reel 1—Layout of roof truss.
Reel 2—Detailing a gusset plate.

Testing of T-square and Triangles   11 min.   Si   B&W   S-C-A
How to check smoothness and straightness of T-square blade and head and the
straightness of the edges of the drawing board.   Demonstrates how to check
accurately the smoothness and straightness of the edges of triangles as well as the
angles of triangles without the use of auxiliary apparatus.

Tracing with Ink   32 min.   Sd   B&W   C-A
Demonstrates tracing on cloth.   Shows cloth attached to drawing board with
tape and powder applied to condition tracing surface.   Procedures for handling
ink bottle, and for filling, adjusting, using, cleaning and sharpening the pens are
shown.   Characteristics of lines and their measurement and control are explained
in detail.   Importance of "order of lettering" to efficient tracing is emphasized.
Lettering triangle is used for guide lines for lettering.   Production of faulty lines
by improper procedures, and use of eraser and soapstone to correct errors are
included.   (work sheet)

Use of T-square and Triangles   20 min.   Si   B&W   S-C-A
This picture demonstrates the basic principles for correct use of the T-square and
Triangles.   Makes demonstrations of:

1. Horizontal lines with the T-square
2. Vertical lines with T-square and Triangle
3. Lines making 60° with the horizontal, also 45°, 30°, 15°, and 75°
4. Parallel lines
5. Perpendicular lines
6. Lines making 30° with an inclined line, also 15°

The picture is divided into 11 sections.   At the end of each the student, on a previously prepared worksheet, solves a suitable problem.

NOTE: These films are available on a rental basis.
        Address: Purdue University Audio-Visual Center,
                Lafayette, Indiana.

Index